Development of the Minkowski Geometry of Numbers

by HARRIS HANCOCK
Ph.D. (Berlin), Dr. Sc. (Paris)

in two volumes

Volume Two

Dover Publications, Inc., New York

Published in the United Kingdom by Constable and Company, Limited, 10 Orange Street, London W.C.2.

This Dover edition, first published in 1964, is an unabridged and unaltered republication of the work first published by The Macmillan Company, New York, in 1939. The 1939 edition was published in one volume, but this edition is published in two volumes.

This edition is published by special arrangement with the Charles Phelps Taft Memorial Fund. The publisher is grateful to the Library of the University of Cincinnati for furnishing a copy of the work for purpose of reproduction.

Library of Congress Catalog Card Number 64-20882

Manufactured in the United States of America

Dover Publications, Inc.
180 Varick Street
New York 14, N.Y.

TABLE OF CONTENTS

CHAPTER XI

PERIODIC APPROXIMATION OF ALGEBRAIC NUMBERS

CHAPTER XII

ON THE APPROXIMATION OF A REAL QUANTITY THROUGH RATIONAL NUMBERS

CHAPTER XVII

THE EXTREME STANDARD BODIES

CHAPTER XVIII

DENSEST PLACEMENT OF CONGRUENT HOMOLOGOUS BODIES

CHAPTER XIX

MISCELLANY

CHAPTER, XX

NEW THEORY OF QUADRATIC FORMS. REGION OF DISCONTINUITY FOR ARITHMETICAL EQUIVALENCE

TABLE OF CONTENTS

CHAPTER XI

PERIODIC APPROXIMATION OF ALGEBRAIC NUMBERS [1]

ART. **115.** Abel (*Oeuvres*, Vol. II, p. 217) made the following remark regarding the problem of the algebraic solution of equations: "Instead of seeking a relation whose existence we do not know, we should ask if such a relation is possible." Following this thought we may also try to approach nearer another as yet unsolved problem in the manifold domain of the solution of equations.

We shall consider here the problem: *What algebraic numbers have analogous periodic approximations as the real algebraic numbers of the second degree through the periodicity of their developments in the usual continued fractions?*

ART. **116. Periodic Chains of Substitutions.** Let α be an arbitrary quantity and put $\sigma=1$ or 2 according as α is real or complex. If α is an *algebraic* number of the nth degree, and that is the root of an irreducible equation of the nth degree in the realm of rational numbers, then (*A. N.*, I, Art. 41) the expression

$$\xi=x_1+\alpha x_2+\cdots+\alpha^{n-1}x_n$$

can never vanish for rational integers $x_1, x_2, \cdots, x_n$ which are not all zero; however, when $n>\sigma$, the quantity ξ may be made arbitrarily small. We shall here make the assumption always that $n>\sigma$. Regarding the approximation of the form ξ to zero we have as shown in the preceding chapter the following theorems:

For the number α we may construct a substitution S taken with respect to an arbitrary real quantity $r\geqq 1$, namely

$$S)\qquad x_h=s_h^{(1)}z_1+s_h^{(2)}z_2+\cdots+s_h^{(n)}z_n \qquad (h=1, 2, \cdots, n),$$

which has the following properties:

[1] Minkowski, *Ges. Abhandl.*, I, p. 357.

a) *All coefficients* $s_h^{(k)}$ *are rational integers and the absolute values of the quotients* $\frac{s_h^{(k)}}{r}$ *are less than a certain quantity that is independent of* r.

b) *The determinant of* S *is* $\neq 0$ *and in absolute value lies below a certain bound that is independent of* r.

c) *If* ξ *is transformed through* S *into*

$$\chi = \rho_1 y_1 + \rho_2 y_2 + \cdots + \rho_n y_n,$$

the absolute values of

$$\rho_1 r^{\frac{n-\sigma}{\sigma}}, \qquad \rho_2 r^{\frac{n-\sigma}{\sigma}}, \qquad \cdots, \qquad \rho_n r^{\frac{n-\sigma}{\sigma}}$$

all lie under certain bounds that are independent of r. (Formula (50), Chap. IX.)

d) *For the ratios* $\rho_1 : \rho_2 : \cdots : \rho_n$ *only a finite number of different systems come under consideration and these do not depend upon* r. (Chap. IX.)

As was shown in Chapter IX, those conditions are always sufficient, if the substitution S, for which the coefficients $s_h^{(k)}$ are numbers of the series $0, \pm 1, \pm 2, \cdots, \pm r$ and the determinant $\neq 0$, is chosen in such a way that first $|\rho_1|$ and then $|\rho_2|$ and finally $|\rho_n|$ become as small as possible. It was seen that the absolute value of the determinant of S is always $\leqq n!$.

Through the substitution S we derive at the same time certain rational approximations for all numbers of the realm $\mathfrak{R}(\alpha)$, if α is real, and if α is complex, for all real numbers of the realm which is composed out of the realm $\mathfrak{R}(\alpha)$ and its conjugate imaginary realm $\mathfrak{R}(\bar{\alpha})$.

Reciprocally, there exists the theorem: *The quantity* α (*if* n *is taken* $>\sigma$) *is necessarily an algebraic number* of the nth degree if with respect to every real quantity $r \geqq 1$ *a substitution* S *for* α *may be derived that corresponds to the conditions* a), b), c), d).

ART. **117.** In the sequel we shall consider α as an algebraic number of the nth degree and $n > \sigma$. Take an unlimited series of increasing numbers $r_1 \geqq 1, r_2, r_3, \cdots$ and corresponding to these numbers construct as indicated above the substitutions $S_1, S_2, S_3, \cdots$. *A substitution of this kind is said to be periodic for the number α if the series of substitutions $Q_1, Q_2, Q_3, \cdots$ derived from them through the composition formulas*

$$S_2 = S_1 Q_1, \qquad S_3 = S_2 Q_2, \qquad \cdots, \qquad S_{j+1} = S_j Q_j, \qquad \cdots$$

neglecting a finite number of initial terms, presents in periodic repetition one and the same finite sequence of substitutions; and that is, *if there is an index j_0 and a positive number p_0 such that for every arbitrary index $j \geqq j_0$ we have always $Q_j = Q_{j+p_0}$.*

We now seek the *character of those algebraic numbers α for which periodic substitutions exist.*

ART. **118.** If the chain $S_1, S_2, S_3, \cdots$ is periodic for α, we have using the above notation

$$Q_j = S_j^{-1} S_{j+1}, \qquad S_j^{-1} S_{j+1} = S_{j+p_0}^{-1} S_{j+p_0+1}, \qquad j \geqq j_0,$$

and therefore also

$$S_{j+p_0} S_j^{-1} = S_{j+p_0+1} S_{j+1}^{-1}, \qquad \text{if} \qquad j \geqq j_0.$$

If we put $S_{j_0+p_0} S_{j_0}^{-1} = P_0$, it follows in general that

$$S_{j+p_0} = P_0 S_j, \qquad S_{j+fp_0} = P_0^f S_j$$

for every index $j \geqq j_0$ and for every exponent $f = 1, 2, 3, \cdots$.

Let φ_j be the linear form into which ξ is transformed through the substitution S_j. Among the infinite number of substitutions $S_{j_0+fp_0}$, where $f = 0, 1, 2, \cdots$, there can appear only a finite number of systems of values in the associated forms $\varphi_{j_0+fp_0}$, since from b) their determinants are limited as are also from d) the ratio of the coefficients $\rho_1 : \rho_2 : \cdots : \rho_n$. Hence we may always find two substitutions $S_{j_0+cp_0} = S$ and $S_{j_0+dp_0} = T$ $(d > c)$ in such a way that first $TS^{-1} = P = P_0^{d-c}$ is an integral substitution with the determinant 1 and in addition and secondly in the two forms $\varphi_{j_0+cp_0} = \varphi$ and $\varphi_{j_0+dp_0} = \psi$ the n coefficients have the same ratios. It follows that $\psi = \theta\varphi$, where θ is a factor considered later. The first requirement is satisfied, if for example we choose S and T, such that their determinants have the same value and in addition to assure integral values we assume that every two corresponding coefficients offer the same residues with respect to the determinant as modulus. The factor θ regarded as the quotient of the coefficients in φ and ψ is like these numbers a quantity of the realm $\Re(\alpha)$. Write $(d-c)p_0 = p$ and observe that

$$Q_j = S_j^{-1}S_{j+1}, \qquad Q_{j+p} = S_{j+p}^{-1}S_{j+p+1}$$

so that $S_{j+p}Q_{j+p} = S_{j+p+1}$. Since $S_{j+p_0} = P_0S_p$ and $S_{j+p} = P_0^{d-c}S_j$, it is seen that $P_0^{d-c}S_jQ_{j+p} = P_0^{d-c}S_{j+1}$, or $Q_{j+p} = S_j^{-1}S_{j+1} = Q_j$, where $j > j_0$. Then from $T = PS$, $\psi = \theta\varphi$ we have $\varphi_{j_0+dp_0} = \theta\varphi_{j_0+cp_0}$, if $j_0 + cp_0 = j$, $\varphi_{j+p} = \theta^f\varphi_j$. Similarly $S_{j+p} = PS_j$ $(j > j_0)$ so that in general

$$S_{j+fp} = P^fS_j, \qquad \varphi_{j+fp} = \theta^f\varphi_j \qquad \text{for} \qquad f = 1, 2, 3, \cdots.$$

Since in the forms φ_j with increasing index j the absolute values of the coefficients decrease towards zero, it follows that $|\theta|$ must be <1.

ART. **119.** If α is a complex quantity, let $\bar{\alpha}$ be its conjugate imaginary. Denote the $n-\sigma$ roots of the irreducible equation which α satisfies, besides α if α is real, and besides α and $\bar{\alpha}$ if α is complex, by $\alpha', \alpha'', \cdots, \alpha^{(n-\sigma)}$. In the realms $\Re(\bar{\alpha}), \Re(\alpha'), \cdots, \Re(\alpha^{(n-\sigma)})$ the numbers conjugate to θ are denoted respectively by $\bar{\theta}, \theta', \cdots, \theta^{(n-\sigma)}$ while the forms conjugate to ξ are $\bar{\xi}, \xi', \cdots, \xi^{(n-\sigma)}$. Through the substitution $TS^{-1} = P = P_0^{d-c}$ (and that is $S_{j_0+dp_0} = PS_{j_0+cp_0}$, or $P = S_{j_0+p}S_{j_0}^{-1}$) the form ξ becomes $\theta\xi$ and due to the irreducibility of the equation of the nth degree which α satisfies we further have $\bar{\xi}$ becoming $\theta\bar{\xi}$; ξ' becoming $\theta\xi'$; $\cdots$ $\xi^{(n-\sigma)}$ becoming $\theta\xi^{(n-\sigma)}$. If t is a variable and E the identical substitution, then the forms $\xi, \cdots, \xi^{(n-\sigma)}$ are transformed through the substitution $tE-P$ into $(t-\theta)\xi$, $\cdots$, $(t-\theta^{(n-1)})\xi^{(n-1)}$ and the determinant of $tE-P$ and that is $|tE-P|$ becomes $=(t-\theta)\cdots(t-\theta^{(n-\sigma)})$. This identical relation in t shows that θ satisfies the equation $|tE-P|=0$. Since P is an integral substitution with determinant $=1$, it is seen that θ is a unit in the realm $\Re(\alpha)$. (Arts. 101 and 105.)

ART. **120.** Let a_0 be a rational integer such that $a_0\alpha$ is an algebraic integer (*A. N.*, Vol. I, p. 122). Then the form $a_0^{n-1}\xi$ has as coefficients only algebraic integers and therefore also in every form $a_0^{n-1}\varphi_j$ the n coefficients $a_0^{n-1}\rho_k$ $(k=1, 2, \cdots, n)$ are algebraic integers different from zero. And the norms of these integers are in absolute values $\geqq 1$.

Due to the property a) of Art. 116 of the substitution S_j it is seen that every absolute value

$$\frac{|\rho_k^{(h)}|}{r_j} \qquad \begin{pmatrix} h=1, \cdots, n-\sigma; \\ k=1, 2, \cdots, n \end{pmatrix}$$

does not lie above a certain limit that is independent of r_j. If we apply the inequalities thus derived for all indices $h=1, 2, \cdots, n-\sigma$ with the exception of one arbitrary index of this series and observe the property c) for S_j (noting the relation $|\rho_k|=|\bar{\rho}_k|$), we derive from the inequality

$$|Nma_0^{n-1}\rho_k| \geqq 0$$

a certain positive lower limit for the one remaining factor $|\rho_k^{(h)}|/r_j$ which is independent of r_j. (See Art. 105.) Accordingly it is seen *that all the absolute values* $\dfrac{|\rho_k^{(h)}|}{r_j}$ *of the form* φ_j *are found between two definite positive quantities that are independent limits; and consequently also the quotients of any two of the conjugate values*

$$\rho_k', \qquad \rho_k'', \qquad \cdots, \qquad \rho_k^{(n-1)} \qquad (k=1, 2, \cdots, n)$$

of all the forms φ_j *are in absolute value situated between two positive finite limits that are independent of* r_j.

If next we consider the relations $\varphi_{j+fp}=\theta^f\varphi_j$ for $f=1, 2, 3, \cdots$, it is seen finally that also the quotients of the absolute values of any two of the $n-1$ quantities

$$(\theta')^f, \qquad (\theta'')^f, \qquad \cdots, \qquad (\theta^{(n-1)})^f$$

must lie between certain two fixed positive finite limits and these limits are at once true for all values $f=1, 2, 3, \cdots$. Hence the unit θ must be such that the following equations

$$|\theta'|=|\theta''|=\cdots=|\theta^{(n-\sigma)}|$$

exist. If we denote the common value of the above absolute values by η and put $|\theta|=\epsilon$ which is also the value of $|\bar{\theta}|$ in case θ is complex, then the equation $Nm\theta=1$ offers the relation $\epsilon^{\sigma}\eta^{n-\sigma}=1$. Since $\epsilon<1$, we must have $\eta>1$. In this manner we have derived the theorem:

In order that an algebraic number α of the nth degree have a periodic substitution, there must be in the realm $\mathfrak{R}(\alpha)$ a unit θ whose absolute value is less than 1, and for which the conjugate units in the conjugate realms (excepting $\bar{\theta}$ in $\mathfrak{R}(\bar{\alpha})$, if α is complex) all have among one another equal absolute values.

ART. 121. The Condition Just Stated Is at the Same Time Sufficient for the Existence of a Periodic Chain of Substitutions for the Number α.

For assume that there exists in $\mathfrak{R}(\alpha)$ a unit θ_0 of the character in question; and let P_0 be the linear substitution through which the n forms ξ, $\bar{\xi}$ (if ξ is complex), ξ', $\cdots$, $\xi^{(n-\sigma)}$ are transformed into $\theta_0\xi$, $\bar{\theta}_0\bar{\xi}$, $\theta_0'\xi'$, $\cdots$, $\theta_0^{(n-\sigma)}\xi^{(n-\sigma)}$. This substitution has only rational coefficients and a determinant $=\pm1$. Through P_0^f, if f is one of the numbers 1, 2, 3, $\cdots$, the forms ξ, $\bar{\xi}$, ξ', $\cdots$, $\xi^{(n-1)}$ are transformed into $\theta_0^f\xi$, $\bar{\theta}_0^f\bar{\xi}$, $(\theta')^f\xi'$, $\cdots$, $(\theta^{(n-\sigma)})^f\xi^{(n-\sigma)}$. Since these powers θ_0^f are all algebraic integers, it is seen that in all the substitutions P_0^f $(f=1, 2, 3, \cdots)$ the coefficients are such rational numbers that their denominators do not exceed a certain limit which is determined by α but which is independent of f, while at the same time their determinants are always $=\pm1$. Thus among the infinite number of substitutions P_0^f there must occur two P_0^c and P_0^d $(d>c)$ such that $P_0^d(P_0^c)^{-1}=P$, say, is a substitution with integral coefficients (Art. 104). If we then put $\theta_0^{d-c}=\theta$ and $|\theta|^{-\frac{\sigma}{n-\sigma}}=\eta$, we have in the series

$$S_1=E, \qquad S_2=P, \qquad S_3=P^2, \qquad \cdots$$

a periodic chain of substitutions for the number α with the properties given in Arts. 116, 117, if in addition for the associated quantities r_j we stipulate that $r_j=\eta^{j-1}$ ($j=1, 2, 3, \cdots$). (See example in Art. 127.)

ART. **122. Units of a Special Character.** We shall now consider further the requirement of the existence of the special unit θ in the realm $\Re(\alpha)$. The integral function of the nth degree in t:

$$F(t)=(t-\theta)\cdots(t-\theta^{(n-\sigma)})$$

has rational integral coefficients. There are σ roots of this equation which have absolute values $\epsilon<1$ while the other $n-\sigma$ roots have absolute values $\eta>1$. In the realm of rational numbers every irreducible factor of $F(t)$ vanishes for at least one of the numbers $\theta, \cdots, \theta^{(n-\sigma)}$ and on account of the irreducibility of the equation with roots $\alpha, \cdots, \alpha^{(n-\sigma)}$ this irreducible factor of $F(t)$ must vanish for all the quantities $\theta, \cdots, \theta^{(n-\sigma)}$, so that $F(t)$ is necessarily the power of an irreducible function. (See *A. N.*, Vol. I, p. 53.) Since only two of the roots of $F(t)$ are in absolute value <1, the power to which the irreducible factor may enter $F(t)$ is at most 2. Thus $F(t)$ is *either* itself irreducible, in which case θ itself determines the realm $\Re(\alpha)$, *or* $F(t)$ is the square of an irreducible function. In this case $\sigma=2$, and as $\theta=f(\alpha)$, say, $=\bar{\theta}=f(\bar{\alpha})$, f denoting a rational function, θ must be real and determines a real sub-realm of the $n/2$ degree of the complex realm $\Re(\alpha)$.

ART. **123.** Due to a theorem of Dirichlet (*A. N.*, Vol. II, p. 233) there exists in every algebraic realm $\Re(\alpha)$ of degree $n>\sigma$ a unit whose absolute value <1. From this it follows at once that in the realm $\Re(\alpha)$ there exists a unit θ of the kind required at least in the following cases:

a) When α is real and $n=2$.

b) When α is real, $n=3$ and $\Re(\alpha)$ has two complex conjugate realms.

c) When α is complex and $n=3$.

d) When α is complex, $n=4$ and $\Re(\alpha)$ has only complex conjugate realms.

e) When α is complex, $n=4$ and the realm $\Re(\alpha)$ has a real sub-realm of the 2nd degree.

f) When α is complex, $n=6$ and $\Re(\alpha)$ has a real sub-realm of degree 3 and the sub-realm has a pair of conjugate complex realms.

In the cases e) and f), $\theta=f(\alpha)$ where f denotes a rational function; and if $f(\alpha)$ is a rational number then is $f(\alpha)=f(\bar{\alpha})=\bar{\theta}$. And the series $\theta', \theta'', \cdots, \theta^{(n-\sigma)}$ has two equal real roots when $n=4$; and when $n=6$ there must be two equal pairs of conjugate imaginary roots.

We may now prove the following theorem. *The six cases just mentioned are the only ones in which the realm $\Re(\alpha)$ offers a unit θ of the kind in question, and therefore the only cases in which the number α has periodic chains of substitution.*

ART. **124.** We shall discuss first the case of a real number α. We then have $\sigma=1$, $\theta=\pm\epsilon$, $\epsilon\eta^{n-1}=1$. We must consider the following possibilities: a) when there are two or more real roots among the $\alpha', \alpha'', \cdots, \alpha^{(n-1)}$, b) when among them there is only one real root, and c) when there is no real root.

a) Consider the first case when there are at least two real roots among $\alpha', \alpha'', \cdots, \alpha^{(n-1)}$, and let $\alpha^{(h)}$ and $\alpha^{(k)}$ be two real quantities. $\theta^{(h)}$ and $\theta^{(k)}$ are then also real, being rational functions of real numbers. Since these quantities can not be equal, although in absolute value they must be equal, we have $\theta^{(h)}=-\theta^{(k)}$ and therefore $(\theta^{(h)})^2=(\theta^{(k)})^2$. But the number $\theta^2=\epsilon^2$ is different from its $n-1$ conjugates. It therefore satisfies an irreducible equation, and its $n-1$ conjugates must also be different among one another (*A. N.*, Vol. I, Art. 68) since we must have the condition $|\theta'|=|\theta''|=\cdots=|\theta^{(n-\sigma)}|$. This case is accordingly impossible.

b) Among the quantities $\alpha', \alpha'', \cdots, \alpha^{(n-1)}$ suppose that *only one* $\alpha^{(g)}$ is real. For $n=2$, this is the case given above under Art. 123, a). If $n>2$, we must have at least one pair of conjugate imaginaries, say $\alpha^{(h)}$, $\alpha^{(k)}$, among α', α'', $\cdots$, $\alpha^{(n-1)}$. The number $\theta^2 = \epsilon^2$ satisfies an irreducible equation of the nth degree and one root is the real quantity $[\theta^{(g)}]^2 = \eta^2$. The other roots are all in absolute value $= \eta^2$. Form the equation of degree $\frac{n(n-1)}{2}$ by taking the products in pairs of the n quantities θ, θ', $\cdots$, $\theta^{(n-1)}$, no two pairs being the same. This equation has $n-1$ roots which in absolute value $= \epsilon\eta$, the remaining roots being in absolute value $= \eta^2$ and among the latter there is one, namely $\theta^{(h)}\theta^{(k)} = \eta^2$. It must accordingly have as roots all the other roots of the above mentioned irreducible equation of the nth degree, one of which is ϵ^2. As it does *not* have ϵ^2 as a root, this case for $n > 2$ is impossible.

c) The numbers α', α'', $\cdots$, $\alpha^{(n-1)}$ are here all complex falling into $\frac{n-1}{2}$ pairs of complex imaginaries. For $n = 3$ we have the case above in Art. 123, b). Next let $n > 3$ and form the equation of the $\frac{n(n-1)}{2}$ degree which has as roots the products of every two of the n quantities θ^{-n+1}, $(\theta')^{-n+1}$, $\cdots$, $(\theta^{(n-1)})^{-n+1}$. This equation has $n-1$ roots of absolute value $(\epsilon\eta)^{-n+1} = \eta^{(n-1)(n-2)}$, while the other roots are all in absolute value $\eta^{-2(n-1)} = \epsilon^2$ and among these there are $n-2$ roots $= \epsilon^2 = \theta^2$. This equation must therefore have all the quantities θ'^2, $\cdots$, $(\theta^{(n-1)})^2$ as roots. The absolute values of these quantities being η^2 we must have $\eta^2 = \eta^{(n-1)(n-2)}$ and that is $n = 3$. The case where $n > 3$ is impossible.

ART. **125.** We must now consider further the case of a complex quantity α. We have here $\sigma = 2$, $\epsilon^2\eta^{n-2} = 1$. We make first the assumption that $\theta = \bar{\theta}$ and is therefore real. θ is here the root of an irreducible equation of the $\frac{n}{2}$ degree. Hence the realm $\mathfrak{R}(\alpha)$ has a real sub-realm of degree $\frac{n}{2}$. And in this sub-realm θ is a unit in absolute value < 1, while the conjugate units in the conjugate realms are equal in absolute value since always the condition

$$|\theta'| = |\theta''| = \cdots = |\theta^{(n-\sigma)}|$$

must be satisfied. Proceeding with this sub-realm as in the similar case of Art. 124 we see that either $\frac{n}{2}=2$ or $=3$. Thus it is clear that associated with $\Re(\theta)$ there are two complex conjugate realms and this leads us to the cases Art. 123, e) and f).

On the other hand we have next the case that $\theta \neq \theta$. θ then satisfies an irreducible equation of the nth degree so that $\Re(\theta) = \Re(\alpha)$ where a) at least two of the quantities α', α'', $\cdots$, $\alpha^{(n-2)}$ are real, or b) only one is real, or c) none is real.

a) Among the quantities α', $\cdots$, $\alpha^{(n-2)}$ suppose that at least two $\alpha^{(h)}$ and $\alpha^{(k)}$ are real. It follows that $\theta^{(h)}$ and $\theta^{(k)}$ are also real and as they can not be equal, due to the irreducibility of the equation which they satisfy, we must have $\theta^{(h)} = -\theta^{(k)}$ since the absolute values of these quantities $=\eta$. We then have $(\theta^{(h)})^2 = (\theta^{(k)})^2$. Hence the rational equation of the nth degree with roots θ^2, $\bar{\theta}^2$, θ'^2, $\cdots$, $(\theta^{(n-2)})^2$ has only double roots and hence also $\theta^2 = \bar{\theta}^2$. Accordingly θ^2 determines a real sub-realm of degree $\frac{n}{2}$ and this is the case Art. 123, e) with $n=4$. Observe that $(\theta^{(h)})^2$ is also real.

b) Among the quantities α', $\cdots$, $\alpha^{(n-2)}$ suppose that there is only one real root $\alpha^{(g)}$. For $n=3$ this falls under the case Art. 123, c). If $n>3$ we have $\frac{n-3}{2}$ pairs of conjugate roots. Observe that $\theta^{(g)} = \pm\eta$, and since $-\theta^{(g)}$ does not satisfy here the same equation with rational coefficients that θ satisfies, there being by hypothesis only one real root, it follows also necessarily that $\theta \neq -\bar{\theta}$ and therefore $\theta^2 \neq \pm\epsilon^2$, $\bar{\theta}^2 \neq \pm\epsilon^2$. Accordingly the rational equations of the nth degree with roots θ^2, $\bar{\theta}^2$, $\cdots$, $(\theta^{(n-2)})^2$ is irreducible and among the roots of this equation there are two *not* real roots in absolute value $=\epsilon^2$ and further one root $=\eta^2$. Next form the rational equation of degree $\frac{n(n-1)}{2}$ which has as roots the products of every two of the quantities $\theta, \bar{\theta}, \theta', \cdots, \theta^{(n-2)}$. This equation has one root $=\epsilon^2$, $2(n-2)$ roots of absolute value $=\epsilon\eta$. The remaining roots are in absolute value $=\eta^2$ and among these there are $\frac{n-3}{2}$ roots $=\eta^2$. Hence they must all be roots of the above irreducible equation which has η^2 as a root. As this is not true the case $n>3$ is impossible.

c) Suppose that the numbers $\alpha', \alpha'', \cdots, \alpha^{(n-2)}$ are all complex, constituting $\frac{n-2}{2}$ pairs of conjugate imaginary quantities. The integer n is here even. For $n=4$ we have the case given above under Art. 123, d). Now let n be $\geqq 6$. Form the equation of the $\frac{n(n-1)}{2}$ degree which has as roots the product of every two of the n quantities $\theta, \cdots, \theta^{(n-2)}$. This equation with rational coefficients has one root $=\epsilon^2$, $2(n-2)$ in absolute value $=\epsilon\eta$, and the remaining roots in absolute value $=\eta^2$, among which there are $\frac{n-2}{2}$ roots $=\eta^2$. Then form another equation of the $\frac{n(n-1)}{2}$ degree whose roots are the $-\frac{n-2}{2}$th power of the roots of the first equation. This new equation with rational coefficients has one root $=\epsilon^{-(n-2)}=\eta^{\frac{(n-2)^2}{2}}$ and $2(n-2)$ roots in absolute value $=(\epsilon\eta)^{\frac{-(n-2)}{2}}=\eta^{\frac{(n-2)(n-4)}{4}}$, the remaining roots are in absolute value $\eta^{-(n-2)}=\epsilon^2$, among which there are $\frac{n-2}{2}=\epsilon^2$. This second equation has no root of absolute value $=\epsilon\eta$, and if *first* we consider the case $n>6$ the two equations under consideration have only the one root ϵ^2 in common. Hence the greatest common divisor of these two equations shows that $\epsilon^2(=\theta\bar{\theta})$ is a rational number. But ϵ^2 being like θ an algebraic unit with norm $= \pm 1$, it follows necessarily that $\epsilon^2 = 1$, which is contrary to the assumption that $\epsilon < 1$. Hence the case $n > 6$ is not permissible.

In *the case* $n = 6$ the first of the equations considered above has one root $= \epsilon^2$, eight roots in absolute value $= \epsilon\eta$, six roots in absolute value $= \eta^2$ while the second equation has one root $= \eta^8$, eight roots in absolute value η^2, six roots in absolute value $= \epsilon^2$ of which two are $= \epsilon^2$. The irreducible equation in the realm of rational numbers having ϵ^2 as a root and therefore entering as a factor in both of the above equations can have only roots in absolute value $= \eta^2$. Since here $\epsilon^2\eta^4 = 1$ and as $\epsilon^2 = \theta\bar{\theta}$ and the other two roots being roots of a cubic and not real must be complex imaginary. We may take θ', θ''' as complex imaginaries as also θ'', $\theta^{(4)}$, it being merely a matter of notation. The roots of this irreducible equation in the realm of rational numbers are accordingly $\epsilon^2 (= \theta\bar{\theta})$, $\theta'\theta'''$, $\theta''\theta^{(4)}$, and is

$$t^3 - g_1 t^2 + g_2 t - 1 = 0,$$

where g_1 and g_2 are rational integers.

Consider next the integral function $F(t)$, irreducible in the realm of rational numbers, which vanishes for $t = \theta$. Suppose that this function $F(t)$ is decomposed into its irreducible factors in the realm of ϵ^2 and that is in $\mathfrak{R}(\epsilon^2)$. Let $G(t)$ be that one of the irreducible factors which has the root $t = \theta$. Since ϵ^2 is real, $G(t)$ has only real coefficients and therefore it must have as a root the conjugate of θ and that is $\bar{\theta} = \frac{\epsilon^2}{\theta}$, so that $G(\epsilon^2/\theta) = 0$. Hence the equation $G(\epsilon^2/t) = 0$ must have as roots all the roots of the equation $G(t) = 0$, which is irreducible in $\mathfrak{R}(\epsilon^2)$. The quantities $\frac{\epsilon^2}{\theta'}$, $\frac{\epsilon^2}{\theta''}$, $\frac{\epsilon^2}{\theta'''}$, $\frac{\epsilon^2}{\theta^{(4)}}$, however, have absolute values $\frac{\epsilon^2}{\eta}$. And this quantity is not equal either to ϵ or to η. Hence the four quantities just written are not roots of $F(t) = 0$, and therefore they are not roots of $G(t) = 0$. Similarly it is seen that $G(t)$ can not have as roots θ', θ'', θ''', $\theta^{(4)}$. We may accordingly write simply $G(t)=(t-\theta)(t-\bar{\theta})$. Thus it is seen that θ is the root of a quadratic equation in $\Re(\epsilon^2)$, with the result that the realm of the sixth degree $\Re(\theta)$, and that is $\Re(\alpha)$, has a real sub-realm of the third degree and the two conjugate realms of the sub-realm are complex. And this is the case given above under Art. 123, f).

The above conditions offer a means of forming more exactly the realm $\Re(\alpha)$. The functions conjugate to $G(t)$ in the realms $\Re(\theta'\theta''')$ and $\Re(\theta''\theta^{(4)})$ are $(t-\theta')(t-\theta''')$ and $(t-\theta'')(t-\theta^{(4)})$.

Observe that if the absolute values of two complex quantities θ' and θ''' are equal, then $\dfrac{\theta'-\theta'''}{\theta'+\theta'''}$ is a pure imaginary and consequently $\left(\dfrac{\theta'-\theta'''}{\theta'+\theta'''}\right)^2$ is a negative real number. Observe further that $\theta'+\theta'''$ and $\theta'\theta'''$ being coefficients of $(t-\theta')(t-\theta''')$ in the realm $\Re(\theta'\theta''')$ are quantities of this realm as is also $\left(\dfrac{\theta'-\theta'''}{\theta'+\theta'''}\right)^2$, which being real and equal to its conjugate $\left(\dfrac{\theta''-\theta^{(4)}}{\theta''+\theta^{(4)}}\right)^2$ in the conjugate imaginary realm $\Re(\theta''\theta^{(4)})$, is a rational number and is therefore equal to the conjugate quantity $\left(\dfrac{\theta-\bar{\theta}}{\theta+\bar{\theta}}\right)^2$ in $\Re(\theta\bar{\theta})$. There being choice in the notation, it is seen that we may write

$$\frac{\theta}{\bar{\theta}}=\frac{\theta'}{\theta'''}=\frac{\theta^{(4)}}{\theta''}=\frac{1}{\delta}$$

say, where δ in absolute value $=1$ and is as θ a unit. Hence δ is *either* $=-1$ *or* it is a root of unity which determines a realm of the 2nd degree. In the first case $\theta=-\bar{\theta}$, $\theta=\pm i\epsilon$, $\theta^2=(\bar{\theta})^2$. In the second case the third, fourth and sixth roots of unity are to be considered in determining δ. Now observe that $\theta=\delta^{1/2}\epsilon$, $\bar{\theta}=\dfrac{1}{\delta^{1/2}}\,\epsilon$ and also $\epsilon\eta^2=\epsilon\theta'\theta''=1$. It is further seen that

$$Nm(\theta+\bar{\theta})=(\theta+\bar{\theta})(\theta'+\theta''')(\theta''+\theta^{(4)})=\frac{\delta+1}{\delta^{1/2}}\left(1+\frac{1}{\delta}\right)(1+\delta).$$

As the left hand side of this expression is a rational number, it is seen that $\frac{\delta+1}{\delta^{1/2}}$ must be rational so that $\delta=\omega^2$, where $1, \omega, \omega^2$ are the cube roots of unity. It follows that $\theta=\pm\omega^2\epsilon$, $\bar{\theta}=\pm\omega\epsilon$ and consequently $\theta+\bar{\theta}=\pm\epsilon$. As seen above $\theta+\bar{\theta}$ was a number of $\Re(\epsilon^2)$, since $\epsilon^2=\theta\bar{\theta}$. It is thus seen that ϵ is a number of $\Re(\epsilon^2)$. Thus, it follows also that $\Re(\alpha)$ is composed of the realm of the third degree of ϵ and the realm of the second degree of ω, $\omega^2=\frac{-1\pm\sqrt{-3}}{2}$.

ART. 126. **The Complex Cubic Irrational Numbers.** In the cases where chains of periodic substitutions for the algebraic number α are possible, the problem is to derive such a chain for α when the value of α is given while the algebraic conjugates of α are unknown. In the case of the real algebraic number of the second degree the required problem was solved through the periodic development in an ordinary continued fraction. It may be shown that when α is a *complex* quantity, being the root of an irreducible equation of the third degree, there exists a completely analogous criterion as was proved by Lagrange for the real algebraic numbers of the second degree namely in the periodicity of the development in continued fractions.

Let α be a complex quantity which in the realm of rational numbers satisfies an irreducible equation of the third degree. The value of the conjugate $\bar{\alpha}$ follows at once, however, the value of a real third root α' for the time being is disregarded. Write

$$\xi=x_1+\alpha x_2+\alpha^2 x_3$$

and for each rational integer $r\geqq 1$ determine a substitution S

$$x_h=s_h^{(1)}y_1+s_h^{(2)}y_2+s_h^{(3)}y_3 \qquad (h=1, 2, 3),$$

where every coefficient $s_h^{(k)}$ is taken from the integers 0, ± 1, $\pm 2, \cdots \pm r$ and determinant $\neq 0$, such that the linear form ξ becomes through S:

$$\varphi = \rho_1 y_1 + \rho_2 y_2 + \rho_3 y_3,$$

where $|\rho_1|$ is as small as possible and finally $|\rho_2|$ is as small as possible and finally $|\rho_3|$ is as small as possible. As we have choice of values between x_1, x_2, x_3 and $-x_1$, $-x_2$, $-x_3$ we shall make the additional assumption that in each vertical row $s_1^{(k)}$, $s_2^{(k)}$, $s_3^{(k)}$ of S the last number different from zero is positive. With this assumption the substitution S is *uniquely determined* through r. And that is we cannot find two systems x_1, x_2, x_3 that are not 0, 0, 0 and that are not the negatives of one another which offer $\xi = \rho$ and $\xi = \sigma$ where $|\rho| = |\sigma|$. For in that case we would have $\frac{\rho\bar{\rho}}{\sigma\bar{\sigma}} = 1$, and if we consider the norm of $\frac{\rho}{\sigma}$ in the cubic realm $\Re(\alpha)$ it is seen that the number $\frac{\rho'}{\sigma'}$ in the realm $\Re(\alpha')$ is rational. And then $\frac{\rho}{\sigma}$ would be rational and necessarily $= \pm 1$ so that the two systems x_1, x_2, x_3 would necessarily be either equal or of opposite values. We may accordingly say that the substitution S *belongs* to r. (See Art. 98.)

We now write $r_1 = 1$ and derive the substitution S_1 which belongs to r_1. This substitution may also belong to $r = 2$, $3, \cdots$. Let $r_2 - 1$ be the largest integer to which S_1 belongs. Then let S_2 be the substitution belonging to r_2, etc. We then have the following theorem:

The chain of substitutions S_1, S_2, S_3, $\cdots$ that are derived in the above manner for the complex cubic irrational number α is periodic.

ART. **127.** In fact, in the realm $\Re(\alpha)$ we may always derive a unit θ_0 (*A. N.*, Vol. I, p. 590) whose absolute value <1 and such that $\theta_0' > 1$. Then as shown in Art. 121 we may derive a power θ_0^f, where $f > 0$, such that $\theta_0^f = \theta$ and is such that the linear substitution P through which the forms ξ, $\bar{\xi}$, ξ' are transformed into $\theta\xi$, $\bar{\theta}\bar{\xi}$, $\theta'\xi'$ has all its coefficients integers and the determinant of P is $=1$.

Writing

$$x_1+\alpha x_2+\alpha^2 x_3=\xi,$$
$$x_1+\bar{\alpha}x_2+(\bar{\alpha})^2 x_3=\bar{\xi},$$
$$x_1+\alpha' x_2+(\alpha')^2 x_3=\xi',$$

where α, $\bar{\alpha}$, α' are the roots of $x^3+ax^2+bx+c=0$, it is seen that

$$x_1=\frac{\begin{vmatrix}\xi, & \alpha, & \alpha^2\\ \bar{\xi}, & \bar{\alpha}, & (\bar{\alpha})^2\\ \xi', & \alpha', & (\alpha')^2\end{vmatrix}}{\begin{vmatrix}1, & \alpha, & \alpha^2\\ 1, & \bar{\alpha}, & (\bar{\alpha})^2\\ 1, & \alpha', & (\alpha')^2\end{vmatrix}}=\frac{\xi\begin{vmatrix}\bar{\alpha}, & (\bar{\alpha})^2\\ \alpha', & (\alpha')^2\end{vmatrix}-\bar{\xi}\begin{vmatrix}\alpha, & \alpha^2\\ \alpha', & (\alpha')^2\end{vmatrix}+\xi'\begin{vmatrix}\alpha, & \alpha^2\\ \bar{\alpha}, & (\bar{\alpha})^2\end{vmatrix}}{(\bar{\alpha}-\alpha)(\alpha'-\bar{\alpha})(\alpha-\alpha')}$$

$$=\xi\frac{\bar{\alpha}\alpha'}{(\bar{\alpha}-\alpha)(\alpha-\alpha')}+\bar{\xi}\frac{\alpha\alpha'}{(\bar{\alpha}-\alpha)(\alpha'-\bar{\alpha})}+\xi'\frac{\alpha\bar{\alpha}}{(\alpha-\bar{\alpha})(\alpha-\alpha')}$$

$$=\xi\frac{-\dfrac{c}{\alpha}}{b+\dfrac{2c}{\alpha}-\alpha^2}+\bar{\xi}\frac{-\dfrac{c}{\bar{\alpha}}}{b+\dfrac{2c}{\bar{\alpha}}-(\bar{\alpha})^2}+\xi'\frac{-\dfrac{c}{\alpha'}}{b+\dfrac{2c}{\alpha'}-(\alpha')^2}.$$

Observe that the coefficients of ξ, $\bar{\xi}$, and ξ' are conjugates in the realms $\Re(\alpha)$, $\Re(\bar{\alpha})$, $\Re(\alpha')$.

Similarly, we have

$$x_2=\xi\frac{\alpha+a}{b+\dfrac{2c}{\alpha}-\alpha^2}+\bar{\xi}\frac{\bar{\alpha}+a}{b+\dfrac{2c}{\bar{\alpha}}-(\bar{\alpha})^2}+\xi'\frac{\alpha'+a}{b+\dfrac{2c}{\alpha'}-(\alpha')^2},$$

$$x_3=\frac{\xi}{b+\dfrac{2c}{\alpha}-\alpha^2}+\frac{\bar{\xi}}{b+\dfrac{2c}{\bar{\alpha}}-(\bar{\alpha}^2)}+\frac{\xi'}{b+\dfrac{2c}{\alpha'}-(\alpha')^2}.$$

Let S: $\qquad x_h=s_h^{(1)}y_1+s_h^{(2)}y_2+s_h^{(3)}y_3 \qquad (h=1, 2, 3)$

be a substitution of the chain formed above, to which this

substitution S belongs so that r is the greatest value among the absolute values of the nine coefficients $s_h^{(k)}$ and let the linear form ξ be transformed through S into

$$\varphi = \rho_1 y_1 + \rho_2 y_2 + \rho_3 y_3.$$

It follows that

$$x_h = s_h^{(1)} y_1 + s_h^{(2)} y_2 + s_h^{(3)} y_3 = \beta_h \varphi + \bar{\beta}_h \bar{\varphi} + \beta_h' \varphi' \quad (h=1, 2, 3);$$

and from this we have

$$s_h^{(k)} = \beta_h \rho_k + \bar{\beta}_h \bar{\rho}_k + \beta_h' \rho_k'. \quad (h, k=1, 2, 3).$$

Due to the property c) of Art. 116 we may determine a positive finite constant M dependent upon α but independent of r, such that $|\rho_1|r^{1/2}$, $|\rho_2|r^{1/2}$, $|\rho_3|r^{1/2}$ are $\leqq M$ for every value of r and by considering the norm as in Art. 120 we may determine a further positive number $\dfrac{M}{N}$ which is independent of r and such that $|\rho_1'|r^{-1}$, $|\rho_2'|r^{-1}$, $|\rho_3'|r^{-1}$ are always $\geqq \dfrac{M}{N}$.

Making use of these inequalities we may prove certain interesting properties for the substitution $T=PS$ if only r is taken greater than a certain definite quantity. Through the substitution $T=PS$ the forms ξ, $\bar{\xi}$, ξ' are transformed into $\theta\varphi$, $\bar{\theta}\bar{\varphi}$, $\theta'\varphi'$. Let the substitution T be

$$x_h = t_h^{(1)} y_1 + t_h^{(2)} y_2 + t_h^{(3)} y_3 \quad (h=1, 2, 3).$$

It then follows that

$$t_h^{(k)} = \theta \beta_h \rho_k + \bar{\theta} \bar{\beta}_h \bar{\rho}_k + \theta' \beta_h' \rho_k' \quad (h, k=1, 2, 3).$$

We then have

$$\frac{t_h^{(k)}}{s_h^{(k)}} = \theta' \frac{1 + \dfrac{\theta \beta_h}{\theta' \beta_h'} \dfrac{\rho_k}{\rho_k'} + \dfrac{\bar{\theta} \bar{\beta}_h}{\theta' \beta_h'} \dfrac{\bar{\rho}_k}{\rho_k'}}{1 + \dfrac{\beta_h}{\beta_h'} \dfrac{\rho_k}{\rho_k'} + \dfrac{\bar{\beta}_h}{\beta_h'} \dfrac{\bar{\rho}_k}{\rho_k'}}.$$

Write $|\theta| = \epsilon$ so that, since $|\bar{\theta}| = \epsilon$, we have $|\theta'| = \dfrac{1}{\epsilon^2}$;

and denote the greatest value of the absolute values among $\frac{\beta_h}{\beta'_h}$ $(h=1, 2, 3)$ by γ. For the ratio $\frac{t_h^{(k)}}{s_h^{(k)}}$ we wish to determine upper and lower limits which are dependent on r and θ' in such a way that as soon as r is taken sufficiently large, it can be shown that the inequality

$$\text{(I)} \qquad \theta' - \frac{1}{2r} < \frac{t_h^{(k)}}{s_h^{(k)}} < \theta' + \frac{1}{2r}$$

is always satisfied.

To secure this result we note that as long as $2\gamma N r^{-3/2} < 1$ it follows that

$$\frac{t_h^{(k)}}{s_h^{(k)}} < \theta' \frac{1+2\epsilon^3\gamma N r^{-3/2}}{1-2\gamma N r^{-3/2}} = \theta'\left(1+\frac{2(\epsilon^3+1)\gamma N r^{-3/2}}{1-2\gamma N r^{-3/2}}\right).$$

Hence we must be able to take r large enough that the inequality

$$\text{(Ia)} \qquad \theta' \frac{2(\epsilon^3+1)\gamma N r^{-3/2}}{1-2\gamma N r^{-3/2}} < \frac{1}{2r}$$

is satisfied. If this is done, then

$$2\theta'(\epsilon^3+1)\gamma N r^{-1/2} < \tfrac{1}{2} - \gamma N r^{-3/2}$$

and that is [1]

$$\text{(Ib)} \qquad [2\theta'(\epsilon^3+1)+r^{-1}]\gamma N r^{-1/2} < \tfrac{1}{2}$$

is satisfied. Hence a necessary and sufficient condition that (Ia) be satisfied is that r be large enough to satisfy (Ib). Since $r^{-1} < 1 < \theta'$, a *sufficient* condition that (Ib) (and consequently (Ia)) be satisfied is that the inequality

$$\text{(II)} \qquad 2\theta'(\epsilon^3+\tfrac{3}{2})\gamma N r^{-1/2} < \tfrac{1}{2}$$

exist. It follows then that (II) is a sufficient condition for the right hand side of (I).

On the other hand, as long as $2\gamma N r^{-3/2} < 1$, it follows that

$$\frac{t_h^{(k)}}{s_h^{(k)}} > \theta' \frac{1-2\epsilon^3\gamma N r^{-3/2}}{1+2\gamma N r^{-3/2}} = \theta'\left(1-\frac{2(\epsilon^3+1)\gamma N r^{-3/2}}{1+2\gamma N r^{-3/2}}\right)$$
$$> \theta'(1-2(\epsilon^3+1)\gamma N r^{-3/2}) > \theta'(1-2(\epsilon^3+\tfrac{3}{2})\gamma N r^{-3/2}).$$

[1] The inequalities (I) and (II) derived by Minkowski (*Ges. Abhandl.*, Vol. I, p. 370) are incorrect.

Using (II) it is seen that the left hand side of (I) is satisfied. Hence also (II) is a sufficient condition for (I).

If the absolute values of all the numbers $s_h^{(k)} \leqq r$ and at least one of these numbers $= \pm r$, we find that the absolute values of the numbers $t_h^{(k)}$ are $< \theta' r + \frac{1}{2}$ and that at least one of these numbers in absolute value is $> \theta' r - \frac{1}{2}$. Hence the greatest among the nine coefficients $t_h^{(k)}$ in absolute value *is equal to the integer that stands nearest to $\theta' r$.* This integer we shall denote by $\bar{r}$. We further find that all the numbers $s_h^{(k)} \neq 0$ and the quotients $\dfrac{t_h^{(k)}}{s_h^{(k)}} > 0$, and consequently in every system $t_1^{(k)}, t_2^{(k)}, t_3^{(k)}$ that appears in T, the last number that is different from zero, namely $t_3^{(k)}$, is > 0 as was assumed to be the case in the corresponding substitution S.

ART. **128.** Reciprocally, if $\bar{r}$ is the largest number to which the matrix T belongs we may obtain an upper and a lower bound for the ratio

$$\frac{s_h^{(k)}}{t_h^{(k)}} = \frac{1}{\theta'} \frac{1 + \dfrac{\beta_h}{\beta_h'} \dfrac{\rho_k}{\rho_k'} + \dfrac{\bar{\beta}_h}{\bar{\beta}_h'} \dfrac{\bar{\rho}_k}{\bar{\rho}_k'}}{1 + \dfrac{\theta}{\theta'} \dfrac{\beta_h}{\beta_h'} \dfrac{\rho_k}{\rho_k'} + \dfrac{\bar{\theta}}{\theta'} \dfrac{\bar{\beta}_h}{\bar{\beta}_h'} \dfrac{\bar{\rho}_k}{\bar{\rho}_k'}},$$

these bounds being dependent on θ' and $\bar{r}$ in such a way that for sufficiently large $\bar{r}$ we have

$$\text{(I}') \qquad \frac{1}{\theta'} - \frac{1}{2\bar{r}} < \frac{s_h^{(k)}}{t_h^{(k)}} < \frac{1}{\theta'} + \frac{1}{2\bar{r}}.$$

To prove this observe that as long as $\bar{r}$ is large enough to make $2\gamma N \bar{r}^{-3/2} < 1$, we have

$$\frac{s_h^{(k)}}{t_h^{(k)}} < \frac{1}{\theta'} \frac{1 + 2\gamma N r^{-3/2}}{1 + 2\epsilon^3 \gamma N r^{-3/2}} < \frac{1}{\theta'} \left(1 + \frac{2(\epsilon^3 + 1)\gamma N r^{-3/2}}{1 - 2\epsilon^3 \gamma N r^{-3/2}}\right).$$

Take $\bar{r}$ sufficiently large that

$$\text{(I}'\text{a)} \qquad \frac{1}{\theta'} \frac{2(\epsilon^3 + 1)\gamma N \bar{r}^{-3/2}}{1 - 2\epsilon^3 \gamma N \bar{r}^{-3/2}} < \frac{1}{2\bar{r}}.$$

We then have

$$\frac{2}{\theta'}(\epsilon^3+1)\gamma N\bar{r}^{-1/2}<\frac{1}{2}-\epsilon^3\gamma N\bar{r}^{-3/2}$$

or

$$\left[\frac{2}{\theta'}(\epsilon^3+1)+\epsilon^3\bar{r}^{-1}\right]\gamma N\bar{r}^{-1/2}<\frac{1}{2}.$$

Hence as $0<\epsilon<1$ we have as a sufficient condition

$$\text{(I'b)} \qquad \left[\frac{2}{\theta'}\left(1+\frac{1}{\epsilon^3}\right)+\bar{r}^{-1}\right]\gamma N\bar{r}^{-1/2}<\frac{1}{2}.$$

But $\bar{r}^{-1}<1/(\theta'\epsilon^3)$ so that the inequality (I'a) will certainly be satisfied if $\bar{r}$ is large enough to satisfy

$$\left[\frac{2}{\theta'}\left(1+\frac{1}{\epsilon^3}\right)+\frac{1}{\theta'\epsilon^3}\right]\gamma N\bar{r}^{-1/2}<\frac{1}{2},$$

or what is the same, if

$$\text{(II')} \qquad \frac{2}{\theta'}\left(1+\frac{3}{2}\cdot\frac{1}{\epsilon^3}\right)\gamma N\bar{r}^{-1/2}<\frac{1}{2}.$$

Hence (II′) is a sufficient condition for the right hand side of (I′).

On the other hand, as long as $2\gamma N\bar{r}^{-3/2}<1$, we have

$$\frac{s_h^{(k)}}{t_h^{(k)}}>\frac{1}{\theta'}\frac{1-2\gamma N\bar{r}^{-3/2}}{1+2\epsilon^3\gamma N\bar{r}^{-3/2}}=\frac{1}{\theta'}\left(1-\frac{2\gamma(\epsilon^3+1)N\bar{r}^{-3/2}}{1+2\gamma\epsilon^3N\bar{r}^{-3/2}}\right),$$

and since $1+2\epsilon^3\gamma N\bar{r}^{-3/2}>1$, and $0<\epsilon<1$, it follows that

$$\begin{aligned}\frac{s_h^{(k)}}{t_h^{(k)}}&>\frac{1}{\theta'}[1-2\gamma(\epsilon^3+1)N\bar{r}^{-3/2}]\\&>\frac{1}{\theta'}\left[1-2\gamma\left(1+\frac{1}{\epsilon^3}\right)N\bar{r}^{-3/2}\right]\\&>\frac{1}{\theta'}\left[1-2\gamma\left(1+\frac{3}{2}\cdot\frac{1}{\epsilon^3}\right)N\bar{r}^{-3/2}\right].\end{aligned}$$

In other words as long as $\bar{r}$ is large enough to satisfy $2\frac{1}{\theta'}\gamma\left(1+\frac{3}{2}\cdot\frac{1}{\epsilon^3}\right)N\bar{r}^{-3/2}<1/(2\bar{r})$, the left hand side of (I′) is satisfied. A sufficient condition that this last inequality be satisfied is that (II′) be satisfied. Thus, (II′) is a sufficient condition for (I′). With this it is seen that the largest in absolute value among the coefficients $s_h^{(k)}$ is equal to the greatest integer that stands next to $(\theta')^{-1}\bar{r}$.

ART. **129.** Consider again, as in Art. 127, any substitution S of the chain and *let* r *be* the smallest integer to which S belongs that satisfies the condition (II) and let $\bar{r}$, the integer standing next to $\theta' r$, satisfy the condition (II′). We may then assert *that* $T=PS$ *is a substitution of the chain and belongs to* $\bar{r}$ *as the lowest integer*. For in T and due to (II) all the coefficients $t_h^{(k)}$ in absolute value are $\leqq \bar{r}$ and in addition in each vertical line of T the last number different from zero is positive. Were the substitution T^* of the chain which belongs to the number $\bar{r}$ different from the substitution T and if the linear form ξ is transformed through T^* into $\theta(\rho_1^* y_1+\rho_2^* y_2+\rho_3^* y_3)$, then we must have either $|\rho_1^*|<|\rho_1|$, or $|\rho_1^*|=|\rho_1|$ and $|\rho_2^*|<|\rho_2|$, or $|\rho_1^*|=|\rho_1|$, $|\rho_2^*|=|\rho_2|$ and $|\rho_3^*|<|\rho_3|$.

In the substitution $S^*=P^{-1}T^*$ due to (II′) all the coefficients in absolute value are

$$<\frac{\bar{r}}{\theta'}+\frac{1}{2}<\frac{1}{\theta'}\left(\theta' r+\frac{1}{2}\right)+\frac{1}{2}<r+1,$$

and therefore as integers also $\leqq r$; and accordingly the form ξ would through the substitution S become $\rho_1^* y_1+\rho_2^* y_2+\rho_3^* y_3$ and S would not be the substitution of the chain belonging to r.

If on the other hand T is such a substitution of the chain which belongs to $\bar{r}>\theta'$ as the lowest number; and if both $\bar{r}$ satisfies the condition (II′) as does also r, where r is the integer standing next to $\theta^{-1}\bar{r}$, then in an analogous manner we see that also $S=P^{-1}T$ *is* a substitution of the chain and belongs to r as the lowest number.

ART. **130.** We next choose in the series $r_1, r_2, r_3, \cdots$ the quantity r_{j_0} such that the inequality (II) with $r=r_{j_0}$ and the inequality (II′) with $\bar{r}=\theta' r_{j_0}-\frac{1}{2}$ are satisfied. We then come with the substitution S_{j_0} in the chain to a later substitution PS_{j_0}, say S_{j_0+p}, and here r_{j_0+p} is the integer standing next to $\theta' r_{j_0}$. The inequality (II) is true of every quantity $r=r_j$ where $j>j_0$ and (II′) is true for every quantity $\bar{r}=r_{j+p}$ where $j>j_0$. Hence with every substitution S_{j+p} $(j>j_0)$ the substitution $P^{-1}S_{j+p}$ will also belong to the chain and as a later term the greater j is. From this it then follows that the substitutions PS_{j_0}, PS_{j_0+1}, PS_{j_0+2}, $\cdots$ all appear in the chain and every substitution comes later than the one previously named here, and on the other hand in this chain no substitution may appear between these individual substitutions, so that in general we have $PS_j=S_{j+p}$ for $j=j_0$, j_0+1, j_0+2, $\cdots$. From these conditions it is seen that

$$S_j^{-1}S_{j+1}=S_{j+p}^{-1}S_{j+p+1}$$

for $j\geqq j_0$; and that is the chain S_1, S_2, S_3, $\cdots$ is in fact periodic. Q.E.D.

EXAMPLE. Prove that for every substitution S of the chain the determinant can only have the values ± 1 or ± 2, and from this fact derive a simple algorithm for the successive formations of the substitutions of the chain.

Minkowski, *Gesammelte Abhandlungen*, Vol. I, p. 371, said that he intended to consider this example, but so far as I know he never did. But see p. 383 and *Diophantische Approximationen*, p. 100.

CHAPTER XII

ON THE APPROXIMATION OF A REAL QUANTITY THROUGH RATIONAL NUMBERS [1]

ART. **131.** Although the theory of approximating a real quantity with the aid of continued fractions has experienced manifold treatments since Euler and Lagrange, one of the most interesting theorems in this domain seems to have been overlooked. Namely, among the different possible developments by means of continued fractions for a real quantity a, where the partial numerators are ± 1 and the partial denominators are positive integers, there is a definite kind of development (and one that is the most rapidly convergent), *for which all the convergents* $\frac{x}{y}$ *may be characterized in the following simple manner: as numerator and denominator of the individual convergents the pairs of integers* x, y *are to be taken for which* $y>0$, *and where* x *and* y *are relatively prime and satisfy the condition*

$$|(x-ay)y|<\tfrac{1}{2}.$$

The case where a is equal to an integer plus $\frac{1}{2}$ is excepted. In a previous paper [2] "On the theory of continued fractions" Minkowski called attention to developments of these continued fractions that were characterized through further remarkable properties. He did not notice, however, in that treatment that the inequality for the convergents just mentioned already completely characterized this development. The following theory he founded by means of purely geometric considerations which becomes intuitively evident in that he made fundamental a *system of two linear*

[1] Minkowski, *Ges. Abhandl.*, Vol. I, p. 320.
[2] *Ibid.*, Vol. I, p. 278; this work, Chapt. X. See also Arts. 63 ff.

forms $\alpha x+\beta y$, $\gamma x+\delta y$ *with integral indeterminates.* An application of the results thus established to the special case $x-ay$, y then offers in particular certain theorems regarding the approximation to a real quantity a.

ART. 132. THEOREM I. *If* $\xi=\alpha x+\beta y$, $\eta=\gamma x+\delta y$ *are two linear forms with arbitrary real coefficients* α, β, γ, δ *and a determinant* $\alpha\delta-\beta\gamma=1$, *then there exist always integers* x, y *which are not both zero and for which we have*

$$|\xi\eta|\leqq\frac{1}{2}.$$

If an integral substitution $x=pX+p'Y$, $y=qX+q'Y$ with determinant $=\pm 1$ is applied to the form $\xi\eta$, we say the form $\xi\eta$ is *equivalent* to the transformed form in the new variables. With the proof of I we may prove the following

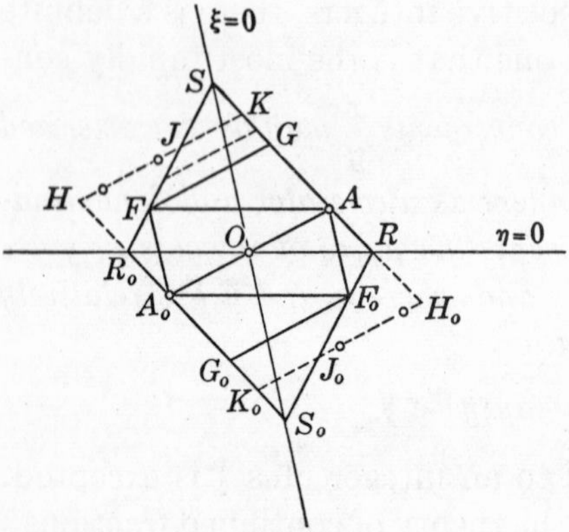

FIG. 75

COROLLARY. *If* $\xi\eta$ *is equivalent neither to the form* XY *nor to the form* $\frac{1}{2}(X^2-Y^2)$, *there exist always integers* x, y *for which* $\xi\neq 0$, $\eta\neq 0$ *and for which* $|\xi\eta|<\frac{1}{2}$.

Proof. Take any system of coordinates in the plane where for each of the two coordinates the distance *unity* may be arbitrarily taken. Let 0 be the origin ($x=0$, $y=0$). Let A be any point different from the origin, say $x=p$, $y=q$. The symmetric point with respect to the origin ($x=-p$, $y=-q$) shall be denoted always by A_0.

The collectivity of the points, for which x and y are integers, is called a *lattice*, and the individual points are called *lattice points*.

If ρ and σ are positive parameters, the four points R, R_0, S, S_0, for which $\xi=\rho$, $\eta=0$; $\xi=-\rho$, $\eta=0$; $\xi=0$, $\eta=\sigma$;

$\xi=0$, $\eta=-\sigma$, form the vertices of a parallelogram with 0 as the center and with the lines $\xi=0$, $\eta=0$ as diagonals. Such a parallelogram is denoted by $\mathfrak{P}(\rho, \sigma)$. The equations of its four sides are $\pm\frac{\xi}{\rho}\pm\frac{\eta}{\sigma}=1$, so that the domain of $\mathfrak{P}(\rho, \sigma)$ is expressed through

$$\left|\frac{\xi}{\rho}\right|+\left|\frac{\eta}{\sigma}\right|\leqq 1.$$

We may choose for ρ and σ such small values that the associated parallelogram $\mathfrak{P}(\rho, \sigma)$ contains no lattice point save the origin. We shall then *keep the ratio* $\rho:\sigma$ *constant* and allow ρ and σ to increase until the parallelogram $\mathfrak{P}(\rho, \sigma)$ takes a lattice point upon *its boundary*, while 0 is the only *inner* lattice point. Let A $(x=p,\ y=q)$ be the lattice point in question, while A_0 $(x=-p, y=-q)$, the symmetric point with respect to the origin, is also on the boundary. For A we may assume that $\eta>0$ or $\eta=0$, while ξ is >0. Thus for A we shall write $\xi=\epsilon\lambda$ and $\eta=\mu$, where both λ and μ are positive or zero and $\epsilon=\pm1$. The integers p, q have no common divisor >1, since the stretch OA has no lattice point between 0 and A. We determine two integers r, s such that $ps-qr=\epsilon$ and write

$$x=p\bar{X}+rY, \qquad y=q\bar{X}+sY.$$

It follows that

$$\epsilon\xi=\lambda\bar{X}+\bar{\lambda}Y, \qquad \eta=\mu\bar{X}+\bar{\mu}Y,$$

where

$$\begin{vmatrix} \lambda, & \bar{\lambda} \\ \mu, & \bar{\mu} \end{vmatrix}=\begin{vmatrix} \epsilon(\alpha p+\beta q), & \epsilon(\alpha r+\beta s) \\ p\gamma+\delta q, & \gamma r+\delta s \end{vmatrix}$$

$$=\epsilon\begin{vmatrix} \alpha, & \gamma \\ \beta, & \delta \end{vmatrix}\begin{vmatrix} p, & r \\ q, & s \end{vmatrix}=\epsilon\cdot1\cdot\epsilon=1.$$

It follows that

$$\bar{X}=\epsilon\xi\bar{\mu}-\bar{\lambda}\eta, \qquad Y=\lambda\eta-\epsilon\xi\mu. \tag{1}$$

Observe that lattice points x, y are lattice points $\bar{X}$, Y. The latter points are found on the line $Y=0$, that is, the line through OA, where $\bar{X}=0$ is the origin, $\bar{X}=1$ is the point A on the line $Y=0$, $\bar{X}=2$ being at a like distance beyond A, etc. We thus have on the line $Y=0$ the lattice points $\bar{X}=\cdots-2, -1, 0, 1, 2, \cdots$. Further lattice points are found on the lines parallel to OY, namely $Y=1$, $Y=-1$, $Y=2$, $Y=-2$, etc., thus making equidistant rows of points in the directions of the axes $\bar{X}=0$ and $Y=0$ with the constant distance $=OA$ between neighboring points. Of these parallel lines the lines $Y=1$ and $Y=-1$ lie next to $Y=0$.

ART. **133.** We assume first that A is *not* a vertex of the parallelogram $\mathfrak{P}(\rho, \sigma)$. In Fig. 75 for the point A, we have $\epsilon=1$ while $\lambda>0$ and $\mu>0$. Let F be the point $\xi=-\epsilon\lambda$, $\eta=\mu$. The parallelogram with vertices A, F, A_0, F_0 is defined through $-\lambda \leqq \xi \leqq \lambda$, $-\mu \leqq \eta \leqq \mu$. This parallelogram excepting its vertices lies entirely within the parallelogram $\mathfrak{P}(\rho, \sigma)$. We shall next assume that A is not a mid-point of one of the sides of $\mathfrak{P}(\rho, \sigma)$. The line parallel to A_0OA through F cuts the boundary of $\mathfrak{P}(\rho, \sigma)$ besides in F in a second point G, where the stretch FG is greater than A_0O, and therefore greater than OA. As F is also not a mid-point, we have $FG>OA$. Hence parallel lines to A_0OA which lie between A_0OA and FG have stretches within $\mathfrak{P}(\rho, \sigma)$ that are $>OA$. Since within $\mathfrak{P}(\rho, \sigma)$ there are no lattice points save O, the line $Y=1$ must lie beyond FG from the origin and that is $Y<1$ for all parallel lines to A_0OA that lie between A_0OA and FG. But from (1) for the point F we have $Y=2\lambda\mu$. It follows that

$$2\lambda\mu<1.$$

With this it is seen that the lattice point A offers the property required in Theorem I and the corollary.

ART. **134.** If A is the middle of a side of $\mathfrak{P}(\rho, \sigma)$, so that $\lambda=\frac{1}{2}\rho$, $\mu=\frac{1}{2}\sigma$, then the line A_0OA, and that is the line $Y=0$, is parallel to one of the sides of $\mathfrak{P}(\rho, \sigma)$. Hence every parallel line to A_0OA which lies within $\mathfrak{P}(\rho, \sigma)$ has with $\mathfrak{P}(\rho, \sigma)$ a stretch $=A_0OA > OA$. The straight lines $Y=\pm 1$ cannot lie within $\mathfrak{P}(\rho, \sigma)$, so that $\mathfrak{P}(\rho, \sigma)$ must lie entirely within the strip $-1 \leqq Y \leqq 1$. Hence we must have for the point F the value $Y \leqq 1$, and that is

$$2\lambda\mu \leqq 1.$$

The point A again has the property required in Theorem I. The equality sign $2\lambda\mu = 1$ (or $\rho\sigma = 2$) exists if a side of $\mathfrak{P}(\rho, \sigma)$ falls on the line $Y=1$. Since this side has a length $=2OA$ (which is twice the distance between two lattice points on $Y=1$), it contains either a lattice point on both of the two halves that are separated by the mid-point or there are lattice points at the mid-point of the side and at the two end-points. In the first case there is a lattice point as in Art. 133, for which $\xi \neq 0$, $\eta \neq 0$ and $|\xi\eta| < \frac{1}{2}$. In the second case all four of the vertices of $\mathfrak{P}(\rho, \sigma)$ would be lattice points as also the four mid-points of the sides. We may then take A as the mid-point of the stretch RS, and hence $\epsilon = 1$. We then have for F the coordinates $Y=1$, $\overline{X}=g$, where g is an integer.

Further writing

$$\overline{X} = X + gY, \qquad Y = Y,$$

we then have A ($\xi = \frac{1}{2}\rho$, $\eta = \frac{1}{2}\sigma$) and F ($\xi = -\frac{1}{2}\rho$, $\eta = -\frac{1}{2}\sigma$) determined through $X=1$, $Y=0$ and $X=0$, $Y=1$. Noting that

$$\xi = \lambda\overline{X} + \overline{\lambda}Y = \lambda(X+gY) + \overline{\lambda}Y,$$

we have for A the value $\frac{1}{2}\rho = \lambda$ and for F we have $-\frac{1}{2}\rho = \lambda g + \overline{\lambda}$ or $\overline{\lambda} = -\frac{1}{2}\rho - \frac{1}{2}g\rho$. And we further have

$$\xi = \tfrac{1}{2}\rho(X-Y), \qquad \eta = \tfrac{1}{2}\sigma(X+Y), \qquad \rho\sigma = 2,$$

and accordingly $\xi\eta = \frac{1}{2}(X^2 - Y^2)$.

ART. **135.** Finally we assume that the lattice point A is a vertex of $\mathfrak{P}(\rho, \sigma)$, and that is, either $\xi = 0$ or $\eta = 0$. It is then self evident that $|\xi\eta| = 0 < \frac{1}{2}$. In either of these cases the lattice point A satisfies the conditions of Theorem I. To see the correctness of the corollary under these conditions, take for example A as the vertex R ($\xi=\rho$, $\eta=0$). We then have from (1) $Y=\rho\eta$. Now keep ρ constant and let σ vary. It is seen that the diagonal R_0R (i.e., A_0OA) of $\mathfrak{P}(\rho, \sigma)$ remains fixed on $Y=0$, while the end-points S_0, S of the other diagonal slide along the line $\xi=0$. By taking σ sufficiently small the parallelogram $\mathfrak{P}(\rho, \sigma)$ lies entirely within the domain $-1<Y<1$ and contains no lattice point

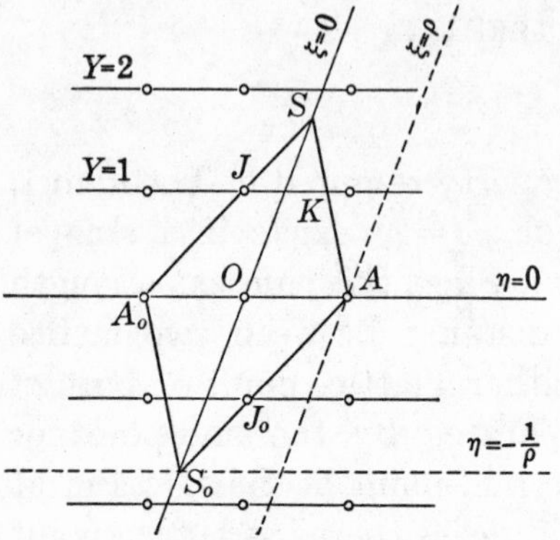

FIG. 76

save O, A_0 and A. If $\sigma=\dfrac{1}{\rho}$, then $\mathfrak{P}(\rho, \sigma)$ reaches the line $Y=1$ with the vertex S ($\xi=0$, $\eta=\sigma$). If this vertex is at the same time a lattice point, let its coordinates be $Y=0$, $\overline{X}=g$; and further put $\overline{X}=X+gY$. We then have for S ($\xi=0$, $\eta=\sigma$; $X=0$, $Y=1$), and for R ($\xi=\rho$, $\eta=0$; $X=1$, $Y=0$). It follows that

$$\xi=\rho X, \qquad \eta=\sigma Y, \qquad \rho\sigma=1, \qquad \xi\eta=XY.$$

On the other hand if the point $\xi=0$, $\eta=\dfrac{1}{\rho}$ does not fall on a lattice point, we may let σ increase beyond $1/\rho$ without at first causing new lattice points to enter $\mathfrak{P}(\rho, \sigma)$. The stretch which the line $Y=1$ cuts out of $\mathfrak{P}(\rho, \sigma)$ becomes at both ends, say J and K, more extended until one of the following cases is reached:

Either, so long as $JK<OA$, one of the end-points, say J, falls on a lattice point A' on the line $Y=1$. Then since $JK<OA$, the parallelogram $\mathfrak{P}(\rho, \sigma)$ does not reach the line $Y=2$ and consequently it contains no other lattice points

save O, A, A_0, A' $(=J)$, A'_0 $(=J_0)$. At the same time A' on $Y=1$ lies closer to S (at which $Y<2$) than it does to the other end-point A_0, these two lattice points A_0 and A' $(=J)$ being on the same side of $\mathfrak{P}(\rho, \sigma)$ and A' not a mid-point. In this case we have for A' as proved in the previous investigation $\xi \neq 0$, $\eta \neq 0$, and $|\xi\eta| < \frac{1}{2}$.

The other possible case is had when OS increases until $JK = OA$, its two end-points thus becoming lattice points. In this situation the upper veterx of $\mathfrak{P}(\rho, \sigma)$ falls upon the line $Y=2$, so that it contains no inner lattice points save 0; but at mid-points of all four sides there appear lattice points. In this case, as seen above in Art. 134, we find $\xi\eta$ equivalent to $\frac{1}{2}(X^2 - Y^2)$. If then we assemble the individual cases considered, we see the correctness of the corollary to Theorem I.

The proof of the inequality $2\lambda\mu \leqq 1$ for the lattice point A, and with it the proof of Theorem I, may also be obtained by considering the *area* of the parallelogram, a concept which leads to a further interesting result: Since in the relation to be derived, namely $|\xi\eta| \leqq \frac{1}{2}$, the role of the forms ξ, η may be interchanged, as also ξ and $-\xi$, admitting also the value of the determinant $= -1$, we may without any essential restriction let A fall on the side RS (Fig. 75), and that is, we may assume that $\epsilon = 1$, and $\frac{\lambda}{\rho} \geqq \frac{\mu}{\sigma}$. Since A is on the side of $\mathfrak{P}(\rho, \sigma)$, we also have

$$(2) \qquad \frac{\lambda}{\rho} + \frac{\mu}{\sigma} = 1.$$

Hence we may write

$$\frac{\lambda}{\rho} = \frac{1}{2} + \omega, \qquad \frac{\mu}{\sigma} = \frac{1}{2} - \omega, \qquad \frac{\lambda\mu}{\rho\sigma} = \frac{1}{4} - \omega^2 \leqq \frac{1}{4}.$$

We may now prove for a parallelogram $\mathfrak{P}(\rho, \sigma)$, which has a lattice point A on its boundary but otherwise 0 as the only inner lattice point, that always

$$(3) \qquad \rho\sigma \leqq 2.$$

It then follows immediately that $\lambda\mu \leqq \frac{1}{2}$. The theorem (3) is, however, more incisive. The area of $\mathfrak{P}(\rho, \sigma)$, and that is the double integral $\int\int dx\,dy$ taken over this domain, is (since the determinant of ξ, η in x, y is $=\pm 1$) $=4\cdot\frac{1}{2}\rho\sigma=2\rho\sigma$. Now let H, K (Fig. 75) be the points of intersection of $Y=1$ with the straight lines S_0R_0 and RS. Observe that the form $\frac{\xi}{\rho}+\frac{\eta}{\sigma}$ is $X\left(\frac{\lambda}{\rho}+\frac{\mu}{\sigma}\right)+\left(\frac{\overline{\lambda}}{\rho}+\frac{\overline{\mu}}{\sigma}\right)Y$, which, due to (2), is $\overline{X}+\left(\frac{\overline{\lambda}}{\rho}+\frac{\mu}{\sigma}\right)Y$, and this with the form Y has a determinant 1 in the variables $\overline{X}$ and Y and therefore also a determinant $=\pm 1$ in x, y. Hence the area of K_0H_0KH is $=4$. If the stretch HK enters the interior of $\mathfrak{P}(\rho, \sigma)$ then K lies on RS between A and S and HK has with $\mathfrak{P}(\rho, \sigma)$ a stretch JK in common which necessarily $\leqq OA$ (otherwise it would have a lattice point on it). Since $JK\leqq OA$, it is seen that J lies on R_0S so that $R_0J\geqq JS$ and the area of the triangle JKS is not greater than that of JHR_0. A comparison of the area of the parallelogram RSR_0S_0 with that of K_0H_0KH shows that $2\rho\sigma\leqq 4$. If, however, the stretch HK does not lie within $\mathfrak{P}(\rho, \sigma)$ so that the parallelogram RSR_0S_0 lies within the parallelogram K_0H_0KH, then likewise we must have $2\rho\sigma\leqq 4$.

ART. **136.** Let ξ and η have the same meaning as in Theorem I of Art. 132. We shall, however, exclude the special cases where the form $\xi\eta$ of the variables x, y is equivalent to the form XY or to the form $\frac{1}{2}(X^2-Y^2)$ in the variables X, Y.

Making these exceptions we shall prove the

THEOREM II. *If $x=p$, $y=q$ are two integers that are relatively prime, and for which $|\xi|>0$ and $|\xi\eta|<\frac{1}{2}$, then we may always find two integers $x=p'$, $y=q'$, such that $pq'-p'q=\pm 1$ and for which also $|\xi\eta|<\frac{1}{2}$ but $|\xi|$ is smaller than in the first instance.*

Proof. Since instead of p, q we may just as well take $-p$, $-q$, let $\xi=\epsilon\lambda$, $\eta=\mu$ where $\lambda>0$, $\mu>0$, $\epsilon=\pm 1$, or let

$\mu=0$, $\lambda>0$, $\epsilon=1$. We determine two integers r, s in any way so that $ps-rq=\epsilon$, and we write $x=pX+rY$, $y=qX+sY$. It follows that $Y=\epsilon(py-qx)$.

Writing as above

$$\epsilon\xi=\lambda\overline{X}+\bar{\lambda}Y, \qquad \eta=\mu\overline{X}+\bar{\mu}Y,$$

it follows that

$$\lambda\bar{\mu}-\mu\bar{\lambda}=1, \qquad Y=\lambda\eta-\mu\epsilon\xi=\epsilon(py-qx).$$

We denote the lattice point A by

$$x=p=p\overline{X}+rY, \qquad y=q=q\overline{X}+sY,$$

so that

$$\overline{X}=1, \qquad Y=0, \qquad \epsilon\xi=\lambda\overline{X}+\bar{\lambda}Y=\lambda, \qquad \eta=r\overline{X}+\bar{\mu}Y=\mu;$$

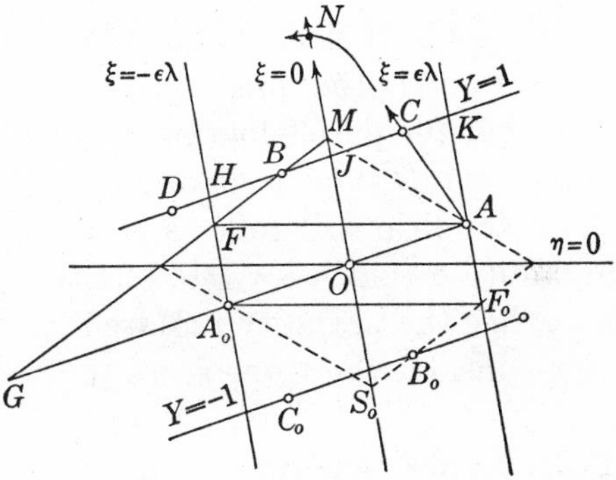

FIG. 77

and if $\mu>0$, we denote the point $\xi=-\epsilon\lambda$, $\eta=\mu$ by F. For F we have $Y=2\lambda\mu$ and that is $Y<1$ due to our assumption regarding the lattice point A, namely, for it $|\xi\eta|<\frac{1}{2}$. The lines $Y=\pm 1$ accordingly inclose the parallelogram with vertices A, F, A_0, F_0 without touching at these points, so that in particular F and F_0 are not lattice points. The straight line $Y=1$ $(=\lambda\eta-\mu\epsilon\xi)$ cuts the lines $\xi=-\epsilon\lambda$, $\xi=0$, $\xi=\epsilon\lambda$ at three points H, J and K for which $\eta=\dfrac{1-\lambda\mu}{\lambda}$, $\eta=\dfrac{1}{\lambda}$ and $\eta=\dfrac{1+\lambda\mu}{\lambda}$, all of which are greater than μ. Since $HJ=JK=OA$, the three points H, J and K on the line $Y=1$ are either all lattice points, or one of the lattice points B lies within the stretch HJ and the other C within the stretch JK. In the latter case let M be the intersection of the line FB (or A_0B in case $\mu=0$) with the line $\xi=0$ and let N be the intersection of the line AC with the line $\xi=0$.

We denote by A' ($x=p'$, $y=q'$) *first* the point J, if J is a lattice point, *secondly* the point B, if J is *not* a lattice point and at the same time if M lies nearer O than does N, so that $OM<ON$, and *thirdly* the lattice point C, when J is not a lattice point and also $OM \geqq ON$.

Since A' lies on the line $Y=1$, we have for all three cases $pq'-qp'=\epsilon=\pm 1$. We may accordingly write for A' the values $\xi=\epsilon'\lambda'$, $\eta=\mu'$, where in the *first* case $\lambda'=0$, while in the *second* case $\epsilon'=-\epsilon$; $\lambda'>0$ and in the *third* case $\epsilon'=\epsilon$, $\lambda'>0$ with $\lambda'<\lambda$ and $\mu'>\mu$ in all three cases. In the first case we take $\epsilon'=-\epsilon$. We shall now understand by the parallelogram $\mathfrak{P}(\rho, \sigma)$ with the vertices R, S, R_0, S_0 the parallelogram with $\xi=0$, $\eta=0$ as diagonals whose boundary contains the lattice points A and A'. The vertex S ($\xi=0$, $\eta=\sigma$) in the first case coincides with J, in the second case with M and in the third case with N. We can show in every case that the parallelogram $\mathfrak{P}(\rho, \sigma)$ contains no inner lattice point save O, and that also A' is not a mid-point. From these conditions it follows as in Art. 133 that $\lambda'\mu'<\frac{1}{2}$ and in addition that $\lambda>\lambda'\geqq 0$. It is seen that the lattice point p', q' has the property required in Theorem II and we shall now consider the three cases just mentioned.

If *first* J is a lattice point, $A'=J$, the parallelogram $\mathfrak{P}(\rho, \sigma)$ only touches the line $Y=1$ at the point J. This parallelogram contains no inner lattice point save O, the lattice points A, A_0, J, J_0 being on the boundary, and J, J_0 at the vertices S, S_0. Further since H falls without this parallelogram, and as $OH=AJ$, the point A lies further from S ($=J$) than S is from the mid-point $\left(\xi=\frac{\epsilon\rho}{2},\ \eta=\frac{\sigma}{2}\right)$ of the side that contains A and S. We therefore have $\lambda>\frac{\rho}{2}$, $\mu<\frac{\sigma}{2}$; $\lambda'<\lambda$, $\mu'>\mu$. We further have $\lambda'=0<\frac{\rho}{2}$, $\mu'=\sigma>\frac{\sigma}{2}$. It may be observed that $\mu>0$. For were $\mu=0$ and A a vertex of $\mathfrak{P}(\rho, \sigma)$, then this parallelogram would have its four vertices at lattice points. Due to Art. 135, the form $\xi\eta$ of the variables x, y would then be equivalent to XY in the variables X, Y.

We make next the assumption that J is not a lattice point. Let G be the intersection of the line FB with the line $Y=0$. The point G in case $\mu>0$ lies on the prolongation of A_0O beyond A_0, and in case $\mu=0$ the point G coincides with A_0. From the two similar triangles GOM and BJM on the one hand and the two similar triangles OAN and JCN on the other we have the proportions

$$(4) \qquad \frac{JM}{OJ+JM}=\frac{BJ}{GO}, \qquad \frac{JN}{OJ+JN}=\frac{JC}{OA}.$$

We have the *second* of the above cases when J is *not* a lattice point where $A'=B$ and $OM<ON$. The parallelogram with vertices M $(=S)$, S_0, N, N_0 is the one in question. For the point M we have always $Y<2$. For *either* on the one hand $BJ<JC$, then since $BJ+JC=A_0O$ and $BJ<\frac{1}{2}A_0O\leqq\frac{1}{2}GO$, it follows from (4) that $JM<OJ$; on *the other* hand if $BJ\geqq JC$, then since $BJ+JC=OA$ so that $JC\leqq\frac{1}{2}OA$, it follows from the second of the relations in (4) that $JN\leqq OJ$ and hence again $JM<OJ$. In both cases we further have $OM<2OJ$ and that is $Y<2$ for the point M. Consequently the parallelogram $\mathfrak{P}(\rho, \sigma)$ lies entirely within the domain $-2<Y<2$. On the line $Y=1$ there is a lattice point at B and another at C exterior to the parallelogram. Hence there are no inner lattice points save at O, while the lattice points A, A_0, B, B_0 are on the boundary. Further since $BC=OA$ the stretch BC at B enters the interior of $\mathfrak{P}(\rho, \sigma)$, but as C falls without the parallelogram the point B is nearer to S $(=M)$ than the mid-point $\xi=-\frac{\epsilon\rho}{2}$, $\eta=\frac{\sigma}{2}$ of the side containing S and B. We thus have $\lambda'<\frac{\rho}{2}$, $\mu'>\frac{\sigma}{2}$. On the other hand the point A is further from S $(=M)$ than the mid-point $\xi = \frac{\epsilon\rho}{2}$, $\eta = \frac{\sigma}{2}$ of the side containing A and S and consequently $\lambda > \frac{\rho}{2}$, $\mu < \frac{\sigma}{2}$, $\lambda' < \lambda$, $\mu' > \mu$.

Regarding the fixing of the lattice point A' in the first two of the above cases, the following may be noted:

From above we had

$$x = p\overline{X} + rY, \qquad y = q\overline{X} + sY,$$

$$\epsilon\xi = \lambda\overline{X} + \overline{\lambda}Y, \qquad \eta = \mu\overline{X} + \overline{\mu}Y,$$

$$Y = \lambda\eta - \mu\epsilon\xi = \epsilon(py - qx).$$

For the point A' we have $\xi = -\epsilon\lambda'$, $\eta = \mu'$ and $0 \leqq \lambda' < \lambda$, $\overline{X} = g$, $Y = 1$ (where g is an integer); and then $p' = gp + r$, $q' = gq + s$. It follows also that $-\epsilon\lambda' = \epsilon(\overline{\lambda} + g\lambda)$, $\mu' = \overline{\mu} + \mu g$, and therefore $0 \leqq -\frac{\overline{\lambda}}{\lambda} - g\lambda < \lambda$, or $0 \leqq -\frac{\overline{\lambda}}{\lambda} - g < 1$. From this it is seen that g is the greatest integer contained in $-\frac{\overline{\lambda}}{\lambda}$, and that is $g = \left[-\frac{\overline{\lambda}}{\lambda}\right]$.

From the relation $Y = 1$ for A' we have $\lambda\mu' + \mu\lambda' = 1$. If $-\frac{\overline{\lambda}}{\lambda}$ is exactly an integer, we have $\lambda' = 0$, $A' = J$. On the other hand suppose that $\lambda' > 0$, and determine M through the equation of the straight line through F and B (through A_0 and B, for $\mu = 0$) and that is $\frac{\eta - \mu'}{\xi + \epsilon\lambda'} = \frac{\eta - \mu}{\xi + \epsilon\lambda}$. Hence for $\xi = 0$, we have for M: $\eta(\lambda - \lambda') = \lambda\mu' - \mu\lambda' = 2\lambda\mu' - 1$. Observing that the coordinates of C are $\xi = -\epsilon\lambda' + \epsilon\lambda$, $\eta = \mu' + \mu$, the equation of the line AC is $\frac{\eta - \mu' - \mu}{\xi + \epsilon\lambda' - \epsilon\lambda} = \frac{\eta - \mu}{\xi - \epsilon\lambda}$. By putting $\xi = 0$, the value η for ON is $\eta\lambda' = \lambda\mu' + \mu\lambda' = 1$. From the inequality $OM < ON$ is derived the inequality $\frac{2\lambda\mu' - 1}{\lambda - \lambda'} < \frac{1}{\lambda'}$; and since $\lambda - \lambda' > 0$, we have finally $2\lambda'\mu' < 1$.

For the *third* case J is *not* a lattice point and $OM \geqq ON$. The point C is now taken for A', so that accordingly for it we have $\xi = \epsilon'\lambda'$, $\eta = \mu'$ and $\epsilon' = \epsilon$. For B the coordinates are $\xi = -\epsilon(\lambda - \lambda')$, $\eta = \mu' - \mu$. It follows at once that $\mu' - \mu > \mu$. From the relation $OM \geqq ON$ we derive as above $2(\lambda - \lambda')(\mu' - \mu) \geqq 1$. The two cases $OM > ON$ and $OM = ON$ are treated separately. Take first $OM > ON$. From $JM > JN$ and $GO \geqq OA$ it follows from (4), namely

$$BJ = \frac{GO}{\dfrac{OJ}{JM} + 1}, \qquad JC = \frac{OA}{\dfrac{OJ}{JN} + 1},$$

that $BJ > JC$ and hence also $\lambda - \lambda' > \lambda'$. Since $BJ + JC = OA$ it is seen that $JC < \frac{1}{2}OA$ and therefore due to (4) we have $JN < OJ$ so that $Y < 2$ for the point N. The parallelogram $\mathfrak{P}(\rho, \sigma)$ therefore does not reach the line $Y = 2$. On the line $Y = 1$ there is a lattice point at C making C, C_0, A and A_0 the lattice points on the boundary and O the only inner lattice point of the parallelogram. Further since B lies without this parallelogram and $AC = OB$ it is seen that AC is greater than the half of the side of $\mathfrak{P}(\rho, \sigma)$ which goes through A and C, so that C is nearer to $S(=N)$ and A farther from S' than the middle $\xi = \frac{\epsilon\rho}{2}$, $\eta = \frac{\sigma}{2}$ of this side. Next let $OM = ON$, so that M and N coincide. In addition assume that $\mu > 0$ so that A is not a vertex of $\mathfrak{P}(\rho, \sigma)$. We then have $GO > A_0O$ and consequently $BJ > JC$, $\lambda - \lambda' > \lambda'$, with the results the same as above only in addition to A, A_0, C, C_0 there are the lattice points B, B_0 on the boundary of $\mathfrak{P}(\rho, \sigma)$. Since OB is parallel to AC, it is seen that B is the middle of a side of the parallelogram so that $\lambda - \lambda' = \frac{\rho}{2}$, $\mu' - \mu = \frac{\sigma}{2}$. However, since neither A nor C is a vertex of $\mathfrak{P}(\rho, \sigma)$, it follows that neither A nor C is the mid-point of a side, and we again have $\lambda' < \frac{\rho}{2} < \lambda$,

$\mu' > \frac{\sigma}{2} > \mu$. Next assume that $\mu = 0$, so that A_0OA is a diagonal of $\mathfrak{P}(\rho, \sigma)$ and the points G and A_0 coincide. It then follows that $BJ = JC = \frac{1}{2}OA$ and therefore $\lambda - \lambda' = \lambda'$ and further $JN = OJ$, $CN = AC = OB$. Under these conditions the parallelogram $\mathfrak{P}(\rho, \sigma)$ with the vertex S reaches to the line $Y = 2$; it has no inner lattice point save O, but both B and C are mid-points of sides. For both B and C there exists the relation $|\xi\eta| = \frac{1}{2}$. This is the case (see Art. 134) where $\xi\eta$ is equivalent to the form $\frac{1}{2}(X^2 - Y^2)$, a case which was excluded.

From the considerations in Arts. 132–135 it follows in every case that the lattice point A' corresponds to the requirements of Theorem II. When the point C is a lattice point (case 3 above) put $\bar{X} = h$, $Y = 1$, where h is an integer. Then for the determination of the lattice point A' $(x = p',$ $y = q')$ from the lattice point $A(x = p,\ y = q)$ the following rule is given: *Denote by g the greatest integer in* $-\frac{\lambda'}{\lambda}$ *and write* $h = g$ *or* $h = g + 1$ *according as*

$$(-\bar{\lambda} - \lambda g)(\bar{\mu} + \mu g) \text{ is } < \text{ or } \geqq \tfrac{1}{2}.$$

We then have $p' = r + ph$, $q' = s + qh$.

ART. **137.** If we change the parameters ρ, σ of the parallelogram $\mathfrak{P}(\rho, \sigma)$ of Art. 132 in such a way that σ is diminished by bringing S and S_0 nearer to O, the sides, however, continuing to go through A, A_0 (and F, F_0), we have, so long as the value σ does not reach a certain limit, a new parallelogram with $\xi = 0$, $\eta = 0$ as diagonals. And this parallelogram clearly contains no other lattice points save A_0, O, A. From this the following theorem is established:

THEOREM III. *If the lattice point* $x = p$, $y = q$ *is such that the integers* p, q *are relatively prime and* $|\xi\eta| < \frac{1}{2}$ *for these values, we may always construct parallelograms*

$$\left|\frac{\xi}{\rho}\right| + \left|\frac{\eta}{\sigma}\right| \leqq 1,$$

which have the lattice point on their boundary and have besides the three lattice points p, q; 0; −p, −q no other lattice point.

If on the other hand a parallelogram of the kind here described exists for a lattice point $x=p$, $y=q$, the proof made for Theorem *I* shows that reciprocally p, q are relatively prime and that $|\xi\eta|<\frac{1}{2}$ for these values of x, y.

Due to this Theorem III we may prove regarding the relation of the two lattice points denoted by A and A' in Art. 132 the following important corollary.

COROLLARY. *There can exist no lattice point x, y different from* A, A_0, A', A'_0 *for which x and y are relatively prime, where* $|\xi\eta|$ *is* $<\frac{1}{2}$ *and at the same time* $\lambda \geqq |\xi| \geqq \lambda'$.

Proof. Assume that there is a lattice point A^* of the kind described, and for it let $|\xi|=\lambda^*$, $\eta=\mu^*$. In the figure we denote by E the point $\xi=\lambda$, $\eta=\mu$, by E' the point $\xi=\lambda'$, $\eta=\mu'$, by R and S the points of intersection of the line EE' with $\eta=0$ and $\xi=0$, by L we denote the point $\xi=\lambda$, $\eta=0$, by L' the point $\xi=\lambda'$, $\eta=0$, and finally by E^* the point $\xi=\lambda^*$, $\eta=\mu^*$. Due to Theorem III it must be possible according to our assumptions to construct a parallelogram $\mathfrak{P}(\rho^*, \sigma^*)$ with $\xi=0$, $\eta=0$ as diagonals on whose boundary the point A^* lies, but which does not contain either A or A'. If R^* and S^* are the vertices $\xi=\rho^*$, $\eta=0$ and $\xi=0$, $\eta=\sigma^*$ of this parallelogram, the stretch R^*S^* must contain the point E^*, but neither E nor E' can belong to the triangle OR^*S^*. Since by hypothesis E^* is necessarily a point within the strip $\lambda' \leqq \xi \leqq \lambda$ and as $\eta \geqq 0$ for this point, it necessarily lies within the four-sided figure $L'LEE'$ and not on the side EE'. However, the parallelogram RSR_0S_0 contains no inner lattice point save O making the existence of the lattice point A^* impossible.

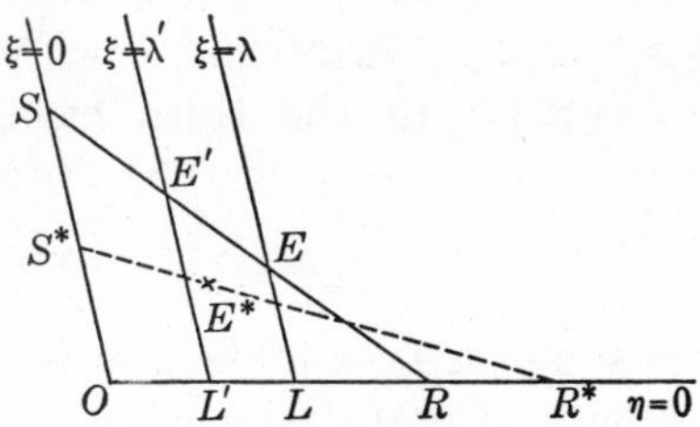

FIG. 78

In a similar manner it is clear that besides A, A_0, A', A'_0 there can exist no other lattice point for which x, y are relatively prime and for which $|\xi\eta| < \frac{1}{2}$ and at the same time $\mu \leqq \eta \leqq \mu'$.

ART. **138.** Through the substitution derived from A and A', namely

$$T: \qquad x = pX + p'Y, \qquad y = qX + q'Y$$

with determinant $pq' - p'q = \pm 1$, the form $\xi\eta$ becomes the equivalent form

$$\varphi X^2 + \chi XY + \psi Y^2 = (\epsilon\lambda X + \epsilon'\lambda' Y)(\mu X + \mu' Y),$$

where $\varphi = \epsilon\lambda\mu$, $\psi = \epsilon'\lambda'\mu'$, $\chi = \epsilon\lambda\mu' + \epsilon'\lambda'\mu = \epsilon(1 + 2\mu\lambda')$, so that $|\varphi| < \frac{1}{2}$, $|\psi| < \frac{1}{2}$, $\chi^2 - 4\varphi\psi = 1$. In the first two cases considered above where $\epsilon = -\epsilon'$, we have $\lambda\mu' + \mu\lambda' = 1$, $\lambda > \lambda' \geqq 0$, $\mu' > \mu \geqq 0$ and $\chi = \epsilon(\lambda\mu' - \mu\lambda') = \epsilon(1 - 2\mu\lambda')$ so that $0 < \epsilon\chi \leqq 1$. In the third case, however, where $\epsilon = \epsilon'$, we have $\lambda\mu' - \mu\lambda' = 1$, $\lambda > 2\lambda' > 0$, $\mu' > 2\mu \geqq 0$ and

$$\chi = \epsilon(\lambda\mu' + \mu\lambda') = \epsilon(1 + 2\mu\lambda').$$

Since here $2\mu\lambda' < \mu'\lambda' < \frac{1}{2}$, it is seen that $1 \leqq \epsilon\chi < \frac{3}{2}$. The relation $(\lambda - \lambda')(\mu' - \mu) \geqq \frac{1}{2}$ gives $\epsilon(\chi - \varphi - \psi) \geqq \frac{1}{2}$. In every case it is seen that ϵ and χ have the same sign, so that when χ is given, ϵ is known, and then ϵ' may be found. An exceptional case arises when $\chi = \pm 1$ (and therefore either $\varphi = 0$ or $\psi = 0$).

Since $pq' - p'q = \pm 1$, it follows on the one hand that p and q are relatively prime as are p' and q' on the other. The other special conditions which exist for the two lattice points $A(\xi = \epsilon\lambda,\ \eta = \mu)$ and $A'(\xi = \epsilon'\lambda',\ \eta = \mu')$ are completely assembled in the following relations:

$$\lambda > 0, \qquad \mu > 0, \qquad \epsilon = \pm 1, \qquad \text{or} \qquad \mu = 0, \qquad \epsilon = 1,$$
$$pq' - p'q = \epsilon,$$

and further:

either $\quad \epsilon' = -\epsilon, \qquad \lambda > \lambda' \geqq 0, \qquad \lambda\mu < \frac{1}{2}, \qquad \lambda'\mu' < \frac{1}{2}$

or $\quad \epsilon' = \epsilon, \qquad \lambda > \lambda' > 0, \qquad \lambda\mu < \frac{1}{2}, \qquad (\lambda - \lambda')(\mu' - \mu) \geqq \frac{1}{2}.$

It may be noted that in the second row of conditions for $\epsilon'=\epsilon$, the inequality $\lambda\mu<\frac{1}{2}$ is a consequence of the remaining equations. For we have here $\lambda\mu'-\lambda'\mu=1$. From $(\lambda-\lambda')(\mu'-\mu)\geqq\frac{1}{2}$ and $\lambda>\lambda'$, it follows first that $\mu'>\mu$. We may write the inequality $(\lambda-\lambda')(\mu'-\mu)\geqq\frac{1}{2}$ in the form $\lambda\mu'+\lambda'\mu-\lambda\mu-\lambda'\mu'\geqq\frac{1}{2}(\lambda\mu'-\lambda'\mu)$ or

$$\tfrac{1}{2}\lambda\mu'+\tfrac{3}{2}\lambda'\mu-\lambda\mu-\lambda'\mu'\geqq 0,$$

and that is $\frac{1}{2}(\lambda-\lambda')(\mu'-2\mu)\geqq\frac{1}{2}\lambda'(\mu'-\mu)$. And from this it is seen that $\mu'-2\mu>0$. If further for $\lambda\mu'$ we put $1+\lambda'\mu$ we have $\frac{1}{2}+2\lambda'\mu\geqq\lambda\mu+\lambda'\mu'$, or $\frac{1}{2}\geqq\lambda\mu+\lambda'(\mu'-2\mu)$, and therefore $\frac{1}{2}>\lambda\mu$.

ART. **139.** If we collect the results of the preceding articles and add the theorems which are had through the interchange of the rôles of ξ and η which exist if we replace ξ, η by η, $-\xi$, there arises the following theorem:

THEOREM IV. *Let $\xi=\alpha x+\beta y$, $\eta=\gamma x+\delta y$ be two linear forms with arbitrary real coefficients and a determinant $\alpha\delta-\beta\gamma=1$, and further suppose that the form $\xi\eta$ in x, y is not equivalent to the form XY or to the form $\frac{1}{2}(X^2-Y^2)$. Then let the collective systems of integers x, y for which x, y are relatively prime and $|\xi\eta|<\frac{1}{2}$ and $\eta>0$, or $\eta=0$, $\xi>0$ be arranged in a series according to increasing values of η.*

For any two successive systems $x=p$, $y=q$ and $x=p'$, $y=q'$ in the series there exists then always

$$pq'-qp'=\pm 1.$$

This series offers a definite first system for which $\eta=0$, $\xi>0$ and therefore $\dfrac{x}{\delta}=\dfrac{y}{-\gamma}$ and >0, if $\dfrac{\delta}{-\gamma}$ is rational; it offers a definite last system for which $\xi=0$, $\eta>0$, and therefore $\dfrac{x}{-\beta}=\dfrac{y}{\alpha}$ and >0, if $\dfrac{-\beta}{\alpha}$ is rational. It is without a first system, if $\dfrac{\delta}{-\gamma}$ is irrational, and it is without a last system, if $\dfrac{-\beta}{\alpha}$ is irrational; it is boundless at both the beginning and end if both $\dfrac{\delta}{-\gamma}$ and $\dfrac{-\beta}{\alpha}$ are irrational.

If the series is without a last system, then in this process $|\xi|$ *converges towards zero, while* η *increases over every bound; if it is without a first term, then with inverse sequence of the systems of the series,* $|\xi|$ *increases over every bound and* η *converges towards zero.*

This last follows from the fact that only a finite number of systems of the series $|\xi|$ or $|\eta|$ can lie between given positive limits. For were $\rho_1 \geqq |\xi| \geqq |\rho_0 > 0$, it would follow from $|\xi\eta| < \frac{1}{2}$ and $|\xi| \geqq \rho_0$ that $|\eta| < \dfrac{1}{2\rho_0}$. However, in a parallelogram $|\xi| \leqq \rho_1$, $|\eta| \leqq \dfrac{1}{2\rho_0}$ there can be only a finite number of lattice points.

The series of lattice points x, y that arise here when arranged according to increasing values of their η, is called *the chain* of the forms ξ, η; a single lattice point $x=p$, $y=q$ is a *term* (joint) of the chain and the substitution formed by means of two consecutive members $x=p$, $y=q$ and $x=p'$, $y=q'$, namely

$$x = pX + p'Y, \qquad y = qX + q'Y,$$

is called a *substitution* of the chain. We denote the consecutive members of a chain by

$$p_i, q_i \qquad (i = \cdots, -2, -1, 0, 1, 2, \cdots).$$

The first term, if such first term exists, is given the index 0, and otherwise any arbitrary term may be given this index 0. For $x=p_i$, $y=q_i$ we write $\xi = \epsilon_i\lambda_i$, $\eta = \mu_i$, so that $\mu_i \geqq 0$, $\lambda_i \geqq 0$, $\epsilon_i = \pm 1$. We further write, when the indices are considered,

$$\frac{\epsilon_i}{\epsilon_{i-1}} = \theta_i \qquad \text{so that} \qquad \epsilon_i = \theta_i\epsilon_{i-1}, \qquad \theta_i = \epsilon_{i-1}\epsilon_i,$$

$$\epsilon_{i+1} = \theta_{i+1}\epsilon_i \qquad \text{or} \qquad \epsilon_i = \epsilon_{i+1}\theta_{i+1}.$$

For any first term we may take $\epsilon_0 = 1$; for any existing last term we write the index $i=w$, where then $\lambda_w = 0$ and for this we choose $\theta_w = -1$. The substitution

$$x = p_{i-1}X_i + p_iY_i, \qquad y = q_{i-1}X_i + q_iY_i$$

or (for brevity) $\begin{pmatrix} p_{i-1}, & p_i \\ q_{i-1}, & q_i \end{pmatrix}$ is denoted by T_i.

In general we have

$$\lambda_{i-1} > \lambda_i, \qquad \mu_{i-1} < \mu_i$$

and further from $Y = \lambda\eta - \mu\epsilon\xi = 1$, we derive $Y_{i-1} = \lambda_{i-1}\eta - \mu_{i-1}\epsilon_{i-1}\xi = 1$, or $\lambda_{i-1}\mu_i - \mu_{i-1}\epsilon_{i-1}\epsilon_i\lambda_i = 1$; and that is

$$(5) \qquad \begin{cases} \lambda_{i-1}\mu_i - \theta_i\mu_{i-1}\lambda_i = 1, \\ \text{and also } p_{i-1}q_i - q_{i-1}p_i = \epsilon_{i-1}. \end{cases}$$

The rule developed at the close of Art. 136, which gives a method of deriving from one term the term immediately following, offers a simple relation among three consecutive members of a chain p_{i-1}, q_{i-1}; p_i, q_i; p_{i+1}, q_{i+1}. We may identify p_i, q_i with the lattice point p, q (ϵ_i with ϵ and λ_i with λ) and further p_{i+1}, q_{i+1} may be identified with p', q'. To determine values r, s which satisfy $p_is - q_ir = \epsilon_i$, write in $\begin{vmatrix} p_i, & r \\ q_i, & s \end{vmatrix}$ the values $r = -\theta_ip_{i-1}$, $s = -\theta_iq_{i-1}$. It follows that $-\theta_i\begin{vmatrix} p_i, & p_{i-1} \\ q_i, & q_{i-1} \end{vmatrix}$ (and this from (1)) $= -\theta_i(-\epsilon_{i-1}) = \epsilon_i$. Hence for (r, s) we have

$$\xi = \epsilon_i\bar{\lambda} = r\alpha + s\beta = -\theta_i(p_{i-1}\alpha + q_{i-1}\beta) = -\theta_{i-1}\epsilon_{i-1}\lambda_{i-1};$$

and therefore for $\bar{\lambda}$ we may write $-\lambda_{i-1}$. Further observing Art. 136, it is seen that

$$\begin{aligned} \epsilon_{i+1}\lambda_{i+1} &= p_{i+1}\alpha + q_{i-1}\beta \\ &= (-\theta_ip_{i-1} + h_ip_i)\alpha + (-\theta_iq_{i-1} + h_iq_i)\beta \\ &= -\theta_i\epsilon_{i-1}\lambda_{i-1} + h_i\epsilon_i\lambda_i. \end{aligned}$$

We accordingly have the following rule:

Denote by g_i the greatest integer in $\frac{\lambda_{i-1}}{\lambda_i}$ and write $h_i = g_i$ or g_{i+1} according as $(\lambda_{i-1} - g_i\lambda_i)(g_i\mu_i - \theta_i\mu_{i-1} <$ or $\geqq \frac{1}{2}$. We *then have* $p_{i+1}=-\theta_{i-1}p_{i-1}+h_ip_i$, $q_{i+1}=-\theta_iq_{i-1}+h_iq_i$, *where in the first case* $\theta_{i+1}=-1$, *while in the second case* $\theta_{i+1}=1$.

Observe that

$$(6)\quad \begin{cases} \begin{pmatrix} p_{i-1}, & p_i \\ q_{i-1}, & q_i \end{pmatrix}\begin{pmatrix} 0, & -\theta_i \\ 1, & h_i \end{pmatrix}=\begin{pmatrix} p_i, & p_{i+1} \\ q_i, & q_{i+1} \end{pmatrix}, \\ \begin{pmatrix} \epsilon_{i-1}\lambda_{i-1}, & \epsilon_i\lambda_i \\ \mu_{i-1}, & \mu_i \end{pmatrix}\begin{pmatrix} 0, & -\theta_i \\ 1, & h_i \end{pmatrix}=\begin{pmatrix} \epsilon_i\lambda_i, & \epsilon_{i+1}\lambda_{i+1} \\ \mu_i, & \mu_{i+1} \end{pmatrix}. \end{cases}$$

It is seen, due to the substitution

$$X_i=-\theta_iY_{i+1},$$
$$Y_i=X_{i+1}+h_iY_{i+1},$$

that we have

$$p_{i-1}X_i+p_iY_i=p_iX_{i+1}+p_{i+1}Y_{i+1},$$
$$q_{i-1}X_i+q_iY_i=q_iX_{i+1}+q_{i+1}Y_{i+1}.$$

In general write $t_i=-\dfrac{X_i}{Y_i}$, so that

$$(7)\quad \frac{-p_{i-1}t_i+p_j}{-q_{i-1}t_i+q_i}=\frac{-p_it_{i+1}+p_{i+1}}{-q_it_{i+1}+q_{i+1}},$$

and

$$(8)\quad t_i=-\frac{X_i}{Y_i}=\frac{-\theta_iY_{i+1}}{Y_i}=\frac{-\theta_i}{\dfrac{Y_i}{Y_{i+1}}}=\frac{\theta_i}{h_i-t_{i+1}}.$$

From (7) and (8) we have more generally

$$(9)\quad \frac{-p_{i-1}t_i+p_i}{-q_{i-1}t_i+q_i}=\frac{-p_{k-1}t_k+p_k}{-q_{k-1}t_k+q_k},\qquad k>i,$$

if

$$(10)\quad t_i=\cfrac{\theta_i}{h_i-\cfrac{\theta_{i+1}}{h_{i+1}-\cdot_{\textstyle\cdot}\cdot\cfrac{-\theta_{k-1}}{h_{k-1}-t_k}}}.$$

And in this we have with respect to the derivation of the numerator and denominator of the right hand side in (9) as derived from the numerator and denominator of the left hand side a similar method of procedure to that employed in the relations (7) and (8).

Observe that when ξ, η have the determinant 1, the same is also true of η, $-\xi$. The chain for η, $-\xi$ is essentially the inverse chain as that for ξ, η. If p_i, q_i the lattice points of the chain for ξ, η are taken in inverse order, and that is, the indices i are decreasing, we have in the systems $x=-\epsilon_i p_i$ $y=-\epsilon_i q_i$ (for which it turns out that $-\xi \geqq 0$) the terms of the chain for η, $-\xi$. For the continuation in this chain we have from (6)

$$(11)\quad \begin{pmatrix} -\epsilon_{i+1}p_{i+1}, & -\epsilon_i p_i \\ -\epsilon_{i+1}q_{i+1}, & -\epsilon_i q_i \end{pmatrix}\begin{pmatrix} 0, & -\theta_{i+1} \\ 1, & h_i \end{pmatrix} = \begin{pmatrix} -\epsilon_i p_i, & -\epsilon_{i-1}p_{i-1} \\ -\epsilon_i q_i, & -\epsilon_{i-1}q_{i-1} \end{pmatrix}.$$

ART. **140.** The following theorem may be added to those in Arts. 136–138.

THEOREM V. *If* $\xi=\alpha x+\beta y$, $\eta=\gamma x+\delta y$ *are two linear forms with arbitrary real coefficients and a determinant* $\alpha\delta-\beta\gamma=1$, *and if* ξ_0, η_0 *are any given real quantities, there always exist integers* x, y *for which we have*

$$|(\xi-\xi_0)(\eta-\eta_0)| \leqq \tfrac{1}{4}.$$

We may consider beforehand the cases where there exists an integral substitution with a determinant $=\pm 1$ through which the form $\xi\eta$ of the variables x, y is transformed into the form XY or into the form $\frac{1}{2}(X^2-Y^2)$ of the new variables X, Y. Let the system $X=X_0$, $Y=Y_0$ correspond to the system of values $\xi=\xi_0$, $\eta=\eta_0$; then from the substitution in question we have (see corollary to Theorem I of Art. 132)

$$(\xi-\xi_0)(\eta-\eta_0)=(X-X_0)(Y-Y_0)$$
$$\text{or}\quad =\tfrac{1}{2}(X-X_0)^2-(Y-Y_0)^2.$$

If we determine X and Y as integers so that $|X-X_0| \leqq \frac{1}{2}$,

$|Y-Y_0|\leqq\frac{1}{2}$, it is seen in the first case, where $\xi\eta$ is equivalent to XY, that $|(\xi-\xi_0)(\eta-\eta_0)|\leqq\frac{1}{2}$. It is to be observed here that in certain cases the equality sign actually occurs, namely when X_0 and Y_0 are both integers increased by $\frac{1}{2}$. In the second case where $\xi\eta$ is equivalent to $\frac{1}{2}(X^2-Y^2)$, we have in fact $|(\xi-\xi_0)(\eta-\eta_0)|\leqq\frac{1}{8}$. We shall henceforth exclude the cases above where $\xi\eta$ is equivalent either to XY or to $\frac{1}{2}(X^2-Y^2)$.

Consider any substitution

$$x=pX+p'Y, \qquad y=qX+q'Y$$

of the chain belonging to ξ, η. We denote the lattice point p, q by A and the lattice point p', q' by A'. From Art. 132 we have a definitely determined parallelogram RSR_0S_0 or $\mathfrak{P}(\rho,\sigma)$, namely $\left|\frac{\xi}{\rho}\right|+\left|\frac{\eta}{\sigma}\right|\leqq 1$ whose boundary goes through both A and A'.

That we be able to make clearer the geometrical drawings we shall interpret the coordinates x, y as such that the parallelogram $\mathfrak{P}(\rho,\sigma)$ shall be a *square* in the usual sense. For p, q let $\xi=\epsilon\lambda$, $\eta=\mu(\lambda\geqq 0,\ \mu\geqq 0,\ \epsilon=\pm 1)$, for p', q' let $\xi=\epsilon'\lambda'$, $\eta=\mu'(\lambda'\geqq 0,\ \mu'\geqq 0,\ \epsilon'=\pm 1)$. We must treat separately the cases considered in Arts. 136–139 where $\epsilon=-\epsilon'$ and where $\epsilon=\epsilon'$.

1°. Let $\epsilon'=-\epsilon$ and $\lambda>\lambda'\geqq 0$, $\mu'>\mu\geqq 0$. The simultaneous appearance of $\mu=0$ and $\lambda'=0$ is excluded, since $\xi\eta$ is not to be equivalent to XY. Let M be the mid-point $\left(\xi=\frac{2\rho}{2},\ \eta=\frac{\sigma}{2}\right)$ of a side of $\mathfrak{P}(\rho,\sigma)$ and let M' be the mid-point $\left(\xi=\frac{\epsilon\rho}{2},\ \eta=\frac{\sigma}{2}\right)$ of the adjacent side of $\mathfrak{P}(\rho,\sigma)$. As shown in Art. 136 the lattice points A and A' are so situated on the boundary of $\mathfrak{P}(\rho,\sigma)$ that by going over the boundary of $\mathfrak{P}(\rho,\sigma)$ in a certain direction the points A, M, (S), A', M', A_0, M_0, (S_0), A'_0, M'_0 follow (see Fig. 79). Note that the sides of $\mathfrak{P}(\rho,\sigma)$ are not drawn in the parallelogram in order to make the figure less complicated. Also note that A is different from M and A' is different from M'.

Since we may change the rôle of ξ and η in that instead of ξ, η, we may also take η, $-\xi$, it is permitted to make

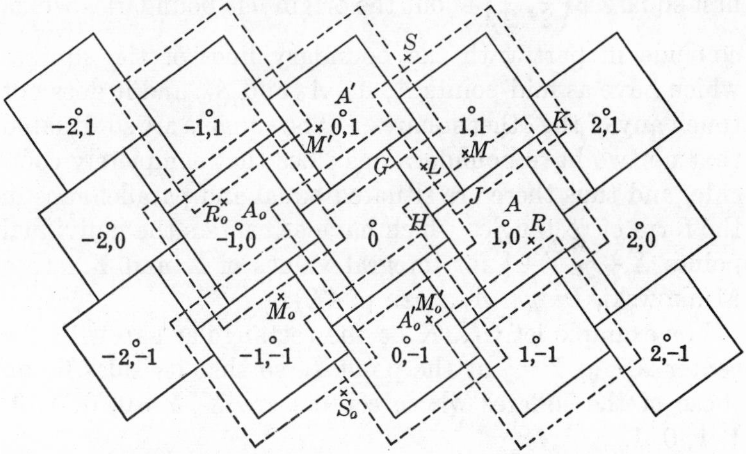

FIG. 79

the assumption $\lambda'\mu' \geqq \lambda\mu$; and, as simultaneously we can not have $\lambda'=0$, $\mu=0$, it is seen that A' and S are different. Observe further that upon each of the sides of the square $\mathfrak{P}(\rho, \sigma)$ the value $\left|\frac{\xi\eta}{\rho\sigma}\right|$ steadily decreases from the middle of a side towards its ends. And, since this ratio has a like value on all four sides with like *distance from the mid-points*, where the concept of distance is employed in the usual sense, it follows that this assumption carries with it the condition that $A'M' \leqq AM$.

We next construct the square $\mathfrak{P}\left(\frac{\rho}{2}, \frac{\sigma}{2}\right)$ whose vertices are situated on $\xi=0$ and $\eta=0$ at half the distances from 0 as the points R, R_0, S, S_0. The boundary of $\mathfrak{P}\left(\frac{\rho}{2}, \frac{\sigma}{2}\right)$ contains the points $X=\pm\frac{1}{2}$, $Y=0$ and $X=0$, $Y=\pm\frac{1}{2}$. Then draw about every individual lattice point as center a square which is equal to the square $\mathfrak{P}\left(\frac{\rho}{2}, \frac{\sigma}{2}\right)$ and with sides parallel to the sides of this square. These squares are indicated in the figure with heavy lines as boundaries. The first square $\mathfrak{P}\left(\frac{\rho}{2}, \frac{\sigma}{2}\right)$ about the origin has boundaries which coincide in part with the boundary lines of the squares which have as mid-points A, A', A_0 and A'_0, and it does not touch any of the other squares. The squares are so situated that no two have boundaries as sides that completely coincide, and thus there are situated equal and parallel gaps in the form of rectangles which have as centers the individual points $X+\frac{1}{2}$, $Y+\frac{1}{2}$ for integral values of X and Y. (See Minkowski, *Dioph. Approx.*, p. 47.)

For example let $GHJK$ be the rectangular gap with the center $X=\frac{1}{2}$, $Y=\frac{1}{2}$ at the point L, so that its sides lie on those of the squares whose centers are X, $Y=0, 0; 1, 0; 1, 1; 0, 1$.

Since AH, $M'GM$, $A'K$ are all parallel to the line $\eta=0$, it is seen that $GH=MA\leqq MS$ and $GK=M'A'<M'S$. It follows that $GH\geqq GK$ and also that $\frac{1}{2}RS\geqq GH$, $\frac{1}{2}RS>GK$. Observe that A' does not coincide with the vertex S. Hence in each of the rectangular gaps one of the sides is smaller and the other at most as great as a side of the square $\mathfrak{P}\left(\frac{\rho}{2}, \frac{\sigma}{2}\right)$.

By the *area* of a figure we understand the value of the integral $\int\int dX\,dY$ taken over its surface. It follows then that the area of the square $\mathfrak{P}\left(\frac{\rho}{2}, \frac{\sigma}{2}\right)$, since $\alpha\delta-\beta\gamma=1$, $pq'-p'q=\pm 1$, is equal to $\frac{1}{2}\rho\sigma$ and the area of the rectangle $GHJK$ is $<\frac{1}{2}\rho\sigma$. Now in the entire plane at each lattice point $X=X^*$, $Y=Y^*$ there is a parallelogram $-\frac{1}{2}\leqq X-X^*\leqq\frac{1}{2}$, $-\frac{1}{2}<Y-Y^*\leqq\frac{1}{2}$ with area 1 and these parallelograms fill the whole plane without gaps and without overlapping. On the other hand there exists for each lattice point X^*, Y^*

a square with center X^*, Y^* with area $\frac{1}{2}\rho\sigma$ and a rectangle with center $X^*+\frac{1}{2}$, $Y^*+\frac{1}{2}$ with an area which is less than $\frac{1}{2}\rho\sigma$ and all these squares and rectangles together fill the entire plane without gaps, and without overlapping. It follows clearly that

$$\frac{1}{2}\rho\sigma<1<2\cdot\frac{1}{2}\rho\sigma. \tag{12}$$

Let the ratio of the distance of the point 0 from the straight line GH be to the distance of the point L from GH, and that is $\frac{1}{2}M'S : \frac{1}{2}M'A'$ as $1 : k-1$, where $1<k<2$. Next construct the square $\mathfrak{P}\left(\frac{k\rho}{2}, \frac{k\sigma}{2}\right)$ with 0 as center and sides parallel to the sides of $\mathfrak{P}\left(\frac{\rho}{2}, \frac{\sigma}{2}\right)$. This is indicated through the dotted lines of the figure (and this square is designated as of the *second kind*). Its boundary passing through L divides the rectangle $GHJK$ into halves, so that such squares about all the lattice points completely cover the plane without any overlapping. Hence the point whose coordinates are the values ξ_0, η_0, the real quantities in question, must fall within or on the boundaries of one of the squares just constructed. If x, y is the lattice point which is the center of this square, it follows that

$$\left|\frac{\xi-\xi_0}{\rho}\right|+\left|\frac{\eta-\eta_0}{\sigma}\right|\leqq\frac{k}{2}. \tag{13}$$

Observe that the square $\mathfrak{P}\left(\frac{k\rho}{2}, \frac{k\sigma}{2}\right)$ about the origin as center is cut by the four squares of like area about the points A, A_0, A', A'_0, which do not overlap one another nor do they reach the center O. And not more than any two of the squares of the second kind overlap one another. Thus the area of $\mathfrak{P}\left(\frac{k\rho}{2}, \frac{k\sigma}{2}\right)$ is necessarily <2, and that is

$$\frac{1}{2}k^2\rho\sigma<2. \tag{14}$$

Noting that the geometric mean of any two positive quantities is $\leqq$ their arithmetic mean, it follows from (2) that

$$\left|\frac{(\xi-\xi_0)(\eta-\eta_0)}{\rho\sigma}\right| \leqq \left(\frac{k}{4}\right)^2,$$

and then from (14) we have

$$|(\xi-\xi_0)(\eta-\eta_0)| < \frac{1}{4},$$

which was to be proved.

2°. Next let $\epsilon=\epsilon'$ and $\lambda>\lambda'>0$, $\mu'<\mu<0$. The lattice points A and A' lie on the same side of $\mathfrak{P}(\rho, \sigma)$; neither of these points can fall on the mid-point of this side. The point A may be one of the vertices of $\mathfrak{P}(\rho, \sigma)$, although A' cannot be a vertex. It is seen from the figure that

$$AA'=OB\geqq OT\ (=\tfrac{1}{2}TT_0=\tfrac{1}{2}RS),$$

where RS is the side of the square $\mathfrak{P}(\rho, \sigma)$ which contains AA'.

The line RS through $A(\lambda, \mu)$ and $A'(\lambda', \mu')$ is

$$\frac{\xi-\lambda}{\eta-\mu}=\frac{\lambda'-\lambda}{\mu'-\mu};$$

and its intercepts on the ξ and η axes are

$$\xi=\lambda-\mu\frac{\lambda'-\lambda}{\mu'-\mu}, \qquad \eta=\mu-\lambda\frac{\mu'-\mu}{\lambda'-\lambda}.$$

Hence

$$RS=\sqrt{\left(\lambda-\mu\frac{\lambda'-\lambda}{\mu'-\mu}\right)^2+\left(\mu-\lambda\frac{\mu'-\mu}{\lambda'-\lambda}\right)^2}$$

$$=\frac{1}{(\mu'-\mu)(\lambda-\lambda')}\sqrt{(\lambda'-\lambda)^2+(\mu'-\mu)^2}=\frac{AA'}{(\mu'-\mu)(\lambda-\lambda')},$$

so that

$$(\mu'-\mu)(\lambda-\lambda')=\frac{AA'}{RS}>\frac{1}{2}.$$

About each lattice point in the plane construct a square equal to the square $\mathfrak{P}\left(\frac{\rho}{2}, \frac{\sigma}{2}\right)$ with sides parallel to the sides of this initial square as shown in Fig. 80. The lattice points are denoted by coordinates X, Y. These squares do not overlap but in general have between one another gaps

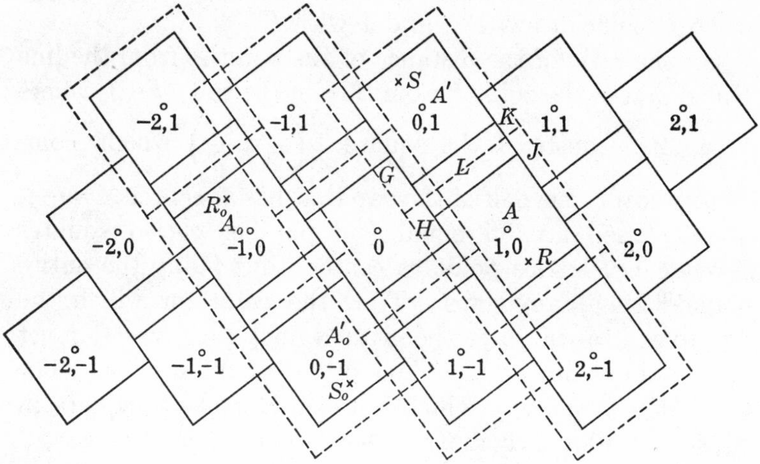

FIG. 80

in the form of rectangles whose mid-points have coordinates $X+\frac{1}{2}$, $Y+\frac{1}{2}$ where X and Y are integers. These gaps are non-existent only when the lattice point $X=-1$, $Y=1$(see Fig. 80) fall on the boundary of $\mathfrak{P}(\rho, \sigma)$, and that is when $(\lambda-\lambda')(\mu'-\mu)=\frac{1}{2}$ as seen above. Neglecting this special case, let $GHJK$ be the rectangular gap whose center is L with coordinates $X=\frac{1}{2}$, $Y=\frac{1}{2}$. Its sides GH, HJ, JK, KG border on the squares whose centers have the coordinates $X, Y=0, 0$; $-1, 0$; $1, 1$; $0, 1$. It is seen that the side GK is equal to the side of the square $\mathfrak{P}\left(\frac{\rho}{2}, \frac{\sigma}{2}\right)$ while the side GH is smaller than the side of a square. The limiting case where $GH=GK$ can only appear when A and A' are both vertices of $\mathfrak{P}(\rho, \sigma)$ which case has been excluded by assuming that $\xi\eta$ was *not* equivalent to the form XY.

It may now be proved by using the same methods as in 1° that the area of the square $\mathfrak{P}\left(\frac{\rho}{2}, \frac{\sigma}{2}\right)$ with that of the rectangle $GHJK$ must be $=1$, and from this it follows that

(15) $$\tfrac{1}{2}\rho\sigma<1<2\cdot\tfrac{1}{2}\rho\sigma.$$

The equation $\frac{1}{2}\rho\sigma=1$ exists if the gaps are zero and that is when H coincides with G and J with K.

Let the ratio of the distance of the point A from the line HJ to that of the point L from this line be as $1 : k-1$, where $1\leqq k<2$. Construct the square $\mathfrak{P}\left(\frac{k\rho}{2}, \frac{k\sigma}{2}\right)$ which completely covers the half of the gap that has as center $X=-\frac{1}{2}$, $Y=\frac{1}{2}$. Then lay off equal and parallel placed squares about every lattice point as center, thus filling the entire plane without any gaps. Thus the point for which the variables ξ, η will have the given values $\xi=\xi_0$, $\eta=\eta_0$ must fall within or on the boundary of one of the squares. For the lattice point x, y which is the center of the square in question we have as above

(16) $$\left|\frac{\xi-\xi_0}{\rho}\right|+\left|\frac{\eta-\eta_0}{\sigma}\right|\leqq\frac{k}{2}.$$

These new squares cover no part of the plane more than twice, while there are certain rectangular gaps each belonging to one square thus giving as in the previous case

(17) $$\tfrac{1}{2}k^2\rho\sigma<2,$$

and from (16) and (17) we again have

$$|(\xi-\xi_0)(\eta-\eta_0)|<\tfrac{1}{4};$$

and at the same time the lattice point x, y may be so chosen that $|\xi-\xi_0|$ lies below any arbitrarily given positive quantity.

ART. **141.** Next let a be any arbitrary real quantity and write $\xi=x-ay$, $\eta=y$. Observe that the form $\xi\cdot\eta$ and that is $(x-ay)y$ can only be equivalent to the form XY if a is an integer and only to a form $\frac{1}{2}(X^2-Y^2)$ if a is an integer increased by $\frac{1}{2}$. In the following we neglect these two cases. The chain for ξ, η has a definite first term p_0, q_0. In the general case treated above when $\eta=0=\gamma x+\delta y$, we have $\frac{x}{\delta}=\frac{y}{-\gamma}$. In the case before us we have $\frac{p_0}{1}=\frac{q_0}{0}$ and >0, so that $p_0=1$, $q_0=0$. For the second term of the chain p_1, q_1, we have $p_0q_1-q_0p_1=\epsilon_0$, so that $q_1=1$; and from

$$|(p_1-aq_1)q_1|<\tfrac{1}{2},$$

it is seen that p_1 is the greatest integer h_0 in $|h_0-a|<\frac{1}{2}$. Hence from (9) of Art. 139 for $i=1$, $t_k=0$, we derive $\frac{p_k}{q_k}=h_0-t_1$. The results derived in Art. 139 may be set forth as follows:

THEOREM VI. *Let a be an arbitrary real quantity that is not an integer nor an integer increased by* $\frac{1}{2}$. *Form in the following manner a series of integral systems* p_i, q_i $(i=0, 1, 2, \cdots)$.

First let $p_0=1$, $q_0=0$ *and then* $q_1=1$ *and* $p_1=h_0$ *the integer next in value to a, so that* $|h_0-a|<\frac{1}{2}$. *In general, if we have come to a system* p_i, q_i *for which* p_i-aq_i *is still* $\neq 0$, *then write down the quotient* $\frac{p_{i-1}-aq_{i-1}}{p_i-aq_i}$. *Let* θ_i *be the sign of this quotient and let* g_i *be the integer that is contained in the absolute value of this quotient. Further write* $h_i=g_i$ *or equal to* g_i+1 *according as* (see Art. 136, end)

$$|\{(p_{i-1}-aq_{i-1})-\theta_i g_i(p_i-aq_i)\}\{g_iq_i-\theta_i q_{i-1}\}|< \quad or \quad \geqq\tfrac{1}{2}.$$

Then write

$$p_{i+1}=h_ip_i-\theta_ip_{i-1},$$
$$q_{i+1}=h_iq_i-\theta_iq_{i-1}.$$

To the series of systems p_i, q_i *thus had, belong the following properties:*

1°. *If a is rational, the series ends with a certain system* p_w, q_w *for which* $p_w-aq_w=0$; *if a is irrational, the series of systems continues indefinitely.*

2°. *For any two consecutive systems we have always*

$$p_iq_{i+1}-q_ip_{i+1}=\theta_1\theta_2\cdots\theta_i=\pm 1.$$

The integers p_i, q_i are always relatively prime.

3°. *We have*

$$\frac{p_k}{q_k}=h_0-\frac{\theta_1|}{|h_1}-\frac{\theta_2|}{|h_2}-\cdots-\frac{\theta_{k-1}|}{|h_{k-1}} \qquad (k=1, 2, \cdots).$$

And here p_k, and q_k are equal to the expressions that are had as numerator and denominator of the right hand side of the above expression when expressed as a quotient of two integral functions of the h_i and θ_i.

4°. *We have $0<q_1<q_2<q_3<\cdots$;*

$$\tfrac{1}{2}>|p_1-aq_1|>|p_2-aq_2|>|p_3-aq_3|>\cdots,$$

and $\left|\frac{p_k}{qk}-a\right|$ decreases with increasing index k.

5°. *For each of the systems p_k, q_k $(k=1, 2, \cdots)$ there exists the inequality*

$$|(p_k-aq_k)q_k|<\tfrac{1}{2}.$$

Inversely: If x, y is any system of relatively prime integers for which $y>0$ and $|(x-ay)y|<\frac{1}{2}$, it is seen that the pair of integers x, y is to be found always among the systems p_i, q_i $(i=1, 2, \cdots)$. (See Corollary to Theorem III.)

From Theorem V it is at once seen that *if b and c are any two real quantities, we can always find* [1] *integers x, y such that*

$$|(x-ay-b)(y-a)|<\tfrac{1}{4},$$

and in addition if a is irrational then $|x-ay-b|$ lies below any given arbitrarily small positive quantity.

The development here defined of continued fractions with convergents $\frac{p_1}{q_1}, \frac{p_2}{q_2}, \cdots$ for the approximation of the quantity a, having regard to the fact that these convergents correspond to the parallelograms with the lines $\xi=x-ay=0$, $\eta=y=0$ as diagonals, may be called the *diagonal continued fraction for a* in contrast to the usual or *normal* continued

[1] This extension of the Tschebyscheff Theorem written in Russian (*Mémoires der Petersburger Akademie*, T. X, Appendix 4, 1866; *Oeuvres*, I.I, p. 679) is also considered on p. 375 of the present volume; see also note at close of this Chapter.

fraction

$$a = l_0 + \frac{1|}{|l_1} + \frac{1|}{|l_2} + \cdots$$

where l_0 is an integer or zero and $l_1, l_2, \cdots$ are positive numbers which refer to parallelograms with the origin as center and with sides parallel to the lines $x - ay = 0$, $y = 0$. This latter development in continued fractions may accordingly be called a *parallel* continued fraction.

Due to a known theorem of Lagrange every pair of integers x, y which are relatively prime, where $y > 0$ and $\left|\frac{x}{y} - a\right| < \frac{1}{2y^2}$, are the numerator and denominator of a convergent of a normal continued fraction. It follows that the diagonal development is more rapidly convergent than the normal development in continued fractions in case the two developments do not coincide.

The diagonal development for a is denoted by

$$a = DC\begin{pmatrix} & \theta_1, & \theta_2, & \cdots \\ h_0, & h_1, & h_2, & \cdots \end{pmatrix},$$

while the parallel chain is denoted by $a = PC(l_0, l_1, l_2, \cdots)$. The geometric concept developed in Arts. 136 ff. of the parallel chain which corresponds to the development of the diagonal chain that is given here, leads to the following rule:

From the series of the systems p_i, q_i ($i = 0, 1, 2, \cdots$) of the diagonal continued fraction for a to derive the convergents of the parallel continued fraction for a we have to extend the first series in such a way that as often as a number $\theta_i = 1$ ($i \geqq 1$) occurs, a new system $p_i - p_{i-1}$, $q_i - q_{i-1}$ must be inserted between the two systems p_{i-1}, q_{i-1} and p_i, q_i.

From this theorem we derive the following rule from which the parallel continued fraction may be derived from the diagonal continued fraction and that is from

$$a = DC\begin{pmatrix} & \theta_1, & \theta_2, & \cdots \\ h_0, & h_1, & h_2, & \cdots \end{pmatrix}$$

to derive

$$a = PC(l_0, l_1, l_2, \cdots)$$

we form the series of numbers $h_0, h_1, h_2, \cdots$ *and have the series of numbers* $l_0, l_1, l_2, \cdots$ *as follows: Instead of every* h_i *we write*

h_i, if $\theta_i = -1, \quad \theta_{i+1} = -1$;
$h_i - 1$, if $\theta_i = 1, \quad \theta_{i+1} = -1$;
$h_i - 1, 1$, if $\theta_i = -1, \quad \theta_{i+1} = 1$; i.e., insert the two terms $h_i - 1, 1$ in the place of h_i;
$h_i - 2, 1$, if $\theta_i = 1, \quad \theta_{i+1} = 1$;

and by θ_0 *we are to understand* -1*, and with this notation we use* $i = 0, 1, 2, \cdots$.

The diagonal continued fractions, says Minkowski, are not only easier to handle on account of their more simple characterization, but they also allow to be recognized all the details regarding the quantities to be put into evidence as in the case of the parallel continued fractions.

EXAMPLE. The parallel continued fraction for $\sqrt{13}$ is

$$\sqrt{13} = PC(3, 1, 1; 1, 1, 6, 1, 1; 1, 1, 6, 1, 1; \cdots)$$

with the convergents

$$\frac{3}{1}, \frac{4}{1}, \frac{7}{2}; \frac{11}{3}, \frac{18}{5}, \frac{119}{35}, \frac{137}{38}, \frac{256}{71}; \frac{393}{109}, \frac{649}{180}, \frac{4287}{1189}, \frac{4936}{1369}, \frac{9223}{2558};$$

The diagonal continued fraction for $\sqrt{13}$ is

$$\sqrt{13} = DC\begin{pmatrix} & +, & -, & +, & +, & -, & +, & +, \\ 4, & 2; & 2, & 8, & 2; & 2, & 8, & 2; \end{pmatrix}$$

with the convergents

$$\frac{4}{1}, \frac{7}{2}; \frac{18}{5}, \frac{137}{38}, \frac{256}{71}; \frac{649}{180}, \frac{4936}{1369}, \frac{9223}{2558}; \cdots$$

which correspond to the

2nd, 3d, 5th, 7th, 8th, $(5k)$th, $(5k+2)$nd, $(5k+3)d$, $\cdots$

convergents of the parallel continued fractions for $\sqrt{13}$.

EXAMPLES

EXAMPLE 1. Observe that

$$p_{i+1} = h_i p_i - \theta_i p_{i-1},$$
$$p_{i+2} = h_{i+1} p_{i+1} - \theta_{i+1} p_i,$$

so that

$$p_{i+2} - p_{i+1} = p_i[h_i(h_{i+1} - 1) - \theta_{i+1}] - (h_{i+1} - \theta_i) p_{i-1}.$$

Hence for $\theta_i=+1$, $\theta_{i+1}=+1$, $p_i=18$, $p_{i-1}=7$, $h_{i+1}=2$, $h_i=8$, $p_{i+2}=256$, $p_{i+1}=137$, we have

$$119=6\cdot 18+11=7\cdot 18-7.$$

If $\theta_i=+1$, $\theta_{i+1}=1$, $p_i=649$, $p_{i-1}=256$, $h_{i+1}=2$, $h_i=8$, $p_{i+2}=9223$, $p_{i+1}=4936$, we have

$$649\cdot 6+393=4287,$$

which verifies the results above for $\sqrt{13}$.

EXAMPLE 2. $p_{i+2}-p_{i+1}=h_{i+1}p_{i+1}-(h_i+\theta_{i+1})p_i+\theta_i p_{i-1}$. If

$$\theta_i=+1,\ \theta_{i+1}=-1;\ p_{i+2}=649,\ p_{i+1}=256,\ p_i=137,\ p_{i-1}=18,$$

we have

$$\begin{aligned}393&=2\cdot 256-137+18\\&=256+137\end{aligned}$$

as given above for $\sqrt{13}$. Similarly if $p_{i+1}=7$, $p_i=4$, $\theta_i=+1$, $\theta_{i+1}=-1$, then

$$11=7+4.$$

EXAMPLE 3. There exists also the development in continued fractions the chain

$$C\begin{pmatrix} & \theta_1, & \theta_2, & \cdots \\ h_0, & h_1, & h_2, & \cdots \end{pmatrix}=h_0-\frac{\theta_1|}{|h_1}-\frac{\theta_2|}{|h_2}-\cdots,$$

where $\theta_1=\pm 1$, $\theta_2=\pm 1$, $\cdots$, and $h_1, h_2, \cdots$, are positive integers such that the remainder

$$\cdots-\frac{\theta_k|}{|h_k}-\frac{\theta_{k+1}|}{|h_{k+1}}-\cdots$$

remains always between $-\frac{1}{2}$ and $+\frac{1}{2}$. For $\sqrt{13}$ this development is

$$\sqrt{13}=C\begin{pmatrix} & 1, & 1, & -1, & 1, & 1, & -1, & 1, & \cdots \\ 4, & 3; & 2, & 7, & 3; & 2, & 7, & 3; & \cdots \end{pmatrix}$$

with the convergents

$$\frac{4}{1},\ \frac{11}{3};\ \frac{18}{5},\ \frac{137}{38},\ \frac{393}{109};\ \frac{649}{180},\ \frac{4936}{1369},\ \frac{14159}{3927};\ \cdots$$

and these are the

2nd, 4th, 5th, 7th, 9th; $\cdots$, $(5k)$th, $(5k+2)$nd, $(5k+4)$th, $\cdots$ convergents in the series of convergents of the parallel continued fraction for $\sqrt{13}$. It is to be observed in this development on the one hand that not every convergent $\frac{x}{y}$ satisfies the condition

$$\left|\frac{x}{y}-\sqrt{13}\right|<\frac{1}{2y^2},$$

and on the other hand that not every fraction which does satisfy this condition is found among the convergents.

EXAMPLE 4. The diagonal continued fraction for the base of the natural logarithm is

$$e=DC\begin{pmatrix} & 1, & -1, & 1, & -1, & \cdots, & & 1, & -1, & \cdots \\ 3, & 3, & & 2, & 5, & & 2, & \cdots, & 2m+1, & & 2, & \cdots \end{pmatrix}$$

with convergents

$$\frac{3}{1}, \frac{8}{3}, \frac{19}{7}, \frac{87}{32}, \frac{193}{71}, \frac{1264}{645}, \frac{2721}{1001}, \cdots.$$

The numerator and denominator of each convergent of this chain offer all the solutions of the condition $-\frac{1}{2}<(x-ey)y<\frac{1}{2}$ and that is of $|\xi\eta|<\frac{1}{2}$ in relatively prime positive integers x, y.

ART. **142.** An infinite diagonal continued fraction

$$(18) \qquad DC\begin{pmatrix} & \theta_1, & \theta_2, & \cdots \\ h_0, & h_1, & h_2, & \cdots \end{pmatrix}$$

for an irrational quantity a is called *periodic*, if there is a positive integer v, such that starting from a certain index j we have always

$$(19) \qquad \theta_k=\theta_{k+v}, \qquad h_k=h_{k+v} \quad (k=j, j+1, j+2, \cdots).$$

The system of values

$$\begin{pmatrix} \theta_j, & \theta_{j+1}, & \cdots, & \theta_{j+v-1} \\ h_j, & h_{j+1}, & \cdots, & h_{j+v-1} \end{pmatrix}$$

is called the *period* of the continued fraction.

We may prove next the following:

If the diagonal chain for an irrational number a is periodic, then a is the root of a quadratic equation with rational coefficients.

We shall use for the chain that is associated with the forms $\xi=x-ay$, $\eta=y$ the notations that were introduced in Art. 139. Through the substitution

$$T_i=\begin{pmatrix} p_{i-1}, & p_i \\ q_{i-1}, & q_i \end{pmatrix}$$

we shall assume that ξ is transformed into $\epsilon_{i-1}\lambda_{i-1}X_i+\epsilon_i\lambda_i y_i$, so that the formula of composition is

$$(1, \; -a)T_i = (\epsilon_{i-1}\lambda_{i-1}, \; \epsilon_i\lambda_i).$$

From formula (6) of Art. 139 we derive more generally the relation

$$(\epsilon_{i-1}\lambda_{i-1}, \; \epsilon_i\lambda_i)\begin{pmatrix}0, & -\theta_i\\ 1, & h_i\end{pmatrix}\begin{pmatrix}0, & -\theta_{i+1}\\ 1, & h_{i+1}\end{pmatrix}\cdots\begin{pmatrix}0, & -\theta_{k-1}\\ 1, & h_{k-1}\end{pmatrix}$$
$$= (\epsilon_{k-1}\lambda_{k-1}, \quad \epsilon_k\lambda_k) \qquad (i<k),$$

and from this we have in particular the relation

$$\epsilon_k\lambda_k = \epsilon_{i-1}\lambda_{i-1}r_{i,k} + \epsilon_i\lambda_i s_{i,k},$$

where $r_{i,k}$, $s_{i,k}$ are certain integers which depend only upon the values $\theta_i, h_i; \theta_{i+1}, h_{i+1}; \cdots; \theta_{k-1}, h_{k-1}$. Observe that with indefinitely increasing k the quantity λ_k converges towards zero, and that the ratio $\frac{\epsilon_{i-1}\lambda_{i-1}}{\epsilon_i\lambda_i}$ is completely determined through the infinite series of the quantities θ_k, h_k for the collective indices $k \geqq i$.

Hence if with any value v the relations (19) exist for all values $k \geqq j$, we have necessarily

$$\frac{\epsilon_{j+v-1}\lambda_{j+v-1}}{\epsilon_{j+v}\lambda_{j+v}} = \frac{\epsilon_{j-1}\lambda_{j-1}}{\epsilon_j\lambda_j}.$$

Write

$$\frac{\epsilon_{j+v-1}\lambda_{j+v-1}}{\epsilon_{j-1}\lambda_{j-1}} = \tau, \qquad \text{where} \qquad 0 < |\tau| < 1.$$

It follows that

$$\epsilon_{j+v-1}\lambda_{j+v-1} = \tau\epsilon_{j-1}\lambda_{j-1},$$

and

$$\epsilon_{j+v}\lambda_{j+v} = \tau\epsilon_j\lambda_j.$$

Since

$$(1, \; -a)T_{j+v} = (\tau\epsilon_{j-1}\lambda_{j-1}, \; \tau\epsilon_j\lambda_j)$$

and

$$(1, \; -a) = (\epsilon_{j-1}\lambda_{j-1}, \; \epsilon_j\lambda_j)T_j^{-1},$$

it follows that

$$(1, \; -a)T_{j+v}T_j^{-1} = (\tau, \; -\tau a).$$

Denote by $\begin{pmatrix} p, & r \\ q, & s \end{pmatrix}$ the scheme of coefficients of the substitution $T_{j+v}T_j^{-1}$. We then have $p-aq=\tau$, $r-as=-\tau a$, or by the elimination of τ, the quadratic equation $(r-as)+(p-aq)a=0$. And in this equation $q\neq 0$, otherwise from above $p=\tau$, where τ is not an integer, since $|\tau|$ lies between 0 and 1.

ART. **143.** We may next prove the inverse theorem:

THEOREM VII. *If an irrational quantity a is the root of a quadratic equation with rational coefficients, then the diagonal continued fraction for a is always periodic.*

Proof. Let

$$n_0a^2+n_1a+n_2=0$$

be the equation for a in which the integers n_0, n_1, n_2 have unity as their greatest common divisor. We then have

$$a=\frac{-n_1\pm\sqrt{n_1^2-4n_0n_2}}{2n_0},$$

so that the integer $D=n_1^2-4n_0n_2$ is positive and on account of the assumed irrationality of a, it is not a perfect square. The second root of the equation $\frac{-n_1\pm\sqrt{D}}{2n_0}$ is denoted by $\bar{a}$.

We put

$$\xi=x-ay=\alpha x+\beta y, \qquad \eta=\frac{1}{a-\bar{a}}(x-\bar{a}y)=\gamma x+\delta y \text{ and } \zeta=y.$$

The forms ξ, η as also ξ, ζ have the determinant 1, and there exists the relation

$$\zeta=\eta+b\xi, \qquad \text{where} \qquad b=-\frac{1}{a-\bar{a}}=\mp\frac{n_0}{\sqrt{D}}\cdot$$

It follows that

$$\mp\sqrt{D}\,\xi\eta=f=n_0x^2+n_1xy+n_2y^2.$$

We consider next the chain for the forms ξ, η. The chain is unbounded at either end; and we shall use for it the notation employed in Art. 139. In addition let ξ_i, η_i

denote the expressions, into which ξ, η are transformed through the substitution T_i and that is

$$T_i: \qquad x=p_{i-1}X+p_iY_i, \qquad y=q_{i-1}X+q_iY_i;$$

and let S_i denote the quadratic scheme $\begin{pmatrix}\epsilon_{i-1}\lambda_{i-1}, & \epsilon_i\lambda_i\\ \mu_{i-1}, & \mu_i\end{pmatrix}$ of the coefficients of ξ_i, η_i so that $\begin{pmatrix}\alpha, & \beta\\ \gamma, & \delta\end{pmatrix}T_i=S_i$.

Through the integral substitution T_i, whose determinant is ±1, the form $f=\pm\sqrt{D}\xi\cdot\eta$ goes into a form

$$f_i=N_0X_i^2+N_1X_iY_i+N_2Y_i^2,$$

where N_0, N_1, N_2 are rational integers and $N_1^2-4N_0N_2=D$. Since D is not a perfect square, it is seen that $N_0\neq0$ and $N_2\neq0$. Comparing this form f_i with the quadratic form $\varphi X^2+\chi XY+\psi Y^2$ of Art. 138, it is seen that the following relations exist: *either*

$$\frac{N_2}{N_0}<0, \quad \frac{N_1}{N_0}>0, \quad |N_0|<\tfrac{1}{2}\sqrt{D}, \quad |N_2|<\tfrac{1}{2}\sqrt{D}, \quad |N_1|<\sqrt{D}$$

or

$$\frac{N_2}{N_0}>0, \qquad \frac{N_1}{N_0}>0, \qquad |N_0|<\tfrac{1}{2}\sqrt{D}, \qquad |N_2|<\tfrac{1}{2}\sqrt{D},$$

$$\sqrt{D}<|N_1|<\tfrac{3}{2}\sqrt{D}, \qquad |N_1-N_0-N_2|>\tfrac{1}{2}\sqrt{D}.$$

In either case there exist only a finite number of possible systems of values for the integral coefficients N_0, N_1, N_2 of a form f_i. It is thus clear that we can find two indices $i=j$ and $i=j+v$, where $v>0$ for which the two forms f_i and f_{i+v} coincide in the coefficients N_0, N_1, N_2.

If we replace the variables X_{j+v}, Y_{j+v} in the forms ξ_{j+v}, η_{j+v} through the variables X_j, Y_j that are found in ξ_j, η_j, we derive the relations

$$\xi_{j+v}=\mathrm{A}\xi_j+\mathrm{B}\eta_j, \qquad \eta_{j+v}=\Gamma\xi_j+\Delta\eta_j,$$

where the coefficients A, B, Γ, Δ are determined through

$S_{j+v} = \begin{pmatrix} \mathrm{A}, & \mathrm{B} \\ \Gamma, & \Delta \end{pmatrix} S_j$. And by means of these relations there must exist the relation $\xi_{j+v}\eta_{j+v} = \xi_j\eta_j$. If the coefficients on either side of this equation are equated, we have $\mathrm{A}\Gamma = 0$, $\mathrm{B}\Delta = 0$, $\mathrm{A}\Delta + \mathrm{B}\Gamma = 1$. Accordingly we must have either

$$(20) \qquad \mathrm{B} = 0, \quad \Gamma = 0, \quad \mathrm{A} = \frac{1}{\Delta} = \tau; \qquad \xi_{j+v} = \tau\xi_j, \quad \eta_{j+v} = \frac{1}{\tau}\eta_j$$

or

$$(20^*) \qquad \mathrm{A} = 0, \quad \Delta = 0, \quad \mathrm{B} = \frac{1}{\Gamma} = \tau; \qquad \xi_{j+v} = \tau\eta_j, \quad \eta_{j+v} = \frac{1}{\tau}\xi_j,$$

where the factor $\tau \neq 0$. The second set of relations, however, are impossible, because in the form η_j the second coefficient has a greater absolute value than the first coefficient, while in the form ξ_{j+v} the contrary must be the case. Hence necessarily the first set of relations must exist and by equating the coefficients in η_j and η_{j+v} it is seen that τ is positive and <1.

From the equations (20) we have

$$S_{j+v} = \begin{pmatrix} \mathrm{A}, & \mathrm{B} \\ \Gamma, & \Delta \end{pmatrix} S_j = \begin{pmatrix} \tau, & 0 \\ 0, & \frac{1}{\tau} \end{pmatrix} S_j,$$

$$\begin{pmatrix} \alpha, & \beta \\ \gamma, & \delta \end{pmatrix} T_{j+v}T_j^{-1} = S_{j+v}T_j^{-1} = \begin{pmatrix} \tau, & 0 \\ 0, & \frac{1}{\tau} \end{pmatrix} S_jT_j^{-1}$$

$$= \begin{pmatrix} \tau, & 0 \\ 0, & \frac{1}{\tau} \end{pmatrix} \begin{pmatrix} \alpha, & \beta \\ \gamma, & \delta \end{pmatrix}.$$

In this relation let $\begin{pmatrix} p, & r \\ q, & s \end{pmatrix}$ be the scheme of the coefficients of the substitution $T_{j+v}T_j^{-1}$, where p, q, r, s are integers such that $ps - qr = \pm 1$. From the relation

$$\begin{pmatrix} \alpha, & \beta \\ \gamma, & \delta \end{pmatrix} \begin{pmatrix} p, & r \\ q, & s \end{pmatrix} = \begin{pmatrix} \tau, & 0 \\ 0, & \frac{1}{\tau} \end{pmatrix} \begin{pmatrix} \alpha, & \beta \\ \gamma, & \delta \end{pmatrix},$$

we have

$$\begin{pmatrix}\alpha p+\beta q, & \alpha r+\beta s\\ \gamma p+\delta q, & \gamma r+\delta s\end{pmatrix}=\begin{pmatrix}\alpha\tau, & \beta\tau\\ \gamma\frac{1}{\tau}, & \delta\frac{1}{\tau}\end{pmatrix}.$$

From this it is seen that if the transformations $x=p\bar{x}+r\bar{y}$, $y=q\bar{x}+s\bar{y}$ are made in ξ, η, these linear forms become $\tau\xi$, $\frac{1}{\tau}\eta$. These two expressions offer the same product as ξ and η. Through the inverse substitution we observe that ξ and η are transformed into $\frac{1}{\tau}\xi$, $\tau\eta$. Hence if we have a lattice point x, y for which x and y are relatively prime and $\xi=\epsilon\lambda$, $\eta=\mu$ ($\mu>0$, $\lambda>0$, $\epsilon=\pm 1$), $\lambda\mu<\frac{1}{2}$, then there exists also another lattice point, for which also x and y are relatively prime and $\xi=\tau\epsilon\lambda$, $\eta=\frac{1}{\tau}\mu$, and further another lattice point for which x and y are relatively prime and $\xi=\frac{1}{\tau}\epsilon\lambda$, $\eta=\tau\mu$; and these two additional lattice points must like the first one enter as terms of the chain for ξ, η.

Due to (20) we have $\epsilon_{j+v}\lambda_{j+v}=\tau\epsilon_j\lambda_j$, $\mu_{j+v}=\frac{1}{\tau}\mu_j$. Further the points $\xi=\epsilon_{j+v+1}\lambda_{j+v+1}$, $\eta=\mu_{j+v+1}$ and $\xi=\tau\epsilon_{j+1}\lambda_{j+1}$, $\eta=\frac{1}{\tau}\mu_{j+1}$, which are both terms of the chain, must be identical. For were $\mu_{j+v+1}>\frac{1}{\tau}\mu_{j+1}$, then the point $\xi=\tau\epsilon_{j+1}\lambda_{j+1}$, $\eta=\frac{1}{\tau}\mu_{j+1}$ would be a term of the chain for which $\mu_{j+v}<\eta<\mu_{j+v+1}$ while $\eta=\mu_{j+v}$ and $\eta=\mu_{j+v+1}$ correspond to two consecutive terms of the chain. If on the other hand $\mu_{j+v+1}<\frac{1}{\tau}\mu_{j+1}$, then we would have $\xi=\frac{1}{\tau}\epsilon_{j+v+1}\lambda_{j+v+1}$, $\eta=\tau\mu_{j+v+1}$ as a term of the chain for which $\mu_j<\eta<\mu_{j+1}$, which likewise is not possible. Hence we must have

$\mu_{j+v+1}=\frac{1}{\tau}\mu_{j+1}$ and accordingly the two points must coincide.

In the same way it may be shown further that

$$\epsilon_{k+v}\lambda_{k+v}=\tau\epsilon_k\lambda_k, \qquad \mu_{k+v}=\frac{1}{\tau}\mu_k \tag{21}$$

for $k=j+2, j+3, \cdots$. We may go backwards in the series of the indices and have the relations (21), which already exist for $k=j-1$ through (20) in sequence for $k=j-2, j-3, \cdots$. Consequently the relations (21) exist for all possible indices.

Further we have for every index i the relation

a) $$S_{i+v}=\begin{pmatrix}\tau, & 0\\ 0, & \frac{1}{\tau}\end{pmatrix}S_i;$$

and from formula (6) of Art. 139 there exists the rule

b) $$S_{i+1}=S_i\begin{pmatrix}0, & -\theta_i\\ 1, & h_i\end{pmatrix}.$$

From the relation a) we have by writing $i=k$ and then $i=k+1$

$$S_{k+v}=\begin{pmatrix}\tau, & 0\\ 0, & \frac{1}{\tau}\end{pmatrix}S_k, \qquad S_{k+v+1}=\begin{pmatrix}\tau, & 0\\ 0, & \frac{1}{\tau}\end{pmatrix}S_{k+1}.$$

It follows from these two relations that

c) $$S_{k+v}S_k^{-1}=S_{k+v+1}S_{k+1}^{-1}.$$

From b) we derive, by writing $i=k$ and then $i=k+v$, the relations

$$S_{k+v}=S_k\begin{pmatrix}0, & \theta_k\\ 1, & h_k\end{pmatrix}, \qquad S_{k+v+1}=S_{k+v}\begin{pmatrix}0, & \theta_{k+v}\\ 1, & h_{k+v}\end{pmatrix},$$

and consequently

$$S_{k+1}S_k^{-1}=\begin{pmatrix}0, & \theta_k\\ 1, & h_k\end{pmatrix}, \qquad S_{k+v+1}S_{k+v}^{-1}=\begin{pmatrix}0, & \theta_{k+v}\\ 1, & h_{k+v}\end{pmatrix}.$$

From c) it is seen that

$$S_{k+1}S_k^{-1}=S_{k+v+1}S_{k+v}^{-1},$$

and therefore

(22) $$\theta_{k+v}=\theta_k, \qquad h_{k+v}=h_k \quad (k=\cdots -2, -1, 0, 1, 2, \cdots).$$

Due to the relations (22) the chain for ξ, η may be regarded as *completely periodic.*

ART. **144.** We return finally to the form $\zeta=y$. Observe that for every term $x=p_i$, $y=q_i$ of the chain for ξ, η we have $\eta>0$ and $|\xi\eta|<\frac{1}{2}$. At the same time it is seen that $\sqrt{D}|\xi\eta|$ is a rational integer. Since this integer $<\frac{1}{2}\sqrt{D}$ it can not be larger than the greatest integer in $\frac{1}{2}\sqrt{D}$. This integer we may write $|\frac{1}{2}\sqrt{D}|=\frac{1}{2}\sqrt{D}-d$, where $0<d<1$. Since, as seen above, $\zeta=y=\eta+b\xi$, it follows from $\sqrt{D}|\xi\eta| \leqq\frac{1}{2}\sqrt{D}-d$, that $|\xi\zeta|\leqq\frac{1}{2}-\frac{d}{\sqrt{D}}+|b\xi^2|, \zeta\geqq\eta-|b\xi|$. Observe in the series of terms of the chain for ξ, η that the quantities $|\xi|$ and $\left|\frac{\xi}{\eta}\right|$ continually decrease. If we continue in this series, we have eventually $|b\xi^2|<\frac{d}{\sqrt{D}}$ and $\left|\frac{\xi}{\eta}\right|<\frac{1}{b}$. We then have $|\xi\zeta|<\frac{1}{2}$, $\zeta>0$, and therefore the systems $x=p_i$, $y=q_i$, which satisfy these conditions, are also terms of the chain for ξ, η.

If, reciprocally, x, y is a term of the chain for the forms ξ, ζ, we must have $\zeta>0$ and $|\xi\zeta|<\frac{1}{2}$. From this it follows that $\sqrt{D}|b\xi^2|\leqq 1-d$, $\eta\geqq\zeta-|b\xi|$. If we proceed in the series of terms of the chain for ξ, ζ so far that $|\sqrt{D}b\xi^2|\leqq 1-d$ and $\left|\frac{\xi}{\zeta}\right|<\frac{1}{|b|}$, it follows here that $\eta>0$ and on the other hand that $\sqrt{D}|\xi\eta|<|\frac{1}{2}\sqrt{D}|+1$. But as $\sqrt{D}|\xi\eta|$ is always an integer, we have $\sqrt{D}|\xi\eta|\leqq[\frac{1}{2}\sqrt{D}]<\frac{1}{2}\sqrt{D}$, and consequently $|\xi\eta|<\frac{1}{2}$. Accordingly it is seen that the system x, y in question is always found among the terms of the chain for ξ, η. Thus the chains for the forms ξ, η and for ξ, ζ starting from certain two terms coincide entirely in the further progress of their terms. Since the individual values θ_i, h_i in a chain may be derived from three consecutive terms in the chain, it is seen that the relations (22) may be transferred starting with a certain index i to the chain for $\xi = x - ay$, $\zeta = y$, and that is the diagonal continued fraction for the quantity a is periodic.

EXAMPLE. In a corresponding relation as the diagonal continued fraction for a stands as the chain which belongs to the forms ξ, η, show that the diagonal continued fraction for the conjugate algebraic number $\bar{a}$ stands as the chain which belongs to the forms $(a-\bar{a})\eta$, $-\frac{1}{a-\bar{a}}\xi$, or what amounts to the same thing to η, $-\xi$. The simple connection of the chain η, $-\xi$ is discussed at the close of Art. 139. From the relation (11) found in that connection it is seen that if $\begin{pmatrix}\theta_j, & \theta_{j+1}, & \cdots, & \theta_{j+v-1}\\ h_j, & h_{j+1}, & \cdots, & h_{j+v-1}\end{pmatrix}$ is a period of the diagonal continued fraction for a, then $\begin{pmatrix}\theta_j, & \theta_{j+v-1}, & \cdots, & \theta_{j+1}\\ h_{j+v-1}, & h_{j+v-2}, & \cdots, & h_j\end{pmatrix}$ will be a period of the diagonal continued fraction for $\bar{a}$.

NOTES

(Continued from p. 452.)

VI. CONTINUED FRACTIONS

A noteworthy application of this theorem is seen in Fig. 81 for diagonal chains. The development for functions of one variable offers a simpler character than the analogous development by means of continued fractions for real quantities. A function $f(z)$ which has a pole for $z = \infty$ admits an expansion in the form

$$c_m z^m + \cdots + c_0 + \frac{c_1}{z} + \frac{c_2}{z^2} + \cdots = F_0(z) - \cfrac{1}{F_1(z) - \cfrac{1}{F_2(z) - \cdot}}.$$

where $F_0(z)$ is an integral rational function of z and $F_1(z)$, $F_2(z)$, $\cdots$ are integral rational functions of degree at least 1. Hence a quotient $\frac{P(z)}{Q(z)}$ of two relatively prime integral rational functions of z is then and only then the approximation fraction for this continued fraction if the development of

$$[P(z) - f(z)Q(z)]Q(z)$$

in decreasing powers of z, begins with a power of z whose exponent is negative. Although there exists a far reaching analogy between the properties of the integral functions and of integers, this analogy in arithmetic seems to have been unnoticed by many mathematicians (Minkowski, I, 321):

It is found in the fact that for any arbitrary real quantity a the fractions x/y which satisfy the inequalities

$$\left|\frac{x}{y}-a\right|<\frac{1}{2y^2}$$

for which therefore $|x-ay|y$ lie within the limits $-\frac{1}{2}$ and $+\frac{1}{2}$, may be arranged as approximations of a definite expansion of a continued fraction

$$a=g_0-\cfrac{1}{g_1-\cfrac{1}{g_2-\cdots}}$$

where g_0 is an integer and $g_1, g_2, \cdots$ are all positive integers. To be noted, however, is that a can not be the half of an odd integer.

To consider more general conditions, let ξ, η be two binary forms in x, y with arbitrary real coefficients and a determinant $=1$ (as a special case we assumed that $\xi=x-ay$, $\eta=y$). It is seen that *there exists a very noteworthy connection among all possible selections of the inequality* $|\xi\eta|<\frac{1}{2}$ *in integers* x, y *which have no common divisor greater than one.* We must assume however that $\xi\cdot\eta$ is not the arithmetical equivalent of the form $\frac{1}{2}(x^2-y^2)$. See in this connection Minkowski, *Diophantische Approximationen*, p. 36. Take the straight lines $\xi=0$, $\eta=0$ at right angles to each other and draw the hyperbolas $\xi\eta=\frac{1}{2}$, $\xi\eta=-\frac{1}{2}$. Construct an arbitrary tangent to the branch of the hyperbola in the first $\xi>\eta$ quadrant and make its image in the other three quadrants, thus forming a quadrilateral with the diagonals $\xi=0$, $\eta=0$.

Such a parallelogram contains always at least one primitive solution (i.e. one consisting of integers that are relatively prime and $x, y\neq 0, 0$) of the inequality $|\xi\eta|<\frac{1}{2}$ and it contains at most two different such solutions where the determinant of the coordinates is always $=\pm 1$. In this connection we do not consider two opposed systems x, y; $-x, -y$ as different. Reciprocally, there corresponds to each primitive solution x, y a tangent parallelogram which contains only this solution (and $-x, -y$); and which contains this primitive solution and in addition another primitive solution with smaller $|\xi|$ where $\xi\neq 0$. By sliding the tangents along the branches of the hyperbola in a continuous manner, we derive in rote parallelograms with one and with two primitive solutions, and we thus have the collectivity of the primitive solutions of the inequality $|\xi\eta| < \frac{1}{2}$ arranged according to decreasing $|\xi|$ and increasing $|\eta|$ and constituting the diagonal chain to the two binary forms ξ, η in terms of x, y.

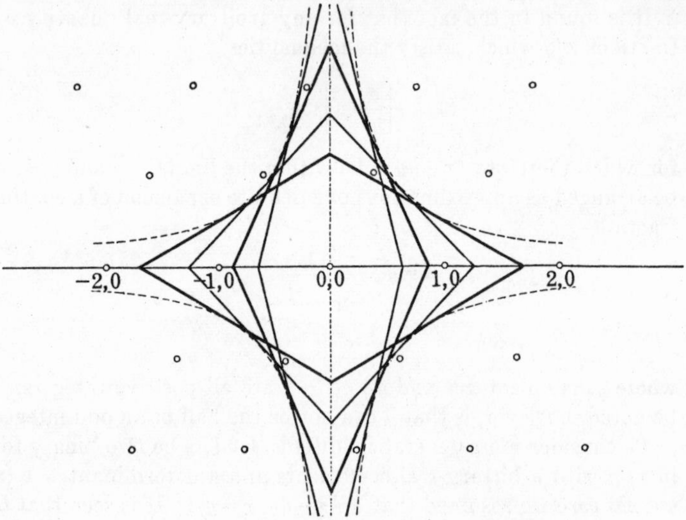

FIG. 81

VII. THE TSCHEBYSCHEFF THEOREM

(1) $$|x-ay-b| < \frac{1}{4|y|},$$

(2) $$\xi = \alpha x + \beta y, \qquad \eta = \gamma x - \delta y, \qquad \alpha\delta - \beta\gamma = 1;$$

(3) $$(\xi - \xi_0)(\eta - \eta_0) < \tfrac{1}{4}.$$

Tschebyscheff was among the first who treated non-homogeneous diophantic inequalities. He treated a theorem of the following kind. If a and b are two arbitrary real quantities, we may always find two integers x and y which satisfy the inequality (1). Instead of the factor $\frac{1}{4}$ on the right Tschebyscheff used a more unfavorable constant. The results which are the most far reaching in this direction are the following: Let ξ, η be two linear forms in x, y with arbitrary real coefficients and a determinant $=1$. By means of two consecutive forms of the above mentioned diagonal chain for ξ, η we are able to construct a system of homologous parallelograms about the individual lattice points as centers whose diagonals are parallel to the lines $\xi = 0$, $\eta = 0$, where no two overlap, but where each is the boundary of the other parallelograms forming a gapless covering of the plane and bounding six or eight other parallelograms. Two different possibilities are offered as seen in the two figures where a parallelogram either abuts with each side on a neighboring parallelogram or only with two sides on two neighboring parallelograms. The heavy parallelograms in general have gaps between them. These we dilate from their centers to homothetic parallelograms in a definite ratio whereby they increase so as to cover a half of the abutting gaps and we thus create new parallelograms which completely cover the plane and in part more than once. It is seen however that part of the plane is covered more than double and consequently the surface area $\iint dx\, dy$ of such a parallelogram is $\leqq 2$. This fact leads to the following theorem:

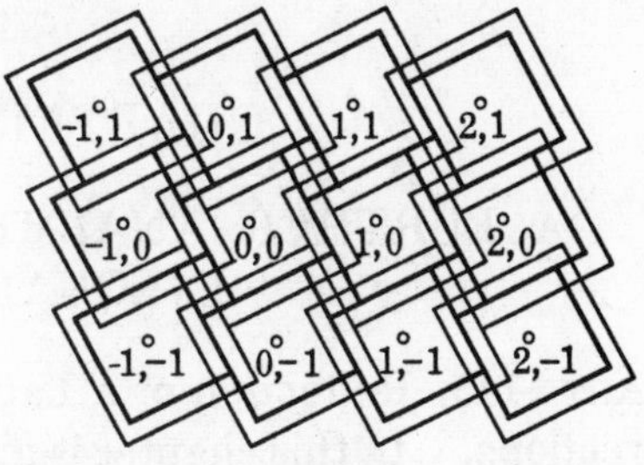

Fig. 79a

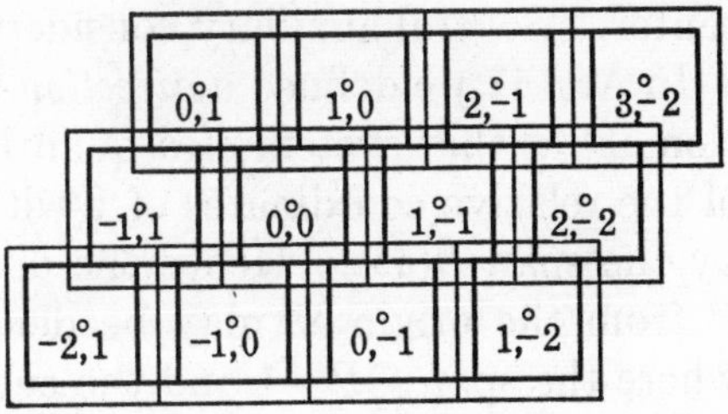

Fig. 80a

In connection with Figs. 79a and 80a, see Fig. 79 on p. 497 and Fig. 80 on p. 501.

If ξ, η are any two real quantities we may always find integers x, y such that the inequality (3) above exists. The previously formulated theorem regarding the expression $x-ay-b$ is only a special case of (3) which is a more general expression.

CHAPTER XIII

A FURTHER ANALYTIC–ARITHMETIC INEQUALITY

ART. **145. Reduction of a Lattice with Respect to Given Directions.** In this chapter is given an essential generalization of the arithmetical theorem that was proposed in Art. 44 regarding bodies that are nowhere concave and have a center. Several auxiliary considerations must be prefaced.

In Art. 17 we defined a *direction* from $\mathfrak{a}$ to $\mathfrak{b}$ (or the direction $\mathfrak{a}\mathfrak{b}$) as that system of n quantities which is had if each of the relative coordinates of $\mathfrak{b}$ with respect to $\mathfrak{a}$ is divided by the span $E(\mathfrak{a}\mathfrak{b})$. Hence the direction of a lattice point P from the origin $\mathfrak{O}$ may be denoted by $x_1, x_2, \cdots, x_n$, where the span $\mathfrak{O}P=1$ and the coordinates of P are $x_1, x_2, \cdots, x_n$. If the coordinates of any point whatever are rational, the direction is said to be *rational.* From every point of a lattice out there lie in the rational directions and only in these rational directions the other points of the lattice.

Let $\mathfrak{O}_h$ $(h=1, 2, \cdots, n)$ represent the point for which $x_h=1$, while all the other coordinates are zero. We may express the fact that a point $\mathfrak{x}$ has the *coordinates* $x_1, x_2, \cdots, x_n$ through the formula

$$(1)\quad \mathfrak{x}-\mathfrak{O}=x_1(\mathfrak{O}_1-\mathfrak{O})+x_2(\mathfrak{O}_2-\mathfrak{O})+\cdots+x_n(\mathfrak{O}_n-\mathfrak{O}),$$

where $\mathfrak{O}_1, \mathfrak{O}_2, \cdots, \mathfrak{O}_n$ are defined above.

Let $\mathfrak{p}, \mathfrak{p}_1, \mathfrak{p}_2, \cdots, \mathfrak{p}_m$ be any $m+1$ points where $\mathfrak{p}$ has the coordinates $p_1, p_2, \cdots, p_n$ and $\mathfrak{p}_h$ has coordinates $p_1^{(h)}, p_2^{(h)}, \cdots, p_n^{(h)}$. Then by the formula

$$(2)\qquad v_1(\mathfrak{p}_1-\mathfrak{p})+v_2(\mathfrak{p}_2-\mathfrak{p})+\cdots+v_m(\mathfrak{p}_m-\mathfrak{p})=0,$$

where $v_1, v_2, \cdots, v_m$ are arbitrary quantities, we understand the system of n equations

$$v_1(p_h^{(1)}-p_h)+v_2(p_h^{(2)}-p_h)+\cdots+v_m(p_h^{(m)}-p_h)=0 \qquad (h=1, 2, \cdots, n).$$

If $\mathfrak{a}$ and $\mathfrak{b}$ are two fixed points and if $\mathfrak{c}$ and $\mathfrak{d}$ go through two sets of points so that always

$$\mathfrak{d}-\mathfrak{b}=\mathfrak{c}-\mathfrak{a},$$

we shall say the set of points $\mathfrak{d}$ is derived from the set of points $\mathfrak{b}$ through the *translation* from $\mathfrak{a}$ to $\mathfrak{b}$ (or through the addition of $\mathfrak{b}-\mathfrak{a}$).

The set of points $\mathfrak{x}$, for which there exists the formula

$$(2') \quad \mathfrak{x}=(1-v_1-v_2-\cdots-v_m)\mathfrak{p}+v_1\mathfrak{p}_1+v_2\mathfrak{p}_2+\cdots+v_m\mathfrak{p}_m$$

and that is the formula

$$(2'') \quad \mathfrak{x}-\mathfrak{p}=v_1(\mathfrak{p}_1-\mathfrak{p})+v_2(\mathfrak{p}_2-\mathfrak{p})+\cdots+v_m(\mathfrak{p}_m-\mathfrak{p}),$$

where $v_1, v_2, \cdots, v_m$ are any quantities whatever, is called the *manifold* (Mannigfaltigkeit) laid through $\mathfrak{p}, \mathfrak{p}_1, \cdots, \mathfrak{p}_m$. Thus a manifold laid through $\mathfrak{O}, \mathfrak{O}_1, \cdots, \mathfrak{O}_n$ is that of all points $(x_1, x_2, \cdots, x_n)$. For writing x_i for $\mathfrak{x}$ in such an expression, we have $x_1=v_1$, and similarly $x_2=v_2, \cdots, x_n=v_n$. Let all the points $\mathfrak{p}_1, \mathfrak{p}_2, \cdots, \mathfrak{p}_m$ be different from $\mathfrak{p}$. The possibility of a relation (2) with values $v_1, v_2, \cdots, v_m$, which are not all zero, denotes then a property entirely of the directions from $\mathfrak{p}$ to $\mathfrak{p}_1, \mathfrak{p}_2, \mathfrak{p}_3, \cdots, \mathfrak{p}_m$. If such a relation exists, these directions are said to be *dependent*, otherwise *independent*. Due to the meaning of (1) the directions $\mathfrak{O}\mathfrak{O}_1, \mathfrak{O}\mathfrak{O}_2, \cdots, \mathfrak{O}\mathfrak{O}_n$ are as a matter of course independent. Paying attention to (1) it is seen that among the directions in any manifold laid through $m+1$ points more than m directions are always dependent, this being true in every case for more than n directions.

If $m \leqq n$, the formula (2), when (1) is taken into account, is only satisfied by the system $v_1=0, v_2=0, \cdots, v_m=0$, if of the matrix where there are more rows than columns

$$\| p_h^{(k)}-p_h \| \qquad \begin{pmatrix} h=1, 2, \cdots, n; \\ k=1, 2, \cdots, m \end{pmatrix}$$

at least one of the m-rowed determinants is not zero. That is to say, if there is at least one mth order determinant that is different from zero, then the v's are all zero. In such a case the directions $\mathfrak{p}\mathfrak{p}_1, \mathfrak{p}\mathfrak{p}_2, \cdots, \mathfrak{p}\mathfrak{p}_m$ are independent and the multiplicity through $\mathfrak{p}, \mathfrak{p}_1, \cdots, \mathfrak{p}_m$ is said to be of the mth *order*. (See my Theory of Maxima and Minima, p. 171.)

Let $\mathfrak{p}_1, \mathfrak{p}_2, \cdots, \mathfrak{p}_n$ be any *lattice* points in independent directions from $\mathfrak{O}$. There belongs then to every point $\mathfrak{x}$ a definite solution of $v_1, v_2, \cdots, v_n$ of the formula

$$(3') \quad x - \mathfrak{O} = v_1(\mathfrak{p}_1 - \mathfrak{O}) + v_2(\mathfrak{p}_2 - \mathfrak{O}) + \cdots + v_n(\mathfrak{p}_n - \mathfrak{O}),$$

and that is there is a definite solution in $v_1, v_2, \cdots, v_n$ of the system of n equations

$$(3) \qquad x_h = p_h^{(1)}v_1 + p_h^{(2)}v_2 + \cdots + p_h^{(n)}v_n \quad (h = 1, 2, \cdots, n).$$

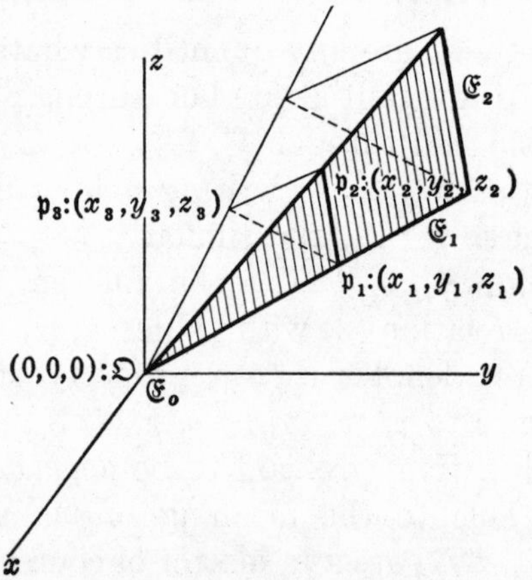

The manifolds[1] in three dimensions are, for example, $\mathfrak{E}_0$, $\mathfrak{E}_1$, $\mathfrak{E}_2$, and $\mathfrak{E}_3$. Selection of the three points $\mathfrak{p}_1$, $\mathfrak{p}_2$, and $\mathfrak{p}_3$, taken together with the origin, where $\mathfrak{O}\mathfrak{p}_1, \mathfrak{O}\mathfrak{p}_2, \mathfrak{O}\mathfrak{p}_3$ are independent directions, determines all these manifolds. The manifold $\mathfrak{E}_0$ is simply $\mathfrak{O}$ itself. The manifold $\mathfrak{E}_1$ is the indefinite straight line through $\mathfrak{O}$ and $\mathfrak{p}_1$. The manifold $\mathfrak{E}_2$, *part* of which is shaded, is the entire plane through $\mathfrak{O}$, $\mathfrak{p}_1$, and $\mathfrak{p}_2$. The manifold $\mathfrak{E}_3$ is the entire space.

FIG. 82

Denote by $\mathfrak{E}_k$ for $k = 1, 2, \cdots, n$ the manifold (*ensemble*) that is laid through $\mathfrak{O}, \mathfrak{p}_1, \mathfrak{p}_2, \cdots, \mathfrak{p}_k$. $\mathfrak{E}_n$ will then be the

[1] For the case $n = 2$, see Art. 155, II.

manifold of all points. Further, $\mathfrak{E}_m$ for $m=1$ or 2 or 3 $\cdots$ or $n-1$ is always defined through $v_{m+1}=0, \cdots, v_n=0$; and $v_1, v_2, \cdots, v_m$ depend for the points of $\mathfrak{E}_m$ only upon $\mathfrak{p}_1, \mathfrak{p}_2, \cdots, \mathfrak{p}_m$. In addition is to be understood by $\mathfrak{E}_0$ the point $\mathfrak{O}$, for which we have $v_1=0, v_2=0, \cdots, v_n=0$. Let two different points $\mathfrak{x}_1$ and $\mathfrak{x}_2$ be expressed through $v_1, v_2, \cdots, v_n$. That one is defined as the *lower* when of the n defining quantities $v_n, v_{n-1}, \cdots, v_2, v_1$ the first one in which the points do not coincide has the lesser value. In the realm

$$0 \leqq v_1, \qquad 0 \leqq v_2, \qquad \cdots, \qquad 0 \leqq v_n$$

it is seen that $\mathfrak{O}$ is lower than any other point; the points in $\mathfrak{E}_1$ are lower than those outside of $\mathfrak{E}_1$; those in $\mathfrak{E}_2$ are lower than those outside of $\mathfrak{E}_2$, etc.

The parallelopipedon

$$(4) \quad 0 \leqq v_1 \leqq 1, \qquad 0 \leqq v_2 \leqq 1, \qquad \cdots, \qquad 0 \leqq v_n \leqq 1$$

contains only a finite number of lattice points, including $\mathfrak{O}$. The point $\mathfrak{p}_1$, which is different from $\mathfrak{O}$, lies in $\mathfrak{E}_1$, and again $\mathfrak{p}_2$, which is outside of $\mathfrak{E}_1$, lies in $\mathfrak{E}_2$, etc.

We thus have in this parallelopipedon a definite lowest lattice point $\mathfrak{r}_1$ different from $\mathfrak{O}$ in $\mathfrak{E}_1$, and again a definite lowest lattice point $\mathfrak{r}_2$ outside of $\mathfrak{E}_1$ and in $\mathfrak{E}_2$, $\cdots$, etc. For these lattice points $\mathfrak{r}_1, \mathfrak{r}_2, \cdots$ we have the formulas

$$(5) \quad \begin{cases} \mathfrak{r}_1-\mathfrak{O}=\beta_1^{(1)}(\mathfrak{p}_1-\mathfrak{O}), \\ \mathfrak{r}_2-\mathfrak{O}=\beta_1^{(2)}(\mathfrak{p}_1-\mathfrak{O})+\beta_2^{(2)}(\mathfrak{p}_2-\mathfrak{O}), \\ \cdots\cdots\cdots\cdots\cdots\cdots\cdots\cdots\cdots \\ \mathfrak{r}_n-\mathfrak{O}=\beta_1^{(n)}(\mathfrak{p}_1-\mathfrak{O})+\beta_2^{(n)}(\mathfrak{p}_2-\mathfrak{O})+\cdots+\beta_n^{(n)}(\mathfrak{p}_n-\mathfrak{O}), \end{cases}$$

where $0<\beta_1^{(1)} \leqq 1, 0<\beta_2^{(2)} \leqq 1, \cdots, 0<\beta_n^{(n)} \leqq 1$. Observe further that there exists no lattice point save $\mathfrak{O}$ for which

$$0 \leqq v_n < \beta_n^{(n)}, \qquad \cdots, \qquad 0 \leqq v_1 < \beta_1^{(1)}. \quad \text{(Cf. Fig. 83.)}$$

If $\mathfrak{x}$ is an arbitrary lattice point, then from the addition of $-y_h(\mathfrak{r}_h-\mathfrak{O})-\cdots-y_1(\mathfrak{r}_1-\mathfrak{O})$ to it where $y_h, \cdots, y_1$ are integers and h is any of the values $n, \cdots, 1$, we always again have a lattice point. We may accordingly so choose the h's uniquely that for this resulting lattice point, which may be called $\mathfrak{r}^{(h)}$, we have

$$0 \leqq v_h < \beta_h^{(h)}, \qquad \cdots, \qquad 0 \leqq v_1 < \beta_1^{(1)}.$$

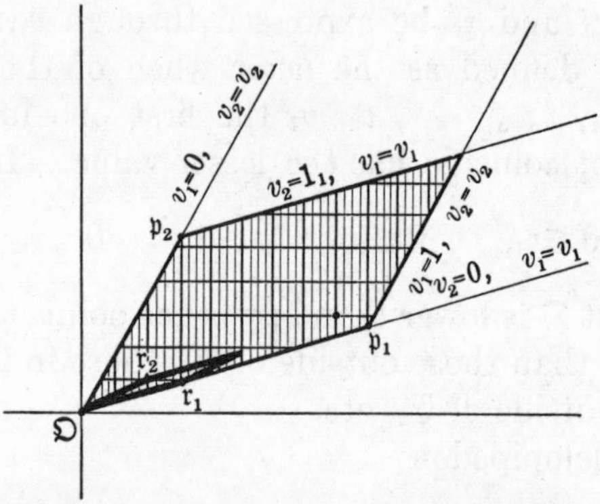

The large, shaded parallelogram is the parallelogram $0 \leqq v_1 \leqq 1$, $0 \leqq v_2 \leqq 1$. The point $\mathfrak{r}_1$ appears as the first lattice point in the manifold $\mathfrak{O}\mathfrak{p}_1$ for $1 \geqq v_1 > 0$. The point $\mathfrak{r}_2$ and the other point interior to the parallelogram (indicated in black) have the smallest possible positive value of v_2 (other than zero), and $\mathfrak{r}_1$ has, at the same time, the smallest positive value of v_1 possible.

In the smaller parallelogram $0 \leqq v_1 \leqq \beta_1^{(1)}$, $0 \leqq v_2 \leqq \beta_2^{(2)}$, if we do not let v_1 assume the value $\beta_1^{(1)}$ or v_2 the value $\beta_2^{(2)}$, then there are no lattice points in the parallelogram defined by $0 \leqq v_1 < \beta_1^{(1)}$, $0 \leqq v_2 < \beta_2^{(2)}$, other than the origin, for which we have $v_1 = v_2 = 0$.

FIG. 83

When this is applied to one of the lattice points $\mathfrak{x} = \mathfrak{r}_k$ $(k > 1)$, and if $h < k$, then

$$(6) \qquad 0 \leqq \beta_h^{(k)} < \beta_h^{(h)} \qquad (\text{if } k > h).$$

Observe next that if $\mathfrak{x}$ is any arbitrary lattice point in $\mathfrak{E}_h$, then for $\mathfrak{r}^{(k)}$ we must always have with a fixed point the result that every lattice point $\mathfrak{x}$ in $\mathfrak{E}_h$ is expressed through

$$\mathfrak{x} - \mathfrak{O} = y_1(\mathfrak{r}_1 - \mathfrak{O}) + y_2(\mathfrak{r}_2 - \mathfrak{O}) + \cdots + y_h(\mathfrak{r}_h - \mathfrak{O}),$$

where the y's are definite integers.

Consider the two expressions

$$\mathfrak{r}_k - \mathfrak{O} = \beta_1^{(k)}(\mathfrak{p}_1 - \mathfrak{O}) + \cdots + \beta_h^{(k)}(\mathfrak{p}_h - \mathfrak{O}) + \cdots + \beta_k^{(k)}(\mathfrak{p}_k - \mathfrak{O}),$$
$$\mathfrak{x} - \mathfrak{O} = y_1(r_1 - \mathfrak{O}) + \cdots + y_h(r_h - \mathfrak{O}),$$

where $\mathfrak{r}_k$ $(k=1, \cdots, n)$ is the lowest lattice point in $\mathfrak{E}_k$ and $\mathfrak{x}$ is an arbitrary lattice point in $\mathfrak{E}_h$. The y's are integers and y_h may have either a positive or negative value. If these two expressions are added and if $y_h>0$, we derive another lattice point, compared to which $\mathfrak{r}_k$ is the lower; if $h=k$, $y=-1$, we have a point in $\mathfrak{E}_{k-1}$; in every other case where $y_h<0$ and that is $y_h=-2, -3, \cdots$ we have, due to (5) and (6), points on the outside of the region (4). Through the relations (5) and (6), and further through the condition that all existing lattice points are expressed by the formula

$$(7)\qquad \mathfrak{x}-\mathfrak{O}=y_1(\mathfrak{r}_1-\mathfrak{O})+y_2(\mathfrak{r}_2-\mathfrak{O})+\cdots+y_n(\mathfrak{r}_n-\mathfrak{O}),$$

where $y_1, \cdots, y_n$ are rational integers, it is seen that $\mathfrak{r}_1, \mathfrak{r}_2, \cdots, \mathfrak{r}_n$ are completely characterized; that is, $\mathfrak{r}_k$ is seen to be the lowest lattice point in (4) outside of $\mathfrak{E}_{k-1}$. Hence also it is clear that these lattice points depend only upon the directions $\mathfrak{O}\mathfrak{p}_1, \mathfrak{O}\mathfrak{p}_2, \cdots, \mathfrak{O}\mathfrak{p}_n$.

Between the coordinates $x_1, x_2, \cdots, x_n$ of an arbitrary point $\mathfrak{x}$ and the values $y_1, y_2, \cdots, y_n$ which satisfy formula (7) for this point there follow from formulas (7) and (1) the relations

$$(7')\qquad \begin{cases} 1)\ x_h=a_h^{(1)}y_1+a_h^{(2)}y_2+\cdots+a_h^{(n)}y_n, \\ 2)\ y_k=b_k^{(1)}x_1+b_k^{(2)}x_2+\cdots+b_k^{(n)}x_n, \end{cases} \qquad (h, k=1, 2, \cdots, n),$$

where $a_1^{(k)}, a_2^{(k)}, \cdots, a_n^{(k)}$ are the $x_1, x_2, \cdots, x_n$ coordinates of $\mathfrak{r}_k$ and $b_1^{(h)}, b_2^{(h)}, \cdots, b_n^{(h)}$ are the determining values (Bestimmungsstücke v_h) $y_1, y_2, \cdots, y_n$ for $\mathfrak{O}_h$. All these quantities are integers. By writing the values of y_k from 2) in 1) and equating the coefficients of the x's on either side of the resulting expressions it is seen that

$$|a_h^{(k)}|\,|b_h^{(k)}|=1.$$

It follows that the determinant $|a_h^{(k)}|=\pm 1$. The introduction of the variables $y_1, y_2, \cdots, y_n$ in the place of $x_1, x_2, \cdots, x_n$ through which the integral systems $x_1, x_2, \cdots, x_n$ are transformed into the integral systems $y_1, y_2, \cdots, y_n$ is called the *reduction* of the lattice with respect to the directions $\mathfrak{D}\mathfrak{p}_1, \mathfrak{D}\mathfrak{p}_2, \cdots, \mathfrak{D}\mathfrak{p}_n$. Observe that these directions were employed in determining the lattice points $\mathfrak{r}_h$ ($h=1, 2, \cdots, n$).

The use of this reduction rests on the simpler presentation which is thereby procured for the multiplicity $\mathfrak{E}_m$. It is seen that with the presentation through the y's the aggregate $\mathfrak{E}_m$ (for $m=0, 1, 2, \cdots, n-1$) is defined through $y_{m+1}=0, y_{m+2}=0, \cdots, y_n=0$. From formulas (7) and (5) we have

$$\begin{aligned}\mathfrak{p}-\mathfrak{D}&=y_1(\mathfrak{r}_1-\mathfrak{D})+y_2(\mathfrak{r}_2-\mathfrak{D})+\cdots+y_n(\mathfrak{r}_n-\mathfrak{D})\\&=y_1\beta_1^{(1)}(\mathfrak{p}_1-\mathfrak{D})+y_2[\beta_1^{(2)}(\mathfrak{p}_1-\mathfrak{D})+\beta_2^{(2)}(\mathfrak{p}_2-\mathfrak{D})]\\&\quad+y_3[\beta_1^{(3)}(\mathfrak{p}_1-\mathfrak{D})+\beta_2^{(3)}(\mathfrak{p}_3-\mathfrak{D})+\beta_3^{(3)}(\mathfrak{p}_3-\mathfrak{D})]+\cdots\\&\quad+y_n[\beta_1^{(n)}(\mathfrak{p}_1-\mathfrak{D})+\beta_2^{(n)}(\mathfrak{p}_2-\mathfrak{D})+\beta_3^{(n)}(\mathfrak{p}_3-\mathfrak{D})+\cdots\\&\qquad\qquad+\beta_n^{(n)}(\mathfrak{p}_n-\mathfrak{D})].\end{aligned}$$

If we equate the coefficients of $\mathfrak{p}_1-\mathfrak{D}, \mathfrak{p}_2-\mathfrak{D}, \cdots, \mathfrak{p}_n-\mathfrak{D}$ in this expression with those in (3′) it is seen that

$$(7'')\qquad \begin{cases} v_1=y_1\beta_1^{(1)}+y_2\beta_1^{(2)}+y_3\beta_1^{(3)}+\cdots+y_n\beta_1^{(n)},\\ v_2=\qquad\qquad y_2\beta_2^{(2)}+y_3\beta_2^{(3)}+\cdots+y_n\beta_2^{(n)},\\ v_3=\qquad\qquad\qquad\qquad y_3\beta_3^{(3)}+\cdots+y_n\beta_3^{(n)},\\ \cdots\cdots\cdots\cdots\cdots\cdots\cdots\cdots\cdots\\ v_n=\qquad\qquad\qquad\qquad\qquad\qquad y_n\beta_n^{(n)}.\end{cases}$$

These equations offer the determinant

$$\Delta=\beta_1^{(1)}\beta_2^{(2)}\cdots\beta_n^{(n)}.$$

The values of $y_1, y_2, \cdots, y_n$ derived from them may be written

$$(8)\qquad \begin{cases} y_1=q_1^{(1)}v_1+q_1^{(2)}v_2+q_1^{(3)}v_3+\cdots+q_1^{(n)}v_n,\\ y_2=\qquad\qquad q_2^{(2)}v_2+q_2^{(3)}v_3+\cdots+q_2^{(n)}v_n,\\ y_3=\qquad\qquad\qquad\qquad q_3^{(3)}v_3+\cdots+q_3^{(n)}v_n,\\ \cdots\cdots\cdots\cdots\cdots\cdots\cdots\cdots\cdots\\ y_n=\qquad\qquad\qquad\qquad\qquad\qquad q_n^{(n)}v_n,\end{cases}$$

where $q_h^{(k)}=0$, when $h>k$.

From (3) we may write

$$y_h = p_h^{(1)} v_1 + p_h^{(2)} v_2 + \cdots + p_h^{(n)} v_n;$$

when the coefficients of $v_1, v_2, \cdots, v_n$ are compared with those in (8) it is seen that the q's are all integers. Observe from (2′) that for a manifold of order m, the quantities $v_{m+1}, \cdots, v_n$ are zero; and from (8) it follows that $y_{m+1}, \cdots, y_n$ are likewise zero.

From (7″) and (8) we have

$$\begin{aligned} v_1 &= \beta_1^{(1)} y_1 + \beta_1^{(2)} y_2 + \beta_1^{(3)} y_3 + \cdots + \beta_1^{(n)} y_n \\ &= \beta_1^{(1)} q_1^{(1)} v_1 + (\beta_1^{(1)} q_1^{(2)} + \beta_1^{(2)} q_2^{(2)}) v_2 \\ &\qquad + (\beta_1^{(1)} q_1^{(3)} + \beta_1^{(2)} q_2^{(3)} + \beta_1^{(3)} q_3^{(3)}) v_3 + \cdots. \end{aligned}$$

By equating the coefficients of the v's on either side of this identity, we have

$$\begin{aligned} &\beta_1^{(1)} q_1^{(1)} = 1, \\ &\beta_1^{(1)} q_1^{(2)} + \beta_1^{(2)} q_2^{(2)} = 0, \quad \text{or} \quad \beta_1^{(2)} q_1^{(1)} q_2^{(2)} = g_1^{(2)},\ g_2^{(2)} \text{ an integer} \\ &\beta_1^{(1)} q_1^{(3)} + \beta_1^{(2)} q_2^{(3)} + \beta_1^{(3)} q_3^{(3)} = 0, \quad \text{or} \quad \beta_1^{(3)} q_1^{(1)} q_2^{(2)} q_3^{(3)} = g_2^{(3)}, \text{ an integer} \\ &\cdots\cdots\cdots\cdots\cdots\cdots\cdots\cdots \\ &\beta_1^{(1)} q_1^{(n)} + \beta_1^{(2)} q_2^{(n)} + \cdots + \beta_1^{(n)} q_n^{(n)} = 0; \end{aligned}$$

and similarly we find

$$\begin{aligned} &\beta_2^{(2)} q_2^{(2)} = 1 \\ &\beta_2^{(2)} q_2^{(3)} + \beta_2^{(3)} q_3^{(3)} = 0 \\ &\beta_2^{(2)} q_2^{(4)} + \beta_2^{(3)} q_3^{(4)} + \beta_2^{(3)} q_4^{(4)} = 0 \\ &\cdots\cdots\cdots\cdots\cdots\cdots \\ &\beta_2^{(2)} q_2^{(n)} + \beta_2^{(3)} q_3^{(n)} + \beta_2^{(3)} q_4^{(n)} + \cdots + \beta_2^{(n)} q_n^{(n)} = 0; \\ &\cdots\cdots\cdots\cdots\cdots\cdots\cdots\cdots \\ &\beta_{n-1}^{(n-1)} q_{n-1}^{(n-1)} = 1, \\ &\beta_{n-1}^{(n-1)} q_{n-1}^{(n)} + \beta_{n-1}^{(n)} q_n^{(n)} = 0; \\ &\cdots\cdots\cdots\cdots \\ &\beta_n^{(n)} q_n^{(n)} = 1. \end{aligned}$$

Noting that $\beta_h^{(h)} q_h^{(h)} = 1$ $(h = 1, 2, \cdots, n)$, it follows from (5) that $q_h^{(h)} > 0$ $(h = 1, 2, \cdots, n)$.

From (7′) and (8) we have

$$\begin{aligned} x_h = a_h^{(1)}[&q_1^{(1)}v_1 + q_1^{(2)}v_2 + q_1^{(3)}v_3 + \cdots + q_1^{(n)}v_n] \\ +a_h^{(2)}[&\qquad\quad q_2^{(2)}v_2 + q_2^{(3)}v_3 + \cdots + q_2^{(n)}v_n] \\ +a_h^{(3)}[&\qquad\qquad\qquad\quad q_3^{(3)}v_3 + \cdots + q_3^{(n)}v_n] \\ +&\cdots\cdots\cdots\cdots\cdots\cdots \\ +a_h^{(n)}[&\qquad\qquad\qquad\qquad\qquad\qquad q_n^{(n)}v_n]; \end{aligned}$$

and from (3) it follows that

$$\begin{aligned} &a_h^{(1)}q_1^{(1)} = p_h^{(1)}, \\ &a_h^{(1)}q_1^{(2)} + a_h^{(2)}q_2^{(2)} = p_h^{(2)}, \\ &a_h^{(1)}q_1^{(3)} + a_h^{(2)}q_2^{(3)} + a_h^{(3)}q_3^{(3)} = p_h^{(3)} \\ &\cdots\cdots\cdots\cdots\cdots\cdots \\ &a_h^{(1)}q_1^{(n)} + a_h^{(2)}q_2^{(n)} + a_h^{(3)}q_3^{(n)} + \cdots + a_h^{(n)}q_n^{(n)} = p_h^{(n)} \\ &\qquad\qquad\qquad\qquad\qquad\qquad (h = 1, 2, \cdots, n). \end{aligned}$$

And that is

$$|a_h^{(k)}|\,|q_h^{(k)}| = |p_h^{(k)}| \qquad (h, k = 1, 2, \cdots, n). \tag{9}$$

In a similar way it may be proved that

$$|b_h^{(k)}|\,|p_h^{(k)}| = q_h^{(k)} \qquad (h, k = 1, 2, \cdots, n). \tag{9^a}$$

Noting the above relations and having regard to (5) and (6), it is seen that if the value of the determinant $|p_h^{(k)}|$ once is given there exists only a finite number of systems for the coefficients $\beta_h^{(k)}$ in (5).

From (9), (9^a) it is further seen that if $m<n$, the number $q_1^{(1)}q_2^{(2)}\cdots q_m^{(m)}$ is always divisible by the greatest common divisor of the m-rowed sub-determinants of the first vertical rows of $|p_h^{(k)}|$, and on the other hand, being a divisor of each of these sub-determinants, is accordingly their greatest common divisor.

Observe that the matrix $|p_h^{(k)}| \begin{pmatrix} k=1, 2, \cdots, m \\ h=1, 2, \cdots, n \end{pmatrix}$ is

$$|p_h^{(k)}| = \begin{vmatrix} a_1^{(1)}q_1^{(1)}, & a_1^{(1)}q_1^{(2)} + a_1^{(2)}q_2^{(2)}, & \cdots, & a_1^{(1)}q_1^{(m)} + \cdots + a_1^{(m)}q_m^{(m)} \\ a_2^{(1)}q_1^{(1)}, & a_2^{(1)}q_1^{(2)} + a_2^{(2)}q_2^{(2)}, & \cdots, & a_2^{(1)}q_1^{(m)} + \cdots + a_2^{(m)}q_m^{(m)} \\ \cdot & \cdot & & \cdot \\ \cdot & \cdot & & \cdot \\ \cdot & \cdot & & \cdot \\ a_n^{(1)}q_1^{(1)}, & a_n^{(1)}q_1^{(2)} + a_n^{(2)}q_2^{(2)}, & \cdots, & a_n^{(1)}q_1^{(m)} + \cdots + a_n^{(m)}q_m^{(m)} \end{vmatrix}.$$

Denote by $h_1, h_2, \cdots, h_m$ any m of the integers $1, 2, \cdots, n$. Observe also that $q_h^{(k)} = 0$ if $h > k$. It is seen that any determinant of the mth order taken from the above matrix is equal to

$$q_1^{(1)} q_2^{(2)} \cdots q_m^{(m)} \,|\, a_{h_i}^{(k)} \,| \qquad \begin{pmatrix} k = 1, 2, \cdots, m \\ i = 1, 2, \cdots, m \end{pmatrix}.$$

If by Laplace's method the determinant

$$1 = |\, a_h^{(k)} \,| \qquad \begin{pmatrix} k = 1, 2, \cdots, n \\ h = 1, 2, \cdots, n \end{pmatrix}$$

is developed in the form $\Sigma A \cdot B$ where A is any determinant of the form $|\, a_{h_i}^{(k)} \,|$, it is clear that the greatest common divisor of the A's must be 1.

ART. **146.** I. *The System of Least Radial-Distances in the Lattice.* We shall now assume that the radial-distances $S(\mathfrak{ab})$ are arbitrary and, as is always the case with accordant (einhellig) radial-distances, that there is a positive lower limit g for all distance coefficients $\dfrac{S(\mathfrak{ab})}{E(\mathfrak{ab})}$ (Art. 20). Further let $\dfrac{G}{n}$ be the largest value among the radial-distances

$$S(\mathfrak{D}\mathfrak{D}_1),\ S(\mathfrak{D}\mathfrak{D}_2),\ \cdots,\ S(\mathfrak{D}\mathfrak{D}_n);\ S(\mathfrak{D}_1\mathfrak{D}),\ \cdots,\ S(\mathfrak{D}_n\mathfrak{D}). \qquad \text{(Art. 17.)}$$

The directions $\mathfrak{D}\mathfrak{D}_1, \mathfrak{D}\mathfrak{D}_2, \cdots, \mathfrak{D}\mathfrak{D}_n$ are independent, and it is clear that there exists a lattice point in n independent directions from $\mathfrak{D}$ with radial-distances $\leqq \dfrac{G}{n}$ from $\mathfrak{D}$.

For points in such radial-distances from $\mathfrak{D}$ the spans from $\mathfrak{D}$ (Cf. end of Art. 20) satisfy the inequalities

$$gE(\mathfrak{ab}) \leqq S(\mathfrak{ab}) \leqq GE(\mathfrak{ab}).$$

Hence with such spans and with such radial-distances from $\mathfrak{D}$ there are found only a finite number of lattice points. Let (G_1) denote the aggregate of all such lattice points that are different from $\mathfrak{O}$ and with radial-distances $\leqq \frac{G}{n}\cdot$ In particular the points $\mathfrak{O}_1, \mathfrak{O}_2, \cdots, \mathfrak{O}_n$ belong to (G_1).

The least quantity which appears among the radial-distances from $\mathfrak{O}$ to the individual points in (G_1) is at the same time the least radial-distance which is to be found from $\mathfrak{O}$ to any lattice point. Denote this radial-distance by M_1, and let (M_1) denote the aggregate of radial-distances of all the points of (G_1) from $\mathfrak{O}$ with values M_1. Let $\mathfrak{p}_1$ be an arbitrary one of such points. If (M_1) contains another point exterior to the ray through $\mathfrak{O}$ and $\mathfrak{p}_1$ let $\mathfrak{p}_2$ be such a point; while if (M_1) contains other points exterior to the manifold through $\mathfrak{O}, \mathfrak{p}_1, \mathfrak{p}_2$ let $\mathfrak{p}_3$ be an arbitrary such point of (M_1), etc. If the order of the manifold laid through $\mathfrak{O}$ and (M_1) in this manner is v_1, we may find any v_1 lattice points $\mathfrak{p}_1, \mathfrak{p}_2, \cdots, \mathfrak{p}_{v_1}$ in (M_1) with v_1 independent directions from $\mathfrak{O}$ and then the manifold laid through $\mathfrak{O}$ and $\mathfrak{p}_1, \mathfrak{p}_2, \cdots, \mathfrak{p}_{v_1}$ is identical with the manifold passed through $\mathfrak{O}$ and (M_1). This manifold may be called $\mathfrak{O}(M_1)$. If $v_1 < n$, then $\mathfrak{O}(M_1)$ does not contain all the points $\mathfrak{O}_1, \mathfrak{O}_2, \cdots, \mathfrak{O}_n$, and therefore in the aggregate (G_1) there are lattice points outside of the manifold $\mathfrak{O}(M_1)$. The aggregate of these points belonging to (G_1) may be called (G_2). We may then let M_2 be the least radial-distance from $\mathfrak{O}$ to the points of (G_2). Note that M_2 is $\leqq \frac{G}{n}$ and that M_2 is at the same time the least radial-distance from $\mathfrak{O}$ to any lattice point outside of the manifolds $\mathfrak{O}(M_1)$.

Next let (M_2) be the aggregate of all points of (G_2) which offer the radial-distance M_2 from $\mathfrak{O}$. Let $\mathfrak{p}_{v_1}+1$ be an arbitrary first point taken from (M_2), and if further (M_2) contains a point outside of the manifold laid through $\mathfrak{O}$, $\mathfrak{p}_1, \cdots, \mathfrak{p}_{v_1}, \mathfrak{p}_{v_1+1}$, let $\mathfrak{p}_{v_1+2}$ be such a point of (M_2), etc. We have in this manner a certain number v_2 of lattice points $\mathfrak{p}_{v_1+1}, \mathfrak{p}_{v_1+2}, \cdots, \mathfrak{p}_{v_1+v_2}$ which are such that the directions from $\mathfrak{O}$ to $\mathfrak{p}_1, \mathfrak{p}_2, \cdots, \mathfrak{p}_{v_1+v_2}$ are all independent, and finally the manifold laid through $\mathfrak{O}, \mathfrak{p}_1, \mathfrak{p}_2, \cdots, \mathfrak{p}_{v_1+v_2}$ comprises also the entire aggregate (M_2). Call this aggregate $\mathfrak{O}(M_1, M_2)$.

The method of procedure is clear if v_1+v_2 is still less than n. We are always led in this manner to a number λ of certain quantities $M_1, M_2, \cdots, M_\lambda$ such that each following is greater than the preceding, while all are $\leqq \frac{G}{n}$; and the definite numbers $v_1, v_2, \cdots, v_\lambda$ are such that

$$v_1+v_2+\cdots+v_\lambda=n.$$

At the same time we have the λ definite manifolds $\mathfrak{O}(M_1)$, $\mathfrak{O}(M_1, M_2), \cdots, \mathfrak{O}(M_1, \cdots, M_\lambda)$ of the orders respectively $v_1, v_1+v_2, \cdots, v_1+v_2+\cdots+v_\lambda$. Each following manifold contains the preceding, and the final one is the manifold of all the lattice points in question. Observe that M_1 is the least radial-distance from $\mathfrak{O}$ to all lattice points different from $\mathfrak{O}$, while M_k $(k>1)$ is the least radial-distance from $\mathfrak{O}$ to all lattice points on the outside of $\mathfrak{O}(M_1, M_2, \cdots, \mathrm{M}_{k-1})$.

Finally, it is possible in one or several ways to choose n lattice points $\mathfrak{p}_1, \mathfrak{p}_2, \cdots, \mathfrak{p}_n$ in n different directions from $\mathfrak{O}$, so that of the n radial-distances

$$S(\mathfrak{O}\mathfrak{p}_1)=S_1, \qquad S(\mathfrak{O}\mathfrak{p}_2)=S_2, \qquad \cdots, \qquad S(\mathfrak{O}\mathfrak{p}_n)=S_n$$

the first v_1 of them are equal to M_1, the v_2 following to M_2, $\cdots$, while the last v_λ are equal to M_λ.

Now let $\mathfrak{q}_1, \mathfrak{q}_2, \cdots, \mathfrak{q}_n$ be any arbitrary n lattice points in n independent directions from $\mathfrak{O}$ and let $\mathfrak{q}_{h_1}, \mathfrak{q}_{h_2}, \cdots, \mathfrak{q}_{h_n}$ be such an arrangement of these points that

$$S(\mathfrak{O}\mathfrak{q}_{h_1}) \leqq S(\mathfrak{O}\mathfrak{q}_{h_2}) \leqq \cdots \leqq S(\mathfrak{O}\mathfrak{q}_{h_n}).$$

Then the differences

$$S(\mathfrak{O}\mathfrak{q}_1)-S(\mathfrak{O}\mathfrak{q}_{h_1}), \qquad S(\mathfrak{O}\mathfrak{q}_2)-S(\mathfrak{O}\mathfrak{q}_{h_2}), \qquad \cdots, \qquad S(\mathfrak{O}\mathfrak{q}_n)-S(\mathfrak{O}\mathfrak{q}_{h_n})$$

are either all zero or the first of these differences, that is not zero, is >0.

Since none of the points $\mathfrak{q}_{h_1}, \mathfrak{q}_{h_2}, \cdots, \mathfrak{q}_{h_n}$ is $\mathfrak{O}$, then if $v_1<n$, the first v_1+1 of them do not all lie in $\mathfrak{O}(M_1)$; and if $v_1+v_2<n$, the first v_1+v_2+1 do not all lie in $\mathfrak{O}(M_1, M_2)$, $\cdots$; and accordingly the n quantities $S(\mathfrak{O}\mathfrak{q}_{h_1}), S(\mathfrak{O}\mathfrak{q}_{h_2}), \cdots$, $S(\mathfrak{O}\mathfrak{q}_{h_n})$ are all $\geqq M_1$; and at least from the v_1+1st on are all $\geqq M_2$; $\cdots$; and accordingly for every value $k=1, 2, \cdots$, n we always have $S(\mathfrak{O}\mathfrak{q}_{h_k}) \geqq S(\mathfrak{O}\mathfrak{p}_k)$. It is thus seen that the differences

$$S(\mathfrak{O}\mathfrak{q}_1)-S_1, \qquad S(\mathfrak{O}\mathfrak{q}_2)-S_2, \qquad \cdots, \qquad S(\mathfrak{O}\mathfrak{q}_n)-S_n$$

are either all zero or positive quantities. Due to this property the quantities $S_1, S_2, \cdots, S_n$ may be called the *least system of independently directed radial-distances in the lattice.*

Write

$$\mu_1=v_1, \qquad \mu_2=v_1+v_2, \qquad \cdots,$$
$$\mu_k=v_1+v_2+\cdots+v_k; \qquad \mu_0=0.$$

Due to Art. 145, instead of $x_1, x_2, \cdots, x_n$ we may, through a linear substitution with integral coefficients and determinant ± 1, introduce such variables that every manifold

$$\mathfrak{O}(M_1, M_2, \cdots, M_{k-1}) \qquad (k=1, 2, \cdots, \lambda)$$

is defined through

$$y_{\mu_{k-1}+1}=0, \qquad y_{\mu_{k-1}+2}=0, \qquad \cdots, \qquad y_n=0.$$

Observe that for $k=1$, the point O is to be taken. Also note that if two lattice points in their coordinates $x_1, x_2, \cdots, x_n$ offer the same residues with respect to an integer p as a modulus the same property is found in the corresponding y-coordinates. For from (7′) we have for any two points p and $\overline{p}$

$$y_k=b_k^{(1)}x_1+b_k^{(2)}x_2+\cdots+b_k^{(n)}x_n,$$
$$\overline{y}_k=b_k^{(1)}\overline{x}_1+b_k^{(2)}\overline{x}_2+\cdots+b_k^{(n)}\overline{x}_n;$$

and if $x_i-\overline{x}_i\equiv 0 \pmod{p}$ $(i=1, 2, \cdots, n,)$ the same is true of $y_i-\overline{y}_i$.

II. From now on the radial-distances $S(\mathfrak{a}\mathfrak{b})$ are assumed to be both accordant (einhellig) and symmetric (wechselseitig). Every point $\mathfrak{a}$ is symmetric with respect to $\mathfrak{O}$ with another point $2\mathfrak{O}-\mathfrak{a}$ having the same radial-distance from $\mathfrak{O}$, since

$$2\mathfrak{O}-\mathfrak{a}-\mathfrak{O}=\mathfrak{O}-\mathfrak{a}.$$

If, further, p is any integer $\geqq 2$ and if the coordinates of any two lattice points $\mathfrak{a}$ and $\mathfrak{b}$ offer the same residues with respect to p, then also

$$\frac{\mathfrak{b}-\mathfrak{a}}{p}+\mathfrak{O}=\frac{\mathfrak{b}+(2\mathfrak{O}-\mathfrak{a})+(p-2)\mathfrak{O}}{p}$$

is a lattice point and its radial-distance from $\mathfrak{O}$ is

$$\leqq\frac{S(\mathfrak{O}\mathfrak{b})+S(\mathfrak{O}\mathfrak{a})}{p}.$$

For the relative coordinates of $\frac{\mathfrak{a}}{p}$ to $\frac{\mathfrak{b}}{p}$ are the same as from $\mathfrak{O}$ to $\frac{\mathfrak{b}-\mathfrak{a}}{p}+\mathfrak{O}$, and $\frac{\mathfrak{b}-\mathfrak{a}}{p}+\mathfrak{O}-\mathfrak{O}=\frac{\mathfrak{b}-\mathfrak{a}}{p}$, and if $\frac{\mathfrak{b}-\mathfrak{a}}{p}+\mathfrak{O}$ is denoted by $\mathfrak{c}$,

$$S(\mathfrak{O}\mathfrak{c})=S\left(\frac{\mathfrak{b}}{p},\quad\frac{\mathfrak{a}}{p}\right)=\frac{1}{p}S(\mathfrak{b}\mathfrak{a})\leqq\frac{1}{p}[S(\mathfrak{b}\mathfrak{O})+S(\mathfrak{O}\mathfrak{a})].$$

If then $p>2$ and $S(\mathfrak{O}\mathfrak{a})$ and $S(\mathfrak{O}\mathfrak{b})$ are both $\leqq M_k$ $(k=1, 2, \cdots, \lambda)$, then this last lattice point lies necessarily in $\mathfrak{O}(M_1, M_2, \cdots, M_{k-1})$ and the values of $y_{\mu_{k-1}+1}, y_{\mu_{k-1}+2}, \cdots, y_n$ must be the same for both $\mathfrak{b}$ and $\mathfrak{a}$.

If $p=3$ there exist not more than 3^n different systems of coordinates for all lattice points $\mathfrak{a}$ for which $S(\mathfrak{O}\mathfrak{a})\leqq M_k$. If $n=2$ and if we take for $S(\mathfrak{O}\mathfrak{x})\leqq 1$, for example, the domain

$$-1\leqq x_1\leqq 1,\qquad -1\leqq tx_2\leqq +1,$$

where $t>1$, then we have $S_1=1$, $S_2=t$; and $\mathfrak{p}_1$ is one of the two points $x_1=\pm 1$, $x_2=0$ while $\mathfrak{p}_2$ may be chosen among all the points for which $-t\leqq x_1\leqq t$, $x_2=\pm 1$. From this example it is seen that in general for *the number of different ways in which we may take n lattice points in n independent directions from* $\mathfrak{O}$ *with least possible radial-distances from* $\mathfrak{O}$ *an upper limit cannot be given that depends only upon n.* This, however, becomes possible as soon as the standard surface of radial-distances, the surface $S(\mathfrak{O}\mathfrak{x})=1$, is everywhere convex, or at least is convex in all rational directions. By this last expression it is to be understood that no stretch $\mathfrak{ab}$ with a rational direction $\mathfrak{ab}$ belongs entirely to this surface, and clearly this property is transmitted to every surface of constant radial-distance.

In general, if the above property exists and if $\mathfrak{a}$ is a point of the aggregate (M_k) and therefore if for this point the coordinates $y_{\mu_{k-1}+1}, y_{\mu_{k-1}+2}, \cdots, y_n$ are not all zero, and if $\mathfrak{b}$ is a lattice point different from $\mathfrak{a}$ and from $2\mathfrak{O}-\mathfrak{a}$, for which we have $S(\mathfrak{O}\mathfrak{b}) \leqq M_k$, then $\mathfrak{a}$ and $\mathfrak{b}$ can never have the residues, modulo 2, of their coordinates the same. For $\mathfrak{b}$ cannot have both for $\mathfrak{a}$ and $2\mathfrak{O}-\mathfrak{a}$ coincidence in the values $y_{\mu_{k-1}+1}, y_{\mu_{k-1}+2}, \cdots, y_n$. Let these values be different for $\mathfrak{b}$ and $\mathfrak{a}$, say. Then the point $\dfrac{\mathfrak{b}+2\mathfrak{O}-\mathfrak{a}}{2}$ does *not* lie in $\mathfrak{O}(M_1, M_2, \cdots, M_{k-1})$ and cannot be a lattice point. For as a point on the line from $2\mathfrak{O}-\mathfrak{a}$ to $\mathfrak{b}$, since these points belong to the domain $S(\mathfrak{O}\mathfrak{x}) \leqq M_k$ and since this stretch has a rational direction, it must have a radial-distance $<M_k$ from $\mathfrak{O}$ which is contrary to the meaning of M_k.

Observe that here $\mathfrak{b}$ may coincide with $\mathfrak{O}$, so that for every lattice point $\mathfrak{p}_k$ there cannot appear more than $2^{n+1}-2$ lattice points, and therefore for the choice of the n points $\mathfrak{p}_1, \mathfrak{p}_2, \cdots, \mathfrak{p}_n$ there are not more than $(2^{n+1}-2)^n$ possibilities. Compare this result with that given in Art. 45, end.

ART. **147. An Application to the Infinite Groups of Integral Linear Substitutions.** We shall insert here an application of the preceding results. Let $B_1, B_2, \cdots, B_w$ be a finite number of different operations of the following character:

The symbol B_γ $(\gamma=1, 2, \cdots, w)$ shall consist in the fact that the n variables $x_1, x_2, \cdots, x_n$ be replaced through n definite expressions

$$(1) \qquad \mathfrak{a}^{(\gamma)} = b_{h1}^{(\gamma)} x_1 + b_{h2}^{(\gamma)} x_2 + \cdots + b_{hn}^{(\gamma)} x_n \quad (h=1, 2, \cdots, n),$$

where the coefficients $b_{hk}^{(\gamma)}$ are integers. Further, each of these linear homogeneous integral substitutions B_γ must be reversible, that is, $|b_{hk}^{(\gamma)}|$ must be different from zero.

Corresponding to each point $\mathfrak{a} : a_1, a_2, \cdots, a_n$ there always exists a definite point $x_1, x_2, \cdots, x_n$ for which the n expressions (1) are equal to $a_1, a_2, \cdots, a_n$. Denote this point by $\mathfrak{a}^{(\gamma)}$. Any n points $\mathfrak{a}_1, \mathfrak{a}_2, \cdots, \mathfrak{a}_n$ which lie in n independent directions from $\mathfrak{O}$ may be expressed through $\mathfrak{a}_1^{(\gamma)}, \mathfrak{a}_2^{(\gamma)}, \cdots, \mathfrak{a}_n^{(\gamma)}$, which system of n points has the same property as $\mathfrak{a}^{(\gamma)}$ above, and this new system, since reciprocally through it the substitutions B_γ may be had, for the different values $\gamma=1, 2, \cdots, w$ will always be different. Finally the w operations are to form a group, and that is, when a second substitution B_δ has been made after a first one B_γ, which resulting operation may be denoted by $B_\gamma B_\delta$, we always have again one of the w substitutions. The number w is called the order of such a finite group and we shall next show that an upper limit may be found that depends only upon the number n.

First it is seen that the determinant of each substitution B_γ must be equal to ± 1. For the w products $B_\gamma B_1, B_\gamma B_2, \cdots, B_\gamma B_w$, neglecting the sequence, produce the substitutions $B_1, B_2, \cdots, B_w$. It is also seen that if $\mathfrak{a}$ is a lattice point, the points $\mathfrak{a}^{(\gamma)}$ are also all lattice points.

Next consider any accordant and symmetric radial-distances $T(\mathfrak{a}\mathfrak{b})$ with a convex standard surface in all rational directions. The properties which belong to the body $T(\mathfrak{O}\mathfrak{x}) \leqq 1$ are seen to belong to each of the bodies $T(\mathfrak{O}\mathfrak{x}^{(\gamma)})$ $(\gamma=1, 2, \cdots, w)$. Write $T(\mathfrak{O}\mathfrak{x}^{(\gamma)}) = T_\gamma(\mathfrak{O}\mathfrak{x})$. Since the w products $B_\gamma B_1, B_\gamma B_2, \cdots, B_\gamma B_w$ are, neglecting the sequence, identical with $B_1, B_2, \cdots, B_w$, it is seen that with every γ the w values $T_1(\mathfrak{O}\mathfrak{x}^{(\gamma)}), T_2(\mathfrak{O}\mathfrak{x}^{(\gamma)}), \cdots, T_w(\mathfrak{O}\mathfrak{x}^{(\gamma)})$, neglecting the sequence, are identical with the values $T_1(\mathfrak{O}\mathfrak{x}), T_2(\mathfrak{O}\mathfrak{x}), \cdots, T_w(\mathfrak{O}\mathfrak{x})$. The realm of points which we call $\mathfrak{K}$, defined through the simultaneous existence of the w inequalities

$$T_1(\mathfrak{O}\mathfrak{x}) \leqq 1, \qquad T_2(\mathfrak{O}\mathfrak{x}) \leqq 1, \qquad \cdots, \qquad T_w(\mathfrak{O}\mathfrak{x}) \leqq 1,$$

has the property that if any point $\mathfrak{x}$ belongs to it, then also the w points $\mathfrak{x}^{(1)}, \mathfrak{x}^{(2)}, \cdots, \mathfrak{x}^{(w)}$ belong to it. Now $\mathfrak{K}$, like each of the bodies $T_\gamma(\mathfrak{O}\mathfrak{x}) \leqq 1$, has $\mathfrak{O}$ as center which is an inner point; and every point of the boundary of $\mathfrak{K}$ lies upon at least one of the surfaces $T_\gamma(\mathfrak{O}\mathfrak{x}) = 1$; and a tac-plane through it to this surface is also a tac-plane to $\mathfrak{K}$. Finally the boundary of $\mathfrak{K}$ can have no stretch with rational direction. For of $2w+1$ arbitrary points of such a stretch, three must lie on one and the same surface $T_\gamma(\mathfrak{O}\mathfrak{x}) = 1$. Hence the boundary of $\mathfrak{K}$ is in all rational directions a convex surface with $\mathfrak{O}$ as center. Now let $S(\mathfrak{a}\mathfrak{b})$ denote the radial-distances for which $\mathfrak{K}$ is the standard body. Then from the preceding article a system of lattice points in n independent directions from $\mathfrak{O}$ and with smallest possible radial-distances $S(\mathfrak{O}\mathfrak{x})$ is had in not more than $(2^{n+1}-2)^n$ ways. Observe that here we have the property $S(\mathfrak{O}\mathfrak{x}^{(\gamma)}) = S(\mathfrak{O}\mathfrak{x})$ $(\gamma = 1, 2, \cdots, w)$. If $\mathfrak{p}_1, \mathfrak{p}_2, \cdots, \mathfrak{p}_n$ represents any system of the kind just described, then $\mathfrak{p}_1^{(\gamma)}, \mathfrak{p}_2^{(\gamma)}, \cdots, \mathfrak{p}_n^{(\gamma)}$ for $\gamma = 1, 2, \cdots, w$ represents such a system. Since any w systems compounded in this way of n points are different, it follows that

$$w \leqq (2^{n+1}-2)^n.$$

With this it is seen that *the order of a finite group of homogeneous linear reversible (umkehrbar) substitutions in n variables is always* $\leqq (2^{n+1}-2)^n$.

ART. 148. **Positive Quadratic Forms and Their Integral Transformations into Themselves.** I. A quadratic form in n variables $x_1, x_2, \cdots, x_n$ and real coefficients

$$f = \sum a_{hk} x_h x_k \qquad (h, k = 1, 2, \cdots, n),$$

where always $a_{kh}=a_{hk}$ is called *positive* when it is positive for all real values of the variables except the system 0, 0, $\cdots$, 0. Let m be any one of the integers 1, 2, $\cdots$, n and h_1, h_2, $\cdots$, h_m any m different integers of the series 1, 2, $\cdots$, n and likewise k_1, k_2, $\cdots$, k_m are any m different integers of the same series. Then the determinant of the m^2 elements a_{hk} $(h=h_1, h_2, \cdots, h_m; k=k_1, k_2, \cdots, k_m)$, h being the index of the horizontal row, and k that of the vertical column, is denoted by

$$D\begin{pmatrix} h_1, & h_2, & \cdots, & h_m \\ k_1, & k_2, & \cdots, & k_m \end{pmatrix}.$$

(See Art. 209, where an example is found.) We may prove that *the necessary and sufficient condition that f be a positive form is that the n determinants*

$$D\begin{pmatrix} 1 \\ 1 \end{pmatrix}=D_1, \quad D\begin{pmatrix} 1, & 2 \\ 1, & 2 \end{pmatrix}=D_2, \quad \cdots, \quad D\begin{pmatrix} 1, & 2, & \cdots, & n \\ 1, & 2, & \cdots, & n \end{pmatrix}=D_n$$

all have positive values.

Observe first that $D_1=a_{11}$ must be positive, for then $x_1=1$, $x_2=0=x_3=\cdots=x_n$ and f must be positive. We may then choose d_1, α_{12}, α_{13}, $\cdots$, α_{1n} uniquely such that if we put

$$f=d_1(x_1+\alpha_{12}x_2+\alpha_{13}x_3+\cdots+\alpha_{1n}x_n)^2+f^{(1)}$$

the form $f^{(1)}$ will contain x_2, x_3, $\cdots$, x_n but no longer x_1. And here $d_1=D_1\leqq 0$. For proof of the theorem, assume that for an integer h which $<n$, it has already been proved that

$$D_1>0, \qquad D_2>0, \qquad \cdots, \qquad D_h>0$$

and that

$$\begin{aligned} f=d_1&(x_1+a_{12}x_2+\cdots+a_{1n}x_n)^2 \\ &+d_2(x_2+a_{23}x_3+\cdots+a_{2n}x_n)^2+\cdots \\ &+d_h(x_h+a_{h,\,h+1}x_{h+1}+\cdots+a_{h,\,n}x_n)^2+f^{(h)}, \end{aligned}$$

where $f^{(h)}$ contains only x_{h+1}, x_{h+2}, $\cdots$, x_n and

$$d_1=\frac{D_1}{D_0}, \qquad d_2=\frac{D_2}{D_1}, \qquad \cdots, \qquad d_h=\frac{D_h}{D_{h-1}} \quad (\text{and } D_0=1).$$

Next let d_{h+1} be the coefficient of x_{h+1}^2 in $f^{(h)}$ and put $x_{h+1}=1$; and if $h+1<n$, put $x_{h+2}=0=\cdots=x_n$.

Further choose the variables so that

$$\frac{1}{2}\frac{\partial f}{\partial x_1}=0, \qquad \frac{1}{2}\frac{\partial f}{\partial x_2}=0, \qquad \cdots, \qquad \frac{1}{2}\frac{\partial f}{\partial x_h}=0.$$

We then have, for the value of f, the relation $f=d_{h+1}$. And from this, if f is to be positive, it follows that $d_{h+1}>0$.

Under the above conditions it is seen that we have also

$$\frac{1}{2}\frac{\partial f}{\partial x_{h+1}}=d_{h+1}.$$

Next observe that

$$(1) \qquad \frac{1}{2}\frac{\partial f}{\partial x_m}=a_{m1}x_1+\cdots+a_{mn}x_n \qquad (m=1, 2, \cdots, n).$$

From the relations

$$\begin{aligned} 0&=a_{11}x_1+a_{12}x_2+\cdots+a_{1h}x_h+a_{1,\,h+1}x_{h+1},\\ 0&=a_{21}x_1+a_{22}x_2+\cdots+a_{2h}x_h+a_{2,\,h+1}x_{h+1},\\ &\cdots\cdots\cdots\cdots\cdots\cdots\cdots\cdots\\ 0&=a_{h1}x_1+a_{h2}x_2+\cdots+a_{hh}x_h+a_{h,\,h+1}x_{h+1},\\ d_{h+1}&=a_{h+1,\,1}x_1+a_{h+1,\,2}x_2+\cdots+a_{h+1,\,h}x_h+a_{h+1,\,h+1}x_{h+1}, \end{aligned}$$

we have $x_{h+1}=1=\dfrac{D_h d_{h+1}}{D_{h+1}}$; and with this it is proved that $D_{h+1}>0$, etc. We are thus able to express f in the form of a sum of squares of n real independent forms, namely,

$$(2) \qquad f=\sum a_{hk}x_hx_k=\xi_1^2+\xi_2^2+\cdots+\xi_n^2,$$

where

$$\xi_h=\sqrt{d_h}(x_h+\alpha_{h,\,h+1}x_{h+1}+\cdots+\alpha_{hn}x_n),$$

$$d_h=\frac{D_h}{D_{h-1}}, \qquad D_h>0 \qquad (h=1, 2, \cdots, n).$$

If $h<k$ and if in f expressed in the form (2) we put all the variables equal to zero except x_1, x_2, $\cdots$, x_h; x_k and put

$x_k=1$ we have, from the resulting system of equations, the expression $x_h+\alpha_{hk}x_k=0$, and then from the linear forms

$$\begin{aligned}0&=a_{11}x_1+a_{12}x_2+\cdots+a_{1h}x_h+a_{1k}x_k,\\0&=a_{21}x_1+a_{22}x_2+\cdots+a_{2h}x_h+a_{2k}x_k,\\&\cdots\cdots\cdots\cdots\cdots\cdots\cdots\cdots\\0&=a_{h1}x_1+a_{h2}x_2+\cdots+a_{hh}x_h+a_{hk}x_k,\end{aligned}$$

we have for the ratio $\frac{x_h}{x_k}$ the value

$$\frac{x_h}{x_k}D_h=\begin{vmatrix}a_{11}, & a_{12}, & \cdots, & a_{1,\,h-1}, & -a_{1k}\\ a_{21}, & a_{22}, & \cdots, & a_{2,\,h-1}, & -a_{2k}\\ \cdot & \cdot & & \cdot & \cdot\\ \cdot & \cdot & & \cdot & \cdot\\ \cdot & \cdot & & \cdot & \cdot\\ a_{h1}, & a_{h2}, & \cdots, & a_{h,\,h-1}, & -a_{hk}\end{vmatrix}$$

and therefore from the above

$$\alpha_{hk}=D\begin{pmatrix}1, & \cdots, & h-1, & h\\ 1, & \cdots, & k-1, & k\end{pmatrix}\div D_h \qquad (h<k). \tag{3}$$

By the determinant D_n of the form f we understand the determinant D_n of the n linear forms

$$\frac{1}{2}\frac{\partial f}{\partial x_1}, \quad \frac{1}{2}\frac{\partial f}{\partial x_2}, \quad \cdots, \quad \frac{1}{2}\frac{\partial f}{\partial x_n}.$$

From (2) it follows that $a_{hh}\geqq d_h$ $(h=1, 2, \cdots, n)$; and since $D_n=d_1d_2\cdots d_n$ it is seen that

$$a_{11}a_{22}\cdots a_{nn}\geqq D_n. \tag{4}$$

A system of n linear forms in n variables may be sufficiently designated through its matrix without naming the variables; and that is, its quadratic system of coefficients may be given. The individual horizontal rows consist of the coefficients of the individual forms, while the vertical rows correspond to the individual variables.

By the matrix of a quadratic form $f(x_1, x_2, \cdots, x_n)$ we shall understand the quadratic system of coefficients of the

n linear forms

$$\frac{1}{2}\frac{\partial f}{\partial x_1}, \qquad \frac{1}{2}\frac{\partial f}{\partial x_2}, \qquad \ldots, \qquad \frac{1}{2}\frac{\partial f}{\partial x_n}.$$

A linear substitution which consists in putting for each of the variables a certain linear form of n new variables is denoted through the matrix of these n forms, A being the matrix of the original n linear forms. After a substitution B is applied to them, the result is denoted by AB. Further, if O denotes the socalled *identical* substitution (for n variables), which consists in the fact that all the variables remain unchanged, we understand (if the determinant of a substitution S is different from zero) by S^{-1} the substitution U for which $SU=0$. A quadratic system of n^2 quantities may be used as a symbol to denote a linear substitution; and by the product of two such systems A and B we understand the system of coefficients belonging to the substitution AB. Finally if in a quadratic system A the lines and columns are interchanged, this substitution may be denoted by $\bar{A}$. We then have the rule $(\overline{AB})=\bar{B}\bar{A}$.

For example, if

$$\begin{aligned}\xi&=a_{11}x_1+a_{12}x_2,\\ \eta&=a_{21}x_1+a_{22}x_2,\end{aligned}$$

and if the substitution

$$\begin{aligned}x_1&=A_{11}X_1+A_{12}X_2,\\ x_2&=A_{21}X_1+A_{22}X_2\end{aligned}$$

is made, the quantities ξ and η become respectively

$$(5)\qquad \left\langle\begin{aligned}&(a_{11}A_{11}+a_{12}A_{21})X_1+(a_{11}A_{12}+a_{12}A_{22})X_2,\\ &(a_{21}A_{11}+a_{22}A_{21})X_1+(a_{21}A_{12}+a_{22}A_{22})X_2;\end{aligned}\right.$$

while if

$$\begin{aligned}\Xi&=A_{11}s+A_{21}t_1, \qquad & s&=a_{11}S+a_{21}T,\\ H&=A_{12}s+A_{22}t_1, \qquad & t&=a_{12}S+a_{22}T,\end{aligned}$$

we have for Ξ and H

$$(6)\qquad \begin{cases}(a_{11}A_{11}+a_{12}A_{21})S+(a_{21}A_{11}+a_{22}A_{21})T,\\(a_{11}A_{12}+a_{12}A_{22})S+(a_{21}A_{12}+a_{22}A_{22})T.\end{cases}$$

When the columns and rows in (5) are interchanged, we have (6).

Observe that if the determinant of the third order

$$\overset{A}{\begin{pmatrix}a_{11}, & a_{12}, & a_{13}\\a_{21}, & a_{22}, & a_{23}\\a_{31}, & a_{32}, & a_{33}\end{pmatrix}} \text{ is multiplied by } \overset{B}{\begin{pmatrix}b_{11}, & b_{12}, & b_{13}\\b_{21}, & b_{22}, & b_{23}\\b_{31}, & b_{32}, & b_{33}\end{pmatrix}} = \text{the deter-}$$

minants of the third order AB; and if $\overset{\bar{B}}{\begin{pmatrix}b_{11}, & b_{21}, & b_{31}\\b_{12}, & b_{22}, & b_{32}\\b_{13}, & b_{23}, & b_{33}\end{pmatrix}}$ is

multiplied by $\overset{\bar{A}}{\begin{pmatrix}a_{11}, & a_{21}, & a_{31}\\a_{12}, & a_{22}, & a_{32}\\a_{13}, & a_{23}, & a_{33}\end{pmatrix}}$ in a similar manner, we have $\bar{B}\bar{A} = \overline{AB}$.

The generalization is evident.

Let A be the matrix of n independent real linear forms $\xi_1, \xi_2, \cdots, \xi_n$. The determinant of A is then different from zero and $f=\xi_1^2+\xi_2^2+\cdots+\xi_n^2$ is a positive quadratic form. The matrix of f thus deformed is $=A\bar{A}$ and the determinant of this form f is equal to the square of the determinant of A. If any linear substitution B is applied to the variables in $\xi_1, \xi_2, \cdots, \xi_n$, the matrix A becomes AB and the form f is transformed into the quadratic form

$$(\overline{AB})AB=\bar{B}\bar{A}AB=\bar{B}fB.$$

The determinant of this new form is thus seen to be equal to the determinant of f multiplied into the square of the determinant of B. Were $\bar{B}fB=f$, it would follow that the determinant of $B=\pm 1$.

II. Let f be a quadratic form in n variables $x_1, x_2, \cdots, x_n$, and put it in the form above, namely

$$f=\xi_1^2+\xi_2^2+\cdots+\xi_n^2.$$

Then $f \leqq 1$ represents a body that is everywhere convex with $\mathfrak{O}$ as the center. This body is called an *ellipsoid*. Take this domain $f \leqq 1$ as the standard body of radial-distances $S(\mathfrak{ab})$ and let $\mathfrak{p}_1, \mathfrak{p}_2, \cdots, \mathfrak{p}_n$ be a system of lattice points in n independent directions from $\mathfrak{O}$ and with the least possible radial-distances $S_1, S_2, \cdots, S_n$ from $\mathfrak{O}$. From Art. 146 it is seen that there are not more than $(2^{n+1}-2)^n$ different such systems $\mathfrak{p}_1, \mathfrak{p}_2, \cdots, \mathfrak{p}_n$. Let $p_1^{(k)}, p_2^{(k)}, \cdots, p_n^{(k)}$ be the coordinates of $\mathfrak{p}_k$ $(k=1, 2, \cdots, n)$ and let P be the squared system of the quantities $p_h^{(k)}$, h being the index of the horizontal rows. If then B is any substitution with integral coefficients through which f is transformed into itself, then the n vertical rows of the system $BP=Q$ are also the coordinates of n such lattice points $\mathfrak{q}_1, \mathfrak{q}_2, \cdots, \mathfrak{q}_n$, which lie in n independent directions from $\mathfrak{O}$ and for which

$$S(\mathfrak{O}\mathfrak{q}_1)=S_1, \qquad S(\mathfrak{O}\mathfrak{q}_2)=S_2, \qquad \cdots, \qquad S(\mathfrak{O}\mathfrak{q}_n)=S_n.$$

And furthermore this system BP for different substitutions B turns out different. With this we have the theorem: *A positive quadratic form in n variables never has more than* $(2^{n+1}-2)^n$ *integral transformations into itself.*

The integral transformations of a positive quadratic form f into itself form a group of finite order. If we have any finite group of integral reversible substitutions for n variables, say $B_1, B_2, \cdots, B_w$, we may take any positive quadratic form φ in n variables arbitrarily. Let $\varphi_1, \varphi_2, \cdots, \varphi_w$ be those forms into which φ is transformed through $B_1, B_2, \cdots, B_w$. Then $\varphi_1+\varphi_2+\cdots+\varphi_w=f$ is also a positive quadratic form; and this form reverts into itself through each of the substitutions B_γ, since we always have

$$B_1B_\gamma, \qquad B_2B_\gamma, \qquad \cdots, \qquad B_wB_\gamma,$$

neglecting the sequence, coinciding with

$$B_1, \qquad B_2, \qquad \cdots, \qquad B_w.$$

It is seen that this group is entirely contained in the group of those integral substitutions through which the form f is transformed into itself. Thus the problem of determining all finite groups of integral substitutions finds solution in the theory of the positive quadratic forms. See Camille Jordan, No. 302, *Traité des substitutions*.

III. If B denotes any quadratic system of n^2 elements and t a constant, then $t^n B$ denotes that system which is derived from B through the multiplication of each of the elements by t.

If

$$B = \|b_{hk}\| \qquad \text{and} \qquad C = \|c_{hk}\| \quad (h, k = 1, 2, \cdots, n)$$

are two quadratic systems of n^2 quantities, we may understand by $B+C$ the quadratic system of the n^2 quantities $b_{hk}+c_{hk}$ $(h, k=1, 2, \cdots, n)$.

If we find the identical substitution among the powers $B, B^2, \cdots$ of a substitution B, it occurring, say, for the first time in B^m, then the substitution B is said to be of the *m-th order*. And if two substitutions with integral coefficients are considered, say

$$B = |b_{hk}| \qquad \text{and} \qquad C = |c_{hk}| \quad (h, k = 1, 2, \cdots, n),$$

then B is said to *be congruent* to C with respect to the modulus, the integer q, if all n^2 congruences $b_{hk} \equiv c_{hk} \pmod{q}$ $(h, k=1, 2, \cdots, n)$ exist.

In *Crelle's Journal*, Vol. 100, p. 449, and Vol. 101, p. 196, Minkowski has proved the following theorem, which is of importance for the theory of finite groups of integral substitutions:

An integral substitution, that is not the identical substitution, of finite order is never congruent to the identical substitution with respect to any integer l which is $\geqq 3$.

Minkowski acknowledges his indebtedness to a remark due to Professor Fabian Franklin in the following proof of the theorem, which is simpler than the one found in *Crelle's Journal:*

Let B be any integral substitution which is different from O, and suppose that it is congruent to the substitution O

either with respect to 4 or with respect to an odd prime integer p. Observe that every number $\geqq 3$ which is not divisible by 4 contains at least one odd prime factor as divisor. Let us understand by q in the first case the prime number 2 and in the other case let p be a prime integer. We are tacitly assuming that all the coefficients in $B-O$ are not zero; let q^{μ} be the highest power of q that divides all the coefficients, and let $\mu \geqq 2$ in the case that $q=2$ while $\mu \geqq 1$, when $q=p$. Write $B=O+q^{\mu}\Psi$ where the coefficients in Ψ are all integers, but are not all divisible by q.

Observe that if t is any integer,

$$B^t=(O+q^{\mu}\Psi)^t=O+tq^{\mu}\Psi+((q^{2\mu}))\equiv O+tq^{\mu}\Psi \pmod{q^{\mu+1}},$$

and that

$$B^t q \equiv O+tq^{\mu+1}\Psi \pmod{q^{\mu+2}}$$

$$\cdots\cdots\cdots\cdots\cdots\cdots\cdots\cdots\cdots$$

$$B^t q^k \equiv O+tq^{\mu+k}\Psi \pmod{q^{\mu+k+1}}.$$

It is thus seen that a power of B with a positive exponent is never equal to O and therefore B is *not* of a finite order.

Due to this theorem it may be proved in a finite group of integral reversible substitutions that no two different substitutions B and C can be congruent with respect to 4 or with respect to an odd prime integer p. For with B and C there enters also the substitution, $B^{-1}C$, in the group which would also be of finite order. This substitution would be $\equiv O$ (mod. 4 or p) and would be different from O.

In any group of the character in question the different substitutions taken with respect to any integer $l \geqq 3$ would offer different residues. But (see above) only such residues appear whose determinant $\equiv \pm 1$ (mod. l). However, for $l=3$, for example, it is seen that the order of a finite group of integral reversible linear substitutions is always $<3^{n^2}$.

This theorem offers a still deeper consequence (See *Crelle's Journal*, Vol. 101, p. 198), namely, that an arbitrary prime integer q appears as a divisor of the order of a finite group at most to a power with the exponent

$$\left[\frac{n}{q-1}\right]+\left[\frac{n}{q(q-1)}\right]+\left[\frac{n}{q^2(q-1)}\right]+\cdots;$$

and in fact this power of q really appears as a divisor of some of these order-numbers. The bracket used here is a function sign to denote the greatest integer which it incloses; and the summation above is to be continued until the last term is zero. The further theorem is proved that among the orders in question only such prime integers which are $\leqq n+1$ can appear, and further, each of these orders divides the integer $(2n)!$

ART. **149. Economy of the Least Radial-Distances.** We shall now resume the discussion of Art. 146, which has been interrupted, with the concepts and notions that were there introduced.

I. Let $S(\mathfrak{a}\mathfrak{b})$ be any given accordant and symmetric (wechselseitig) radial-distances, and let $\mathfrak{p}_1, \mathfrak{p}_2, \cdots, \mathfrak{p}_n$ be a system of n lattice points in n independent directions from $\mathfrak{O}$ and having the smallest possible radial-distances $S_1, S_2, \cdots$, S_n from $\mathfrak{O}$. Let $p_1^{(k)}, p_2^{(k)}, \cdots, p_n^{(k)}$ be the coordinates of $\mathfrak{p}_k$ $(k=1, 2, \cdots, n)$, and let P denote the substitution

$$(1) \qquad x_h=p_h^{(1)}v_1+p_h^{(2)}v_2+\cdots+p_h^{(n)}v_n \qquad (h=1, 2, \cdots, n).$$

The determinant of P is a rational integer which is different from zero; denote its absolute value by N. This quantity N gives the volume of the parallelopipedon defined through

$$(2) \qquad o\leqq v_1\leqq 1, \qquad o\leqq v_2\leqq 1, \qquad \cdots, \qquad o\leqq v_n\leqq 1.$$

For write formula (1) in the form

$$(3) \qquad \mathfrak{x}-\mathfrak{O}=v_1(\mathfrak{p}_1-\mathfrak{O})+v_2(\mathfrak{p}_2-\mathfrak{O})+\cdots+v_n(\mathfrak{p}_n-\mathfrak{O}).$$

The point symmetric to $\mathfrak{p}_k$ with respect to the origin is $2\mathfrak{O}-\mathfrak{p}_k$.

The lattice in $v_1, v_2, \cdots, v_n$, that is, the assemblage of all points with integral values of $v_1, v_2, \cdots, v_n$, is entirely embodied in the lattice in $x_1, \cdots, x_n$ being identical with it in the particular case $N=1$.

Through the translation of the realm

$$(4) \qquad o \leqq v_1 < 1, \qquad o \leqq v_2 < 1, \qquad \cdots, \qquad o \leqq v_n < 1$$

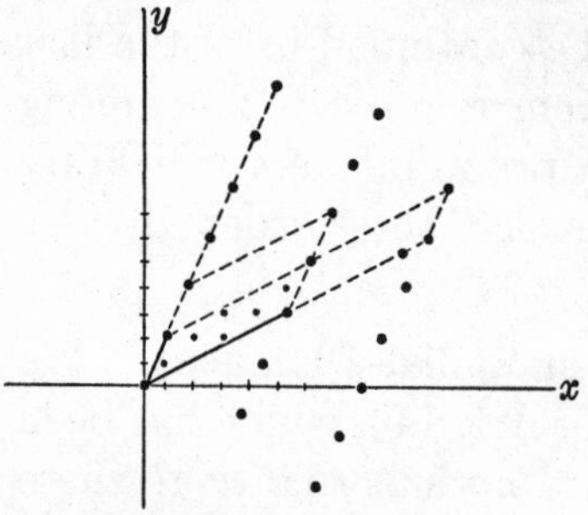

Suppose $\mathfrak{p}_1=(1,2)$, $\mathfrak{p}_2=(5,3)$.

$$\left.\begin{aligned} x_1 &= v_1+5v_2 \\ x_2 &= 2v_1+3v_2 \end{aligned}\right\}; \qquad |\Delta| = N = 7.$$

The origin counts as one of the seven lattice points.

FIG. 84

from $\mathfrak{O}$ to all lattice points in $v_1, v_2, \cdots, v_n$ we entirely cover the manifold of the points $\mathfrak{x}$ and in so doing we produce each point $\mathfrak{x}$ in one way. We conclude from this condition, if we wish to compute the volume of the parallelopipedon (2) by applying the theorem of Art. 39, III, that the number of lattice points that are present in the realm (4) is equal to this volume and that is N. Through these N lattice points we have through the addition of

$$v_1(\mathfrak{p}_1-\mathfrak{O})+v_2(\mathfrak{p}_2-\mathfrak{O}) + \cdots + v_n(\mathfrak{p}_n-\mathfrak{O}),$$

when $v_1, v_2, \cdots, v_n$ go over all integral values, the complete lattice in $x_1, x_2, \cdots, x_n$.

II. Due to the properties of accordant and symmetric (wechselseitig) radial-distances, it follows from (3) that

$$S(\mathfrak{O}\mathfrak{x}) \leqq S_1|v_1| + S_2|v_2| + \cdots + S_n|v_n|.$$

Denote by $\mathfrak{D}$ the domain of those points $\mathfrak{x}$ for which

$$(6) \qquad |v_1| + |v_2| + \cdots + |v_n| \leqq 1.$$

This domain is included within the one expressed through (2) and is a nowhere concave body with $\mathfrak{O}$ as its center. It may be decomposed into 2^n cells (see Art. 23), each having one vertex in $\mathfrak{O}$, one in $\mathfrak{p}_1$ or in $2\mathfrak{O}-\mathfrak{p}_1$, one in $\mathfrak{p}_2$ or in $2\mathfrak{O}-\mathfrak{p}_2$, $\cdots$, one in $\mathfrak{p}_n$ or in $2\mathfrak{O}-\mathfrak{p}_n$. These cells are in their inner points completely separated by the n planes $v_k=0$ $(k=1, 2, \cdots, n)$. And each one of them has a volume $\frac{1}{n!}N$ so that the volume of $\mathfrak{D}=2^n\frac{N}{n!}$, the value of N being of course different from the parallelopipedon formed from (2). (See Art. 42.)

Next let $\mathfrak{x}$ be any point on the inside of $\mathfrak{D}$ and in the manifold $\mathfrak{O}(M_1, M_2, \cdots, M_k)$ but not already in the manifold $\mathfrak{O}(M_1, M_2, \cdots, M_{k-1})$, where k is any of the numbers $1, 2, \cdots, \lambda$ (See Art. 146, I). It follows that the last of the quantities $v_1, v_2, \cdots, v_n$ that is not zero has for $\mathfrak{x}$ an index taken from the series $\mu_{k-1}+1, \cdots, \mu_n$; and it further follows from (5) that

$$S(\mathfrak{O}\mathfrak{x})<M_k. \tag{7}$$

Due to the meaning of the quantities M_k it is seen that the point $\mathfrak{x}$ can never be a lattice point, with the result that $\mathfrak{D}$ has no lattice point within its interior save $\mathfrak{O}$. Applying the theorem of Art. 44 to $\mathfrak{D}$, it is seen that the volume of $\mathfrak{D}$ must be $\leqq 2^n$, and consequently

$$\frac{2^nN}{n!}\leqq 2^n, \qquad \text{or} \qquad N\leqq n! \tag{7'}$$

Thus it is seen that the integer N can have only a finite number of values and in this inequality we perceive *not improperly a certain economy of least radial-distances.*

To this property of the numbers $\mathfrak{p}_h^{(k)}$, others may be added, which are not, however, of such general scope: Let $m<n$ and among the points $\mathfrak{p}_1, \mathfrak{p}_2, \cdots, \mathfrak{p}_n$ take any m, say $\mathfrak{p}_{k_1}, \mathfrak{p}_{k_2}, \cdots, \mathfrak{p}_{k_m}$, where $k_1<k_2<\cdots<k_m$.

Let the manifold laid through $\mathfrak{O}$ and these m points be $\mathfrak{E}$. Take next any n independent rational directions, and let the first m of them be the directions from $\mathfrak{O}$ to $\mathfrak{p}_{k_1}, \mathfrak{p}_{k_2}, \cdots, \mathfrak{p}_{k_m}$. Then perform the *reduction of the lattice* in the sense of Art. 145, and denote by $y_1, y_2, \cdots, y_n$ the new variables that are introduced. Then every point of $\mathfrak{E}$ is determined through its values $y_1, y_2, \cdots, y_m$ which suffer no restriction, and $\mathfrak{E}$ appears defined through $y_{m+1}=0$, $y_{m+2}=0$, $\cdots$, $y_n=0$. The various lattice points in $\mathfrak{E}$ correspond exactly to the collective integral systems of values of $y_1, y_2, \cdots, y_m$, and that is, so to speak, in the manifold of the systems $y_1, y_2, \cdots, y_m$. Here it is seen that the determinant of the coordinates $y_1, y_2, \cdots, y_m$ for the m points $\mathfrak{p}_{k_1}, \mathfrak{p}_{k_2}, \cdots, \mathfrak{p}_{k_m}$ (due to the last remark in Art. 145) is equal to the greatest common divisor of all of the m-row determinants formed from the matrix

$$||\mathfrak{p}_k^{(h)}||\begin{pmatrix} k=k_1, & k_2, & \cdots, & k_m; \\ h=1, & 2, & \cdots, & n \end{pmatrix}.$$

Denote this positive divisor by $N(k_1, k_2, \cdots, k_m)$. Accordingly we observe that the points $\mathfrak{p}_{k_1}, \mathfrak{p}_{k_2}, \cdots, \mathfrak{p}_{k_m}$ among the different systems possible in $\mathfrak{E}$ of m lattice points in m different directions from $\mathfrak{O}$ are seen to form necessarily a system with least possible radial-distances from $\mathfrak{O}$, because the m arbitrary directions in $\mathfrak{E}$ together with the $n-m$ directions not contained in $\mathfrak{E}$ present n independent directions in $\mathfrak{O}\mathfrak{p}_1, \mathfrak{O}\mathfrak{p}_2, \cdots, \mathfrak{O}\mathfrak{p}_n$.

We may now apply the theorem contained in the inequality (7) to this lattice of the integral systems $y_1, y_2, \cdots, y_m$ in $\mathfrak{E}$ and arrive at the conclusion that $N(k_1, k_2, \cdots, k_m) \leqq m!$. For $m=1$, this inequality indicates that the coordinates of each point $\mathfrak{p}_k$ are always n integers whose greatest common divisor is unity.

III. There exists a definite integral substitution Q with determinant $=\pm 1$, for $x_1, x_2, \cdots, x_n$, say

$$Q:\quad x_h = q_h^{(1)}y_1 + q_h^{(2)}y_2 + \cdots + q_h^{(n)}y_n \quad (h=1, 2, \cdots, n),$$

such that these equations for the substitution $P^{-1}Q=C^{-1}$ take the special form

$$(8)\qquad \begin{aligned} v_1 &= \gamma_1^{(1)}y_1 + \gamma_1^{(2)}y_2 + \cdots + \gamma_1^{(n)}y_n, \\ v_2 &= \qquad\quad\ \gamma_2^{(2)}y_2 + \cdots + \gamma_2^{(n)}y_n, \\ &\cdots\cdots\cdots\cdots\cdots\cdots\cdots\cdots \\ v_n &= \qquad\qquad\qquad\qquad\quad \gamma_n^{(n)}y_n, \end{aligned}$$

with the characterization that

$$\gamma_h^{(k)}=0, \qquad \text{when} \qquad h>k$$

and also

$$0<\gamma_h^{(h)}, \qquad 0\leqq\gamma_h^{(k)}<\gamma_h^{(h)} \qquad (h<k).$$

The introduction of this substitution was denoted in Art. 145 as the *Reduction of the lattice with regard to the directions* $\mathfrak{op}_1, \mathfrak{op}_2, \cdots, \mathfrak{op}_n$, where instead of the letters a, β, q formerly used we have here q, γ, c. The origin is now denoted by $\mathfrak{O}$.

The values $y_1, y_2, \cdots, y_n$ which belong to a definite point $\mathfrak{p}_k$ appear as the coefficients of v_k in the inverse substitution $C=Q^{-1}P$:

$$(9) \qquad \begin{aligned} y_1 &= c_1^{(1)}v_1+c_1^{(2)}v_2+\cdots+c_1^{(n)}v_n, \\ y_2 &= \qquad\quad c_2^{(2)}v_2+\cdots+c_2^{(n)}v_n, \\ &\cdots\cdots\cdots\cdots\cdots\cdots\cdots\cdots \\ y_n &= \qquad\qquad\qquad\qquad c_n^{(n)}v_n, \end{aligned}$$

these values all being integral.

The determinant of these linear expressions C is $N=c_{(1)}^{(1)}c_{(2)}^{(2)}\cdots c_{(n)}^{(n)}$ and when they are solved with respect to the v's and the results compared with those in (8) it is seen that all the products $N\gamma_{(h)}^{(k)}$ are integers $\geqq 0$ and $\leqq N$. And from the fact that $N\leqq n!$ (due to which circumstance the domain $\mathfrak{D}$ has within its interior no lattice point save $\mathfrak{o}$) it is clear that for $C=Q^{-1}P$ *only a finite number of different integral substitutions come into question.*

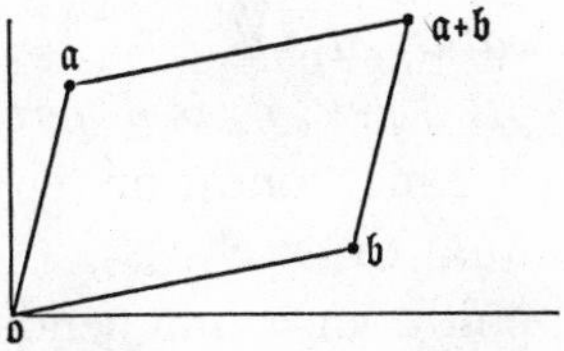

$S(\mathfrak{oa})+S(\overline{\mathfrak{aa}+\mathfrak{b}})\geqq S(\overline{\mathfrak{oa}+\mathfrak{b}})$.

FIG. 85

Next write

$$S(\mathfrak{ox})=f(y_1, y_2, \cdots, y_n)=\varphi(v_1, v_2, \cdots, v_n)$$

and observe (see Fig. 85) that $S(\mathfrak{oa})=S(\mathfrak{b}, \mathfrak{a}+\mathfrak{b})$.

Since

$$S(\mathfrak{ob})=S(\overline{\mathfrak{aa}+\mathfrak{b}}),$$

it follows that

$$S(\mathfrak{oa})+S(\mathfrak{ob})\geqq S(\overline{\mathfrak{oa}+\mathfrak{b}}),$$

or

$$f(a_1, a_2, \cdots, a_n)+f(b_1, b_2, \cdots, b_n) \geqq f(a_1+b_1, a_2+b_2, \cdots, a_n+b_n).$$

Writing $a_1=0$, $b_2=0$, we have as a particular case

$$f(0, a_2)+f(b_1, 0) \geqq f(b_1, a_2),$$

and

$$f(x, y, z) \leqq f(x, y, 0)+f(0, 0, z) \leqq f(x, 0, 0)+f(0, y, 0)+f(0, 0, z).$$

Further, the function $f(y_1, y_2, \cdots, y_n)$ has a *positive* value for all values of the y's except $y_1=0=y_2=\cdots=y_n$.

Hence with respect to the manifold $\mathfrak{O}(M_1, M_2, \cdots, M_k)$ (see Art. 146, I) we have (replacing $\mathfrak{o}$ for $\mathfrak{O}$).

(10) $$f(y_1, y_2, \cdots, y_n) \geqq S_h.$$

For the point $\mathfrak{p}_h$ in particular we have (Cf. formulas (5), (6) and (7) of Art. 145) $y_h=c_h^{(h)}>0$ and $S(\mathfrak{o}\mathfrak{p}_h)=S_h$. Taking account of the inequalities $S_1 \leqq S_2 \leqq \cdots \leqq S_n$ we have the following:

The radial-distance S_h always represents the *minimum among all the values of* $f(y_1, y_2, \cdots, y_n)$ *for such integral values* $y_1, y_2, \cdots, y_n$, *where at least one of the integers* y_h, $y_{h+1}, \cdots, y_n$ *is different from zero.*

This condition characterizes completely the system of quantities $S_1, S_2, \cdots, S_n$. For if we have any n lattice points in n independent directions from $\mathfrak{o}$, the determinant of their coordinates is different from zero. Consequently not more than $h-1$ of the points can have all $n-h+1$ coordinates $y_h, y_{h+1}, \cdots, y_n$ equal to zero and always exhibit at least $n-h+1$ of its radial-distances $\geqq S_h$ from $\mathfrak{o}$.

If of the quantities $v_h, v_{h+1}, \cdots, v_n$ for a point at least one is different from zero, it follows from (9) that one of the values $y_h, y_{h+1}, \cdots, y_n$ for this point is different from zero. Hence we find in (10) in particular the inequalities

(11) $$\varphi(v_1, v_2, \cdots, v_n) \geqq S_h$$

for every such system of integral values $v_1, v_2, \cdots, v_n$ where in the series $v_h, v_{h+1}, \cdots, v_n$ at least one number is different from zero. S_h itself appears more simply in this presentation directly as the value of $\varphi(v_1, v_2, \cdots, v_n)$, if we put $v_h = 1$ and the other v's all zero.

The domain $\mathfrak{D}$ here appears as a particular case of the body that is treated in Art. 54; from the considerations there in Art. 54, I, end, it is to be noticed that in the inequality $N \leqq n!$ above, the equality sign can never enter if $n \geqq 3$.

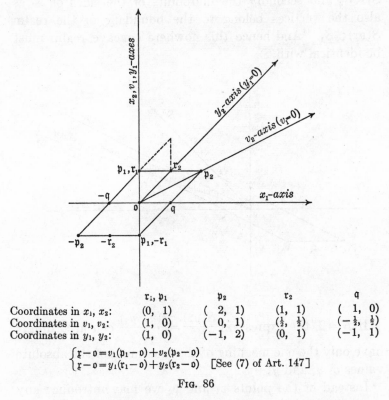

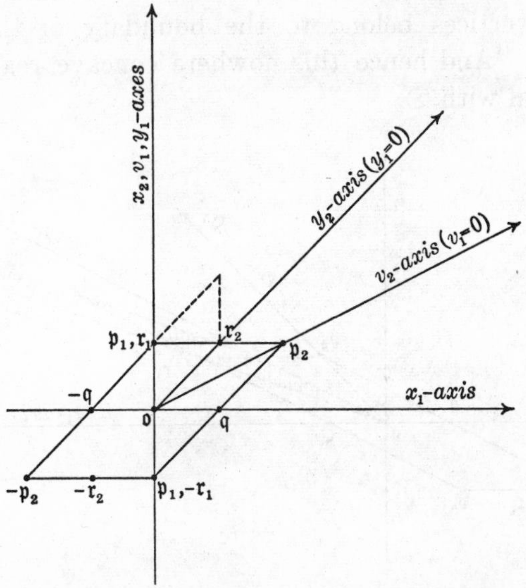

	$\mathfrak{r}_1, \mathfrak{p}_1$	$\mathfrak{p}_2$	$\mathfrak{r}_2$	$\mathfrak{q}$
Coordinates in x_1, x_2:	(0, 1)	(2, 1)	(1, 1)	(1, 0)
Coordinates in v_1, v_2:	(1, 0)	(0, 1)	$(\frac{1}{2}, \frac{1}{2})$	$(-\frac{1}{2}, \frac{1}{2})$
Coordinates in y_1, y_2:	(1, 0)	(−1, 2)	(0, 1)	(−1, 1)

$$\begin{cases} \mathfrak{x} - \mathfrak{o} = v_1(\mathfrak{p}_1 - \mathfrak{o}) + v_2(\mathfrak{p}_2 - \mathfrak{o}) \\ \mathfrak{x} - \mathfrak{o} = y_1(\mathfrak{r}_1 - \mathfrak{o}) + y_2(\mathfrak{r}_2 - \mathfrak{o}) \end{cases}$$ [See (7) of Art. 147]

FIG. 86

In the case $n = 2$ the domain $\mathfrak{D}$ is a parallelogram with $\mathfrak{o}$ as the only lattice point in the interior and four lattice points at the vertices. We then have $N = 1$ or $N = 2$. In the first case C is the identical substitution. In the second case (since here $N(k_1)$ above is 1 and $N(k_2)=1$), the substitution C^{-1} can only be

$$v_1=y_1+\tfrac{1}{2}y_2, \qquad v_2=\tfrac{1}{2}y_2.$$

And here the points $v_1=\pm\frac{1}{2}$, $v_2=\pm\frac{1}{2}$ are lattice points being the midpoints of the sides of $\mathfrak{D}$. The radial-distances from $\mathfrak{o}$ to these two points from $\mathfrak{o}$ on the one hand due to (5) $\leqq\frac{1}{2}S_1+\frac{1}{2}S_2$ and on the other hand, as they do not lie on the line $y_2=0$, they are $\geqq S_2$. Hence we have here *first* $S_1=S_2$ and secondly the midpoints of the sides of $\mathfrak{D}$ as also the vertices belong to the boundary of the realm $S(\mathfrak{o}\mathfrak{x})\leqq S_1$. And hence this nowhere concave realm must be identical with $\mathfrak{D}$.

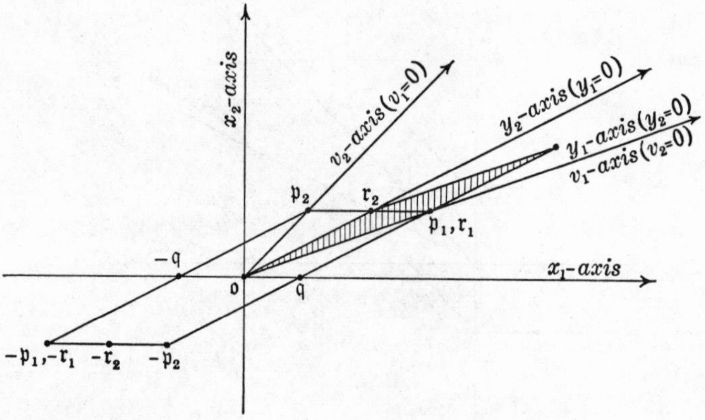

FIG. 87

If $N=2$, the expression $\dfrac{S(\mathfrak{o}\mathfrak{x})}{S_1}=\dfrac{f(y_1, y_2)}{S_1}$ can accordingly have only the one meaning of the maximum of the absolute values of y_1 and y_1+y_2.

Instead of the points $\mathfrak{p}_1$ and $\mathfrak{p}_2$ we may introduce any two points non-symmetric with respect to $\mathfrak{o}$ of the vertices and midpoints of the sides of $\mathfrak{D}$, both points *not* being vertices, and here we have a determinant of value 1 for N.

		$\mathfrak{r}_1, \mathfrak{p}_1$	$\mathfrak{p}_2$	$\mathfrak{r}_2$	$\mathfrak{q}$
Coordinates in	x_1, x_2	$(3, 1)$	$(1, 1)$	$(2, 1)$	$(1, \quad 0)$
Coordinates in	v_1, v_2	$(1, 0)$	$(0, 1)$	$(\frac{1}{2}, \frac{1}{2})$	$(\frac{1}{2}, -\frac{1}{2})$
Coordinates in	y_1, y_2	$(1, 0)$	$(-1, 2)$	$(0, 1)$	$(1, -1)$

The shaded parallelogram is the region

$$0 \leqq y_1 \leqq 1, \qquad 0 \leqq y_2 \leqq 1.$$

The large parallelogram is the parallelogram

$$|v_1| + |v_2| \leqq 1,$$

and has for its four corners the coordinates in the v's $(1, 0)$, $(0, 1)$, $(-1, 0)$, and $(0, -1)$. The midpoints of the sides have the coordinates $(\frac{1}{2}, \frac{1}{2})$, $(-\frac{1}{2}, \frac{1}{2})$, $(-\frac{1}{2}, -\frac{1}{2})$, and $(\frac{1}{2}, -\frac{1}{2})$ in the v's and in the y's, respectively $(0, 1)$, $(-1, +1)$, $(0, -1)$, and $(+1, -1)$.

$$\begin{cases} \mathfrak{x} - \mathfrak{o} = v_1(\mathfrak{p}_1 - \mathfrak{o}) + v_2(\mathfrak{p}_2 - \mathfrak{o}) \\ \mathfrak{x} - \mathfrak{o} = y_1(\mathfrak{r}_1 - \mathfrak{o}) + y_2(\mathfrak{r}_2 - \mathfrak{o}) \end{cases}$$

IV. Let J be the volume of the standard body of radial-distances $S(\mathfrak{a}\mathfrak{b})$, which is defined here through $\varphi(v_1, v_2, \cdots, v_n) \leqq 1$. For a point $\mathfrak{p}_h$ $(h = 1, 2, \cdots, n)$ all the values v_1, $v_2, \cdots, v_n$ are put $= 0$, save v_h which is made $= 1$; and we thus have $S(\mathfrak{o}\mathfrak{p}_h) = S_p$, so that $\mathfrak{p}_h$ always lies on the boundary of the body

$$\mathfrak{B} = \varphi\left(\frac{v_1}{S_1}, \frac{v_2}{S_2}, \cdots, \frac{v_n}{S_n}\right) \leqq 1.$$

The volume of this body (in $x_1, x_2, \cdots, x_n$) is $S_1 S_2 \cdots S_n J$, as seen as follows:
Write

$$\frac{v_i}{S_i} = \bar{v}_i \qquad (i = 1, 2, \cdots, n).$$

Hence

$$\begin{aligned} v_1 &= S_1 \bar{v}_1, \\ v_2 &= \qquad S_2 \;{}_2, \\ &\cdots\cdots\cdots\cdots \\ v_n &= \qquad\quad S_n \bar{v}_n. \end{aligned}$$

It follows that

$$D(v_1, v_2, \cdots, v_n) = S_1 S_2 \cdots S_n D(\bar{v}_1, \bar{v}_2, \cdots, \bar{v}_n)$$

and (Art. 42, end) in $x_1, x_2, \cdots, x_n$

$$\text{Vol. } \mathfrak{B} = S_1 S_2 \cdots S_n J.$$

This body with the n points $\mathfrak{p}_1, \mathfrak{p}_2, \cdots, \mathfrak{p}_n$, since it is nowhere concave, and has $\mathfrak{o}$ as center, contains the entire domain $\mathfrak{D}$.

It will be proved in the next sections that *with accordant and symmetric radial-distances $S(\mathfrak{a}\mathfrak{b})$ there exists for the system of the n quantities* $S_1, S_2, \cdots, S_n$ always the inequality

$$(12) \qquad S_1 S_2 \cdots S_n J \leqq 2^n.$$

The inequality $N \leqq n!$ is a simple consequence of this theorem.

If we collect into powers those of the quantities $S_1, S_2, \cdots, S_n$ that are equal, the inequality (12) may be written

$$(12') \qquad M_1^{v_1} M_2^{v_2} \cdots M_\lambda^{v_\lambda} J \leqq 2^n.$$

This inequality carries with it the one proved in Art. 44, namely $M_1^n J \leqq 2^n$, and coincides with this latter inequality when $\lambda = 1$. Thus the inequality has already in Art. 44 been proved for the latter case. In Art. 46 it was found to be characteristic for the existence of the equality $M_1^n J = 2^n$ that the least radial-distance from the lattice point to a variable point reaches as a maximum the value $\frac{1}{2} M_1$. Now in particular the radial-distance from the lattice point to the midpoint of the line $\mathfrak{o}\mathfrak{p}_n$ has the value $\frac{1}{2} S_n = \frac{1}{2} M_\lambda$, and the existence of the equation $M_1^n J = 2^n$ requires before everything else that $S_1 = S_2 = \cdots = S_n$ and that is that $\lambda = 1$. This would be inferred also from the existence of the inequality (12). In what follows we shall prove first the inequality (12) for the case $n = 2$.

We may then, as is made clear from the last remark in III, choose always the lattice points $\mathfrak{p}_1$ and $\mathfrak{p}_2$ with radial-distances S_1 and S_2 from $\mathfrak{o}$ in such a way that

$$\mathfrak{o} + v_1(\mathfrak{p} - \mathfrak{o}) + v_2(\mathfrak{p}_2 - \mathfrak{o})$$

offers every lattice point by taking integral values of v_1 and v_2 and that is the determinant of the coordinates of $\mathfrak{p}_1$ and $\mathfrak{p}_2$ is ± 1.

If we put $S(\mathfrak{o}\mathfrak{x}) = \varphi(v_1, v_2)$, we have from (5)

$$\varphi(1, 0) = S(\mathfrak{o}\mathfrak{p}_1) = S_1 \qquad \text{and} \qquad \varphi(0, 1) = S(\mathfrak{o}\mathfrak{p}_2) = S_2.$$

And among the inequalities (11) we have in particular the following:

$$\varphi(0, 1) \geqq \varphi(1, 0).$$

Since we may equally as well put $2\mathfrak{o} - \mathfrak{p}_1$ in the place of $\mathfrak{p}_1$, which is the same as the substitution of $-v$ for v, we have as particular cases of (11)

$$\varphi(-1, 1) \geqq \varphi(0, 1)$$

and we may, without any limitation, assume that

$$\varphi(1, 1) \geqq \varphi(-1, 1).$$

In other words we take that one of the points $\mathfrak{p}_1'$, $\mathfrak{p}_1''$, as the point $\mathfrak{p}_1$, which causes $\varphi(1, 1)$ to be $\geqq \varphi(-1, 1)$.

Observe that $\varphi(-1, 1) \leqq \varphi(-1, 0) + \varphi(0, 1)$, and

$$\varphi(-1, 0) = \varphi(1, 0).$$

Due to the properties of $S(\mathfrak{a}\mathfrak{b})$ we have

$$\varphi(-v_1, -v_2) = \varphi(v_1, v_2),$$
$$\varphi(y\beta_1, y\beta_2) = y\varphi(\beta_1, \beta_2), \qquad y > 0.$$

If in the formula

$$\varphi(a_1, a_2) + \varphi(b_1, b_2) \geqq \varphi(a_1 + b_1, a_2 + b_2),$$

we put

$$a_1 = y\beta_1 - z\gamma_1, \qquad a_2 = y\beta_2 - z\gamma_2,$$
$$b_1 = \quad z\gamma_1, \qquad b_2 = \quad z\gamma_2,$$

we have

$$\varphi(y\beta_1 - z\gamma_1, y\beta_2 - z\gamma_2) + z\varphi(\gamma_1, \gamma_2) \geqq y\varphi(\beta_1, \beta_2),$$

if $y > 0$ and $z > 0$. If t_1, t_2 are two positive quantities, we further have

$$\varphi(\pm t, 0) = t_1\varphi(1, 0), \qquad \varphi(0, \pm t_2) = \pm t_2\varphi(0, 1),$$
$$\varphi(\mp t_1, -t_2) = \varphi(\pm t_1, t_2).$$

If $t_1 > t_2$,then

$$\varphi(\pm t_1, t_2) \geqq t_1\varphi(\pm 1, 1) - (t_1 - t_2)\varphi(0, 1) \geqq t_2\varphi(\pm 1, 1);$$

if $t_1 = t_2$, then

$$\varphi(\pm t_1, t_2) = t_2\varphi(\pm 1, 1);$$

if $t_1 < t_2$, then

$$\varphi(\pm t_1, t_2) \begin{cases} \geqq t_2\varphi(\pm 1, 1) - (t_2 - t_1)\varphi(1, 0) \geqq t_1\varphi(\pm 1, 1), \\ \geqq t_2\varphi(0, 1) - t_1\varphi(1, 0) \geqq (t_2 - t_1)\varphi(0, 1). \end{cases}$$

If in the last of these formulas, we put $t_2 = 2$, $t_1 = 1$, we again have

$$\varphi(0, 1) \geqq \varphi(1, 0).$$

From these formulas it is seen that *for integral values* of v_1, v_2 the value $\varphi(v_1, v_2)$ *first* is always $\geqq \varphi(1, 0)$ if v_1, v_2 are not *both* zero and *secondly* $\varphi(v_1, v_2) \geqq \varphi(0, 1)$ if $v_2 \neq 0$, and *thirdly* $\varphi(v_1, v_2) \geqq \varphi(-1, 1)$ if $v_2 \neq 0$ and $v_1 \neq 0$. In this manner the inequalities

$$(13) \qquad \varphi(1, 1) \geqq \varphi(-1, 1) \geqq \varphi(0, 1) \geqq \varphi(1, 0)$$

of themselves indicate that $\varphi(1, 0) = S_1$ and $\varphi(0, 1) = S_2$ and that besides $\varphi(-1, 1) = S_3$ denotes for the function $S(\mathfrak{o}\mathfrak{x})$ an a priori fixed value with respect to the lattice. These values S_1, S_2, S_3 are characterized through the following condition: If we consider any three lattice points different from the origin, of which no two are in the same straight line with $\mathfrak{o}$, it is seen that the radial-distances of these lattice points from $\mathfrak{o}$ when arranged according to their magnitudes are always $\geqq S_1$, $\geqq S_2$, $\geqq S_3$ and in particular the case may occur that all three equality signs may exist at the same time.

Let us consider next the realm $\varphi(v_1, v_2) \leqq S_2$. It has as center $\mathfrak{o}$ and contains other lattice points in its interior only if $S_1 < S_2$ and then only on the line $v_2 = 0$. Observe again Figs. 86 and 87 and consider the two cases:

$$1°, \quad \text{when} \quad S_1 = S_2$$
$$2°, \quad \text{when} \quad S_1 < S_2.$$

1°. To prove the statement for $S_1 = S_2$ we need only assume that there is a lattice point interior, say $\mathfrak{q}$; then this point will have $S(\mathfrak{o}\mathfrak{q}) < S(\mathfrak{o}\mathfrak{p}_2)$ from which it follows that $\mathfrak{p}_1$, $\mathfrak{p}_2$ are not a set of points having a system of least radial-distances. This, however, is contradictory to our hypothesis.

2°. Consider the inequality $S_1 < S_2$. $S(\mathfrak{o}\mathfrak{p}_1) = S_1$ is the least radial-distance from $\mathfrak{o}$ to a lattice point. Assume a lattice point $\mathfrak{q}$ interior to $\varphi(v_1, v_2) \leqq S_2$ but not on $v_2 = 0$, then $S(\mathfrak{o}\mathfrak{p}_2) > S(\mathfrak{o}\mathfrak{q}) \geqq S(\mathfrak{p}_1)$. But this is contradictory to hypothesis, since $S(\mathfrak{o}\mathfrak{p}_2) = S_2$ was the smallest radial-distance from $\mathfrak{o}$ to lattice points not in the manifold $\mathfrak{o}\mathfrak{p}_1$. Therefore any lattice points other than $\mathfrak{o}$ interior to $\varphi(v_1, v_2) \leqq S_2$ must be on the line $v_2 = 0$.

There are now two cases: either (I) this realm $\varphi(v_1, v_2) \leqq S_2$ lies entirely between the lines $v_2 = \pm 1$; or (II) there are points in $\varphi(v_1, v_2) \leqq S_2$ for which we have $v_2 > 1$.

CASE I: Boundary points are the only points of $\varphi(v_1, v_2) \leqq S_2$ which may lie on $v_2 = 1$. Due to the nowhere-concave property then, $\varphi(v_1, v_2) \leqq S_2$ has either the single point (0, 1) or a whole line-segment of points in common with $v_2 = 1$.

If $S(\mathfrak{o}\mathfrak{x}) \leqq 1$ is an *everywhere convex* body, the point (0, 1) is the only point which may belong to both the body and the line $v_2 = 1$. (This is seen in Case I.)

CASE II: We may consider the possibility of a lattice point of the realm $v_2 \geqq 2$ belonging to the boundary of $\varphi(v_1, v_2) = S_2$.

Consider all points

$$(\pm a, b), \qquad a > 0, \qquad b \geqq 2.$$

Suppose first $a > b$. Then as above

$$\varphi(\pm a, b) \geqq b\varphi(\pm 1, 1) \geqq b\varphi(0, 1) \geqq 2\varphi(0, 1) \geqq 2S_2,$$

so that if $a>b$ no points can be on $\varphi(v_1, v_2) \leqq S_2$. On the other hand, if $a<b$ then

$$\varphi(\pm a, b) \geqq a\varphi(+1, 1) \geqq a\varphi(0, 1) \geqq aS_2$$

and

$$\varphi(\pm a, b) \geqq (b-a)\varphi(0, 1) \geqq (b-a)S_2.$$

The only possibility that

$$\varphi(\pm a, b) = S_2$$

is that

$$a=1, \qquad b=2.$$

The points to be considered are then $v_1=1$, $v_2=2$ and $v_1=-1$, $v_2=2$.

Let us first consider the point $(-1, 2)$. From the definition of the body $\varphi(v_1, v_2) \leqq S_2$ we know that the point $(0, 1)$ is on the boundary and the point $(1, 0)$ is either within or on the boundary. Now any straight line through the point $(0, 1)$ either passes through both $(1, 0)$ and $(-1, 2)$ or else it separates one of these points from the origin (we are not considering the v_2-axis). It is seen that if $(1, 0)$ is within the body $\varphi(v_1, v_2) \leqq S_2$, due to its nowhere concave property, the point $(-1, 2)$ must be exterior to it.

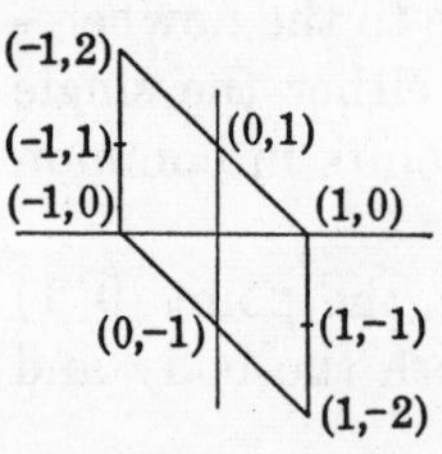

Fig. 88

Assume that $(-1, 2)$ is on the boundary. It is seen that $(1, 0)$ is on the boundary and it follows that $(-1, 0)$ is on the boundary. Then in order that $(-1, 1)$ be not within $\varphi(v_1, v_2) \leqq S_2$ the line segment joining $(-1, 2)$ to $(-1, 0)$ must be a portion of the boundary. Since the body is symmetric with respect to the origin and as the line segment joining $(1, 0)$ to $(-1, 2)$ is also a portion of the boundary we have the body $\varphi(v_1, v_2) \leqq S_2$ as seen in Fig. 88.

We see that for this body, necessarily

$$\varphi(-1, 2) = \varphi(-1, 1) = \varphi(0, 1) = \varphi(1, 0),$$

and consequently $S_1 = S_2 = S_3$.

If we consider the points (1, 1) and (−1, 1) we see that (1, 1) is here exterior to $\varphi(v_1, v_2) \leqq S_2$ and consequently we have also

$$\varphi(1, 1) > \varphi(-1, 1)$$

so that the inequalities in (13) take the form

$$\varphi(1, 1) > \varphi(-1, 1) = \varphi(0, 1) = \varphi(1, 0).$$

Thus the condition that the point (1, 2) be a boundary point leads to a body which has the conditions

$$\varphi(-1, 1) > \varphi(1, 1)$$

imposed so that the point (1, 2) can never lie on the body $\varphi(v_1, v_2) \leqq S_2$.

From the above considerations it is seen that if $S(\mathfrak{ox}) \leqq 1$ is everywhere convex the first and second inequalities in (13) cannot exist simultaneously. However, by subjecting $\varphi(v_1, v_2)$ to the transformations

$$\begin{vmatrix} 1, & 0 \\ 0, & 1 \end{vmatrix}, \qquad \begin{vmatrix} -1, & 0 \\ 0, & -1 \end{vmatrix}$$

we see that the resulting function still satisfies the inequalities (13) due to symmetry about the origin.

EXAMPLES

1. If the first equality sign in (13) holds, prove that it is possible to add to these transformations

$$\begin{vmatrix} 1, & 0 \\ 0, & -1 \end{vmatrix} \quad \text{and} \quad \begin{vmatrix} -1, & 0 \\ 0, & 1 \end{vmatrix}.$$

2. If the third equality sign in (13) holds, it is possible to add to the first two transformations the two

$$\begin{vmatrix} 0, & 1 \\ 1, & 0 \end{vmatrix} \quad \text{and} \quad \begin{vmatrix} 0, & -1 \\ -1, & 0 \end{vmatrix}.$$

3. If both the first and third hold we are able to add to these six transformations

$$\begin{vmatrix} 0, & -1 \\ 1, & 0 \end{vmatrix} \quad \text{and} \quad \begin{vmatrix} 0, & 1 \\ -1, & 0 \end{vmatrix}.$$

4. If the second equality in (13) holds we are able to add to the first two transformations the two

$$\begin{vmatrix} 1, & 1 \\ 0, & -1 \end{vmatrix} \quad \text{and} \quad \begin{vmatrix} -1, & -1 \\ 0, & 1 \end{vmatrix}.$$

5. If both the second and third hold we may add to these

$$\begin{vmatrix} 1, & 1 \\ -1, & 0 \end{vmatrix}, \quad \begin{vmatrix} -1, & -1 \\ 1, & 0 \end{vmatrix}, \quad \begin{vmatrix} 0, & -1 \\ 1, & 1 \end{vmatrix},$$

$$\begin{vmatrix} 0, & 1 \\ -1, & -1 \end{vmatrix}, \quad \begin{vmatrix} -1, & 0 \\ 1, & 1 \end{vmatrix}, \quad \begin{vmatrix} 1, & 0 \\ -1, & -1 \end{vmatrix}.$$

6. That these are the only transformations with determinant ± 1 to which we may subject $\varphi(v_1, v_2)$ and still maintain the properties in (13) is not obvious. Consider this problem.

The inequality $S_1^2 J \leqq 4$ follows from the condition that the realm $\varphi(v_1, v_2) \leqq S_1$ has on its interior besides $\mathfrak{O}$ no other lattice point (see Art. 44).

Next let $S_1 < S_2$ and consider the realm

$$\varphi\left(\frac{v_1}{S_1}, \frac{v_2}{S_2}\right) \leqq 1.$$

This realm coincides along the line $v_2 = 0$ with $S(v_1, v_2) \leqq S_1$; on the other hand from $\varphi(v_1, v_2) \leqq S_2$ it follows that if for every point $v_1 = \beta_1$, $v_2 = \beta_2$ of this lattice realm we take always the point $v_1 = \frac{S_1}{S_2}\beta_1$, $v_2 = \beta_2$ where $\frac{S_1}{S_2} < 1$ we have the result that $\varphi\left(\frac{v_1}{S_1}, \frac{v_2}{S_2}\right) \leqq 1$ contains within its interior no lattice point save $\mathfrak{o}$. And from this it follows through the same general theorem that $S_1 S_2 J \leqq 4$, thus proving (12) for the case $n = 2$.

Observe further that if $S_1 < S_2$ and if the realm

$$\varphi\left(\frac{v_1}{S_1}, \frac{v_2}{S_2}\right) \leqq 1$$

is *cut* through by $v_2 = 1$, then on the boundary of this realm there are only four lattice points, namely $v_1 = \pm 1$, $v_2 = 0$; and $v_1 = 0$, $v_2 = \pm 1$. We then have from Art. 46, $S_1 S_2 J < 4$. If, however, in this realm we have *everywhere* $-1 \leqq v_2 \leqq 1$, then let $v_1 + \tau v_2 = 1$ be a straight line through $v_1 = 1$, $v_2 = 0$, which must exist, that does not cut this realm. Then the domain $\varphi\left(\frac{v_1}{S_1}, \frac{v_2}{S_2}\right) \leqq 1$ lies entirely in the parallelogram $-1 \leqq v_2 \leqq 1$, $-1 \leqq v_1 + \tau v_2 \leqq 1$. And the equality sign in $S_1 S_2 J \leqq 4$ appears only if the realm coincides with this

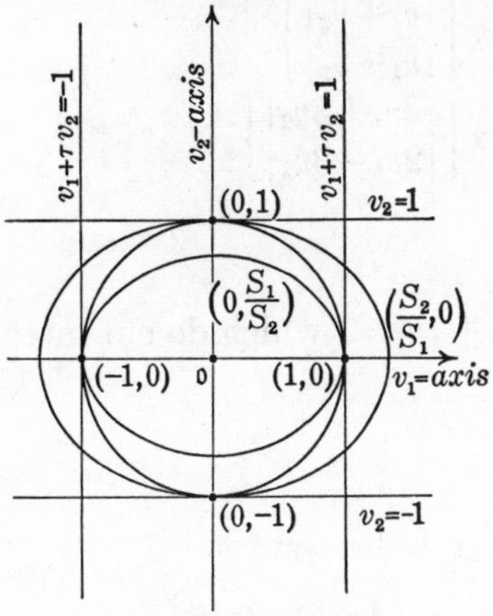

FIG. 89a

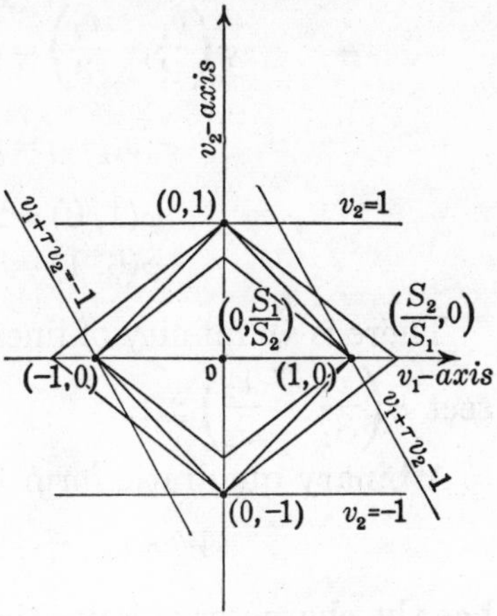

FIG. 89b

parallelogram, and then $\varphi(v_1, v_2)$ is identical with the maximum of the values $S_1 v_1 + \tau S_2 v_2$ and $S_2 v_2$. See Figs. 89a and 89b.

In Fig. 89a

$$\varphi\left(\frac{v_1}{S_1}, \frac{v_2}{S_2}\right) = \sqrt{v_1^2 + v_2^2}.$$

Suppose $S_1 = 3$, $S_2 = 4$.

$$\varphi\left(\frac{v_1}{3}, \frac{v_2}{4}\right) = \sqrt{v_1^2 + v_2^2},$$

$$\varphi(v_1, v_2) = \sqrt{9v_1^2 + 16v_2^2},$$

$$\varphi(1, 0) = 3 (= S_1),$$

$$\varphi(0, 1) = 4 (= S_2).$$

The only line $v_1 + \tau v_2 = 1$ which does not intersect

$$\varphi\left(\frac{v_1}{S_1}, \frac{v_2}{S_2}\right) \leqq 1$$

is that one for which $\tau = 0$, namely the line $v_1 = 1$.

In Fig. 89b

$$\varphi\left(\frac{v_1}{S_1},\ \frac{v_2}{S_2}\right)=\max\left\{\begin{matrix}|v_1+v_2|\\|v_1-v_2|\end{matrix}\right\}$$

then $\dfrac{S_1}{S_2}=\dfrac{2}{3}$. Suppose $S_1=2$, $S_2=3$,

$$\varphi\left(\frac{v_1}{2},\ \frac{v_2}{3}\right)=\max\left\{\begin{matrix}|v_1+v_2|\\|v_1-v_2|\end{matrix}\right\},$$

$$\varphi(v_1,\ v_2)=\max\left\{\begin{matrix}|2v_1+3v_2|\\|2v_1-3v_2|\end{matrix}\right\},$$

$$\varphi(1,\ 0)=2,$$

$$\varphi(0,\ 1)=3.$$

There is an infinity of lines $v_1+\tau v_2=1$ which do not intersect $\varphi\left(\dfrac{v_1}{S_1},\ \dfrac{v_2}{S_2}\right)\leqq 1$.

A binary quadratic form

$$W=w_{11}x_1^2+2w_{12}x_1x_2+w_{22}x_2^2$$

has the character of a positive form (Art. 148) if

$$w_{11}w_{22}-w_{12}^2=D>0 \qquad \text{and} \qquad w_{11}>0.$$

Such a form may always [1] be transformed into a reduced form

$$F=a_{11}y_1^2+2a_{12}y_1y_2+a_{22}y_2^2,$$

where

$$a_{11}+2a_{12}+a_{22}\geqq a_{11}-2a_{12}+a_{22}\geqq a_{22}\geqq a_{11}. \tag{i}$$

The proof of this follows from (13), namely

$$a_{11}+2a_{12}+a_{22}\geqq a_{11}-2a_{12}+a_{22}\geqq a_{22}\geqq a_{11}.$$

Further writing $y_1=1$, $y_2=0$ in $\sqrt{F}$, we find that $S_1^2=a_{11}$ and similarly $S_2^2=a_{22}$,

$$S_3^2=a_{11}-2a_{12}+a_{22}.$$

Writing W in the form

$$W=\frac{(w_{11}x_1+w_{12}x_2)^2}{w_{11}}+\frac{w_{22}w_{11}-w_{12}^2}{w_{11}}x_2^2;$$

[1] Lagrange, *Works*, 1773, Vol. III, p. 698.

or, writing

$$w_{11}x_1+w_{12}x_2=\xi_1,$$
$$x_2=\xi_2,$$

we have

$$W=\frac{\xi_1^2}{w_{11}}+\frac{\xi_2^2}{\dfrac{w_{11}}{D}}.$$

And area of ellipse $W=1$, is $\dfrac{\pi w_{11}}{\sqrt{D}}$. Observing that

$$x_1=\frac{\xi_1}{w_{11}}-\frac{w_{12}}{w_{11}}\xi_2,$$
$$x_2=\xi_2,$$

with determinant $=\dfrac{1}{w_{11}}$ we have (Art. 42, end)

$$J=\frac{\pi}{\sqrt{D}}.$$

If we take for $S(\mathfrak{o}\mathfrak{x})$ the square root of W, it follows from the last theorems that it is possible to transform W through integral substitutions and determinant $=\pm 1$ into the form F where

$$a_{11}+2a_{12}+a_{22}\geqq a_{11}-2a_{12}+a_{22}\geqq a_{22}\geqq a_{11}$$

and from $S_1S_2J<4$, it follows that

$$a_{11}a_{22}<\left(\frac{4}{\pi}\right)^2 D.$$

Making use of the identity

$$\frac{4}{3}(a_{11}a_{22}-a_{12}^2)\equiv a_{11}a_{22}+\frac{1}{3}(a_{11}+2a_{12})(a_{11}-2a_{12})+\frac{a_{11}}{3}(a_{22}-a_{11})$$

and noting the inequalities (i), it is seen that

$$a_{11}a_{22}\leqq \tfrac{4}{3}D.$$

CHAPTER XIV

THE ARITHMETIC OF THE ELLIPSOID

ART. 150. **Finiteness of the Number of Classes of Positive Quadratic Forms.** Let $W = \Sigma w_{hk} x_h x_k$ $(h, k = 1, 2, \cdots, n)$ be a *positive* quadratic form in n variables $x_1, x_2, \cdots, x_n$ and a determinant which we call Δ.

Take the *ellipsoid* $W \leqq 1$ as the standard body of radial-distances. We may calculate the volume of this body as follows:

From Art. 148, we have

$$\Sigma a_{ij} x_i x_j = \xi_1^2 + \cdots + \xi_n^2,$$

where the determinant of the ξ's is $\bar{\Delta} = \sqrt{\Delta}$.

Then we wish the volume of

$$\xi_1^2 + \cdots + \xi_n^2 \leqq 1,$$

or what is the same thing,

$$\frac{(\xi_1\sqrt{n})^2 + \cdots + (\xi_n\sqrt{n})^2}{n} \leqq 1,$$

or

$$\left(\frac{(\xi_1\sqrt{n})^2 + \cdots + (\xi_n\sqrt{n})^2}{n}\right)^{1/2} \leqq 1.$$

But from Art. 54, the volume of

$$\left(\frac{|v_1|^k + \cdots + |v_n|^k}{n}\right)^{1/k} \leqq 1$$

is

$$2^n \left(\frac{\pi}{2}\right)^s \frac{\left(\Gamma\left(1+\frac{1}{k}\right)\right)^r 2^{-\frac{2s}{k}} \left(\Gamma\left(1+\frac{2}{k}\right)\right)^s}{n^{-\frac{n}{k}} \Gamma\left(1+\frac{n}{k}\right)} \cdot \frac{1}{\Delta},$$

where r of the forms $v_1, \cdots, v_n$ are real and $2s$ of them are imaginary, and $\bar{\bar{\Delta}}$ is the determinant of $v_1, \cdots, v_n$.

Applying this, we have

$$v_i = \xi_i\sqrt{n}, \qquad \bar{\bar{\Delta}} = n^{n/2}\bar{\Delta} = n^{n/2}\sqrt{\Delta}, \qquad r = n, \qquad s = 0, \qquad k = 2,$$

so that

$$J = 2^n \frac{\left(\Gamma\left(1+\frac{1}{2}\right)\right)^n}{n^{-\frac{n}{2}}\Gamma\left(1+\frac{n}{2}\right)} \cdot \frac{1}{n^{n/2}\sqrt{\Delta}}$$

$$= 2^n \frac{\left[\frac{1}{2}\Gamma\left(\frac{1}{2}\right)\right]^n}{\Gamma\left(1+\frac{n}{2}\right)} \cdot \frac{1}{\sqrt{\Delta}} = \frac{\left[\Gamma\left(\frac{1}{2}\right)\right]^n}{\Gamma\left(1+\frac{n}{2}\right)} \cdot \frac{1}{\sqrt{\Delta}}.$$

I. Let $\mathfrak{p}_1, \mathfrak{p}_2, \cdots, \mathfrak{p}_n$ be n lattice points in independent directions from $\mathfrak{o}$ and having the least possible radial-distances $S_1, S_2, \cdots, S_n$ from $\mathfrak{o}$. Let the coordinates of $\mathfrak{p}_k$ $(k = 1, 2, \cdots, n)$ be $p_1^{(k)}, p_2^{(k)}, \cdots, p_n^{(k)}$ and let P denote the substitution:

$$P: \qquad x_h = p_h^{(1)}v_1 + p_h^{(2)}v_2 + \cdots + p_h^{(n)}v_n \qquad (h = 1, 2, \cdots, n).$$

The number of different substitutions which may be used for P has (see Art. 146) an upper limit which depends only upon n.

We may next determine corresponding to P (and in fact in an infinite number of ways) an integral substitution with determinant ± 1,

$$Q: \qquad x_h = q_h^{(1)}y_1 + q_h^{(2)}y_2 + \cdots + q_h^{(n)}y_n \qquad (h = 1, 2, \cdots, n),$$

such that for the substitution $P^{-1}Q = C^{-1}$ (Art. 149, III) the equations become

$$C^{-1}: \qquad \begin{aligned} v_1 &= \gamma_1^{(1)}y_1 + \gamma_1^{(2)}y_2 + \cdots + \gamma_1^{(n)}y_n, \\ v_2 &= \qquad\quad\ \gamma_2^{(2)}y_2 + \cdots + \gamma_2^{(n)}y_n, \\ &\cdots\cdots\cdots\cdots\cdots\cdots\cdots\cdots \\ v_n &= \qquad\qquad\qquad\qquad\quad \gamma_n^{(n)}y_n, \end{aligned}$$

where in these expressions for v_k, when $k \geqq 1$, the variables $y_1, y_2, \cdots, y_{k-1}$ are wanting.

Let W be transformed through the substitution Q into F, a form in $y_1, y_2, \cdots, y_n$, F and W having the same determinant.

Due to formula (10) of Art. 149 it is seen that S_h^2 (for $h=1, 2, \cdots, n$) is expressed always as the *minimum* among all the values of F for such integral systems $y_1, y_2, \cdots, y_n$ where at least one of the numbers $y_h, y_{h+1}, \cdots, y_n$ is different from zero. In particular we have

(1) $$S_1^2 \leqq S_2^2 \leqq \cdots \leqq S_n^2,$$

and we always have $F \geqq S_k^2$ if integers are written for $y_1, y_2, \cdots, y_n$ and the last among them *that is different from* zero is y_k. Next take for the form given in Art. 148, I, namely

$$F = \eta_1^2 + \eta_2^2 + \cdots + \eta_n^2,$$

where $\eta_1, \eta_2, \cdots, \eta_n$ are linear forms in the y's and where always η_h contains only $y_h, y_{h+1}, \cdots, y_n$; and consider the form

$$F^* = \frac{\eta_1^2}{S_1^2} + \frac{\eta_2^2}{S_2^2} + \cdots + \frac{\eta_n^2}{S_n^2}.$$

Through this form inversely there may be derived by operating with Q^{-1} a form W^* in the variables $x_1, x_2, \cdots, x_n$. The volume of the ellipsoid $W^* \leqq 1$ is seen to be equal to $S_1 S_2 \cdots S_n J$. (Cf. IV of preceding Article.)

If $x_1, x_2, \cdots, x_n$ represents any lattice point except $\mathfrak{o}$, the corresponding values $y_1, y_2, \cdots, y_n$ that are had through Q are always integral and are not all zero. Suppose that among them y_k is the last that is different from zero; then if $k<n$, the quantities $\eta_{k+1}, \eta_{k+2}, \cdots, \eta_n$ are also zero for the point and we therefore have for the point

$$F = \eta_1^2 + \eta_2^2 + \cdots + \eta_k^2 \geqq S_k^2;$$

and consequently, due to (1),

$$W^* = F^* = \frac{\eta_1^2}{S_1^2} + \frac{\eta_2^2}{S_2^2} + \cdots + \frac{\eta_k^2}{S_k^2} \geqq \frac{\eta_1^2 + \eta_2^2 + \cdots + \eta_k^2}{S_k^2} \geqq 1.$$

It follows that *the ellipsoid $W^* \leqq 1$ has in its interior no lattice point save* $\mathfrak{o}$. Hence, due to Art. 54 the volume of this ellipsoid $<2^n$. We thus come here to the inequality

$$S_1 S_2 \cdots S_n J < 2^n \tag{2}$$

which is treated more fully in Art. 152.

II. Through the substitution P let the form W become $\Phi = \Sigma a_{hk} v_h v_k$. We then have $a_{hh} = S_h^2$ $(h = 1, 2, \cdots, n)$ and therefore

$$0 < a_{11} \leqq a_{22} \leqq \cdots \leqq a_{nn}, \tag{3}$$

and (2) becomes [1]

$$a_{11} a_{22} \cdots a_{nn} < \left(\frac{2^n \Gamma\left(1 + \frac{n}{2}\right)}{\Gamma\left(\frac{1}{2}\right)^n} \right)^2 \Delta. \tag{4}$$

We then have from Art. 149 (11) always $\Phi \geqq a_{kk}$ if for $v_1, v_2, \cdots, v_n$ are written integers and where v_k is the last which is different from zero. Writing $v_k = 1$, $v_h = \pm 1$ $(h < k)$ and the remaining of the arguments $v_1, v_2, \cdots, v_n$, in case $n > 2$, equal zero, it follows that $a_{hk} \pm 2a_{hk} + a_{kk} \geqq a_{kk}$; and therefore

$$-a_{hh} \leqq 2a_{hk} \leqq a_{hh} \qquad (h < k). \tag{5}$$

Let N be the absolute value of the determinant of P, so that the determinant of the form Φ is equal to ΔN^2.

Due to Art. 148 (4) we have

$$a_{11} a_{22} \cdots a_{nn} \geqq \Delta N^2; \tag{6}$$

and therefore from (4)

$$N < \frac{2^n \Gamma\left(1 + \frac{n}{2}\right)}{\left(\Gamma\left(\frac{1}{2}\right)\right)^n}. \tag{7}$$

From this it is seen that N can only have a finite number of

[1] Minkowski, *Ges. Abhandl.*, I, p. 269.

values for any integer n as has already been shown more generally in Art. 149.

Due to Art. 149, III, it is seen that corresponding to the definite substitution P we may so choose a substitution Q with determinant ± 1 and *uniquely* such that the coefficients in $P^{-1}Q=C^{-1}$ satisfy the further conditions:

$$0<\gamma_h^{(h)}, \qquad 0\leqq\gamma_h^{(k)}\leqq\gamma_h^{(h)}, \qquad h<k \qquad (h, k=1, 2, \cdots, n).$$

In the future we shall assume that C^{-1} has been chosen in this manner.

Since $C=Q^{-1}P$ consists only of integral coefficients and since $\frac{1}{\gamma_h^{(k)}}$ is found among these, and since N is the determinant of C, it is seen below that the quantities $\gamma_h^{(h)}$ are all $\leqq 1$ while all products $N\gamma_h^{(k)}$ are integers $\geqq 0$ and $\leqq N$. Taking this into consideration and having regard to (7) it is seen that for every value of n there are only a finite number of different substitutions for C^{-1}.

Remark. $W=\sum_{h=1,k=1}^{n,n} w_{h,k}x_hx_k$ is a positive quadratic form with determinant Δ.

P: $$x_h=p_h^{(1)}v_1+\cdots+p_h^{(n)}v_n \qquad (h=1, 2, \cdots, n).$$

N is the absolute value of the determinant of P.

Q: $$x_h=q_h^{(1)}y_1+\cdots+q_h^{(n)}y_n \qquad (h=1, 2, \cdots, n).$$

The determinant of Q is ± 1.

$P^{-1}Q=C^{-1}$: $$\begin{cases} v_1=\gamma_1^{(1)}y_1+\cdots+\gamma_1^{(n)}y_n, \\ \cdots\cdots\cdots\cdots\cdots\cdots \\ v_n= \qquad\qquad \gamma_n^{(n)}y_n, \end{cases}$$

where

$$0<\gamma_h^{(h)}, \qquad 0\leqq\gamma_h^{(h)}<\gamma_h^{(h)}, \qquad h<k \quad (h, k=1, 2, \cdots, n).$$

N is of course also the determinant of C, since $C=Q^{-1}P$.

In the inverse of C^{-1}, namely C, in the expression giving y_h, the coefficient of v_h is seen to be $\frac{1}{\gamma_h^{(h)}}$, which therefore must be an integer. Consequently $\gamma_h^{(h)}\leqq 1$.

Since $(N\gamma_h^{(k)})$ is an integer and bounded (since both N and $\gamma_h^{(k)}$ are bounded) there is only a finite number of possible values for

$(N\gamma_h^{(k)})$. Since there is only a finite number of possibilities for N there is also then only a finite number for $\gamma_h^{(k)}$.

$$\left.\begin{array}{ll}\text{Since a)} & W \to F \text{ by } Q \\ \text{and b)} & W \to \Phi \text{ by } P\end{array}\right\}, \quad \text{we have} \quad \Phi \to F \text{ by } P^{-1}Q = C^{-1}.$$

From b) see Art. 148, I, end, we have $\Phi = \bar{P}WP$.

III. By a *class* of positive quadratic forms we understand the collectivity of all forms which are derived from one such form through all possible integral substitutions with a determinant ± 1. As an initial class any one of a class may be used. The forms W and F above belong to the same class.

A form W is called *integral* if all its coefficients w_{hk} are integers. If the form W above is integral, the same is also true of the form $\Phi = \bar{P}WP$. Hence as positive integers the numbers $a_{11}, a_{22}, \cdots, a_{nn}$ must all be $\geqq 1$, and then from the inequalities (4) and (5), as soon as the value Δ is given, we can have only a finite number of different integral systems for the quantities a_{hk}. Since on the one hand the number of different forms Φ to which all existing positive integral forms with a given determinant Δ lead, is finite, and on the other hand again from these forms Φ through a finite number of substitutions C^{-1} are had forms F from all the classes W, we have the theorem:

Corresponding to every positive integer Δ there is always only a finite number of classes of integral positive quadratic forms in n variables with the determinant Δ.

This theorem for an arbitrary number of variables n was first proved by Hermite in a letter to Jacobi (*Crelle's Journal*, Vol. 40, pp. 261–315) and in fact through the setting up of certain inequalities which have to do with positive quadratic forms. These are similar to the relations developed here regarding the manner in which the coefficients of the forms enter into the inequalities; however, the numerical constants which enter into them are in the methods of Hermite less definitive.

CHAPTER XV

COMPUTATION OF A VOLUME THROUGH SUCCESSIVE INTEGRATIONS

Art. **151.** The manner similar to the proof of the inequality $M^n J \leqq 2^n$ in Art. 44 is connected in detail with the considerations from which the concept of volume exists; further, the general proof of the inequality (Art. 149 (12))

$$M_1^{\mathfrak{v}_1} M_2^{\mathfrak{v}_2} \cdots M_\lambda^{\mathfrak{v}_\lambda} J \leqq 2^n$$

rests mainly upon a peculiar manner of expressing the volume J. For this we shall first develop certain necessary lemmas.

The manifold of all points $x_1, x_2, \cdots, x_n$ will be denoted by $\mathfrak{X}$. A given assemblage of points $\mathfrak{P}$ may be characterized as a nowhere concave body in $\mathfrak{X}$ through the following properties:

1°. That a straight line has in common with an assemblage of points either no point, or one point, or a portion of the line (or ray);

2°. That in the assemblage exist $n+1$ definite points which do not lie in a plane. For with such points the assemblage of points due to 1° will contain the entire cell (Art. 23) which is determined through these points as vertices, and therefore at all events the assemblage contains inner points (Art. 25).

If then $\mathfrak{c}$ is any inner point of $\mathfrak{P}$, and if we consider the property 1° first alone for the straight lines that pass through $\mathfrak{c}$, we recognize at once the existence of definite radial-distances $S(\mathfrak{ab})$ through which $\mathfrak{P}$ may be expressed as the body (*Körper*) $S(\mathfrak{cx}) \leqq 1$ (Art. 21).

In 1° there exists, however, the further property that

3°. *As soon as any two points belong to* $\mathfrak{P}$ *the same is true of every point lying on the line* (*or ray*) *that joins these two points;* and with this is proved that the radial-distance $S(\mathfrak{ab})$, here introduced, is accordant (*einhellig*) (Art. 22) and that $\mathfrak{P}$ is a nowhere concave body (Art. 31).

If the property 1° exists for an assemblage of points $\mathfrak{P}$ without the existence of the property 2°, then take a point $\mathfrak{p}$ in $\mathfrak{P}$. The assemblage $\mathfrak{P}$ may consist only of this one point. In the other event we may choose in $\mathfrak{P}$ a definite *extreme* number m of points in independent directions from $\mathfrak{p}$, where now necessarily $m<n$. Let $\mathfrak{p}_1, \mathfrak{p}_2, \cdots, \mathfrak{p}_m$ be such points. It is seen that the point assemblage $\mathfrak{P}$ lies entirely in the manifold that is laid through $\mathfrak{p}, \mathfrak{p}_1, \mathfrak{p}_2, \cdots, \mathfrak{p}_m$ (Art. 145) and therefore actually has *no inner point* in $\mathfrak{X}$.

Form the matrix of the relative coordinates of $\mathfrak{p}_1, \mathfrak{p}_2, \cdots, \mathfrak{p}_m$ with respect to $\mathfrak{p}$. Among the m-row determinants of this matrix let the one taken with respect to the coordinates $x_1, x_2, \cdots, x_m$ be different from zero. This means merely that of the n axes we designate the m of them that offer an m-row determinant $\neq 0$ by the notation $x_1, x_2, \cdots, x_m$. At least one of these determinants must be $\neq 0$, since the m directions are independent.

The above manifold may be characterized through $n-m$ definite equations

$$\begin{aligned}
x_{m+1} &= a_{m+1} + a_{m+1}^{(1)}x_1 + a_{m+1}^{(2)}x_2 + \cdots + a_{m+1}^{(m)}x_m,\\
x_{m+2} &= a_{m+2} + a_{m+2}^{(1)}x_1 + a_{m+2}^{(2)}x_2 + \cdots + a_{m+1}^{(m)}x_m,\\
&\cdots\cdots\cdots\cdots\cdots\cdots\cdots\cdots\cdots\\
x_n &= a_n \quad + a_n^{(1)}x_1 \;\; + a_n^{(2)}x_2 \;\; + \cdots + a_n^{(m)}x_m;
\end{aligned}$$

and every point in this manifold is given already through its coordinates $x_1, x_2, \cdots, x_m$ whose variability is unlimited.

The systems $x_1, x_2, \cdots, x_m$ which belong to the points of the assemblage $\mathfrak{P}$ constitute with respect to the properties 1° and 2° a nowhere concave realm in the collectivity of all systems $x_1, x_2, \cdots, x_m$.

If we return to the results of Arts. 20 and 25, it appears that the property 1°, taken by itself, has besides the property 3° a still further property:

4°. *That the given assemblage of points is a closed one,* and

5°. That for the span of points in it from $\mathfrak{o}$ there exists an upper limit, or what amounts to the same thing, that *for the values of the coordinates* $x_1, x_2, \cdots, x_n$ *there exist upper and lower limits.* On the other hand it is also clear that the properties 5°, 4°, 3° have reciprocally as a consequence 1°, so that the property 1° is entirely equivalent to the content of 3°, 4°, 5°. In other words, and to recapitulate:

A point-set $\mathfrak{P}$ is a nowhere concave body in $\mathfrak{X}$ if and only if

1°. *Every straight line has in common with it no point, one point, or a segment of points.*

2°. *There exist* $n+1$ *points in it not in the same plane.*

1° measures the nowhere-concave condition.

2° insures that the body is immersed in $\mathfrak{X}$, that is, that it is n-dimensional. If 2° were not satisfied, the body could serve only as boundary in n-space, i.e., could have no inner points.

From property 1° we have immediately

3°. *If two points belong to* $\mathfrak{P}$ *every point of the segment joining them belongs to* $\mathfrak{P}$.

From Arts. 20 and 25, we see that 1° implies also

4°. $\mathfrak{P}$ *is a closed point-set.*

5°. *The coordinates of the points of* $\mathfrak{P}$ *are bounded.*

Conversely, 3°, 4°, 5° taken together imply 1°, so that we have the equivalence

$$(1°) \sim (3°, 4°, 5°).$$

FIG. 90

Note that 5° prevents the body's being infinite, and 4° prevents a gap in the boundary, such as in Fig. 90.

I. Let $f(x_1, x_2, \cdots, x_n)$ be any function which satisfies the following conditions:

$$\text{(I)} \qquad f(x_1, x_2, \cdots, x_n) > 0$$

(unless $x_1 = 0 = x_2 = \cdots = x_n$, in which case and only in this case $f(0, 0, \cdots, 0) = 0$),

$$f(tx_1, tx_2, \cdots, tx_n) = tf(x_1, x_2, \cdots, x_n), \qquad \text{if} \qquad t > 0;$$

(II) $$f(x_1+y_1, x_2+y_2, \cdots, x_n+y_n) \leqq f(x_1, x_2, \cdots, x_n) + f(y_1, y_2, \cdots, y_n).$$

Here $f(x_1, x_2, \cdots, x_n)$ will always be a *continuous* function of $x_1, x_2, \cdots, x_n$ (see Art. 18); and due to this condition there always exists a *positive* factor g, which satisfies the n inequalities

(1) $$g\,|x_h| \leqq f(x_1, x_2, \cdots, x_n) \qquad (h = 1, 2, \cdots, n).$$

for every possible system of values $x_1, x_2, \cdots, x_n$. (See Arts. 20 and 38.)

The realm which is defined through

$$f(x_1, x_2, \cdots, x_n) \leqq 1$$

presents the *most general* nowhere concave body with $\mathfrak{o}$ in the interior. This realm is denoted by $\mathfrak{K}$ and its boundary by $\mathfrak{F}$.

Further, we shall introduce those radial-distances $S(\mathfrak{ab})$ for which $\mathfrak{K}$ forms the standard body. Next let m be any integer $< n$ and for every point $\mathfrak{x}$ distribute the coordinates $x_1, x_2, \cdots, x_n$ into two groups, the coordinates $x_1, x_2, \cdots, x_m$ being denoted as the *first projection* of $\mathfrak{x}$ and $x_{m+1}, x_{m+2}, \cdots, x_n$ as the *second*. Denote the first by $\mathfrak{x}'$ and the second by $\mathfrak{x}''$. For the point $\mathfrak{x}$ write $\mathfrak{x}', \mathfrak{x}''$. By $\mathfrak{X}'$ is to be understood the manifold of all systems of values $x_1, x_2, \cdots, x_m$, while $\mathfrak{X}''$ denotes the manifold of all systems of values $x_{m+1}, x_{m+2}, \cdots, x_n$.

We may define the concepts *hypercube, span, direction, straight line, translation, dilation, closed assemblages of points, inner, exterior, boundary, nowhere concave body, volume* in $\mathfrak{X}'$ as also in $\mathfrak{X}''$, if simply in the preceding usage of the analogous concepts for $\mathfrak{X}$ we write instead of $x_1, x_2, \cdots, x_n$ merely $x_1, x_2, \cdots, x_m$ or merely $x_{m+1}, x_{m+2}, \cdots, x_n$.

For example, if $\mathfrak{a}(=a_1, a_2, \cdots, a_n)$ and $\mathfrak{b}(=b_1, b_2, \cdots, b_n)$ are two points in $\mathfrak{X}$ by the span of $\mathfrak{a}'$ to $\mathfrak{b}'$ in $\mathfrak{X}'$ we understand the maximum of the values $b_1-a_1, b_2-a_2, \cdots, b_m-a_m$ by the span of $\mathfrak{a}''$ to $\mathfrak{b}''$ in $\mathfrak{X}''$ is to be understood the maximum among the values $b_{m+1}-a_{m+1}, b_{m+2}-a_{m+2}, \cdots, b_n-a_n$. These spans may be denoted by $E'(\mathfrak{a}'\mathfrak{b}')$ and $E''(\mathfrak{a}''\mathfrak{b}'')$, respectively. The span $E(\mathfrak{a}\mathfrak{b})$ in $\mathfrak{X}$ is accordingly the greater among these two spans.

If $\mathfrak{C}'$ denotes an assemblage of the first projections $\mathfrak{c}'$, and $\mathfrak{C}''$ an assemblage of the second projections $\mathfrak{c}''$, then by $\mathfrak{C}', \mathfrak{C}''$ is to be understood the assemblage of all possible points $\mathfrak{c}', \mathfrak{c}''$.

In this connection we may put $\mathfrak{X}=\mathfrak{X}', \mathfrak{X}''$.

By $\mathfrak{C}'+\mathfrak{b}'-\mathfrak{a}'$ we understand the assemblage of all systems (points $\mathfrak{c}'+\mathfrak{b}'-\mathfrak{a}'$). Write

$$f(x_1, x_2, \cdots, x_n)=S(\mathfrak{o}\mathfrak{x})=\varphi(\mathfrak{x}', \mathfrak{x}'').$$

If we keep constant the system

$$\mathfrak{x}''=\mathfrak{c}'' \quad (\text{or } x_{m+1}=c_{m+1}, x_{m+2}=c_{m+2}, \cdots, x_n=c_n),$$

then $\varphi(\mathfrak{x}', \mathfrak{c}'')$ forms a continuous function of the remaining variables $x_1, x_2, \cdots, x_m$. If then $\mathfrak{c}'$ is any definite first projection, we can have $\varphi(\mathfrak{x}', \mathfrak{c}'')\leqq\varphi(\mathfrak{c}', \mathfrak{c}'')$ from (1) only if the absolute values of $x_1, x_2, \cdots, x_m$ are all $\leqq\dfrac{\varphi(\mathfrak{c}', \mathfrak{c}'')}{g}$.

A hypercube is defined in $\mathfrak{X}'$ through this condition, and in this hypercube as a continuous function, $\varphi(\mathfrak{x}', \mathfrak{c}'')$ has a definite minimum (Art. 36). And this minimum thus presents the *least* value of $\varphi(\mathfrak{x}', \mathfrak{c}'')$ with *arbitrary variable* $\mathfrak{x}'$ and will be denoted by

$$f''(c_{m+1}, c_{m+2}, \cdots, c_n) \quad \text{or} \quad S''(\mathfrak{o}''C'') \quad \text{or also by} \quad \psi(\mathfrak{c}'').$$

From (I) we may derive for the function f'' the corresponding conditions:

$$f''(x_{m+1}, x_{m+2}, \cdots, x_n)>0,$$

if $x_{m+1}, x_{m+2}, \cdots, x_n$ are not all simultaneously zero,

$$f''(0, 0, \cdots, 0)=0;$$

and

$$f''(tx_{m+1}, tx_{m+2}, \cdots, tx_n) = tf''(x_{m+1}, x_{m+2}, \cdots, x_n),$$

where $t>0$. If, further, $x_{m+1}, x_{m+2}, \cdots, x_n$ and $y_{m+1}, y_{m+2}, \cdots, y_n$ are any second projections, we may always find corresponding to them such first projections $x_1, x_2, \cdots, x_m$ and $y_1, y_2, \cdots, y_m$ that

$$f(x_1, x_2, \cdots, x_n) = f''(x_{m+1}, x_{m+2}, \cdots, x_n),$$
$$f(y_1, y_2, \cdots, y_n) = f''(y_{m+1}, y_{m+2}, \cdots, y_n);$$

and since, due to the meaning of f'', we always have for arbitrary values of $x_1+y_1, x_2+y_2, \cdots, x_n+y_n$ the relation

$$f''(x_{m+1}+y_{m+1}, x_{m+2}+y_{m+2}, \cdots, x_n+y_n) \leqq f(x_1+y_1, x_2+y_2, \cdots, x_n+y_n),$$

it follows from (II) that

$$f''(x_{m+1}+y_{m+1}, x_{m+2}+y_{m+2}, \cdots, x_n+y_n) \leqq f''(x_{m+1}, x_{m+2}, \cdots, x_n) + f''(y_{m+1}, y_{m+2}, \cdots, y_n).$$

Accordingly the realm $f''(x_{m+1}, x_{m+2}, \cdots, x_n)$ is found also to be nowhere concave in $\mathfrak{X}''$, and also has the system $\mathfrak{o}''$ (and that is $x_{m+1}=0, \cdots, x_n=0$) as an inner point. This realm is denoted by $\mathfrak{K}''$.

Corresponding to a projection $\mathfrak{c}''$ there exists then and only then in the assemblage of points $\mathfrak{X}'$, $\mathfrak{c}''$ a point of $\mathfrak{K}$, if there exists a system $\mathfrak{X}'$ for which $\varphi(\mathfrak{X}', \mathfrak{c}'') \leqq 1$, and therefore if $\psi(\mathfrak{c}'') \leqq 1$. From this it is seen that $\mathfrak{K}''$ *consists exactly of the collectively different projections* $\mathfrak{X}''$ *which exist for the points of* $\mathfrak{K}$.

If $\mathfrak{c}''$ denotes any system (point) of $\mathfrak{K}''$, the assemblage of those systems $\mathfrak{x}'$ for which $\mathfrak{x}'$, $\mathfrak{c}''$ is a point of $\mathfrak{K}$ is denoted by $\mathfrak{K}'(\mathfrak{c}'')$. The collectivity of the points in question of $\mathfrak{K}$ may be denoted by $\mathfrak{K}'(\mathfrak{c}'')$, $\mathfrak{c}''$.

If we pay attention to the property 1° of the body $\mathfrak{K}$, especially for the straight lines that are laid in the manifold $\mathfrak{x}'$, $\mathfrak{c}''$, there appears exactly the property corresponding to 1° for the realm $\mathfrak{K}'(\mathfrak{c}'')$ with respect to the straight lines of the manifold $\mathfrak{X}'$. Therefore $\mathfrak{K}'(\mathfrak{c}'')$ will always represent a nowhere concave body in $\mathfrak{x}'$, if this realm has an *interior*[1] in $\mathfrak{X}'$. This, however, is always the case when $\mathfrak{c}''$ is a system in the *interior* of $\mathfrak{X}''$, and for which therefore $\psi(\mathfrak{c}'')<1$. For in this case corresponding to $\mathfrak{c}''$ there exists a system $\mathfrak{c}'$, for which $\varphi(\mathfrak{c}', \mathfrak{c}'')=\psi(\mathfrak{c}'')$ which is <1, and consequently $\mathfrak{c}', \mathfrak{c}''$ is an inner point of $\mathfrak{K}$. This condition carries with itself the fact that the system (point) $\mathfrak{c}'$ as an inner point of $\mathfrak{X}'(\mathfrak{c}'')$ is a point in $\mathfrak{X}'$. If on the other hand $\mathfrak{c}''$ belongs to the *boundary* of $\mathfrak{K}''$, and accordingly $\psi(\mathfrak{c}'')=1$, then similarly the realm $\mathfrak{K}'(\mathfrak{c}'')$ may exist in $\mathfrak{X}'$ without having an inner point in it.

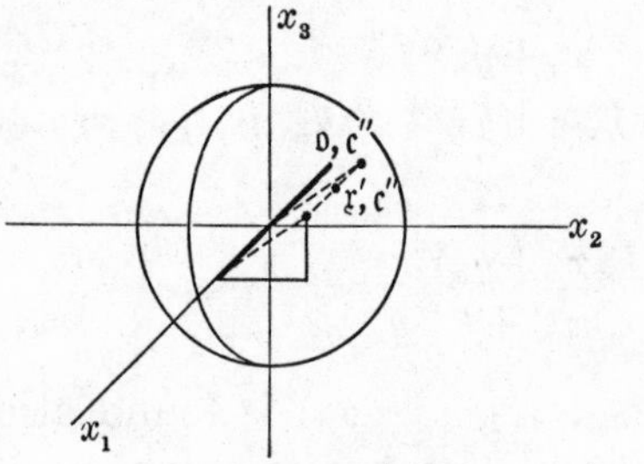

FIG. 91a

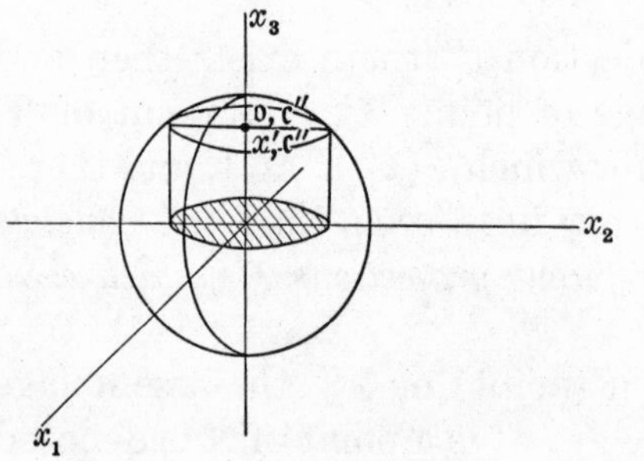

FIG. 91b

EXAMPLE:

$f(x_1, x_2, x_3)=\varphi(\mathfrak{x}', \mathfrak{x}'')$

$=\sqrt{x_1^2+x_2^2+x_3^2}$

$\mathfrak{K}$ is the sphere

$\sqrt{x_1^2+x_2^2+x_3^2}\leqq 1.$

Case $n=3$, $m=1$.

$f''(\mathfrak{c}_2, \mathfrak{c}_3)=$ min. of $\sqrt{x_1^2+c_2^2+c_3^2}$ as x_1 varies $=\sqrt{c_2^2+c_3^2}$ $=\psi(\mathfrak{c}'')$.

$\mathfrak{K}''$ is the circle, in the x_2x_3 plane.

$\mathfrak{K}'(\mathfrak{c}'')$ is the central line segment in heavy ink.

Case $n=3$, $m=2$.

$f''(\mathfrak{c}_3)=$ min. of $\sqrt{x_1^2+x_2^2+c_3^2}$ as x_1 and x_2 vary.

$\mathfrak{K}''$ is the central line segment in heavy ink.

$\mathfrak{K}'(\mathfrak{c}'')$ is the central ruled circle, in the x_1x_2 plane.

Regarding the points of the boundary of $\mathfrak{K}$, that is of the surface $\mathfrak{F}$, the following may be said: First, if $\mathfrak{c}''$ is an inner system point of $\mathfrak{K}$, there exist associated with $\mathfrak{c}''$ certain systems $\mathfrak{c}'$ for which $\varphi(\mathfrak{c}', \mathfrak{c}'')<1$; and then as shown above,

[1] *Interior* here means an assemblage of inner points. See also Art. 25, end.

$\mathfrak{e}'$, $\mathfrak{c}''$ is an inner system of $\mathfrak{K}'(\mathfrak{c}'')$. If, on the other hand, corresponding to the same $\mathfrak{c}''$, we have a system f', such that $\varphi(f', \mathfrak{c}'')=1$, and accordingly f', $\mathfrak{c}''$ is a point of $\mathfrak{F}$, then we may take an arbitrary system $\mathfrak{c}'$ such that $\varphi(\mathfrak{c}', \mathfrak{c}'')<1$; and it is then seen that the point $\mathfrak{e}'$, $\mathfrak{c}''$ of the boundary of $\mathfrak{K}$ belongs to the stretch of the straight line through $\mathfrak{c}'$, $\mathfrak{c}''$ and f', $\mathfrak{c}''$ and this condition shows at once $\mathfrak{e}'$ as belonging to the boundary of $\mathfrak{K}'(\mathfrak{c}'')$ in $\mathfrak{K}'(\mathfrak{c}'')$.

Hence there arise in the case $\psi(\mathfrak{c}'')<1$ the points which in the domain $\mathfrak{K}'(\mathfrak{c}'')$, $\mathfrak{c}''$ belong to the surface $\mathfrak{F}$, definitely from the boundary of $\mathfrak{K}'(\mathfrak{c}'')$ in $\mathfrak{X}'$.

If, secondly, $\mathfrak{e}''$ is a system of the boundary of $\mathfrak{K}''$ and if $\mathfrak{e}'$ is then any system of $\mathfrak{K}'(\mathfrak{e}'')$, it follows from

$$1\geqq\varphi(\mathfrak{e}', \mathfrak{e}'')\geqq\psi(\mathfrak{e}'')=1$$

that we have always $\varphi(\mathfrak{e}', \mathfrak{e}'')=1$ and consequently $\mathfrak{e}'$, $\mathfrak{e}''$ belongs always to $\mathfrak{F}$.

In this case $\psi(\mathfrak{e}'')=1$, the realm $\mathfrak{K}'(\mathfrak{e}'')$, $\mathfrak{e}''$ in every point belongs to $\mathfrak{F}$.

II. In the manifold $\mathfrak{X}$ we take any net $\mathfrak{N}$ of hypercubes with side δ (see Art. 37). Let $q_1, q_2, \cdots, q_n$ be the midpoint of any one of these hypercubes and observe that $q_1+l_1\delta$, $q_2+l_2\delta, \cdots, q_n+l_n\delta$ for the different integral systems l_1, $l_2, \cdots, l_n$ represent the midpoints of all the hypercubes of the net.

Next let A be the number *multiplied by* δ^n of all the hypercubes of $\mathfrak{N}$ in which every point is an inner point of $\mathfrak{K}$. If there do *not* exist such points, write $A=0$. And if there do exist such points let $\mathfrak{A}$ be the domain of such hypercubes and let $\mathfrak{A}_0$ be the domain of all the remaining hypercubes of $\mathfrak{N}$. If $A=0$, we shall understand by $\mathfrak{A}_0$ the entire manifold $\mathfrak{X}$. Let $\mathfrak{U}$ be the realm of all the hypercubes of $\mathfrak{N}$ which have at least one point in common with $\mathfrak{K}$ and let U be the number of these hypercubes multiplied by δ^n. Finally let $\mathfrak{U}_0$ be the realm of all hypercubes of $\mathfrak{N}$ that are not counted in $\mathfrak{U}$. Next vary the net $\mathfrak{N}$ in such a way that δ decreases toward zero. The point $q_1, q_2, \cdots, q_n$ may be fixed or it may be allowed to vary. The two quantities A and U both converge, as seen in Art. 39, to one and the same positive limit J, the *volume* of $\mathfrak{K}$. Observe that A and $\mathfrak{U}_0$ have no point of $\mathfrak{K}$ in common. In an analogous manner we have from Art. 40 a definite volume for each assemblage of points which is formed out of combinations of all different points of a finite number of *given bodies that are nowhere concave,* where the individual bodies may cover arbitrarily one another. An assemblage of points of this nature is looked upon as *closed* (Art. 25); and every point of the boundary is seen to be a point of condensation of inner points. Hence if two such assemblages of points have the first containing the second, without being identical with it, then there exists in the first a point which is an exterior point for the second, and hence with regard to the remark above there exists an inner point of the first assemblage of points which is an exterior point of the second. Consequently there exists a hypercube which belongs entirely to the first assemblage of points and has no inner point of the second. *It is accordingly clear that the volume of the first assemblage is at least greater than that of the second by as much as the volume of this hypercube.*

Hence A is the volume of $\mathfrak{A}$ (insofar as a realm $\mathfrak{A}$ exists) and always $J > A$; and further U is the volume of $\mathfrak{U}$ and always $U > J$. It may be remarked further that $\mathfrak{A}$ lies entirely within $\mathfrak{K}$ while U_0 is entirely exterior to $\mathfrak{K}$. Every hypercube of $\mathfrak{A}_0$ has at least one point of the exterior or boundary of $\mathfrak{K}$ while every point of $\mathfrak{U}$ has at least one point within or on the boundary of $\mathfrak{K}$. Finally on the one hand $\mathfrak{A}$ and A_0 and on the other $\mathfrak{U}_0$ and U have their boundary in common. Neither $\mathfrak{A}$ nor $\mathfrak{U}_0$ has a point of $\mathfrak{F}$; but each point of the boundary of $\mathfrak{U}_0$, as does each point of the boundary of U_0, has from a point of the boundary $\mathfrak{F}$ a span which is $\leqq \delta$, if we consider that a stretch from an inner point to an exterior point of $\mathfrak{K}$ must always pass through a point of $\mathfrak{F}$.

Consider next any hypercube of $\mathfrak{N}$ with center $q_1 + l_1\delta$, $q_2 + l_2\delta$, $\cdots$, $q_n + l_n\delta$. It is seen that all the points $\mathfrak{x}'$, $\mathfrak{x}''$

of this hypercube are had if on the one hand $\mathfrak{x}'$ fills a certain hypercube with the side δ in $\mathfrak{X}'$ and on the other hand $\mathfrak{x}''$ independent of $\mathfrak{x}'$ fills a certain hypercube in $\mathfrak{X}''$ with side δ, namely the one $q_{m+1}+l_{m+1}\delta, q_{m+2}+l_{m+2}\delta, \cdots, q_n+l_n\delta$ as midpoint. Hence for all hypercubes in question for $\mathfrak{X}'$ and $\mathfrak{X}''$ there arise definite nets of hypercubes $\mathfrak{N}'$ and $\mathfrak{N}''$ for the two manifolds $\mathfrak{X}'$ and $\mathfrak{X}''$.

With regard to the net $\mathfrak{N}''$ we shall employ the symbols $\mathfrak{A}''$ and $\mathfrak{U}''$ for the realm $\mathfrak{K}''$ in a manner corresponding to the one used above for $\mathfrak{A}$ and $\mathfrak{U}$ in $\mathfrak{K}$ with regard to the net $\mathfrak{N}$. Further we shall understand by A'' multiplied by δ^{n-m} and U'' multiplied by δ^{n-m} the number of hypercubes of $\mathfrak{N}''$ that appear in $\mathfrak{A}''$ and $\mathfrak{U}''$. Finally let $\mathfrak{s}''$ go over all the midpoints of hypercubes of $\mathfrak{N}''$ (and that is of systems $\mathfrak{x}''$ of the form $q_{m+1}+l_{m+1}\delta, q_{m+2}+l_{m+2}\delta, \cdots, q_n+l_n\delta$ (where $l_{m+1}, l_{m+2}, \cdots, l_n$ are integers) which are inner points of $\mathfrak{K}''$. And let j'' be the number of such different systems $\mathfrak{s}''$. It follows at once that

$$A'' \leqq j''\delta^{n-m} \leqq U''.$$

Due to the constitution of $\mathfrak{K}''$ as outlined in I, if δ approaches zero, A'', U'' and with them $j''\delta^{n-m}$ all converge toward a definite positive limit J'', the *volume* of $\mathfrak{K}''$ in $\mathfrak{X}''$. In an analogous manner it is seen, if $\mathfrak{c}''$ is any system of $\mathfrak{K}''$, that the realm $\mathfrak{K}'(\mathfrak{c}'')$ has a definite volume in $\mathfrak{X}'$. For this realm $\mathfrak{K}'(\mathfrak{c}'')$ with respect to the net $\mathfrak{N}'$ we may adopt the notation $A'(\mathfrak{c}'')$, $\mathfrak{A}'(\mathfrak{c}'')$, $\mathfrak{A}'_0(\mathfrak{c}'')$, $U'(\mathfrak{c}'')$, $\mathfrak{U}'(\mathfrak{c}'')$, $\mathfrak{U}'_0(\mathfrak{c}'')$ corresponding to symbols used above for the net $\mathfrak{N}$ in $\mathfrak{K}$. In particular $A'(\mathfrak{c}'')$ multiplied by δ^m and $U'(\mathfrak{c}'')$ multiplied by δ^m denote the number of hypercubes of the net $\mathfrak{N}'$ which appear in $\mathfrak{A}'(\mathfrak{c}'')$ and $\mathfrak{U}'(\mathfrak{c}'')$.

If $\mathfrak{c}''$ is an inner point of $\mathfrak{K}''$ or if it belongs to the boundary of $\mathfrak{K}''$ but if $\mathfrak{K}'(\mathfrak{c}'')$ has in $\mathfrak{X}'$ an inner point, then if δ tends toward zero, it is seen that both $A'(\mathfrak{c}'')$ and $U'(\mathfrak{c}'')$ converge toward a definite limit $J'(\mathfrak{c}'')$ and for this limit there exist for the individual nets $\mathfrak{N}''$ always the inequalities $A'(\mathfrak{c}'') < J'(\mathfrak{c}'') < U'(\mathfrak{c}'')$. But if $\mathfrak{c}''$ belongs to the boundary of $\mathfrak{K}''$ and if in addition $\mathfrak{K}'(\mathfrak{c}'')$ has no inner point, it follows on the one hand that $A'(\mathfrak{c}'')=0$ for every net $\mathfrak{N}''$ and on the other hand $U'(\mathfrak{c}'')$ converges toward zero, if δ decreases to zero, and hence in this case we have to ascribe a volume $J'(\mathfrak{c}'')=0$ to the body $\mathfrak{K}'(\mathfrak{c}'')$ in $\mathfrak{X}'$. Hence with respect to the single nets $\mathfrak{N}''$ we have always $J'(\mathfrak{c}'')<U'(\mathfrak{c}'')$.

As often as $\mathfrak{c}'$, $\mathfrak{c}''$ is the midpoint of one of the hypercubes in the realm $\mathfrak{A}$ of the net $\mathfrak{N}$, it is clear that $\mathfrak{c}''$ is one of the systems denoted in general by δ'' and then $\mathfrak{c}'$ appears as the midpoint of one of the hypercubes of $\mathfrak{N}'$ which net offers the realm $\mathfrak{A}'(\mathfrak{c}'')$. If on the other hand we take any one of the systems δ'' and let $\mathfrak{c}'$ be midpoint of one of those hypercubes of $\mathfrak{N}'$ which net offers the correlated realm $U'(\delta'')$, then $\mathfrak{c}'$, δ'' is the midpoint of such a hypercube of the net $\mathfrak{N}$ which is to be counted as belonging to the realm $\mathfrak{U}$. Accordingly we have

$$(2) \qquad A \leqq \delta^{n-m}\Sigma A'(\delta''), \qquad \delta^{n-m}\Sigma U'(\delta'') \leqq U,$$

and at the same time

$$(3) \qquad \delta^{n-m}\Sigma A'(\delta'') \leqq \delta^{n-m}\Sigma J'(\delta'') \leqq \delta^{n-m}\Sigma U'(\delta''),$$

where the summations are to be taken over all the systems of the form $q_{m+1}+l_{m+1}\delta$, $q_{m+2}+l_{m+2}\delta$, $\cdots$, $q_n+l_n\delta$, l_{m+1}, l_{m+2}, $\cdots$, l_n being integers, and these systems lie within the body $\mathfrak{K}''$; and N. B., they may also extend to points both within and on the boundary of $\mathfrak{K}''$.

Due to these inequalities with decreasing δ the quantities A and U and with them the expression $\delta^{n-m}\Sigma J'(\delta'')$ converge to the volume J of $\mathfrak{K}$. This result may be expressed as follows:

The integral $\int dx_1\, dx_2 \cdots dx_n$ *may be computed if we integrate first with respect to* $x_1, x_2, \cdots, x_m$ *and then with respect to* $x_{m+1}, x_{m+2}, \cdots, x_n$.

III. Let $\mathfrak{p}$ denote a definite point, while $\mathfrak{q}$ is an arbitrary variable point in a closed assemblage of points $\mathfrak{Q}$. Then in this system of quantities (due to the theorem in Art. 36) there is a definite minimum of the spans $E(\mathfrak{p}\mathfrak{q})$. We may prove first that $E(\mathfrak{p}\mathfrak{Q})$ is a continuous function of $\mathfrak{p}$.

Let $E(\mathfrak{p}_1 q_1)$ be the minimum span from the point $\mathfrak{p}_1$ to the points in $\mathfrak{Q}$. Let $E(\mathfrak{p}_2\mathfrak{q}_2)$ be the minimum span from the point $\mathfrak{p}_2$ to the points in $\mathfrak{Q}$. Then $E(\mathfrak{p}_1\mathfrak{q}_1)$ differs from $E(\mathfrak{p}_2\mathfrak{q}_2)$ by less than $E(\mathfrak{p}_1\mathfrak{p}_2)$; for suppose not. Then either

$$(1) \qquad E(\mathfrak{p}_1\mathfrak{q}_1)-E(\mathfrak{p}_2\mathfrak{q}_2)>E(\mathfrak{p}_1\mathfrak{p}_2)$$

or

$$(2) \qquad E(\mathfrak{p}_2\mathfrak{q}_2)-E(\mathfrak{p}_1\mathfrak{q}_1)>E(\mathfrak{p}_1\mathfrak{p}_2)=E(\mathfrak{p}_2\mathfrak{p}_1).$$

In the first case, since from the accordant property we have

$$E(\mathfrak{p}_1\mathfrak{q}_2)\leqq E(\mathfrak{p}_1\mathfrak{p}_2)+E(\mathfrak{p}_2\mathfrak{q}_2),$$

we see that

$$E(\mathfrak{p}_1\mathfrak{q}_1)>E(\mathfrak{p}_1\mathfrak{q}_2),$$

which is impossible since $E(\mathfrak{p}_1\mathfrak{q}_1)$ was a minimum. Similarly it may be proved that the second case is impossible.

Due to the relation $E(\mathfrak{p}\mathfrak{q})\geqq E(\mathfrak{o}\mathfrak{q})-E(\mathfrak{o}\mathfrak{p})$ there exists this minimum when $E(\mathfrak{p}\mathfrak{q})$ with $E(\mathfrak{o}\mathfrak{q})$ increases above every limit, even in the case where there does not exist an *upper limit* for the span $E(\mathfrak{o}\mathfrak{q})$ in $\mathfrak{Q}$. This minimum of $E(\mathfrak{p}\mathfrak{q})$ in $\mathfrak{Q}$ may be denoted by $E(\mathfrak{p}\mathfrak{Q})$. In Art. 26 this notation is used in a different sense. This quantity $E(\mathfrak{p}\mathfrak{Q})$ (since for two different points $\mathfrak{p}$ it cannot differ by more than their interchangeable span) is a continuous function of the coordinates and consequently (Art. 36) it has a definite *minimum* in every closed assemblage $\mathfrak{P}$ of $\mathfrak{p}$ in which there exists an upper limit for the spans $E(\mathfrak{o}\mathfrak{p})$. *Hence if* $\mathfrak{P}$ *and* $\mathfrak{Q}$ *are two closed assemblages of points, which have no point in common and in at least one of them the span from* $\mathfrak{o}$ *does not exceed every limit, there exists a definite positive minimum for the spans from the points in* $\mathfrak{P}$ *to the points in* $\mathfrak{Q}$.

Next let $\mathfrak{c}''$ be any definite system of $\mathfrak{R}''$. If a positive quantity κ is taken arbitrarily, we may take the side δ of the net $\mathfrak{N}$ so small that $A'(\mathfrak{c}'')>J'(\mathfrak{c}'')-\kappa$ and $U'(\mathfrak{c}'')<J'(\mathfrak{c}'')+\kappa$. Observe that the assemblage of points

$U'_0(\mathfrak{c}'')$, $\mathfrak{c}''$ never has a point on the boundary $\mathfrak{F}$, and there consequently exists a *positive* minimum of the spans of this assemblage of points to the points of $\mathfrak{F}$. Let ϵ be a *positive* quantity not greater than this minimum. If $\mathfrak{x}''$ is any system point of $\mathfrak{K}''$ which belongs at the same time to the realm $E''(\mathfrak{c}''\mathfrak{x}'') \leqq \epsilon$ there lies in every hypercube which contributes to $\mathfrak{U}'(\mathfrak{x}'')$ at least one system (point) $\mathfrak{x}'$ of $\mathfrak{K}'(\mathfrak{x}'')$ and then there appears $\mathfrak{x}'$, $\mathfrak{x}''$ as a point of $\mathfrak{K}$ with a span $<\epsilon$ from the point $\mathfrak{x}'$, $\mathfrak{c}''$. Hence the latter point can never

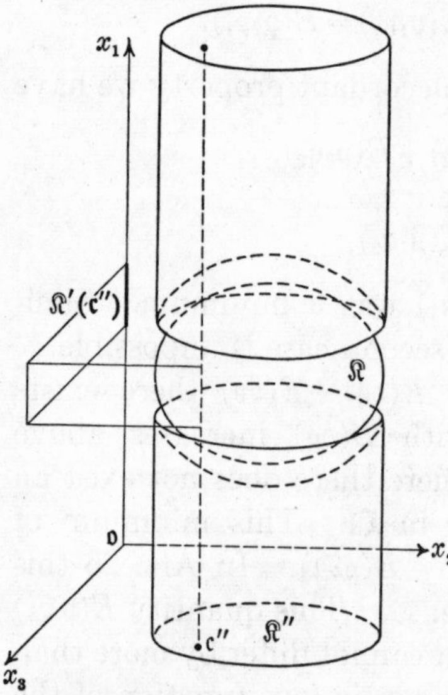

FIG. 92a

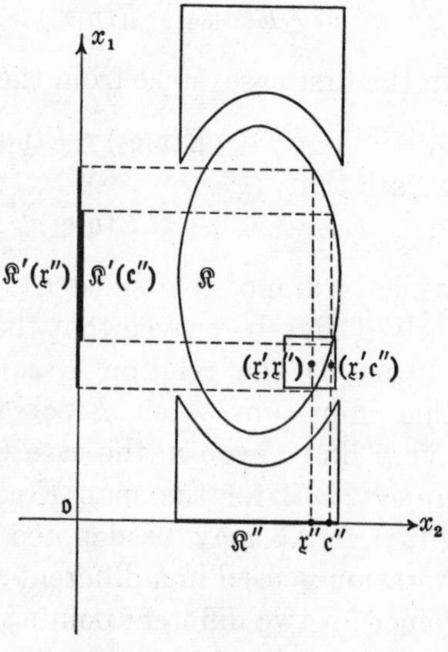

FIG. 92b

belong to $\mathfrak{U}'_0(\mathfrak{c}'')$, $\mathfrak{c}''$ and hence $\mathfrak{x}'$ forms an inner system of $\mathfrak{U}'(\mathfrak{c}'')$.

In this way it is seen that every hypercube of $\mathfrak{U}'(\mathfrak{x}'')$ belongs also to $\mathfrak{U}'(\mathfrak{c}'')$ and we accordingly have $\mathfrak{U}'(\mathfrak{c}'') \geqq \mathfrak{U}'(\mathfrak{x}'')$. And from this it follows finally that

$$J'(\mathfrak{x}'') - J'(\mathfrak{c}'') < \kappa, \tag{4}$$

so long as $\mathfrak{x}''$ lies in $\mathfrak{K}''$ and $E''(\mathfrak{c}''\mathfrak{x}'') < \epsilon$.

Next let $\mathfrak{c}''$ be in particular an inner point of $\mathfrak{K}''$, then (see remark at end of I) the assemblage of points $\mathfrak{A}'(\mathfrak{c}'')$, $\mathfrak{c}''$

can never have a point of $\mathfrak{F}$; we then again have a definite *positive* minimum of the spans of this assemblage to $\mathfrak{F}$; let ϵ be a positive quantity that is not greater than this new minimum. If $\mathfrak{x}''$ is any system of the realm $E''(\mathfrak{c}''\mathfrak{x}'')<\epsilon$ and if $\mathfrak{c}'$ is any arbitrary system of $\mathfrak{A}'(\mathfrak{c}'')$, then the point $\mathfrak{c}', \mathfrak{c}''$ has a span $<\epsilon$ from the point $\mathfrak{c}', \mathfrak{x}''$ and the last point must also be an inner point of $\mathfrak{K}$. With this it is seen that $\mathfrak{x}''$ is at all events a system (point) of $\mathfrak{K}''$ and the realm $\mathfrak{A}'(\mathfrak{x}'')$ contains every system of $\mathfrak{A}'(\mathfrak{c}'')$ so that $A'(\mathfrak{x}'') \geqq A'(\mathfrak{c}'')$.

From this we have finally

$$J'(\mathfrak{x}'')-J'(\mathfrak{c}'')>-\kappa, \tag{5}$$

so long as $E''(\mathfrak{c}''\mathfrak{x}'')<\epsilon$.

In a certain sense this last result may be extended to systems $\mathfrak{c}''$ of the boundary of $\mathfrak{K}''$; for let $\mathfrak{c}''$ and $\mathfrak{b}''$ be any two systems of $\mathfrak{K}''$ (which may be inner points or points of the boundary of $\mathfrak{K}''$), then every definite third system of the stretch $\mathfrak{b}\mathfrak{c}''$ in $\mathfrak{X}''$ is expressed through

$$\mathfrak{t}''=t\mathfrak{b}''+(1-t)\mathfrak{c}''$$

with a value $t>0$ and <1. If then we hold a system $\mathfrak{b}'$ of $\mathfrak{K}'(\mathfrak{b}'')$ fixed and let $\mathfrak{c}'$ vary arbitrarily in the assemblage of points $\mathfrak{K}'(\mathfrak{c}'')$, then due to the nature of the realm $\mathfrak{K}$, the system expressed through $\mathfrak{t}'=t\mathfrak{b}'+(1-t)\mathfrak{c}'$ is always found in the assemblage $\mathfrak{K}'(t'')$ and we accordingly have for every value $t>0$ and <1 at all events

$$J'(t'')\geqq(1-t)^m J'(\mathfrak{c}''). \tag{6}$$ (See Art. 156.)

More definitely we have the following proof of this inequality.

Let $\mathfrak{b}''$ and $\mathfrak{c}''$ be in $\mathfrak{K}'(\mathfrak{b}'')$ and $\mathfrak{K}'(\mathfrak{c}'')$ respectively. Then the points $\mathfrak{b}', \mathfrak{b}''$ and $\mathfrak{c}', \mathfrak{c}''$ are in the body $\mathfrak{K}$. Therefore the point $t(\mathfrak{b}', \mathfrak{b}'')+(1-t)(\mathfrak{c}', \mathfrak{c}'')$ is in $\mathfrak{K}$ since the body is nowhere concave, and consequently the point $t\mathfrak{b}'+(1-t)\mathfrak{c}'$ is in $\mathfrak{K}'(\mathfrak{t}'')$. This is true for every point $\mathfrak{b}'$ in $\mathfrak{K}'(\mathfrak{b}'')$ and every point $\mathfrak{c}'$ in $\mathfrak{K}'(\mathfrak{c}'')$.

So that, keeping $\mathfrak{b}'$ fixed, we see that $\mathfrak{K}'(\mathfrak{t}'')$ includes the domain generated by $t\mathfrak{b}'+(1-t)\mathfrak{c}'$ as $\mathfrak{c}'$ varies over the domain $\mathfrak{K}'(\mathfrak{c}'')$. But the domain generated by $t\mathfrak{b}'+(1-t)\mathfrak{c}'$ is that obtained from $\mathfrak{K}'(\mathfrak{c}'')$ by the transformation

$$\bar{c}_i' - tb_i' = (1-t)c_i' \qquad (i=1, 2, \cdots, m),$$

whose determinant is $(1-t)^m$. Consequently the volume of the domain generated by $t\mathfrak{b}'+(1-t)\mathfrak{c}'$ as $\mathfrak{c}'$ varies is equal to $(1-t)^m J'(\mathfrak{c}'')$, and since it is included in $\mathfrak{K}'(\mathfrak{t}'')$ we have

$$J'(\mathfrak{t}'') \geqq (1-t)^m J'(\mathfrak{c}'').$$

The relations (4), (5), (6) show that *the quantity* $J'(\mathfrak{x}'')$ *expresses a continuous function of the variables* $x_{m+1}, x_{m+2}, \cdots, x_n$ *of* $\mathfrak{x}''$ *in the entire interior of* $\mathfrak{K}''$, *and further on every arbitrary stretch in* $\mathfrak{K}''$, *even if this stretch extends to the boundary of* $\mathfrak{K}''$ *or lies wholly in it.*

IV. In conclusion we may add certain remarks which have a place in connection with the proof of the inequality $S_1S_2\cdots S_nJ \leqq 2^n$, where the question arises as to when does the equality sign occur in the expression just written.

Let $\mathfrak{b}''$ and $\mathfrak{c}''$ be any two systems of $\mathfrak{K}''$ and in addition suppose that $J(\mathfrak{c}'')>0$. Then the system $x_1, x_2, \cdots, x_m, t$ belonging to all those points $\mathfrak{x}$ of $\mathfrak{K}$, for which $\mathfrak{x}''$ has the form $\mathfrak{t}''=t\mathfrak{b}''+(1-t)\mathfrak{c}''$ where $0\leqq t\leqq 1$ (due to properties 1° and 2°) presents a nowhere concave body in the manifold of all possible systems $x_1, x_2, \cdots, x_m, t$. Then not only does equation (6) exist, but also another theorem due to Brunn, proof of which is found in Art. 156 and which exists as stated in the following inequality:

$$(7) \qquad \sqrt[m]{J'(t'')} \geqq t\sqrt[m]{J'(\mathfrak{b}'')}+(1-\mathrm{t})\sqrt[m]{J'(\mathfrak{c}'')}.$$

From the following it is seen that there are cases where $J'(\mathfrak{x}'')$ is constant as $\mathfrak{x}''$ varies over $\mathfrak{K}''$. If in addition we have $J'(\mathfrak{b}'')=J'(\mathfrak{c}'')$, then the inequality (7) becomes $J'(\mathfrak{t}'')\geqq J'(\mathfrak{c}'')$. If only for *one value* t which is >0 and <1 we require the existence of the equality sign, then, as is also proved in Art. 156, it is necessary (and later shown to be sufficient) that the bodies $\mathfrak{K}'(t'')$ which belong to the different systems $\mathfrak{t}''$ of the stretch $\mathfrak{b}''\mathfrak{c}''$ may all be had through translations in $\mathfrak{X}'$ of the one body $\mathfrak{K}'(\mathfrak{c}'')$.

In virtue of this last remark it may be determined next *under what conditions the quantity* $J'(\mathfrak{x}'')$ *for the system* $\mathfrak{x}''$ *in* $\mathfrak{K}''$ *is always constant,* $=J'(\mathfrak{o}'')$. It is seen that every body $\mathfrak{K}'(\mathfrak{x}'')$ is had through a translation of $\mathfrak{K}'(\mathfrak{o}'')$.

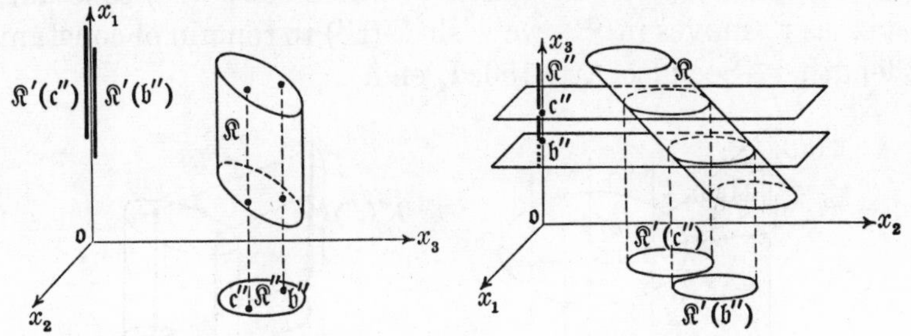

Case 1. $m=1$, $n=3$ Case 2. $m=2$, $n=3$

FIG. 93

Let $\mathfrak{b}''$ and $\mathfrak{c}''$ be any two systems of $\mathfrak{K}''$. Then by the above theorem, $\mathfrak{K}'(\mathfrak{b}'')$ can be derived from $\mathfrak{K}'(\mathfrak{o}'')$ by the translation in $\mathfrak{X}'$ from $\mathfrak{o}'$ to a certain system $\mathfrak{b}'$, and $\mathfrak{K}'(\mathfrak{c}'')$ can be derived from it by a translation from $\mathfrak{o}'$ to some point $\mathfrak{c}''$. So that

$$\mathfrak{K}'(\mathfrak{b}'')=\mathfrak{K}'(\mathfrak{o}'')+\mathfrak{b}'-\mathfrak{o}',$$
$$\mathfrak{K}'(\mathfrak{c}'')=\mathfrak{K}'(\mathfrak{o}'')+\mathfrak{c}'-\mathfrak{o}'.$$

If we use the above equalities for fixed points in $\mathfrak{K}'(\mathfrak{o}'')$, then $\mathfrak{K}'(\mathfrak{b}'')$ and $\mathfrak{K}'(\mathfrak{c}'')$ will be used to represent single points of the domains $\mathfrak{K}'(\mathfrak{b}'')$ and $\mathfrak{K}'(\mathfrak{c}'')$. Multiplying them (with this understanding) by t and $(1-t)$ respectively and adding, we get

$$t\mathfrak{K}'(\mathfrak{b}'')+(1-t)\mathfrak{K}'(\mathfrak{c}'')=\mathfrak{K}'(\mathfrak{o}'')+t(\mathfrak{b}'-\mathfrak{o}')+(1-t)(\mathfrak{c}'-\mathfrak{o}').$$

The point represented by the left side lies in $\mathfrak{K}'(t'')$ as was stated on p. 584. This is the case no matter which point of $\mathfrak{K}'(\mathfrak{o}'')$ we started with. And so the whole domain (due to the nature of a nowhere concave body)

$$\mathfrak{K}'(\mathfrak{o}'')+t(\mathfrak{b}'-\mathfrak{o}')+(1+t)(\mathfrak{c}'-\mathfrak{o}')$$

lies in $\mathfrak{K}'(t'')$. See Figs. 94a and 94b.

We have in Figs. 94a and 94b a nowhere concave body in x_2x_3 and also a nowhere concave body on the x_1 (or y_1) axis.

THEOREM. Show how to generate in three dimensions (here) a body (nowhere concave) which has $J'(\mathfrak{x}'')$ constant, viz. as $\mathfrak{x}''$ moves in $\mathfrak{K}''$, we wish $\mathfrak{K}'(\mathfrak{x}'')$ to remain of constant length. (See also Art. 156, I, end.)

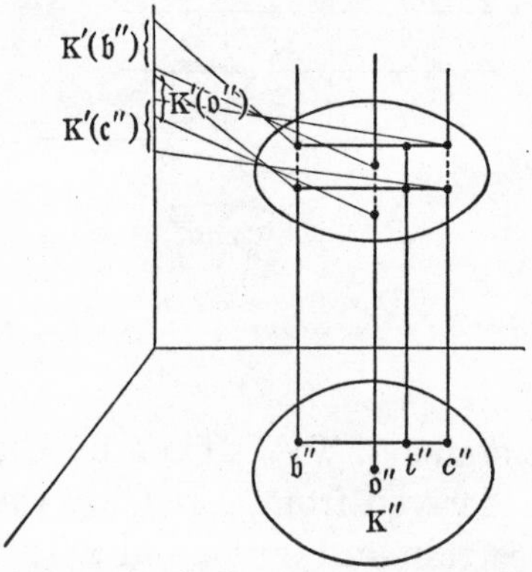

FIG. 94a

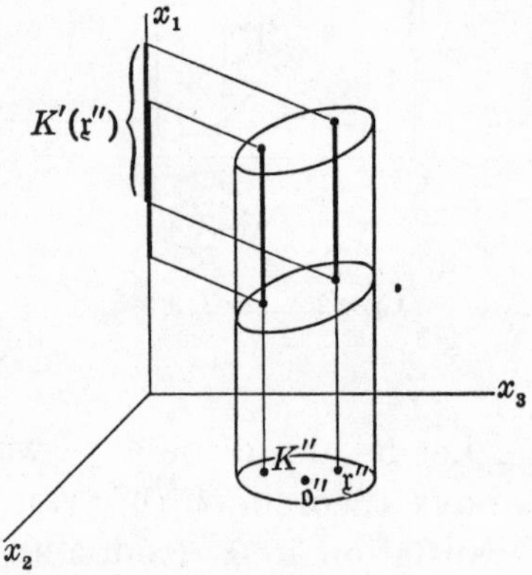

FIG. 94b

Such a body is generated as follows: Choose any $\mathfrak{x}''$ in $\mathfrak{K}''$ and for it from

$$x_1=y_1+a_1^{(2)}x_2+a_1^{(3)}x_3 \tag{8}$$

we get a range of x_1's by allowing y_1 to range over $\mathfrak{K}'(\mathfrak{o}'')$, thus determining an element of an oblique cylinder. Similarly for another $\mathfrak{x}''$ we get another element of the cylinder. The obliquity of the cylinder depends on the a's.

If in general the realm $\mathfrak{K}'(\mathfrak{t}'')$ is to be derived through a translation from $\mathfrak{K}'(\mathfrak{o}'')$, then the only translation that can be taken is the one from $\mathfrak{o}'$ to $t\mathfrak{b}'+(1-t)\mathfrak{c}'$. For if we subject a definite assemblage of points in $\mathfrak{X}'$ (which is such that in it the spans from $\mathfrak{o}'$ do not exceed a definite limit) to any real translation in $\mathfrak{x}'$ (that is not merely the translation from $\mathfrak{o}'$ to $\mathfrak{o}'$) then for at least one of the m coordinates $x_1, x_2, \cdots, x_m$ the upper and the lower limit in the assemblage of points experiences the same change; and consequently either the lower limit in question experiences an increase or the upper limit a decrease; in each case the assemblage of points would no longer retain certain of its original systems (points) after the translation.

Since $x_{m+1}=0, x_{m+2}=0, \cdots, x_n=0$; that is, $\mathfrak{o}''$ is a point within $\mathfrak{K}''$, we have in $\mathfrak{K}''$ such systems $\mathfrak{x}''$ where of the quantities $x_{m+1}, x_{m+2}, \cdots, x_n$ only one, say x_k, is not $=0$, this being a point on the x_k-axis. Suppose we have such a system $\mathfrak{x}''$, for example, with $x_k=\xi_k$, and let $\mathfrak{a}_k'$ be such a system that the translation through which $\mathfrak{K}'(\mathfrak{o}'')$ goes into $\mathfrak{K}'(\mathfrak{x}'')$ is expressed through the translation from $\mathfrak{o}'$ to $\xi_k(\mathfrak{a}_k'-\mathfrak{o}')$. In the case of three variables let $m=1$, then in the expression $x_1=y_1+a_1^{(2)}x_2+a_1^{(3)}x_3$, by putting $a_1^{(2)}=0=a_1^{(3)}$, we have, when $\mathfrak{x}''$ ranges over $\mathfrak{K}''$, a right cylinder with constant altitude and faces parallel to the x_2x_3 plane. (See Fig. 93.) When $a_1^{(2)}$ and $a_1^{(3)}$ are different from zero we have merely to incline the faces differently. (See Fig. 94.)

In general make the substitution

$$
(9)\qquad \begin{aligned}
x_1 &= y_1+a_1^{(m+1)}x_{m+1}+a_1^{(m+2)}, x_{m+2}+\cdots+a_1^{(n)}x_n,\\
&\cdots\cdots\cdots\cdots\cdots\cdots\cdots\cdots\cdots\cdots\\
x_m &= y_m+a_m^{(m+1)}x_{m+1}+a_m^{(m+2)}x_{m+2}+\cdots+a_m^{(n)}x_n,
\end{aligned}
$$

where the coefficients $a_h^{(k)}\begin{pmatrix}h=1,\ 2,\ \cdots,\ m\\ k=m+1,\ \cdots,\ n\end{pmatrix}$ are arbitrary and take in $\mathfrak{X}''$ a nowhere concave body $\mathfrak{K}''$ and an arbitrary nowhere concave body $\mathfrak{K}'(\mathfrak{o}'')$ in $\mathfrak{X}'$. Then let $x_{m+1}, x_{m+2}, \cdots, x_n$ go over all systems of $\mathfrak{K}''$ and independently of them let $y_1, y_2, \cdots, y_m$ go over all systems of $x_1, x_2, \cdots, x_m$ of $\mathfrak{K}'(\mathfrak{o}'')$. It is seen that $x_1, x_2, \cdots, x_m, \cdots, x_n$ describes such a nowhere concave body $\mathfrak{K}$ in $\mathfrak{X}$, *for which* $J'(\mathfrak{x}'')$ in $\mathfrak{X}''$ *is always constant, and every nowhere concave body* $\mathfrak{K}$, *for which* $J'(\mathfrak{x}'')$ *is in* $\mathfrak{x}''$ *constant, can be had through this procedure and always only through an assumption regarding* $\mathfrak{K}''$, $\mathfrak{K}'(\mathfrak{o}'')$ *and the quantities* $a_h^{(k)}$.

Again let $\mathfrak{K}$ be an arbitrary nowhere concave body but now with $\mathfrak{o}$ as the midpoint. In this case $\mathfrak{K}''$ has $\mathfrak{o}''$ as *midpoint* and $\mathfrak{K}'(\mathfrak{o}'')$ has its midpoint in $\mathfrak{o}'$. Next arrange in pairs $\mathfrak{b}''$, $\mathfrak{c}''$ the systems of $\mathfrak{K}$ with $\mathfrak{o}''$ as midpoint of the stretch $\mathfrak{b}''\mathfrak{c}''$. It is seen that the two assemblages of points $\mathfrak{K}'(\mathfrak{b}'')$, $\mathfrak{b}''$ and $\mathfrak{K}'(\mathfrak{c}'')$, $\mathfrak{c}''$ are symmetric to each other with respect to $\mathfrak{o}$, so that $J'(\mathfrak{b}'')=J'(\mathfrak{c}'')$; and from the inequality (7) we have $J'(\mathfrak{o}'')\geqq J'(\mathfrak{c}'')$. *It is thus evident in the case of a body* $\mathfrak{K}$ *with* $\mathfrak{o}$ *as center that* $J'(\mathfrak{o}'')$ *is always the maximum among all the values* $J'(\mathfrak{x}'')$ *in* $\mathfrak{K}''$.

In that case we find the expression $\delta^{n-m}\Sigma J'(\mathfrak{o}'')$ which was considered in (3) and in which the sum contains j'' terms, $\leqq j''\delta^{n-m}J'(\mathfrak{o}'')$. When δ tends towards zero, the expression (3) has on the one hand the limit J and on the other hand $j''\delta^{n-m}$ approaches J'', which is the volume of $\mathfrak{K}''$ in $\mathfrak{X}''$. From this it is seen finally that for a body with $\mathfrak{o}$ as center there exists the inequality

$$(10) \qquad J\leqq J'(\mathfrak{o}'')J''.$$

We may add that the equality sign enters here only if $J'(\mathfrak{x}'')$ is everywhere in $\mathfrak{K}''$ constant $[=J'(\mathfrak{o}'')]$, that is when $\mathfrak{K}$ offers the peculiar character that is expressed in (9). For if there exists in $\mathfrak{K}''$ a system $\mathfrak{c}''$ for which $J'(\mathfrak{c}'')<J'(\mathfrak{o}'')$, and if we denote by v' any positive quantity $<J'(\mathfrak{o}'')-J'(\mathfrak{c}'')$, we may (see (4)) always form a hypercube which is situated entirely in $\mathfrak{K}''$ and for whose systems $\mathfrak{x}''$ we always have

$$J'(\mathfrak{x}'')\leqq J'(\mathfrak{o}'')-v'.$$

If v'' is the volume of this hypercube in $\mathfrak{X}''$, we have through the investigation in II,

$$J'(\mathfrak{o}'')J''\geqq J+v'v''.$$

CHAPTER XVI

PROOF OF THE NEW ANALYTIC–ARITHMETIC INEQUALITY

ART. **152.** We shall now prove in general the inequality that was stated in (12) of Art. 149, namely

(1) $$S_1S_2\cdots S_nJ \leqq 2^n.$$

Let n be an arbitrary integer (>1) and in the manifold of the n coordinates $x_1, x_2, \cdots, x_n$ consider any arbitrary accordant (einhellig) and symmetric radial-distances $S(\mathfrak{ab})$.

First of all determine such a system of n lattice points $\mathfrak{p}_1, \mathfrak{p}_2, \cdots, \mathfrak{p}_n$ that the radial-distances $S(\mathfrak{op}_1), S(\mathfrak{op}_2), \cdots, S(\mathfrak{op}_n)$ are in ascending magnitude as small as possible. The magnitude of these radial-distances is expressed through the quantities $S_1, S_2, \cdots, S_n$. Next observe that if $y_1, y_2, \cdots, y_n$ are any linear homogeneous expressions in $x_1, x_2, \cdots, x_n$ with integral coefficients and a determinant ± 1, then the lattice in the y's is precisely the same as the lattice in the x's; and every body with a definite volume in the x's has the same volume in the y's (Art. 42). Hence all quantities of the inequality (1) have the same significance for $y_1, y_2, \cdots, y_n$ as they had for $x_1, x_2, \cdots, x_n$; and it will accordingly be sufficient to prove the theorem expressed in (1) for the variables $y_1, y_2, \cdots, y_n$.

We may introduce these new variables in a special relation to the points $\mathfrak{p}_1, \mathfrak{p}_2, \cdots, \mathfrak{p}_n$, and in such a way that the reduction of the lattice with respect to the directions $\mathfrak{op}_1, \mathfrak{op}_2, \cdots, \mathfrak{op}_n$ is performed as in Art. 145. For simplicity we may *assume that $x_1, x_2, \cdots, x_n$ are themselves the coordinates with which the reduction just mentioned is associated.* Accordingly we will have in particular for the point $\mathfrak{p}_h$ for the indices $h=1, 2, \cdots, n-1$ always $x_{h+1}=0, x_{h+2}=0, \cdots, x_n=0$. And through this associated condition the meaning of the assumption made here becomes essential for the following.

I. Among the quantities $S_1, S_2, \cdots, S_n$ assume as in Art. 146 that the ν_1 first ones are equal, as are the ν_2 that follow these, $\cdots$, and finally the ν_λ last ones are equal among themselves. Then write $\mu_0=0,\ \mu_1=\nu_1,\ \mu_2=\nu_1+\nu_2$, and finally $\mu_\lambda=\nu_1+\nu_2+\cdots+\nu_\lambda=n$. We thus have

$$\begin{aligned} S_1 &= S_2=\cdots=S_{\mu_1}=M_1,\\ S_{\mu_1+1} &= S_{\mu_1+2}=\cdots=S_{\mu_2}=M_2,\\ &\cdots\cdots\cdots\cdots\cdots\cdots\\ S_{\mu_{\lambda-1}+1} &= S_{\mu_{\lambda-1}+2}=\cdots=S_{\mu_\lambda}=M_\lambda, \end{aligned}$$

where, when $\lambda>1$, $M_1<M_2\cdots<M_\lambda$. Observe that M_1 is the least radial-distance magnitude from $\mathfrak{o}$ to all the lattice points, and further, if $\lambda>1$ for the numbers $\kappa=1, 2, \cdots, \lambda-1$, *the quantity* M_{k+1} *is always the least radial-distance from* $\mathfrak{o}$ *to all the lattice points outside of the manifold laid through* $\mathfrak{o}, \mathfrak{p}_1, \mathfrak{p}_2, \cdots, \mathfrak{p}_{\mu_\kappa}$; and conforming to our assumption regarding the coordinates $x_1, x_2, \cdots, x_n$ this last manifold is defined through the equations $x_{\mu_\kappa+1}=0$, $x_{\mu_\kappa+2}=0, \cdots, x_n=0$.

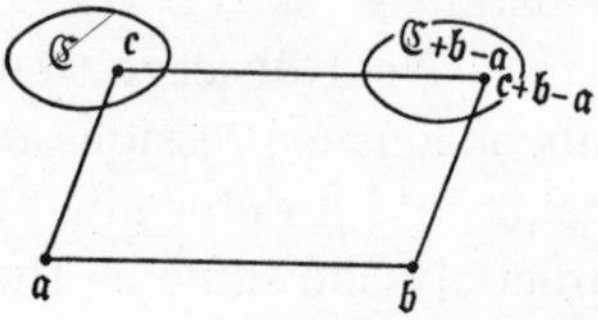

FIG. 95

If $\mathfrak{a}$ and $\mathfrak{b}$ are two points and $\mathfrak{C}$ an assemblage of points, then the assemblage of points, which arise from $\mathfrak{C}$ through the translation from $\mathfrak{a}$ to $\mathfrak{b}$, is denoted symbolically (Art. 145) through $\mathfrak{C}+\mathfrak{b}-\mathfrak{a}$.

If $\mathfrak{a}$ and $\mathfrak{b}$ are two points then the point set $\mathfrak{C}$ goes over into $\mathfrak{C}+\mathfrak{b}-\mathfrak{a}$ by a translation from $\mathfrak{a}$ to $\mathfrak{b}$. When the first set is represented by $\mathfrak{C}(\mathfrak{a})$ the second set will be represented by $\mathfrak{C}(\mathfrak{b})$. That is, the second set has the same relation to $\mathfrak{b}$ as the first set has to $\mathfrak{a}$.

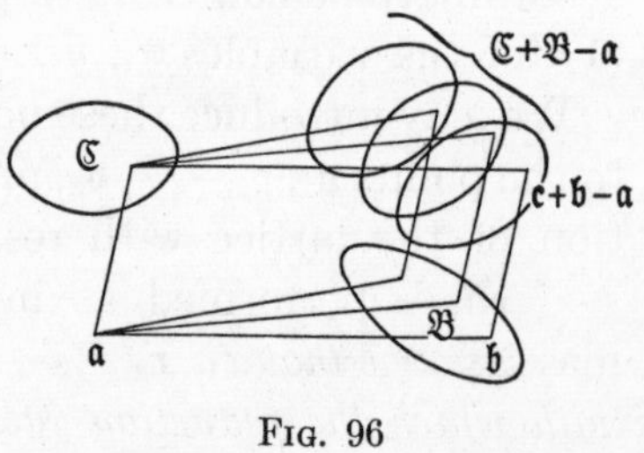

FIG. 96

If $\mathfrak{a}$ is a point and $\mathfrak{B}$ is a point set then $\mathfrak{C}$ goes into $\mathfrak{C}+\mathfrak{B}-\mathfrak{a}$ by all the translations from $\mathfrak{a}$ to $\mathfrak{B}$. When the first set is called $\mathfrak{C}(\mathfrak{a})$ the second set is called $\mathfrak{C}(\mathfrak{B})$.

Thus we see that if $\mathfrak{a}$ is a point and if $\mathfrak{B}$ and $\mathfrak{C}$ are two assemblages of points and if $\mathfrak{b}$ and $\mathfrak{c}$ are two variable points in these assemblages, then by $\mathfrak{C}+\mathfrak{B}-\mathfrak{a}$ we shall understand the union of all assemblages of points $\mathfrak{C}+\mathfrak{b}-\mathfrak{a}$, and that is the assemblages of all different points which may be expressed in at least one way in the form $\mathfrak{c}+\mathfrak{b}-\mathfrak{a}$. If $\mathfrak{B}$ denotes an assemblage of points $\mathfrak{b}$, then by $\mathfrak{C}(\mathfrak{B})$ may be denoted the union of all bodies $\mathfrak{C}(\mathfrak{b})$ and that is the assemblage $\mathfrak{C}(\mathfrak{a})+\mathfrak{B}-\mathfrak{a}$. Let G denote the quantity given for the radial-distances in Art. 17, where due to Art. 146 the quantities $M_1, M_2, \cdots, M_\lambda$ are all $\leqq \frac{G}{n}$ and as in Art. 20 let g be a positive lower limit of all distance coefficients $\frac{S(\mathfrak{ab})}{E(\mathfrak{ab})}$. Further, for $\kappa=1, 2, \cdots, \lambda$ denote the bodies $S(\mathfrak{o}\mathfrak{x}) \leqq \frac{1}{2}M_\kappa$ by $\mathfrak{P}_\kappa(\mathfrak{o})$, which are assemblages of points. By $\mathfrak{G}$ denote the lattice (collective lattice points) and by $\mathfrak{g}$ denote any lattice point. $\mathfrak{P}_\kappa(\mathfrak{G})$ will then denote the union of all bodies $\mathfrak{P}_\kappa(\mathfrak{g})$, that is the collective realms of all lattice points $\mathfrak{x}$ which have the property of having radial-distances $\leqq \frac{1}{2}M_\kappa$ from their respective lattice points.

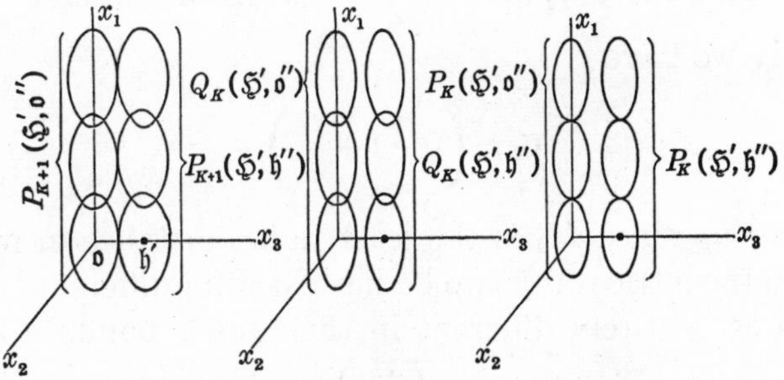

FIG. 96a FIG. 96b FIG. 96c

II. Next let Ω be any positive odd integer and let $\mathfrak{h}$ go through only those lattice points which have a span $\leqq \frac{\Omega}{2}$

from $\mathfrak{o}$ and which therefore also have spans $\leqq \frac{\Omega-1}{2}$ from $\mathfrak{o}$. These are the points for which each of the coordinates $x_1, x_2, \cdots, x_n$ is equal to one of the Ω integers $0, \pm 1, \pm 2, \pm \frac{\Omega-1}{2}$. The number of such lattice points is Ω^n, and the assemblage of them (their collectivity) denoted by $\mathfrak{H}$.

The following investigation is based upon the treatment of the realms $\mathfrak{P}_1(\mathfrak{H}), \mathfrak{P}_2(\mathfrak{H}), \cdots, \mathfrak{P}_\lambda(\mathfrak{H})$. By $\mathfrak{P}_\kappa(\mathfrak{H})$ due to the stipulation in I is to be understood the union of all the Ω^n bodies $\mathfrak{P}_\kappa(\mathfrak{h})$ with respect to the individual Ω^n points $\mathfrak{h}$, where $\mathfrak{P}_\kappa(\mathfrak{h})$ denotes that the points of the associated bodies $S(\mathfrak{h}\mathfrak{x})$ are $\leqq \frac{1}{2}M_\kappa$. As in Art. 40 it is seen that the entire realm $\mathfrak{P}_\kappa(\mathfrak{H})$ has a definite volume. For $\lambda > 1$ it is clear that when $\kappa = 1, 2, \cdots, \lambda-1$ we always have $\mathfrak{P}_\kappa(\mathfrak{H})$, a body within the body $\mathfrak{P}_{\kappa+1}(\mathfrak{H})$; and in all cases $\mathfrak{P}_\lambda(\mathfrak{H})$ is the most comprehensive realm that comes under consideration. Denote the volume of $\mathfrak{P}_\lambda(\mathfrak{H})$ by Π_λ. Since $M_\lambda \leqq \frac{G}{n}$; and, as a radial-distance which is $\leqq \frac{G}{2n}$ from a point, has a span that is $\leqq \frac{G}{2ng}$ from it, it is seen that $\mathfrak{P}_\lambda(\mathfrak{H})$ is entirely enclosed in the body that has a span $\leqq \frac{\Omega-1}{2} + \frac{G}{2ng}$ from $\mathfrak{o}$; and consequently we have

$$\text{(2)} \qquad \Pi_\lambda \leqq \left(\Omega - 1 + \frac{G}{ng}\right)^n.$$

Secondly, since M_1 is the least radial-distance in magnitude in the lattice, any two bodies $\mathfrak{P}_1(\mathfrak{h})$ for different lattice-points are entirely different in their inner points. Every such body has a volume $= \left(\frac{M_1}{2}\right)^n J$, where J is the volume of the body $S(\mathfrak{o}\mathfrak{x}) \leqq 1$. Accordingly it is seen that the volume of $\mathfrak{P}_1(\mathfrak{H}) = \Omega^n \left(\frac{M_1}{2}\right)^n J$. In the case $\lambda = 1$, this remark in connection with (2) is sufficient to prove fully the inequality (1). If $\lambda > 1$, we may reach this goal by bringing the different realms $\mathfrak{P}_1(\mathfrak{H})$, $\mathfrak{P}_2(\mathfrak{H})$, $\cdots$, $\mathfrak{P}_\lambda(\mathfrak{H})$ sequentially in association.

III. We next assume that $\lambda > 1$. Let κ have one of the values $1, 2, \cdots, \lambda - 1$ and let

$$\mathfrak{P}_\kappa(\mathfrak{H}) \qquad \textit{be compared with} \qquad \mathfrak{P}_{\kappa+1}(\mathfrak{H}).$$

Write $\mu_\kappa = m$ and denote, as in Art. 151, for a point $x_1, x_2, \cdots, x_n$, or $\mathfrak{x}$ the *system* $x_1, x_2, \cdots, x_m$ by $\mathfrak{x}'$ and the *system* $x_{m+1}, \cdots, x_n$ by $\mathfrak{x}''$ and write for $\mathfrak{x}$ itself $\mathfrak{x}', \mathfrak{x}''$.

Let $\mathfrak{X}$, $\mathfrak{X}'$, $\mathfrak{X}''$ denote the manifold respectively of all points $\mathfrak{x}$, of all *systems* $\mathfrak{x}'$, or all systems $\mathfrak{x}''$, and further apply all the concepts and abbreviations which were defined at the beginning of Art. 151 for the separation of $\mathfrak{X}$ into $\mathfrak{X}'$, $\mathfrak{X}''$. For example, the manifold of all points for which $x_{m+1} = 0$, $x_{m+2} = 0$, $\cdots$, $x_n = 0$ may be expressed through $\mathfrak{X}', \mathfrak{o}''$.

Finally the following may be added: Let $\mathfrak{a}', \mathfrak{x}''$ be a point and for an associated assemblage of points in $\mathfrak{X}'$ use the symbol $\mathfrak{E}'(\mathfrak{a}', \mathfrak{x}'')$. Then the assemblage of points in $\mathfrak{X}'$ which may be derived from this assemblage through the translation in $\mathfrak{X}'$ from $\mathfrak{a}'$ to $\mathfrak{b}'$ is denoted by $\mathfrak{E}(\mathfrak{b}', \mathfrak{x}'')$; and if $\mathfrak{B}'$ denotes an *assemblage of systems* $\mathfrak{b}$ in $\mathfrak{X}'$, then by $\mathfrak{E}'(\mathfrak{B}', \mathfrak{x}'')$ is to be understood the union of all realms $\mathfrak{E}'(\mathfrak{b}', \mathfrak{x}'')$ composed of the individual systems $\mathfrak{b}'$. The magnitude $M_{\kappa+1}$ denotes the least radial-distance from $\mathfrak{o}$ to all lattice points outside of the manifold $\mathfrak{X}', \mathfrak{o}''$, and that is the least magnitude for possible values $S(\mathfrak{a}, \mathfrak{b})$ if $\mathfrak{a}$ and $\mathfrak{b}$ are lattice points and with different systems $\mathfrak{a}''$ and $\mathfrak{b}''$.

By definition $M_{\kappa+1}$ is the least radial-distance from $\mathfrak{o}$ to lattice points not in the manifold determined by the points $\mathfrak{o}, \mathfrak{p}_1, \mathfrak{p}_2, \cdots, \mathfrak{p}_{\mu_\kappa}$, that is, the manifold:

$$x_{\mu_\kappa+1} = 0, \qquad x_{\mu_\kappa+2} = 0, \qquad \cdots, \qquad x_n = 0.$$

If we take $\mu_\kappa = m = 1$, $n = 3$, then $M_{\kappa+1}$ is the least radial-distance from $\mathfrak{o}$ to points not on the x_1-axis. It is this fact that makes $\mathfrak{P}_{\kappa+1}(\mathfrak{H}', \mathfrak{o}'')$ and $\mathfrak{P}_{\kappa+1}(\mathfrak{H}', \mathfrak{h}'')$ distinct.

Now observe that the Ω^n points $\mathfrak{h}=\mathfrak{h}', \mathfrak{h}''$ exactly exist from $\mathfrak{H}$, if $\mathfrak{h}'$ goes over a definite assemblage $\mathfrak{H}'$ of Ω^m systems in $\mathfrak{X}'$ and in addition $\mathfrak{h}''$, completely independent of $\mathfrak{h}'$, goes over a definite assemblage $\mathfrak{H}'$ of Ω^{n-m} systems in $\mathfrak{X}''$. The collective assemblage $\mathfrak{H}$ is thus distributed with Ω^{n-m} groups of the general expression $\mathfrak{H}'$, $\mathfrak{h}''$ which correspond to the Ω^{n-m} single systems $\mathfrak{h}''$ of $\mathfrak{H}''$. From the meaning thus given of $M_{\kappa+1}$ it is seen that the corresponding realms $\mathfrak{P}(\mathfrak{H}', \mathfrak{h}'')$ for different $\mathfrak{h}''$ *are entirely different among one another* in their inner points for these different groups.

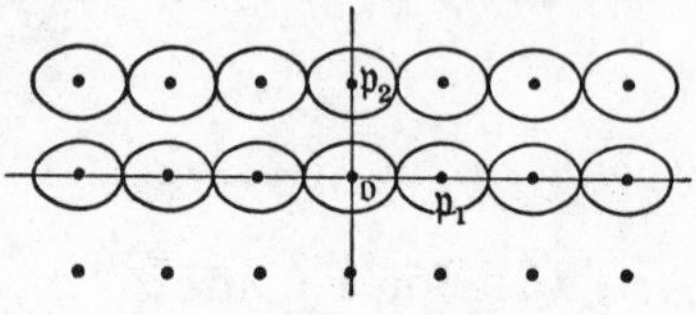

FIG. 97

Given $S(\mathfrak{a}, \mathfrak{b})$ such that

$$S(\mathfrak{o}\mathfrak{p}_1)=S_1, \qquad S(\mathfrak{o}\mathfrak{p}_2)=S_2, \qquad S_1<S_2,$$

then $M_1=S_1$, $M_2=S_2$. Take $m=1$. In the figure below the bodies are $S(\mathfrak{g}\mathfrak{x})\leqq\frac{1}{2}M_1$ or $\mathfrak{P}_1(\mathfrak{g})$. The upper row composes $\mathfrak{P}_1(\mathfrak{H}', \mathfrak{h}'')$ and the lower row the body $\mathfrak{P}_1(\mathfrak{H}', \mathfrak{o}'')$. The bodies in the figure above are $S(\mathfrak{g}\mathfrak{x})\leqq\frac{1}{2}M_2$ or $P_2(\mathfrak{g})$. The upper row forms the body $P_2(\mathfrak{H}', \mathfrak{h}'')$ and the lower row the body $P_2(\mathfrak{H}', \mathfrak{o}'')$. The two bodies $\mathfrak{P}_2(\mathfrak{H}', \mathfrak{o}'')$ and $\mathfrak{P}_2(\mathfrak{H}', \mathfrak{h}'')$ have no inner points in common.

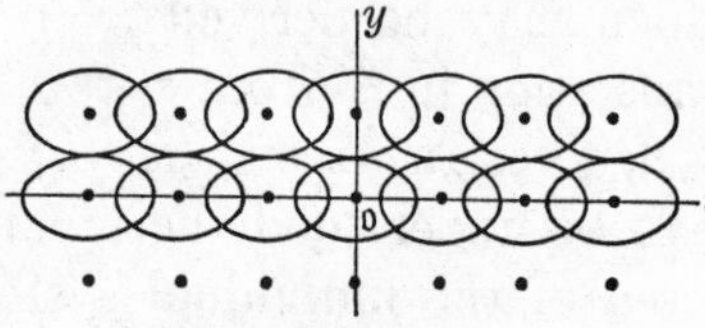

FIG. 98

Since $M_\kappa<M_{\kappa+1}$ the same inequality holds for a greater reason for the different realms $\mathfrak{P}_\kappa(\mathfrak{H}', \mathfrak{h}'')$. It is seen that $\mathfrak{P}_{\kappa+1}(\mathfrak{H}', \mathfrak{h}'')$ exists from $\mathfrak{P}_{\kappa+1}(\mathfrak{H}', \mathfrak{o}'')$ and on the other hand $\mathfrak{P}_\kappa(\mathfrak{H}', \mathfrak{h}'')$ from $\mathfrak{P}_\kappa(\mathfrak{H}', \mathfrak{o}'')$ from the translation $\mathfrak{o}'$, $\mathfrak{o}''$, to $\mathfrak{o}'$, $\mathfrak{h}''$ so that the volumes of the realms of this kind for each $\mathfrak{h}''$ are always the same as for $\mathfrak{h}''=\mathfrak{o}''$. For $\kappa=1, 2, \cdots, \lambda$ we denoted the bodies $S(\mathfrak{o}\mathfrak{x})\leqq\frac{1}{2}M_\kappa$ by $\mathfrak{P}_\kappa(\mathfrak{o})$, and

by $\mathfrak{P}_\kappa(\mathfrak{H})$ was denoted the union of the Ω^n bodies $\mathfrak{P}_\kappa(\mathfrak{h})$ where $\mathfrak{h}$ goes over the Ω^n lattice points in the restricted region. The volume of $\mathfrak{P}_\lambda(\mathfrak{H})$ was denoted above by Π. For $\kappa=1, 2, \cdots, \lambda-1$ put the volume of $P_\kappa(\mathfrak{H})$ equal to $\Omega^{n-m_\kappa}\Pi_\kappa$, thus defining Π_κ. We then have from II:

$$\mathfrak{P}_1(\mathfrak{H})=\Omega^n M_1^n \frac{J}{2^n}\cdot$$

Since

$$\mathfrak{P}_1(\mathfrak{H})=\Omega^{n-\mu_1}\Pi_1;$$

and as

$$\mu_1=v_1, \qquad n=v_1+v_2+\cdots+v_\lambda$$

it follows that

$$\Pi_1=\Omega^{v_1}M_1^{v_1+v_2+\cdots+v_\lambda}\frac{J}{2^n}\cdot \tag{3}$$

It is then seen that the volume of $\mathfrak{P}_\kappa(\mathfrak{H}', \mathfrak{o}'')$ is equal to Π_κ; and from $\mathfrak{P}_{\kappa+1}(\mathfrak{H})=\Omega^{n-\mu_{\kappa+1}}\Pi_{\kappa+1}$, or

$$\Omega^{n-m}\mathfrak{P}_{\kappa+1}(\mathfrak{H}', \mathfrak{o}'')=\Omega^{n-\mu_{\kappa+1}}\Pi_{\kappa+1},$$

it follows, since $\mu_{\kappa+1}-\mu_\kappa=v_{\kappa+1}$, that

$$\mathfrak{P}_{\kappa+1}(\mathfrak{H}', \mathfrak{o}'')=\frac{\Pi_{\kappa+1}}{\Omega^{v_{\kappa+1}}}\cdot$$

Our problem has to do next with a comparison of the two realms $\mathfrak{P}_\kappa(\mathfrak{H}', \mathfrak{o}'')$ and $\mathfrak{P}_{\kappa+1}(\mathfrak{H}', \mathfrak{o}'')$.

Observe that the assemblage of points $\mathfrak{H}'$, $\mathfrak{o}''$ considered here consists only of those lattice points of $\mathfrak{H}$ which lie in the manifold $\mathfrak{X}'$, $\mathfrak{o}''$.

IV. Put $\dfrac{M_{\kappa+1}}{M_\kappa}=q$ where $q>1$. We may derive $\mathfrak{P}_{\kappa+1}(\mathfrak{o})$ from $\mathfrak{P}_\kappa(\mathfrak{o})$, if for a point $\mathfrak{x}'$, $\mathfrak{x}''$ of $\mathfrak{P}_\kappa(\mathfrak{o})$ we substitute the point $\mathfrak{y}'$, $\mathfrak{y}''$ for which

$$\begin{aligned} \mathfrak{y}'-\mathfrak{o}' &=q(\mathfrak{x}'-\mathfrak{o}'),\\ \mathfrak{y}''-\mathfrak{o}''&=q(\mathfrak{x}''-\mathfrak{o}''). \end{aligned} \tag{4}$$

This operation may be carried out through two successive processes, and on this fact rest essentially the further conclusions: instead of transposing $\mathfrak{x}'$, $\mathfrak{x}''$ directly into $\mathfrak{y}'$, $\mathfrak{y}''$

by means of (4), we may first make the change $\mathfrak{x}'$, $\mathfrak{x}''$ into $\mathfrak{y}'$, $\mathfrak{x}''$ and then change $\mathfrak{y}'$, $\mathfrak{x}''$ into $\mathfrak{y}'$, $\mathfrak{y}''$.

Let the realm in which $\mathfrak{P}_\kappa(\mathfrak{o})$ is transformed by the first process alone be denoted by $\mathfrak{Q}_\kappa(\mathfrak{o})$. Due to this transformation the body $\mathfrak{P}_\kappa(\mathfrak{o})$ is elongated in $\mathfrak{X}'$, unchanged in $\mathfrak{X}''$. This domain will be again a nowhere concave body. The volume of $\mathfrak{Q}_\kappa(\mathfrak{H}', \mathfrak{o}'')$ may be denoted by X_κ. In Art. 151 is found a particular expression for the volume of a single nowhere concave body by taking into consideration a separation of $\mathfrak{X}=\mathfrak{X}', \mathfrak{X}''$, as exists here. This may be done now for the realms $\mathfrak{P}_\kappa(\mathfrak{H}',\mathfrak{o}'')$ and $\mathfrak{Q}_\kappa(\mathfrak{H}', \mathfrak{o}'')$. In this way the volume of the second realm is shown to be the greater. On the other hand there exists between the volumes of $\mathfrak{Q}_\kappa(\mathfrak{H}', \mathfrak{o}'')$ and $\mathfrak{P}_{\kappa+1}(\mathfrak{H}', \mathfrak{o}'')$ a simple equation, which we shall now derive.

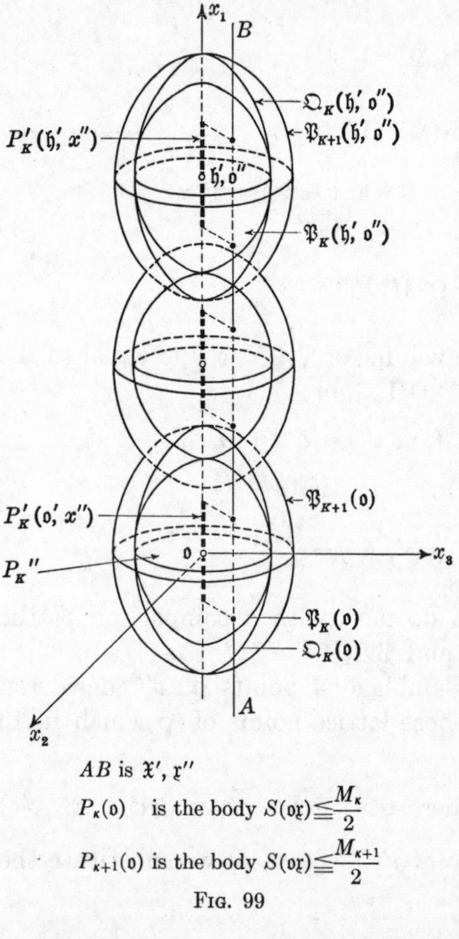

AB is $\mathfrak{X}', \mathfrak{x}''$

$P_\kappa(\mathfrak{o})$ is the body $S(\mathfrak{o}\mathfrak{x}) \leqq \dfrac{M_\kappa}{2}$

$P_{\kappa+1}(\mathfrak{o})$ is the body $S(\mathfrak{o}\mathfrak{x}) \leqq \dfrac{M_{\kappa+1}}{2}$

FIG. 99

For an arbitrary system $\mathfrak{x}''$ let $S''(\mathfrak{o}''\mathfrak{x}'')$ denote always the *minimum* among all values, which $S(\mathfrak{o}\mathfrak{x})$ takes for the points $\mathfrak{x}$ in the assemblage of points $\mathfrak{X}'$, $\mathfrak{x}''$. (See Fig. 99 for case $n=3$.) Denote by P''_κ the realm in $\mathfrak{X}''$ that is defined through $S''(\mathfrak{o}''\mathfrak{x}'') \leqq \frac{1}{2}M_\kappa$. In the realm $\mathfrak{P}''_\kappa$ the system $\mathfrak{x}''$ moves for the points $\mathfrak{x}$ in $\mathfrak{P}_\kappa(\mathfrak{o})$ exactly as it does for the points $\mathfrak{x}$ in $\mathfrak{Q}_\kappa(\mathfrak{o})$ and we have precisely the same systems $\mathfrak{x}''$ in the body $\mathfrak{P}_\kappa(\mathfrak{h}', \mathfrak{o}'')$ as in the body $\mathfrak{Q}_\kappa(\mathfrak{h}', \mathfrak{o}'')$, and consequently also in the collective realms $\mathfrak{P}_\kappa(\mathfrak{H}', \mathfrak{o}'')$ and $\mathfrak{Q}_\kappa(\mathfrak{H}', \mathfrak{o}'')$. For a system $\mathfrak{x}''$ of $\mathfrak{p}_\kappa''$ we are to understand by $\mathfrak{P}_\kappa'(\mathfrak{o}', \mathfrak{x}'')$ and $\mathfrak{Q}_\kappa'(\mathfrak{o}', \mathfrak{x}'')$ always the assemblages of those systems $\mathfrak{x}'$ for which we find $\mathfrak{x}', \mathfrak{x}''$ as a point of $\mathfrak{P}_\kappa(\mathfrak{o})$ or of $\mathfrak{Q}_\kappa(\mathfrak{o})$. Then, due to (4), there exists in $\mathfrak{X}'$ the assemblage of points $\mathfrak{Q}_\kappa'(\mathfrak{o}', \mathfrak{x}'')$ through dilation of the assemblage $\mathfrak{P}_\kappa'(\mathfrak{o}', \mathfrak{x}'')$ from the system $\mathfrak{o}'$ in the ratio $q:1$ Then, as indicated in III, we shall have to take in $\mathfrak{P}_\kappa'(\mathfrak{H}', \mathfrak{x}'')$ and $\mathfrak{Q}_\kappa'(\mathfrak{H}', \mathfrak{x}'')$ the assemblages of all the systems $\mathfrak{x}'$ for which $\mathfrak{x}', \mathfrak{x}''$ gives a point of $\mathfrak{P}_\kappa'(\mathfrak{H}', \mathfrak{o}'')$ or of $\mathfrak{Q}_\kappa'(\mathfrak{H}', \mathfrak{o}'')$. Similarly as for the realm $\mathfrak{P}_\kappa'(\mathfrak{o}', \mathfrak{x}'')$ there also exist for the assemblages $\mathfrak{P}_\kappa'(\mathfrak{H}', \mathfrak{x}'')$ and $\mathfrak{Q}_\kappa'(\mathfrak{H}', \mathfrak{x}'')$ definite volumes in $\mathfrak{X}'$. We denote them by $\Pi_\kappa'(\mathfrak{x}'')$ and $X_\kappa'(\mathfrak{x}'')$. If the volume of $\mathfrak{P}_\kappa'(\mathfrak{o}', \mathfrak{x}'')$ is zero in $\mathfrak{X}'$, a case which may arise for systems $\mathfrak{x}''$ upon the boundary of $\mathfrak{P}_\kappa''$, we shall then have also $\Pi_\kappa'(\mathfrak{x}'')=0$ and $X_\kappa'(\mathfrak{x}'')=0$. Let the realm $\mathfrak{P}_\kappa'(\mathfrak{o}', \mathfrak{x}'')$ have a volume in $\mathfrak{X}'$ that is different from zero; it then has inner points in $\mathfrak{X}'$ and is a nowhere concave body in $\mathfrak{X}'$. Let $\mathfrak{a}'$ be an arbitrary system taken from within this realm. Due to (4) let $\mathfrak{b}'$ be the system in $\mathfrak{Q}'(\mathfrak{o}', \mathfrak{x}'')$ for which

$$\mathfrak{b}'-\mathfrak{o}'=q(\mathfrak{a}'-\mathfrak{o}').$$

The relation $\mathfrak{y}'-\mathfrak{b}'=q(\mathfrak{x}'-\mathfrak{o}')$ may be replaced by

$$\mathfrak{y}'-\mathfrak{b}'=[\mathfrak{y}'-(\mathfrak{b}'-\mathfrak{a}')]-\mathfrak{a}'=q(\mathfrak{x}'-\mathfrak{a}');$$

and from this it is seen that through the dilation of the realm $\mathfrak{P}_\kappa'(\mathfrak{o}', \mathfrak{x}')$ from the system $\mathfrak{a}'$ in the ratio $q:1$ there exists the realm $\mathfrak{Q}_\kappa'(\mathfrak{o}', \mathfrak{x}'')-(\mathfrak{b}'-\mathfrak{a}')$.

We suppose for definiteness that $q=\frac{3}{2}$. We then have the relation $\mathfrak{b}'-\mathfrak{o}'=\frac{3}{2}(\mathfrak{a}'-\mathfrak{o}')$, where $\mathfrak{a}'$ is a point in $\mathfrak{P}_\kappa'(\mathfrak{o}', \mathfrak{x}'')$ and $\mathfrak{b}'$ is the corresponding point in $\mathfrak{Q}_\kappa'(\mathfrak{o}', \mathfrak{x}'')$.

Also, if $\mathfrak{x}'$ and $\mathfrak{y}'$ are any pair of such corresponding points, we have

$$\mathfrak{y}'-\mathfrak{o}'=\frac{3}{2}(\mathfrak{x}'-\mathfrak{o}'),$$

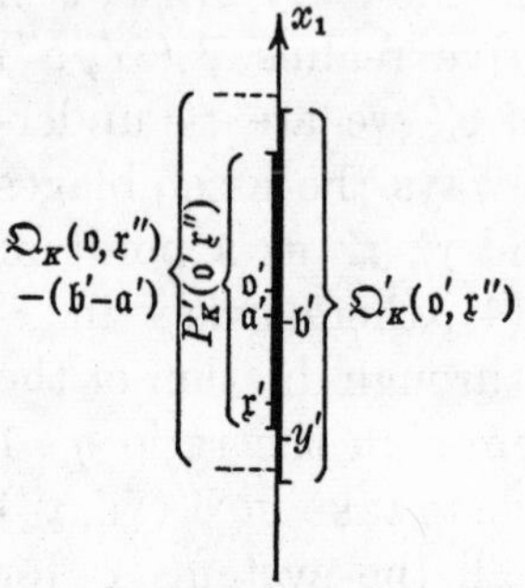

Fig. 100

and subtracting the two equations, we get

$$\mathfrak{y}'-\mathfrak{b}'=\frac{3}{2}(\mathfrak{x}'-\mathfrak{a}'),$$

or

$$[\mathfrak{y}'-(\mathfrak{b}'-\mathfrak{a}')]-\mathfrak{a}'=\frac{3}{2}(\mathfrak{x}'-\mathfrak{a}').$$

So that if instead of dilating $\mathfrak{P}'_\kappa(\mathfrak{o}, \mathfrak{x}'')$ out from $\mathfrak{o}$ we dilate it out from any other inner point, we get the body

$$\mathfrak{Q}'_\kappa(\mathfrak{o}', \mathfrak{x}'')-(\mathfrak{b}'-\mathfrak{a}').$$

Consequently $\mathfrak{P}'_\kappa(\mathfrak{o}', \mathfrak{x}'')$ lies entirely within the realm $\mathfrak{Q}'_\kappa(\mathfrak{o}', \mathfrak{x}'')-(\mathfrak{b}'-\mathfrak{a}')$, when $\mathfrak{a}'$ and $\mathfrak{b}'$ are corresponding points of $\mathfrak{P}'_\kappa(\mathfrak{o}', \mathfrak{x}'')$ and $\mathfrak{Q}'_\kappa(\mathfrak{o}', \mathfrak{x}'')$.

In a similar manner, through dilating any realm $\mathfrak{P}'_\kappa(\mathfrak{h}', \mathfrak{x}'')$ from $\mathfrak{a}'+\mathfrak{h}'-\mathfrak{o}'$ in the ratio $q:1$, the realm $\mathfrak{Q}'_\kappa(\mathfrak{h}', \mathfrak{x}'')-(\mathfrak{b}'-\mathfrak{a}')$ is produced. Observe that $\mathfrak{a}'+\mathfrak{h}'-\mathfrak{o}'$ is an inner system of $\mathfrak{P}'_\kappa(\mathfrak{h}', \mathfrak{x}'')$ and that this realm is a nowhere concave body in $\mathfrak{X}'$. These conditions taken together show clearly that the first realm $\mathfrak{P}'_\kappa(\mathfrak{h}', \mathfrak{x}'')$ lies wholly in the interior of the one named in the second place. With this it is further seen that $\mathfrak{P}'_\kappa(\mathfrak{H}, \mathfrak{x}'')$ lies entirely within the interior of the realm $\mathfrak{Q}'_\kappa(\mathfrak{H}, \mathfrak{x}'')$ and therefore is of *less* volume than the body last mentioned. From this, however, it is seen that $\mathfrak{Q}'_\kappa(\mathfrak{H}', \mathfrak{x}'')$ is produced through the translation from $\mathfrak{a}'$ to $\mathfrak{b}'$, and that in this process the volume in $\mathfrak{X}'$ remains unchanged. From this nothing other has arisen than that

$$\Pi'_\kappa(\mathfrak{x}'')<X'_\kappa(\mathfrak{x}''), \tag{5}$$

in which we observe that the inequality sign must exist here.

To apply next the results of (2) in Art. 151 to the realms $\mathfrak{P}_\kappa(\mathfrak{H}', \mathfrak{o}'')$ and $\mathfrak{Q}_\kappa(\mathfrak{H}', \mathfrak{o}'')$ take a net of hypercubes in $\mathfrak{X}''$, with side δ, and form the two summations $\Sigma\Pi_\kappa'(\mathfrak{x}'')\delta^{n-m}$ and $\Sigma X_\kappa'(\mathfrak{x}'')\delta^{n-m}$ in such a way that for $\mathfrak{x}''$ we have all the mid-points of the net that are inner points of the realm $\mathfrak{P}_\kappa''$. The volumes of $\mathfrak{P}_\kappa(\mathfrak{H}', \mathfrak{o}'')$ and $\mathfrak{Q}_\kappa(\mathfrak{H}', \mathfrak{o}'')$ appear as the limiting values of these summations when δ approaches zero. And in this way of forming the volumes Π_κ and X_κ it follows at once from (5) that

$$\Pi_\kappa \leqq X_\kappa \qquad (\kappa=1, 2, \cdots, \lambda-1). \tag{6}$$

See Minkowski, *Geom. der Zahlen*, p. 217.

The results of III, Art. 151 may be applied to the realms $\mathfrak{P}_\kappa(\mathfrak{H}', \mathfrak{o}'')$ and $\mathfrak{Q}(\mathfrak{H}', \mathfrak{o}'')$ and we recognize therefrom that $\Pi_\kappa'(\mathfrak{x}'')$ and $X_\kappa(\mathfrak{x}'')$ are continuous functions of the coordinates $x_{m+1}, x_{m+2}, \cdots, x_n$ of $\mathfrak{x}''$ everywhere for inner points of $\mathfrak{P}_\kappa''$. A similar consideration to that given at the end of Art. 151 shows that from the result (5) the sign $<$ is always true in the inequality (6), which condition, however, is not essential in what follows.

Observing that $q=\dfrac{M_{\kappa+1}}{M_\kappa}$, it is seen that the body $\mathfrak{P}_{\kappa+1}(\mathfrak{o})$ is described by $\mathfrak{y}', \mathfrak{y}''$ when $\mathfrak{y}', \mathfrak{x}''$ moves in $\mathfrak{Q}_\kappa$ and $\mathfrak{y}''-\mathfrak{o}'' =q(\mathfrak{x}''-\mathfrak{o}'')$. An arbitrary body $\mathfrak{Q}_\kappa(\mathfrak{h}', \mathfrak{o}'')$ is generated through $\mathfrak{y}'+\mathfrak{h}'-\mathfrak{o}', \mathfrak{x}''$ under the same conditions and simultaneously the point $\mathfrak{y}'+\mathfrak{h}'-\mathfrak{o}', \mathfrak{y}''$ describes the body $\mathfrak{P}_{\kappa+1}(\mathfrak{h}', \mathfrak{o}'')$.

Between two bodies thus joined through $\mathfrak{y}''-\mathfrak{o}'' =q(\mathfrak{x}''-\mathfrak{O}'')$ exists simply the connection that for a point of the first body, the coordinates of a point being $a_1, a_2, \cdots, a_m, a_{m+1}, \cdots, a_n$, there enters in the second body always the point with coordinates $a_1, a_2, \cdots, a_m, qa_{m+1}, \cdots, qa_n$. As the system $\mathfrak{h}'$ offers no change in this result, the above statement may be made word for word for the connection between the two realms $\mathfrak{Q}_\kappa(\mathfrak{H}', \mathfrak{o}'')$ and $\mathfrak{P}_{\kappa+1}(\mathfrak{H}', \mathfrak{o}'')$ and it is seen that the volume of $\mathfrak{P}_{\kappa+1}(\mathfrak{H}', \mathfrak{o}'')$ is simply q^{n-m} times the volume of $\mathfrak{Q}_\kappa(\mathfrak{H}', \mathfrak{o}'')$. (Cf. Art. 42.) We thus have

$$\Pi_{\kappa+1}=\Omega^{v_{\kappa+1}}\frac{M_{\kappa+1}^{v_{\kappa+1}+\cdots+v_\lambda}}{M_{\kappa}^{v_{\kappa+1}+\cdots+v_\lambda}}X_\kappa \qquad (\kappa=1, 2, \cdots, \lambda-1). \tag{7}$$

in which $\Pi_{\kappa+1}$ is the volume of the body $\mathfrak{P}_{\kappa+1}(\mathfrak{H}', \mathfrak{o}'')$. X_κ is the volume of $\mathfrak{Q}_\kappa(\mathfrak{H}', \mathfrak{o}'')$, while $M_{\kappa+1}$ denotes the least radial-distance from $\mathfrak{o}$ to all lattice points that lie without the manifold laid through $\mathfrak{o}, \mathfrak{p}_1, \mathfrak{p}_2, \cdots, \mathfrak{p}_{\mu_\kappa}$.

V. If equation (3) is multiplied by those in (7) for $\kappa=1, 2, \cdots, \lambda-1$, we have

$$\Pi_\lambda=\Omega^n\frac{X_{\lambda-1}}{\Pi_{\lambda-1}}\cdot\frac{X_{\lambda-2}}{\Pi_{\lambda-2}}\cdots\frac{X_1}{\Pi_1}\cdot M_1^{v_1}M_2^{v_2}\cdots M_\lambda^{v_\lambda}\cdot\frac{J}{2^n}\cdot \tag{8}$$

By using the inequalities (6) and (2) we are then led to

$$M_1^{v_1}M_2^{v_2}\cdots M_\lambda^{v_\lambda}J\leqq\left(1-\frac{1}{\Omega}+\frac{G}{ng\Omega}\right)^n 2^n.$$

When Ω increases indefinitely, this inequality becomes

$$M_1^{v_1}M_2^{v_2}\cdots M_\lambda^{v_\lambda}J\leqq 2^n.$$

and with this we come to the following theorem which is a generalization of the one found in Art. 44:

Let $f(x_1, x_2, \cdots, x_n)$ be any function of $x_1, x_2, \cdots, x_n$ which satisfies the following conditions:

$$\begin{cases} f(0, 0, \cdots, 0)=0, \\ f(x_1, x_2, \cdots, x_n)>0, \text{ unless } x_1=0=x_2=\cdots=x_n, \\ f(tx_1, \cdots, tx_n)=tf(x_1, x_2, \cdots, x_n), \text{ if } t>0, \end{cases}$$
$$f(x_1+y_1, \cdots, x_n+y_n)\leqq f(x_1, \cdots, x_n)+f(y_1, \cdots, y_n),$$
$$f(-x_1, \cdots, -x_n)=f(x_1, \cdots, x_n).$$

We further assume that the integral $\int\int\cdots\int dx_1, dx_2, \cdots, dx_n$, the integration being taken in positive directions over the realm $f(x_1, x_2, \cdots, x_n)\leqq 1$, has a definite positive value J. There exists at least one system of n^2 integers $p_h^{(k)}$ ($h, k=1, 2, \cdots, n$) for which the determinant $|p_h^{(k)}|$ ($h, k=1, 2, \cdots, n$)

is different from zero and for which the inequality

$$(9)\qquad f(p_1^{(1)}, p_2^{(1)}, \cdots, p_n^{(1)}) \cdots (p_1^{(n)}, p_2^{(n)}, \cdots, p_n^{(n)}) \leqq \frac{2^n}{J}$$

is satisfied. The value of the determinant $|p_h^{(k)}|$ *in this presentation is always* $\leqq n!$ (See the remark in Art. 149 (12); see also Art. 85.)

EXAMPLES

1. Consider the function

$$\begin{aligned}
f(x, y, z) &= |x| + |y| + |z|.\\
f(0, 0, 0) &= 0;\\
f(x, y, z) &> 0, \qquad \text{if} \qquad x^2+y^2+z^2 \neq 0;\\
f(tx, ty, tz) &= |tx| + |ty| + |tz|\\
&= t[|x| + |y| + |z|]\\
&= ft(x, y, z), \qquad t > 0;\\
(x_1+x_2, y_1+y_2, z_1+z_2) &= |x_1+x_2| + |y_1+y_2| + |z_1+z_2|\\
&\leqq |x_1| + |x_2| + |y_1| + |y_2| + |z_1| + |z_2|\\
&= f(x_1, y_1, z_1) + f(x_2, y_2, z_2);\\
f(-x, -y, -z) &= |-x| + |-y| + |-z|\\
&= |x| + |y| + |z|\\
&= f(x, y, z).
\end{aligned}$$

Consider $\iiint dx\, dy\, dz$ over the region $|x| + |y| + |z| \leqq 1.$ We have

$$\begin{aligned}
\text{Volume} &= 8\int_0^1\int_0^{1-x}\int_0^{1-x-y} dx\, dy\, dz = 8\int_0^1\int_0^{1-x}(1-x-y)\,dx\, dy\\
&= 8\int_0^1 \frac{(1-x)^2}{2}dx = 4\int_0^1 (1-2x+x^2)\,dx\\
&= \frac{4}{3}\cdot
\end{aligned}$$

Hence $J = \frac{4}{3}\cdot$

Consider the systems (0, 0, 1), (1, 1, 0), (−1, 1, 1).

$$|p_h^{(k)}| = \begin{vmatrix} 0, & 0, & 1\\ 1, & 1, & 0\\ -1, & 1, & 1\end{vmatrix} = 2 < 3!$$

Also

$$f(0, 0, 1)\cdot f(1, 1, 0)\cdot f(-1, 1, 1) \leqq \frac{8}{J} = 6.$$

The equality sign holds here.

For the systems (0, 0, 1), (1, 1, 0), (−1, 1, 0),

$$|p_h^{(k)}|=\begin{vmatrix} 0, & 0, & 1 \\ 1, & 1, & 0 \\ -1, & 1, & 0 \end{vmatrix}=2<3!$$

$$f(0,0,1)\cdot f(1,1,0)\cdot f(-1,1,0)=1\cdot 2\cdot 2=4<6.$$

2. Let the standard body be the ellipsoid, the square root of which is

$$(x,y,z)=\sqrt{\frac{x^2}{a^2}+\frac{y^2}{b^2}+\frac{z^2}{c^2}}\leqq 1.$$

We have

$$f(0,0,0)=0,$$
$$f(x,y,z)>0,\qquad x^2+y^2+z^2\neq 0,$$
$$f(tx,ty,tz)=\sqrt{\frac{t^2x^2}{a^2}+\frac{t^2y^2}{b^2}+\frac{t^2z^2}{c^2}}=t\sqrt{\frac{x^2}{a^2}+\frac{y^2}{b^2}+\frac{z^2}{c^2}}=tf(x,y,z),\qquad t>0.$$

Now

$$f(x_1+x_2,y_1+y_2,z_1+z_2)=\sqrt{\frac{x_1^2+2x_1x_2+x_2^2}{a^2}+\frac{y_1^2+2y_1y_2+y_2^2}{b^2}+\frac{z_1^2+2z_1z_2+z_2^2}{c^2}}$$

and we wish to show that this is

$$\leqq\sqrt{\frac{x_1^2}{a^2}+\frac{y_1^2}{b^2}+\frac{z_1^2}{c^2}}+\sqrt{\frac{x_2^2}{a^2}+\frac{y_2^2}{b^2}+\frac{z_2^2}{c^2}}=f(x_1,y_1,z_1)+f(x_2,y_2,z_2)$$

or that

$$\left[\frac{x_1x_2}{a^2}+\frac{y_1y_2}{b^2}+\frac{z_1z_2}{c^2}\right]^2\leqq\left(\frac{x_1^2}{a^2}+\frac{y_1^2}{b^2}+\frac{z_1^2}{c^2}\right)\left(\frac{x_2^2}{a^2}+\frac{y_2^2}{b^2}+\frac{z_2^2}{c^2}\right).$$

Writing

$$A_1=\frac{x_1}{a},\quad B_1=\frac{y_1}{b},\quad C_1=\frac{z_1}{c};\qquad A_2=\frac{x_2}{a},\quad B_2=\frac{y_2}{b},\quad C_2=\frac{z_2}{c},$$

we then show that

$$(A_1A_2+B_1B_2+C_1C_2)^2\leqq(A_1^2+B_1^2+C_1^2)(A_2^2+B_2^2+C_2^2)$$

or

$$2(A_1A_2B_1B_2+A_1A_2C_1C_2+B_1B_2C_1C_2)$$
$$\leqq A_1^2B_2^2+A_1^2C_2^2+A_2^2B_1^2+B_1^2C_2^2+A_2^2C_1^2+B_2^2C_1^2$$

or

$$(A_1B_2-A_2B_1)^2+(A_1C_2-A_2C_1)^2+(B_1C_2-B_2C_1)^2\geqq 0,$$

which is obviously satisfied.

Consider $\iiint dx\,dy\,dz$ over the domain

$$\sqrt{\frac{x^2}{a^2}+\frac{y^2}{b^2}+\frac{z^2}{c^2}}\leqq 1.$$

We have

$$J=\int_{-a}^{a}\int_{-b\sqrt{1-\frac{x^2}{a^2}}}^{b\sqrt{1-\frac{x^2}{a^2}}}\int_{-c\sqrt{1-\frac{x^2}{a^2}-\frac{y^2}{b^2}}}^{c\sqrt{1-\frac{x^2}{a^2}-\frac{y^2}{b^2}}}dx\,dy\,dz$$

$$=2c\int_{-a}^{a}\int_{-b\sqrt{1-\frac{x^2}{a^2}}}^{b\sqrt{1-\frac{x^2}{a^2}}}\sqrt{1-\frac{x^2}{a^2}-\frac{y^2}{b^2}}dx\,dy$$

$$=\pi bc\int_{-a}^{a}\left(1-\frac{x^2}{a^2}\right)dx$$

$$=\frac{4}{3}\pi abc.$$

Now let us take $a=\frac{1}{2}$, $b=1$, $c=\frac{3}{2}$ so that $J=\pi$ and

$$f(x,\,y,\,z)=\sqrt{4x^2+y^2+\frac{4}{9}z^2}.$$

The only sets of integral values with determinant $\neq 0$ satisfying the inequality (9) above are the eight sets

$$\begin{vmatrix}\pm1, & 0, & 0\\ 0, & \pm1, & 0\\ 0, & 0, & \pm1\end{vmatrix}=\pm1.$$

We have

$$f(\pm1,\,0,\,0)\cdot f(0,\,\pm1,\,0)\cdot f(0,\,0,\,\pm1)=2\cdot1\cdot\frac{2}{3}=\frac{4}{3}\leqq\frac{8}{\pi}\cdot$$

ART. 153. **Additional Lemmas Regarding Volumes.** Before making application of the preceding results, we may take up the question of the appearance of the equality sign in formula (9) of Art. 152. To understand the nature of this case certain additional lemmas regarding volumes are necessary, and these we shall proceed to derive.

Let $\mathfrak{Q}(\mathfrak{o})$ be an arbitrary nowhere concave body with $\mathfrak{o}$ in its interior; let t be any real number such that $1>t>0$; and let $\mathfrak{P}(\mathfrak{o})$ be that body which arises from $\mathfrak{Q}(\mathfrak{o})$ by dilation about $\mathfrak{o}$ in the ratio $t:1$. Let $\mathfrak{D}$ be a point set consisting of a *finite* number of points $\mathfrak{d}_1, \cdots, \mathfrak{d}_k$. By $\mathfrak{P}(\mathfrak{d}_i)$ we shall mean the body $\mathfrak{P}(\mathfrak{o})+\mathfrak{d}_i-\mathfrak{o}$, and by $\mathfrak{Q}(\mathfrak{d}_i)$ we shall mean the body $\mathfrak{Q}(\mathfrak{o})+\mathfrak{d}_i-\mathfrak{o}$. Denote by $\mathfrak{P}(\mathfrak{D})$

the point set composed of all the bodies $\mathfrak{P}(\mathfrak{d}_i)$ and by $\mathfrak{Q}(\mathfrak{D})$ the point set composed of all the points of all the bodies $Q(\mathfrak{d}_i)$. Further denote the volume of $\mathfrak{Q}(\mathfrak{d}_i)$ (which is the same for each of the points $\mathfrak{d}_i$) by Q and the volume of $\mathfrak{P}(\mathfrak{d}_i)$ by P. Denote the volume of $\mathfrak{Q}(\mathfrak{D})$ by X and that of $\mathfrak{P}(\mathfrak{D})$ by Π.

LEMMA I. *The volumes of $\mathfrak{P}(\mathfrak{D})$ and of $\mathfrak{Q}(\mathfrak{D})$ satisfy the relations*

$$\text{(1) and (2)} \qquad X > \Pi \geqq t^n X,$$

where $1 > t > 0$.

Since $t < 1$, $\mathfrak{P}(\mathfrak{d}_i)$ is entirely in the *interior* of $\mathfrak{Q}(\mathfrak{d}_i)$ $(i = 1, \cdots, k)$ and, consequently, is in the *interior* of $\mathfrak{Q}(\mathfrak{D})$.

1) Therefore $X > \Pi$.

Introducing the radial-distances $S(\mathfrak{a}\mathfrak{b})$ for which $\mathfrak{Q}(\mathfrak{o})$ is the standard body, we have $S(\mathfrak{o}\mathfrak{x}) \leqq 1$ for points within and on the boundary of $\mathfrak{Q}(\mathfrak{o})$ and $S(\mathfrak{o}\mathfrak{x}) \leqq t$ for points within and on the boundary of $\mathfrak{P}(\mathfrak{o})$. Similarly, for points of $\mathfrak{Q}(\mathfrak{d}_i)$ we have $S(\mathfrak{d}_i\mathfrak{x}) \leqq 1$, and for points of $\mathfrak{P}(\mathfrak{d}_i)$ we have $S(\mathfrak{d}_i\mathfrak{x}) \leqq t$.

With reference to the fixed points $\delta_1, \delta_2, \cdots, \delta_k$ we shall define k domains $\mathfrak{Q}(\mathfrak{d}_i)$ as follows:

Denote by X_{l1} that portion of $\mathfrak{Q}(\mathfrak{d}_l)$ $(l = 1, 2, \cdots, k)$ which does not lie in any other of the bodies $\mathfrak{Q}(\mathfrak{d}_i)$ $(i = 1, 2, \cdots, k)$; by X_{l2}, that portion or those portions of $\mathfrak{Q}(\mathfrak{d}_l)$ which lie in one and only one of the other $\mathfrak{Q}(\mathfrak{d}_i)$; $\cdots$; by X_{lj} those portions of $\mathfrak{Q}(\mathfrak{d}_l)$ which lie in $j-1$ and only $j-1$ of the other $\mathfrak{Q}(\mathfrak{d}_i)$. Thus there are k regions constituting $\mathfrak{Q}(\mathfrak{d}_l)$ as thus defined, some of which may be devoid of points. These regions are, in addition, non-overlapping and the k regions taken together constitute $\mathfrak{Q}(\mathfrak{d}_l)$. Thus we have, if Q denotes the volume of $\mathfrak{Q}(\delta_l)$,

$$Q = \sum_{j=1}^{k} X_{lj} \qquad (l = 1, 2, \cdots, k).$$

Of the k regions thus introduced suppose that only j different regions occur that have overlapped in $\mathfrak{Q}(\delta_l)$, and, writing

$$\mathfrak{Q}_j = \sum_{i=1}^{k} \mathrm{X}_{ij},$$

it is seen that Q_j is j times the portion of $\mathfrak{Q}(\mathfrak{D})$ which is contained in j and only j of the bodies $\mathfrak{Q}(\mathfrak{d}_i)$. We thus have (cf. Figs. 100a, 100b, 100c, in example below)

$$(2^a) \qquad \mathrm{X} = \sum_{j=1}^{k} \frac{Q_j}{j} = \sum_{j=1}^{k} \sum_{i=1}^{k} \frac{\mathrm{X}_{ij}}{j}.$$

Similarly we may define the corresponding portions Π_{ij} of the bodies $\mathfrak{P}(\mathfrak{d}_i)$ and have

$$(2^b) \qquad \Pi = \sum_{j=1}^{k} \frac{P_j}{j} = \sum_{j=1}^{k} \sum_{i=1}^{k} \frac{\Pi_{ij}}{j}.$$

Write

$$(3) \qquad \mathfrak{x} - \mathfrak{d}_i = t(\mathfrak{y} - \mathfrak{d}_i)$$

and note that as $\mathfrak{y}$ describes the body $\mathfrak{Q}(\mathfrak{d}_l)$ then $\mathfrak{x}$ describes the body $\mathfrak{P}(\mathfrak{d}_l)$ and conversely. Let us define $\mathfrak{R}_{lj}$ as that portion of $\mathfrak{P}(\mathfrak{d}_l)$ described by $\mathfrak{x}$ as $\mathfrak{y}$ describes the portion X_{lj} of $\mathfrak{Q}(\mathfrak{d}_l)$. Let R_{lj} denote the volume of $\mathfrak{R}_{lj}$.

We shall next prove that for every point δ_l the following relations exist for the volumes in question, namely,

$$(4) \qquad \left\{ \begin{aligned} R_{lk} &\quad \text{contains} \quad \Pi_{lk}, \\ R_{l,\,k-1} + R_{lk} &\quad \text{contains} \quad \Pi_{l,\,k-1} + \Pi_{lk}, \\ &\cdots\cdots\cdots\cdots\cdots\cdots \\ R_{l2} + \cdots + R_{lk} &\quad \text{contains} \quad \Pi_{l2} + \cdots + \Pi_{lk}, \\ \text{and} \qquad & \\ R_{l1} + \cdots + R_{lk} &= P(\mathfrak{d}_l) = \Pi_{l1} + \cdots + \Pi_{lk}. \end{aligned} \right.$$

To prove this observe that with the substitution (3) any point $\mathfrak{x}$ of $P(\mathfrak{d}_l)$ which is common to j of the $\mathfrak{P}(\mathfrak{d}_i)$ is transformed into a point $\mathfrak{y}$ of $Q(\mathfrak{d}_l)$ which is common to *at least* j of the $\mathfrak{Q}(\mathfrak{d}_i)$.

This follows at once if it is shown that whenever $\mathfrak{x}$ is an inner point of $P(\mathfrak{d}_l)$ and $P(\mathfrak{d}_m)$ $(m = 1, 2, \cdots, k)$ the corresponding $\mathfrak{y}$ is common to both $\mathfrak{Q}(\mathfrak{d}_l)$ and $\mathfrak{Q}(\mathfrak{d}_m)$. Due to our assumptions $S(\mathfrak{d}_l\mathfrak{x})<t$ and $S(\mathfrak{d}_m\mathfrak{x})<t$, the conclusion that we seek is $S(\mathfrak{d}_l\mathfrak{y})<1$ and $S(\mathfrak{d}_m\mathfrak{y})<1$.

From the substitution $\mathfrak{x}-\mathfrak{d}_l=t(\mathfrak{y}-\mathfrak{d}_l)$ we derive $S(\mathfrak{d}_l\mathfrak{x})=tS(\mathfrak{d}_l\mathfrak{y})$ so that $S(\mathfrak{d}_l\mathfrak{x})<t$ implies that $S(\mathfrak{d}_l\mathfrak{y})<1$. An upper bound for the quantity $S(\mathfrak{d}_m\mathfrak{y})$ is found by use of the inequality $S(\mathfrak{d}_m\mathfrak{y})\leqq S(\mathfrak{d}_m\mathfrak{x})+S(\mathfrak{x}\mathfrak{y})$. By rearranging the transformation in the form $\mathfrak{y}-\mathfrak{x}=(1-t)(\mathfrak{y}-\mathfrak{d}_l)$, we have $S(\mathfrak{x}\mathfrak{y})=(1-t)S(\mathfrak{d}_l\mathfrak{y})$. Hence under our hypothesis we have $S(\mathfrak{x}\mathfrak{y})<1-t$, and, consequently, $S(\mathfrak{d}_m\mathfrak{y})<1$.

Hence from (4) there exist the following relations among the volumes R_{lj} and Π_{lj} $(j=1, 2, \cdots, k)$, namely,

$$\sum_{j=s}^{k} R_{lj} \geqq \sum_{j=s}^{k} \Pi_{lj} \qquad (s=2, 3, \cdots, k)$$

and

$$\sum_{j=1}^{k} R_{lj} = \sum_{j=1}^{k} \Pi_{lj}.$$

If we subtract each one of the inequalities in turn from the equality we transform the set of inequalities to

$$\sum_{j=1}^{s} R_{lj} \leqq \sum_{j=1}^{s} \Pi_{lj} \qquad (s=1, 2, \cdots, k-1)$$

and the equality is as before

$$\sum_{j=1}^{k} R_{lj} = \sum_{j=1}^{k} \Pi_{lj}.$$

Accordingly we may write

$$\sum_{j=1}^{k} \frac{R_{lj}}{j} \leqq \sum_{j=1}^{k} \frac{\Pi_{lj}}{j} \qquad (j=1, 2, \cdots, k).$$

As $\mathfrak{d}_l$ is an arbitrary point of $\mathfrak{D}$, this inequality is valid for each value of $l=1, 2, \cdots, k$. Therefore,

$$\sum_{i=1}^{k} \sum_{j=1}^{k} \frac{R_{ij}}{j} \leqq \sum_{i=1}^{k} \sum_{j=1}^{k} \frac{\Pi_{ij}}{j}.$$

The relation between any volume R_{ij} and the corresponding X_{ij} is seen to be $R_{ij}=t^n X_{ij}$. Hence the above inequality becomes

$$t^n \sum_{i=1}^{k} \sum_{j=1}^{k} \frac{X_{lj}}{j} \leqq \sum_{i=1}^{k} \sum_{j=1}^{k} \frac{\Pi_{ij}}{j}.$$

Since the double summations are respectively X and Π, we have finally

$$\Pi \geqq t^n X.$$

EXAMPLE. Suppose that $\mathfrak{D}$ consists of three arbitrary points, $\mathfrak{d}_1$, $\mathfrak{d}_2$, $\mathfrak{d}_3$.

Figure I shows X_{11}, X_{12}, and X_{13} as the portions ruled respectively horizontally, diagonally, and doubly. X_{12} is the sum of the two diagonally ruled regions, wherever they *do not overlap*.

Figure II shows Π_{11} and Π_{12} as the horizontally ruled portion and the diagonally ruled portion, respectively. Π_{13} is zero in this example.

Figure III shows $t^n X_{11}$, $t^n X_{12}$, and $t^n X_{13}$ as the regions corresponding to X_{11}, X_{12}, and X_{13} in Fig. I.

From the considerations above we have

$$t^n X_{13} \geqq \Pi_{13},$$
$$t^n X_{12} + t^n X_{13} \geqq \Pi_{12} + \Pi_{13}$$

and since the body in Fig. II about $\mathfrak{d}_1$ is the same as that in Fig. III about $\mathfrak{d}$, we have

$$t^n X_{11} + t^n X_{12} + t^n X_{13} = \Pi_{11} + \Pi_{12} + \Pi_{13}.$$

Subtraction of the two inequalities from this equality gives us the three inequalities

$$\sum_{i=1}^{l} t^n X_{1i} \leqq \sum_{i=1}^{l} \Pi_{1i} \qquad (l=1, 2, 3).$$

We accordingly have

$$\sum_{i=1}^{l} \frac{t^n X_{1i}}{i} \leqq \sum_{i=1}^{l} \frac{\Pi_{1i}}{i},$$

and, in particular,

$$\sum_{i=1}^{3} t^n \frac{X_{1i}}{i} \leqq \sum_{i=1}^{3} \frac{\Pi_{1i}}{i}.$$

As these inequalities hold for every point $\mathfrak{d}_j$, we may write

$$\sum_{j=1}^{3} \sum_{i=1}^{3} t^n \frac{X_{ji}}{i} \leqq \sum_{j=1}^{3} \sum_{i=1}^{3} \frac{\Pi_{ji}}{i}.$$

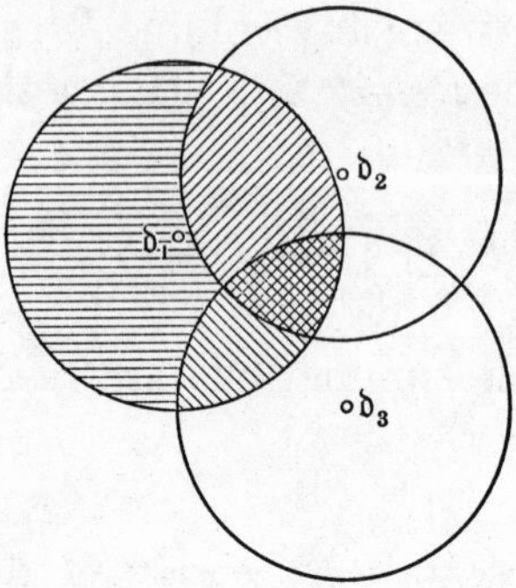

FIG. 100a

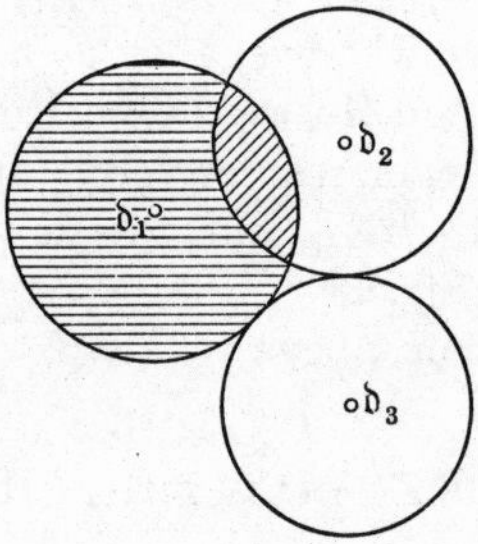

FIG. 100b

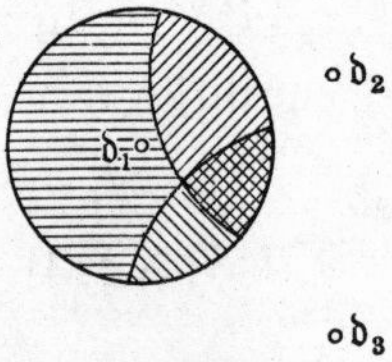

FIG. 100c

It is easily seen that

$$\sum_{j=1}^{3}\sum_{i=1}^{3}\frac{X_{ji}}{i}=X$$

and

$$\sum_{j=1}^{3}\sum_{i=1}^{3}\frac{\Pi_{ji}}{i}=\Pi,$$

so that

$$\Pi\geqq t^{n}X.$$

LEMMA II. Let $\mathfrak{G}$ be the collective lattice points in general, and let $\mathfrak{P}(\mathfrak{o})$ and $\cdot\mathfrak{P}(\mathfrak{o})$ be two nowhere concave bodies with $\mathfrak{o}$ an inner point. Let $\cdot\mathfrak{P}(\mathfrak{o})$ be contained entirely within $\mathfrak{P}(\mathfrak{o})$. Further let there be a point $\mathfrak{j}$ such that the body $\cdot\mathfrak{P}(\mathfrak{j})$ has at most points on the boundary in common with the entire realm $\mathfrak{P}(\mathfrak{G})$. Further let $\mathfrak{H}$ be any finite assemblage of lattice points.

Next derive a new body $\mathfrak{Q}(\mathfrak{o})$ by dilating from $\mathfrak{o}$ the body $\mathfrak{P}(\mathfrak{o})$ in the ratio $1+\theta:1$, where $0<\theta<1$. Let Π, $\cdot\Pi$ and X be the volumes of $\mathfrak{P}(\mathfrak{H})$, $\cdot\mathfrak{P}(\mathfrak{H})$ and $\mathfrak{Q}(\mathfrak{H})$. We may prove the inequality

$$\mathrm{X} \geqq \Pi + \cdot\Pi\theta^n. \tag{5}$$

On the one hand let $\mathfrak{P}(\mathfrak{o})$ and on the other hand let $\cdot\mathfrak{P}(\mathfrak{o})$ be standard bodies of radial-distances. Denote the first radial-distances by $S(\mathfrak{ab})$ and the second by $\cdot S(\mathfrak{ab})$. Since $\cdot\mathfrak{P}(\mathfrak{o})$ is situated entirely within $\mathfrak{P}(\mathfrak{o})$, we have for the boundary of $\mathfrak{P}(\mathfrak{o})$, that is, when $S(\mathfrak{ox})=1$, then always $\cdot S(\mathfrak{ox}')\geqq 1$, and for arbitrary points $\mathfrak{a}$ and $\mathfrak{b}$ we have always $\cdot S(\mathfrak{ab})\geqq S(\mathfrak{ab})$.

Further, $\mathfrak{P}(\mathfrak{G})$ is to have no inner point of $\cdot\mathfrak{P}(\mathfrak{j})$ within itself. Hence for every point $\mathfrak{x}$ of $\mathfrak{P}(\mathfrak{G})$ we have always $\cdot S(\mathfrak{jx})\geqq 1$ and in the closed realm $\mathfrak{P}(\mathfrak{G})$ there must be at least one point $\mathfrak{l}$ for which $\cdot S(\mathfrak{jl})$ has its smallest value. Hence all the points on the line $\mathfrak{jl}$ except $\mathfrak{l}$ do *not* belong to $\mathfrak{P}(\mathfrak{G})$ and hence at all events $\mathfrak{l}$ must be upon the boundary of $\mathfrak{P}(\mathfrak{G})$. It follows also that $\cdot S(\mathfrak{jl})\geqq 1$. Since $\theta\leqq 1$, there must be on the line $\mathfrak{jl}$ a definite point $\mathfrak{k}$ for which $\cdot S(\mathfrak{kl})=\theta$ and $\cdot S(\mathfrak{jk})=\cdot S(\mathfrak{jl})-\theta$. Denote the realm $\cdot S(\mathfrak{kx})\leqq\theta$ by $\cdot\mathfrak{Q}(\mathfrak{k})$. For inner points $\mathfrak{x}$ of this body we then have $\cdot S(\mathfrak{jx})\leqq\cdot S(\mathfrak{jk})+\cdot S(\mathfrak{kx})<\cdot S(\mathfrak{jl})$. Hence the inner points of $\mathfrak{Q}(\mathfrak{k})$ as those of $\cdot\mathfrak{P}(\mathfrak{j})$ fall nowhere within $\mathfrak{P}(\mathfrak{G})$.

Since $\mathfrak{l}$ belongs to the boundary of $\mathfrak{P}(\mathfrak{G})$, we have at least one lattice point $\mathfrak{g}$ for which $S(\mathfrak{gl})=1$. Next determine a point $\mathfrak{f}$ through the relation $\mathfrak{g}-\mathfrak{f}=\mathfrak{l}-\mathfrak{k}$ or $\mathfrak{g}-\mathfrak{l}=\mathfrak{f}-\mathfrak{k}$. It may be proved as follows that the body $\mathfrak{Q}(\mathfrak{f})$ and that is the realm $S(\mathfrak{fx})\leqq 1+\theta$ includes the body $\mathfrak{P}(\mathfrak{g})$ and also the body

$\cdot\mathfrak{Q}(\mathfrak{k})$. For we have

$$S(\mathfrak{f}\mathfrak{g})=S(\mathfrak{k}\mathfrak{l})\leqq\cdot S(\mathfrak{k}\mathfrak{l})=\theta,$$

and on the other hand $S(\mathfrak{f}\mathfrak{k})=S(\mathfrak{g}\mathfrak{l})=1$. For a point $\mathfrak{x}$ in $\mathfrak{P}(\mathfrak{g})$ we have $S(\mathfrak{g}\mathfrak{x})\leqq 1$, and hence also

$$S(\mathfrak{f}\mathfrak{x})\leqq S(\mathfrak{f}\mathfrak{g})+S(\mathfrak{g}\mathfrak{x})\leqq\theta+1.$$

Also for a point $\mathfrak{x}$ in $\cdot\mathfrak{Q}(\mathfrak{k})$ we have $\cdot S(\mathfrak{k}\mathfrak{x})\leqq\theta$ and for a greater reason $S(\mathfrak{k}\mathfrak{x})\leqq\theta$. Hence for such points $\mathfrak{x}$ in $\cdot\mathfrak{Q}(\mathfrak{k})$ we have

$$S(\mathfrak{f}\mathfrak{x})\leqq S(\mathfrak{f}\mathfrak{k})+S(\mathfrak{k}\mathfrak{x})\leqq 1+\theta.$$

Observe that since the two realms $\cdot\mathfrak{Q}(\mathfrak{k})$ and $\mathfrak{P}(\mathfrak{G})$ are distinct in their inner points, the two realms

$$\cdot\mathfrak{Q}(\mathfrak{k})+\mathfrak{h}-\mathfrak{o}\ (=\cdot\mathfrak{Q}(\mathfrak{h})+\mathfrak{k}-\mathfrak{o})$$

and $\mathfrak{P}(\mathfrak{G})+\mathfrak{h}-\mathfrak{o}$ are distinct in their inner points. We observe that this last realm is nothing other than $\mathfrak{P}(\mathfrak{G})$ if $\mathfrak{h}$ denotes a lattice point. It follows further, since $\mathfrak{Q}(\mathfrak{f})$ contains both $\mathfrak{P}(\mathfrak{g})$ and $\cdot\mathfrak{Q}(\mathfrak{k})$, that the realm $\mathfrak{Q}(\mathfrak{h})+\mathfrak{f}-\mathfrak{o}$ contains $\mathfrak{P}(\mathfrak{h})+\mathfrak{g}-\mathfrak{o}$ and $\cdot\mathfrak{Q}(\mathfrak{h})+\mathfrak{k}-\mathfrak{o}$ and consequently $\mathfrak{Q}(\mathfrak{H})+\mathfrak{f}-\mathfrak{o}$ contains the two realms differing in their inner points, namely $\mathfrak{P}(\mathfrak{H})+\mathfrak{g}-\mathfrak{o}$ and $\cdot\mathfrak{Q}(\mathfrak{H})+\mathfrak{k}-\mathfrak{o}$. The volumes of these three realms are however the same as the volumes of $\mathfrak{Q}(\mathfrak{H})$, $\mathfrak{P}(\mathfrak{H})$, and $\cdot\mathfrak{Q}(\mathfrak{H})$, while from Lemma I the volume of $\cdot\mathfrak{Q}(\mathfrak{H})$ is $\geqq\theta^n\cdot\Pi$. With this the inequality (5) is proved. (See theorem, Art. 40, II.)

Example. Prove that instead of making use of the condition regarding $\cdot\mathfrak{P}(\mathfrak{j})$, that is that points $\mathfrak{x}$ are to lie within the realm $\cdot S(\mathfrak{j}\mathfrak{x})\leqq 1$, we may impose the condition regarding $\cdot\mathfrak{Q}$, that is that $\cdot S(\mathfrak{j}\mathfrak{x})\leqq\theta$ has no inner points within $\mathfrak{P}(\mathfrak{G})$.

Lemma III. The hypercube $\mathfrak{E}(\mathfrak{o}\mathfrak{x})\leqq\frac{1}{2}$, that is, the body of spans $\leqq\frac{1}{2}$ from $\mathfrak{o}$ may be denoted by $\mathfrak{B}$ or by $\mathfrak{B}(\mathfrak{o})$. We denote as above any lattice point by $\mathfrak{g}$. Observe that the individual bodies $\mathfrak{B}(\mathfrak{g})$ are distinct as to their inner points. Their union $\mathfrak{B}(\mathfrak{G})$ coincides with the entire manifold $\mathfrak{X}$.

Let $\mathfrak{P}(\mathfrak{o})$ be an arbitrary nowhere concave body with $\mathfrak{o}$ an inner point, and by $\mathfrak{P}$ we are to understand the assemblage of all the points which are simulatneously inner points of $\mathfrak{B}$ and $\mathfrak{P}(\mathfrak{G})$ including the boundaries of these assemblages. Evidently there is a definite volume of this assemblage $\mathfrak{P}$. For let C be the side of a hypercube with $\mathfrak{o}$ as center (Figs. 101a, 101b) which includes entirely $\mathfrak{P}(\mathfrak{o})$. Then in a body $\mathfrak{P}(\mathfrak{g})$ there exists for every point $\mathfrak{x}$ the inequality

$$E(\mathfrak{o}\mathfrak{g}) \leqq E(\mathfrak{o}\mathfrak{x}) + E(\mathfrak{x}\mathfrak{g}),$$

where $E(\mathfrak{o}\mathfrak{x}) < \frac{1}{2}$ and $E(\mathfrak{x}\mathfrak{g}) \leqq \frac{1}{2}C$; and hence in $\mathfrak{P}(\mathfrak{g})$ there can be inner points of $\mathfrak{B}$ only if $E(\mathfrak{o}\mathfrak{g}) < \frac{1}{2} + \frac{1}{2}C$. It is evident that this condition can be satisfied for only a finite nu ber of lattice points. Hence there is only a finite number of ways of exhibiting a system $\mathfrak{G}_0$ of lattice points for which we have points $\mathfrak{x}$ on the *interior* of $\mathfrak{B}$ which exist on the one hand with respect to every point $\mathfrak{g}$ of $\mathfrak{G}_0$ always within the interior of $\mathfrak{P}(\mathfrak{g})$ and which on the other hand with respect to every other lattice point $\mathfrak{g}$ are always on the exterior of $\mathfrak{P}(\mathfrak{g})$. With each such system $\mathfrak{G}_0$ we are to understand by $\mathfrak{P}\{\mathfrak{G}_0\}$ the assemblage of all points $\mathfrak{x}$ of the nature indicated together with the boundary of this assemblage. For each realm $\mathfrak{P}\{\mathfrak{G}_0\}$ (Cf. Art. 40, I) there is a definite volume. It is seen that $\mathfrak{P}$ consists of the union of all such realms $\mathfrak{P}\{\mathfrak{G}_0\}$ and these realms, when there are more than one system $\mathfrak{G}_0$, are among one another in their inner points, entirely distinct. Thus the sum of their volumes is the volume of $\mathfrak{P}$. Denote it by P.

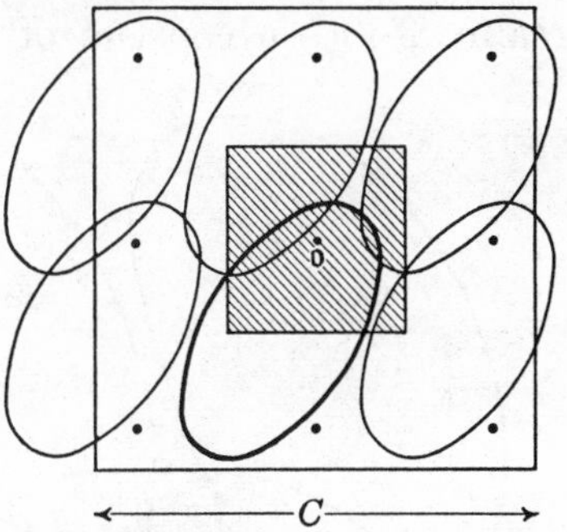

Shaded portions constitute $\mathfrak{P}$
Small square is $\mathfrak{B}(\mathfrak{o})$
Heavy oval is $\mathfrak{P}(\mathfrak{o})$
FIG. 101a

Let $\mathfrak{H}$ be a finite assemblage of lattice points; let ω denote the number of such points; and let Π denote the volume of $\mathfrak{P}(\mathfrak{H})$. We then have the inequality

$$\Pi \geqq \omega P. \tag{6}$$

For $\mathfrak{P}(\mathfrak{G})$ consists exactly of all the realms $\mathfrak{P}+\mathfrak{g}-\mathfrak{o}$; and these realms, like the realms $\mathfrak{P}(\mathfrak{g})$ in which they lie, are entirely different in their interior points. And again every realm $\mathfrak{P}+\mathfrak{g}-\mathfrak{o}$ consists of the realms $\mathfrak{P}\{\mathfrak{G}_0\}+\mathfrak{g}-\mathfrak{o}$ with

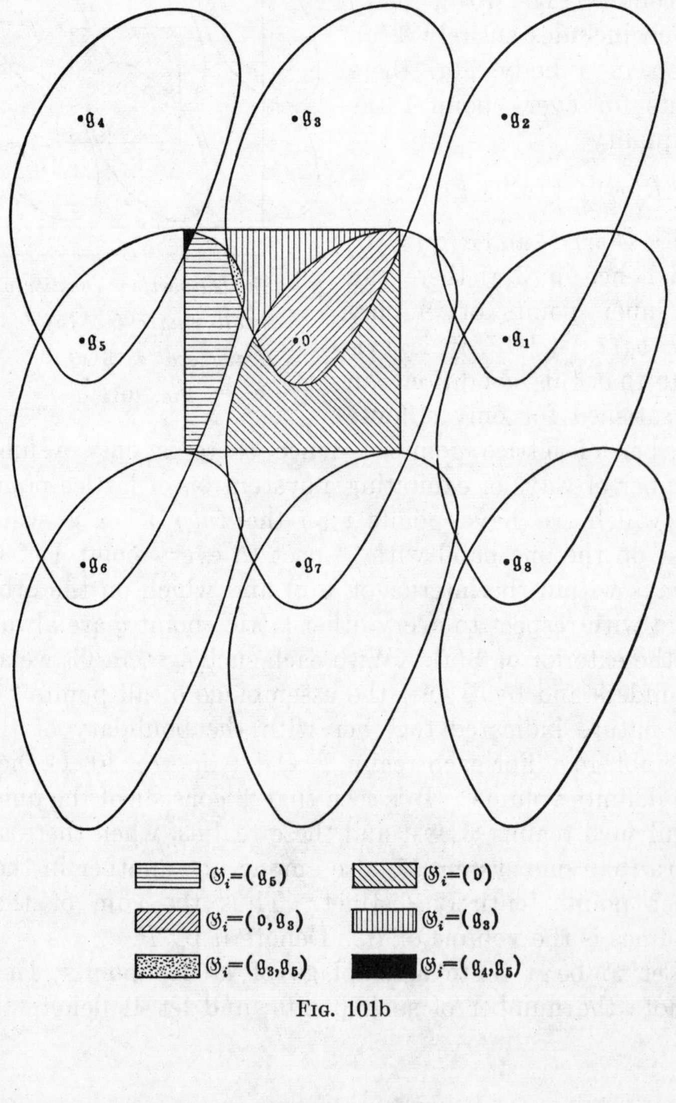

FIG. 101b

respect to the existing systems $\mathfrak{G}_0$. And thus $\mathfrak{P}(\mathfrak{G})$ is composed of the realms $\mathfrak{P}\{\mathfrak{G}_0\}+\mathfrak{g}-\mathfrak{o}$ on the one hand with respect to the collective systems $\mathfrak{G}_0$, on the other hand with respect to the collective lattice points $\mathfrak{g}$, while all these realms are entirely different in their inner points.

Now choose at pleasure a lattice point in each assemblage which may be called $\mathfrak{g}_0$. Then $\mathfrak{P}\{\mathfrak{G}_0\}$ belongs in particular entirely to $\mathfrak{P}(\mathfrak{g})$, and correspondingly for an arbitrary lattice point $\mathfrak{h}$ it is seen that $\mathfrak{P}(\mathfrak{h})$ always includes the realm $\mathfrak{P}(\mathfrak{G}_0\}+\mathfrak{h}-\mathfrak{g}_0$. Thus in the case of every system $\mathfrak{G}_0$ it is seen that $\mathfrak{P}(\mathfrak{H})$ includes at least ω of the realms $\mathfrak{P}\{\mathfrak{G}_0\}+\mathfrak{g}-\mathfrak{o}$; and from this it follows that $\Pi \geqq \omega P$.

Finally let Ω be any positive odd integer, and now let $\mathfrak{H}$ be in particular the assemblage of those lattice points which have spans $\leqq \dfrac{\Omega-1}{2}$ from $\mathfrak{o}$. The number of these lattice points is Ω^n. The spans from $\mathfrak{o}$ to points on the interior of $\mathfrak{P}(\mathfrak{H})$ are $<\dfrac{\Omega-1}{2}+\frac{1}{2}C$, where C is defined as above. On the other hand this span in a region $\mathfrak{P}+\mathfrak{g}-\mathfrak{o}$ is always $\geqq E(\mathfrak{o}\mathfrak{g})-\frac{1}{2}$. Hence $\mathfrak{P}(\mathfrak{H})$ must be taken entirely from those realms $\mathfrak{P}+\mathfrak{g}-\mathfrak{o}$ for which the lattice point $\mathfrak{g}$ satisfies the condition

$$E(\mathfrak{o}\mathfrak{g})-\tfrac{1}{2}<\frac{\Omega-1}{2}+\tfrac{1}{2}C.$$

The number of lattice points which satisfy this inequality is certainly less than $(\Omega+1+C)^n$, and hence we have, with the assumed nature of $\mathfrak{H}$, the inequality

$$\Pi<(\Omega+1+C)^n P.$$

On the other hand, from (6) we have $\Omega^n P<\Pi$, and from these two inequalities we have the result that, *with the special meaning which at present is given to* Π, *with indefinite increase of the number* Ω, *the quotient* $\dfrac{\Pi}{\Omega^n}$ *converges to the quantity* P.

CHAPTER XVII

THE EXTREME STANDARD BODIES

ART. **154.** Again let $\mathfrak{G}$ denote the collective assemblage of lattice points, $\mathfrak{g}$ being an arbitrary one of them.

By a *remainder realm* [1] (*Restbereich*) is to be understood a nowhere concave body $\mathfrak{R}$ with $\mathfrak{o}$ as center, for which the individual bodies $\mathfrak{R}+\mathfrak{g}-\mathfrak{o}$ are entirely distinct as to their inner points, and collectively they cover the entire manifold $\mathfrak{X}$. The nature of such remainder realms was discussed in Arts. 46–49. The simplest remainder realm in $\mathfrak{X}$ is the hypercube $E(\mathfrak{o}\mathfrak{x}) \leqq \frac{1}{2}$ which again we shall denote by $\mathfrak{B}$.

In Art. 152 was derived for arbitrary accordant and symmetric radial-distances $S(\mathfrak{a}\mathfrak{b})$ the inequality

$$(1) \qquad M_1^{v_1} M_2^{v_2} \cdots M_\lambda^{v_\lambda} J \leqq 2^n.$$

By $\mathfrak{o}(M_1, M_2, \cdots, M_k)$ we are to understand as in Art. 146 the manifold laid through the collective lattice points which have the property $S(\mathfrak{o}\mathfrak{g}) \leqq M_k$. No limitations are imposed (Cf. Arts. 147, I and 152) if the coordinates are supposed to stand in such a relation to the body $S(\mathfrak{o}\mathfrak{x}) \leqq 1$ that for $k=1, 2, \cdots, \lambda-1$ the manifold $\mathfrak{o}(M_1, M_2, \cdots, M_k)$ is defined through $x_{\mu_k+1}=0$, $x_{\mu_k+2}=0$, $\cdots$, $x_n=0$. Under such conditions the realm $S(\mathfrak{o}\mathfrak{x}) \leqq 1$ is said to be *prepared* (*eingerichtet*).

A body $S(\mathfrak{o}\mathfrak{x}) \leqq 1$ is said to be *extreme* if in the inequality (1) there exists the equality sign. In the sequel is established the existence of *extreme standard bodies*. For the case $\lambda=1$ the appearance of the equality sign in (1) (Cf. Arts. 46, I and 149, IV) is of the same significance as the appearance of a remainder realm among the sheaf of bodies $S(\mathfrak{o}\mathfrak{x}) \leqq$constant. This remainder realm corresponds to the value constant $=\dfrac{1}{2}M=\dfrac{1}{J^{1/n}}$.

[1] Minkowski, *Geom. d. Zahlen*, p. 224; *Ges. Abhandl.*, II, p. 120.

We shall now assume that $\lambda > 1$ and that $v_1, v_2, \cdots, v_\lambda$ (whose sum is n) are given in any manner. It will be found as characteristic for the extreme standard bodies in question that they arise in a certain way out of the remainder realms in manifolds of the $v_1^{st}, v_2^{nd}, \cdots, v_\lambda^{th}$ order.

As in Art. 152, we let Ω be any odd integer and let $\mathfrak{H}$ be the collectivity of the Ω^n lattice points with spans $\leqq \frac{\Omega-1}{2}$ from $\mathfrak{o}$. Further let $\mathfrak{P}_\kappa(\mathfrak{o})$ denote the body $S(\mathfrak{o}\mathfrak{x}) \leqq \frac{M_\kappa}{2}$ for $\kappa = 1, 2, \cdots, \lambda$. Let $S(\mathfrak{o}\mathfrak{x}) \leqq 1$ be prepared for $x_1, x_2, \cdots, x_n$. If κ takes one of the values $1, 2, \cdots, \lambda-1$, let the distribution of $x_1, x_2, \cdots, x_n$ to κ be made in two groups $x_1, x_2, \cdots, x_{\mu_\kappa}$, and $x_{\mu_\kappa+1}, x_{\mu_\kappa+2}, \cdots, x_n$ in a similar manner as was made above in Art. 152, III for the comparison of the volumes of $\mathfrak{P}_\kappa(\mathfrak{H})$ and $\mathfrak{P}_{\kappa+1}(\mathfrak{H})$. The realms $\mathfrak{X}, \mathfrak{B}, \mathfrak{G}, \mathfrak{H}$ are all four in every case so arranged that in them $\mathfrak{x}'$ and $\mathfrak{x}''$ run completely independent of one another. Thus every general distribution of a point for these realms presents certain distributions: $\mathfrak{X}', \mathfrak{X}''; \mathfrak{B}', \mathfrak{B}''; \mathfrak{G}', \mathfrak{G}''; \mathfrak{H}', \mathfrak{H}''$. Whenever clearness demands, the number κ will be added as a lower index for the individual systems $\mathfrak{x}'$ or $\mathfrak{x}''$, for example, $\mathfrak{G}'_\kappa$ denotes the assemblage of all integers $x_1, x_2, \cdots, x_{\mu_\kappa}$ so that to speak of the lattice points in $\mathfrak{X}'_1$ and $\mathfrak{B}'_\kappa$ denotes the corresponding realm for $\mathfrak{X}'$ in $x_1, x_2, \cdots, x_{\mu_\kappa}$ as $\mathfrak{B}$ for $\mathfrak{X}$ in $x_1, x_2, \cdots, x_{\mu_\kappa}, x_{\mu_\kappa+1}, \cdots, x_n$; that is, a remainder realm in $\mathfrak{X}'_\kappa$. Finally $\mathfrak{H}'_\kappa$ denotes the collectivity of lattice points $\mathfrak{g}'_\kappa$ of $\mathfrak{G}'_\kappa$ in number Ω^{μ_κ}. If in the realm $\mathfrak{P}_\kappa(\mathfrak{o})$ $[\kappa = 1, 2, \cdots, \lambda-1]$ for every point $\mathfrak{x} = \mathfrak{x}'_\kappa, \mathfrak{x}''_\kappa$ we make the substitution $\mathfrak{y}'_\kappa, \mathfrak{x}''$ where $y'_\kappa - \mathfrak{o}'_\kappa = \frac{M_{\kappa+1}}{M_\kappa}(\mathfrak{x}'_\kappa - \mathfrak{o}'_\kappa)$, we have the body designated above by $\mathfrak{Q}_\kappa(\mathfrak{o})$. Further denote the volumes of $\mathfrak{P}_\kappa(\mathfrak{H}'_\kappa, \mathfrak{o}''_\kappa)$ and $\mathfrak{Q}(\mathfrak{H}', \mathfrak{o}''_\kappa)$ $(\kappa = 1, 2, \cdots, \lambda-1)$ by Π_κ and X_κ, and in addition denote the volume $\mathfrak{P}_\lambda(\mathfrak{H})$ by Π_λ. Observe that the inequality (1) existed out of the equation Art. 152, (8) and the λ inequalities

$$\Pi_\kappa \leqq X_\kappa \ (\kappa = 1, 2, \cdots, \lambda-1), \qquad \Pi_\lambda \leqq \left(\Omega - 1 + \frac{\mathfrak{G}}{ng}\right)^n.$$

I. We may next introduce a new additional quantity X_λ. Every quantity $\mathfrak{x}$ (Cf. Art. 149, (3)) may be expressed in the form

$$\mathfrak{x}=\mathfrak{o}+v_1(\mathfrak{p}_1-\mathfrak{o})+\cdots+v_n(\mathfrak{p}_n-\mathfrak{o})$$

with definite values given to $v_1, \cdots, v_n$. The lattice in $v_1, v_2, \cdots, v_n$ is entirely embodied in the lattice $\mathfrak{G}$. Observe that a remainder realm in $v_1, v_2, \cdots, v_n$ may be defined through

$$-\tfrac{1}{2}\leqq v_k\leqq\tfrac{1}{2} \qquad [k=1, 2, \ldots, n];$$

and by writing $v_\kappa=g_\kappa\pm\bar{v}_\kappa$, where $\bar{v}_\kappa$ is situated within this remainder realm, g_κ being an integer, we may express the point $\mathfrak{x}$ above in the form

$$\mathfrak{x}-\Sigma g_\kappa\mathfrak{p}_\kappa=\mathfrak{o}+\bar{v}_1(\mathfrak{p}_1-\mathfrak{o})+\cdots+\bar{v}_n(\mathfrak{p}_n-\mathfrak{o}).$$

Hence the point $\mathfrak{x}$ is so situated with respect to at least one lattice point from which its radial-distance to $\mathfrak{x}$ is always (Art. 24, end)

$$\leqq\tfrac{1}{2}S(\mathfrak{o}\mathfrak{p}_1)+\tfrac{1}{2}S(\mathfrak{o}\mathfrak{p}_2)+\cdots+\tfrac{1}{2}S(\mathfrak{o}\mathfrak{p}_n)\leqq\frac{n}{2}M_\lambda.$$

It is further seen that every point $\mathfrak{x}$ has also a least radial-distance from one among the lattice $\mathfrak{G}$ with the above as an upper limit. Denote this radial-distnace by $\varphi_\lambda(\mathfrak{x})$. For points on the boundary of the realm $\mathfrak{P}_\lambda(\mathfrak{G}'_{\lambda-1}, \mathfrak{o}''_{\lambda-1})$ it is clear that $\varphi_\lambda(\mathfrak{x})=\tfrac{1}{2}M_\lambda$. The function $\varphi_\lambda(\mathfrak{x})$ takes for itself, however, all possible values that it can have in an arbitrary remainder realm, for example in $\mathfrak{B}$. It is accordingly a continuous function of $\mathfrak{x}$ (Art. 46, (1)) and has a definite maximum value in $\mathfrak{B}$ (and with it at the same time a definite maximum for the entire manifold $\mathfrak{X}$). Denote this maximum value by $\tfrac{1}{2}N_\lambda$. That is, $\varphi_\lambda(\mathfrak{x})$ has a minimum value in $\mathfrak{B}$ for every point $\mathfrak{x}$. Denote the largest of these minimal values by $\tfrac{1}{2}N_\lambda$. We thus have $M_\lambda\leqq N_\lambda\leqq nM_\lambda$. Denote the body $S(\mathfrak{O}\mathfrak{x})\leqq\tfrac{1}{2}N_\lambda$ by $\mathfrak{Q}_\lambda$ and by X_λ understand the volume $\mathfrak{Q}_\lambda(\mathfrak{H})$. (See Fig. 102.) Since $M_\lambda\leqq N_\lambda$, the realm $\mathfrak{Q}_\lambda(\mathfrak{H})$ contains entirely within itself the realm $\mathfrak{P}_\lambda(\mathfrak{H})$

and in consequence we have

$$\Pi_\lambda \leqq X_\lambda.$$

On the other hand, since $N_\lambda \leqq nM_\lambda \leqq \mathfrak{G}$, the body $\mathfrak{Q}_\lambda(\mathfrak{H})$ lies

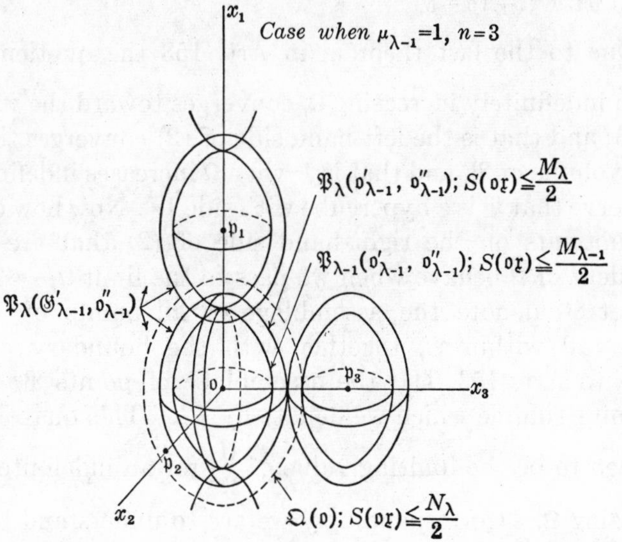

M_λ is the least radial-distance from $\mathfrak{o}$ to lattice points not on the x_1 axis

FIG. 102

entirely within the body of the spans $\dfrac{\Omega-1}{2}+\dfrac{\mathfrak{G}}{2g}$ from $\mathfrak{o}$; and from this it follows that

$$X_\lambda \leqq \left(\Omega-1+\frac{\mathfrak{G}}{g}\right)^n.$$

The equation (8) of Art. 152 is

$$\Pi_\lambda = \Omega_n \frac{X_{\lambda-1}}{\Pi_{\lambda-1}} \cdot \frac{X_{\lambda-2}}{\Pi_{\lambda-2}} \cdots \frac{X_1}{\Pi_1} M_1^{v_1} \cdots M_\lambda^{v_\lambda} \frac{J}{2^n},$$

which, if multiplied on both sides by X_λ, is

$$\text{(2)} \qquad \frac{X_\lambda}{\Omega^n} = \frac{X_\lambda}{\Pi_\lambda} \cdot \frac{X_{\lambda-1}}{\Pi_{\lambda-1}} \cdots \frac{X_1}{\Pi_1} M_1^{v_1} \cdots M_\lambda^{v_\lambda} \frac{J}{2^n}.$$

We further have the λ inequalities $\Pi_\kappa \leqq X_\kappa$ ($\kappa=1, 2, \cdots, \lambda$).

Observe that the 2λ quantities Π_κ and X_κ are essentially dependent on Ω^n.

The meaning of N_λ *consists in the fact that the realm* $\mathfrak{Q}_\lambda(\mathfrak{G})$ *fills up the entire manifold* $\mathfrak{X}$, *and accordingly coincides with* $\mathfrak{B}+\mathfrak{G}-\mathfrak{o}$.

Due to the last theorem in Art. 153 the quotient $\frac{X_\lambda}{\Omega^n}$, with indefinitely increasing Ω, converges toward the volume of $\mathfrak{B}$; and that is the left-hand side of (2) converges toward the volume of $\mathfrak{B}$, and that is 1 when Ω increases indefinitely. Observe that $\mathfrak{B}$ is a hypercube with side 1. Now how do the λ quotients on the right-hand side of (2) that are independent of Ω behave when we pass to the limit $\Omega \to \infty$?

Let $\mathfrak{P}_\lambda$ denote the assemblage of all points of $\mathfrak{P}_\lambda(\mathfrak{G})$ that fall within $\mathfrak{B}$, together with the boundary points. Due to Art. 153, III, the assemblage of points $\mathfrak{P}_\lambda$ has a definite volume which we denote by P_λ. This quantity P_λ is seen to be the limiting value of $\frac{\Pi_\lambda}{\Omega^n}$ for an indefinitely increasing Ω. Correspondingly we are to understand by $\mathfrak{Q}_\lambda$ the entire realm $\mathfrak{B}$. For this volume write Q_λ, so that $Q_\lambda = 1$. The quotient $\frac{X_\lambda}{\Pi_\lambda}$ converges then in the limit $\Omega \to \infty$, to $\frac{Q_\lambda}{P_\lambda}$; and from $\Pi_\lambda \leqq X_\lambda$ we have $P_\lambda \leqq Q_\lambda$. We may next introduce quantities P_κ, Q_κ $(\kappa = 1, 2, \cdots, \lambda-1)$ and study among them the inequalities that correspond to the above. Let κ take any of the values $1, 2, \cdots, \lambda-1$, and belonging to a definite value of κ we make the corresponding distribution of the points $\mathfrak{x}=\mathfrak{x}', \mathfrak{x}''$ and connected with these distributions we use the notations such as $\mathfrak{X}'$, $\mathfrak{G}'$, $\mathfrak{B}'$, etc. For example, $\mathfrak{G}'$, $\mathfrak{B}'$ denote the corresponding assemblages with respect to $\mathfrak{X}'$ as $\mathfrak{G}$, $\mathfrak{B}$ do with respect to $\mathfrak{X}$.

We shall further denote the assemblage of all systems (points) $\mathfrak{x}''$ of the body $\mathfrak{P}_\kappa(\mathfrak{o})$ as in Art. 152 by $\mathfrak{P}_\kappa''$. If we denote any point in $\mathfrak{P}_\kappa(\mathfrak{o})$ by $\mathfrak{f}=\mathfrak{f}', \mathfrak{f}''$, then any body $\mathfrak{P}_\kappa(\mathfrak{x}', \mathfrak{o}'')$ consists always exactly of the points $\mathfrak{x}'+\mathfrak{f}'-\mathfrak{o}'$,

$\mathfrak{f}''$ and the collective realm $\mathfrak{P}_\kappa(\mathfrak{X}', \mathfrak{o}'')$ consists simply of $\mathfrak{X}'$, $\mathfrak{P}_\kappa''$; and that is $\mathfrak{P}_\kappa(\mathfrak{X}', \mathfrak{o}'') \sim \mathfrak{X}', \mathfrak{P}_\kappa''$. The transition from $\mathfrak{P}_\kappa(\mathfrak{o})$ to $\mathfrak{Q}_\kappa(\mathfrak{o})$ now takes place through a change only of $\mathfrak{f}'$ among the points $\mathfrak{f}', \mathfrak{f}''$. We shall understand by $\mathfrak{P}_\kappa$ and $\mathfrak{Q}_\kappa$ the assemblage of all points of $\mathfrak{P}_\kappa(\mathfrak{G}', \mathfrak{o}'')$ and $\mathfrak{Q}_\kappa(\mathfrak{G}', \mathfrak{o}'')$ that are inner points of $\mathfrak{B}$, $\mathfrak{P}_\kappa''$, the boundaries in all cases being included. Through similar considerations as those of Art. 153, III, it is seen that the volumes of $\mathfrak{P}_\kappa$ and $\mathfrak{Q}_\kappa$ which volumes we denote by P_κ and Q_κ, are the values to which the quotients $\frac{\Pi_\kappa}{\Omega^{\mu_\kappa}}$ and $\frac{X_\kappa}{\Omega^{\mu_\kappa}}$ converge when Ω increases without limit. Hence the ratio $\frac{X_\kappa}{\Pi_\kappa}$ converges for $\Omega \to \infty$, toward $\frac{Q_\kappa}{P_\kappa}$; and from $\Pi_\kappa \leqq X_\kappa$ we have

$$P_\kappa \leqq Q_\kappa \qquad (\kappa = 1, 2, \ldots, \lambda - 1).$$

If next we let $\Omega \to \infty$, equation (2) becomes

$$1 = \frac{Q_\lambda}{P_\lambda} \cdots \frac{Q_1}{P_1} M_1^{\mathfrak{v}_1} \cdots M_\lambda^{\mathfrak{v}_\lambda} \frac{J}{2^n};$$

and the quantities that appear in this expression are independent of Ω. It is clear that the equality sign can appear in (1) only if in each of the λ inequalities $P_\kappa \leqq Q_\kappa$ $(\kappa = 1, 2, \cdots, \lambda)$ the equality sign exists.

II. For every index κ the difference between the case $P_\kappa < Q_\kappa$ and the case $P_\kappa = Q_\kappa$ stamps itself in a certian way on the realm $\mathfrak{P}_\kappa(\mathfrak{o})$ alone. Let κ have one of the values $1, \cdots, \lambda - 1$, and use the distribution $\mathfrak{x} = \mathfrak{x}', \mathfrak{x}''$ that belongs to this κ. Then for every point $\mathfrak{x}', \mathfrak{x}''$ there is a definite least radial-distance to the assemblage of points $\mathfrak{X}', \mathfrak{o}''$ and it always coincides with the least radial-distance from $\mathfrak{o}$ to the assemblage of points $\mathfrak{X}', \mathfrak{X}''$. This radial-distance was denoted by $S''(\mathfrak{o}'', \mathfrak{x}'')$ in Art. 152, IV. The points of the lattice $\mathfrak{G}$ which are situated in the assemblage of points $\mathfrak{X}', \mathfrak{o}''$ constitute the lattice points of the assemblage $\mathfrak{G}'$, $\mathfrak{o}''$, and for every point $\mathfrak{x}$ there is a least radial-distance to this new assemblage $\mathfrak{G}', \mathfrak{o}''$ (which assemblage here is $\mathfrak{G}_\kappa'$,

$\mathfrak{o}_\kappa''$). It is clear that we always have $S''(\mathfrak{o}''\mathfrak{x}'') \leqq \varphi_\kappa(\mathfrak{x})$, since the expression on the right-hand side has reference to integers, and that on the left to any points of the same assemblage of points.

Further we have for any two arbitrary points $\mathfrak{a}$ and $\mathfrak{b}$ necessarily always (due to the accordant properties of the function)

$$\varphi(\mathfrak{b}) \leqq \varphi(\mathfrak{a}) + S(\mathfrak{a}\mathfrak{b}). \tag{3}$$

This function $\varphi_\kappa(\mathfrak{x})$ has in the points of the boundary of the realm $\mathfrak{P}_\kappa(\mathfrak{G}', \mathfrak{o}'')$ always the value $\frac{1}{2}M_\kappa$; in the inner points of this realm it is $\leqq \dfrac{M_\kappa}{2}$; and without this realm it is $> \dfrac{M_\kappa}{2}$. Further the function $\varphi_\kappa(\mathfrak{x})$ takes in the entire realm $\mathfrak{X}'$, $\mathfrak{P}_\kappa''$ all the values which it takes in $\mathfrak{B}'$, $\mathfrak{P}_\kappa''$. From this it is seen that $\varphi_\kappa(\mathfrak{x})$ is a continuous function of the coordinates of $\mathfrak{x}$ and therefore has in the closed realm $\mathfrak{B}'$, $\mathfrak{P}_\kappa''$ a definite maximum which (as above) call $\frac{1}{2}N_\kappa$. This quantity also denotes the maximum of $\varphi_\kappa(\mathfrak{x})$ in the entire realm $\mathfrak{X}'$, $\mathfrak{P}_\kappa''$. *It is seen that* we have $N_\kappa > M_\kappa$ or $N_\kappa = M_\kappa$, the first sign (i.e. $>$) when $\mathfrak{P}_\kappa(\mathfrak{G}', \mathfrak{o}'')$ does *not* fill the entire realm $\mathfrak{X}'$, $\mathfrak{P}_\kappa''$, the second (i.e. the equality sign) when $\mathfrak{P}_\kappa(\mathfrak{G}', \mathfrak{o}'')$ covers $\mathfrak{X}'$, $\mathfrak{P}_\kappa''$.

Since $\mathfrak{X}'$, $\mathfrak{P}_\kappa''$ coincides with the realm defined as $\mathfrak{P}_\kappa(\mathfrak{X}', \mathfrak{o}'')$ corresponding to any point of $\mathfrak{X}'$, $\mathfrak{P}_\kappa''$, there is always at least one point of $\mathfrak{X}'$, $\mathfrak{o}''$ such that the radial-distance of the two points $\leqq \frac{1}{2}M_\kappa$. The realm $\mathfrak{X}'$, $\mathfrak{o}''$ is the complex of all points of the expression

$$\mathfrak{o} + v_1(\mathfrak{p}_1 - \mathfrak{o}) + v_2(\mathfrak{p}_2 - \mathfrak{o}) + \cdots + v_{\mu_\kappa}(\mathfrak{p}_{\mu_\kappa} - \mathfrak{o}).$$

(As in Art. 149, (3)) integral values of $v_1, v_2, \cdots, v_{\mu_\kappa}$ of this expression give lattice points, that is, points of $\mathfrak{G}'$, $\mathfrak{o}''$. Hence it is seen that every point of $\mathfrak{X}'$, $\mathfrak{o}''$ offers a radial-distance to some point of $\mathfrak{G}'$, $\mathfrak{o}''$ which radial-distance is $\leqq \dfrac{\mu_\kappa}{2} M_\kappa$. And from this result it follows that

$$\frac{N_\kappa}{2} \leqq \left(\frac{\mu_\kappa + 1}{2}\right) M_\kappa \qquad \text{or} \qquad N_\kappa \leqq (\mu_\kappa + 1) M_\kappa.$$

However, this upper limit for N_κ is not used in the sequel.

We may next prove that the condition $Q_\kappa = P_\kappa$ coincides entirely with $N_\kappa = M_\kappa$. The latter equation means that $\mathfrak{P}_\kappa(\mathfrak{G}', \mathfrak{o}_\kappa'')$ occupies the entire realm $\mathfrak{P}_\kappa(\mathfrak{X}', \mathfrak{o}_\kappa'')$. We are to understand always by $\mathfrak{P}_\kappa'(\mathfrak{o}', \mathfrak{x}'')$ and $\mathfrak{Q}_\kappa'(\mathfrak{o}, \mathfrak{x}'')$ the com-

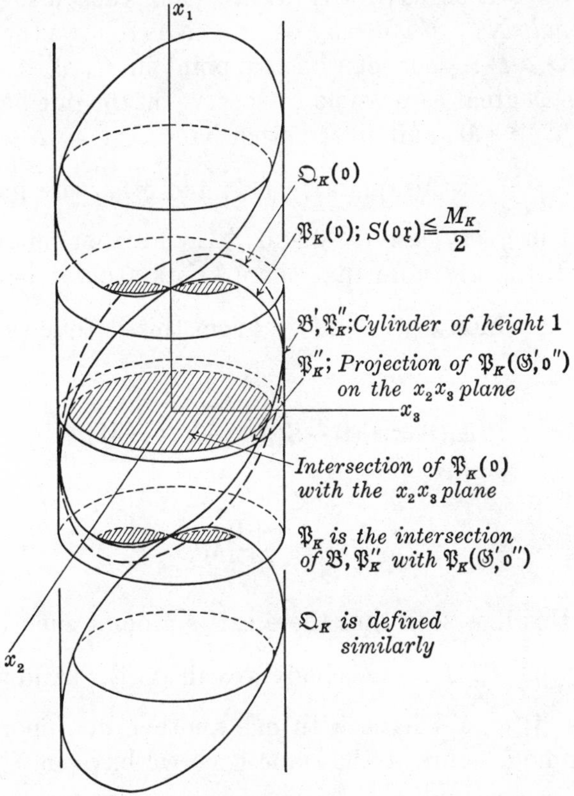

FIG. 103

plex of all those systems (points) $\mathfrak{x}'$ for which $\mathfrak{x}', \mathfrak{x}''$ is a point out of $\mathfrak{P}_\kappa(\mathfrak{o})$ or out of $\mathfrak{Q}_\kappa(\mathfrak{o})$; and then $\Pi_\kappa'(\mathfrak{x}'')$ and $X_\kappa'(\mathfrak{x}'')$ are to denote the volumes of $\mathfrak{P}_\kappa'(\mathfrak{H}', \mathfrak{x}'')$ and $\mathfrak{Q}_\kappa'(\mathfrak{H}', \mathfrak{x}'')$ in $\mathfrak{X}'$. Due to Art. 152, IV the realm $\mathfrak{Q}_\kappa'(\mathfrak{o}', \mathfrak{x}'')$ may through translations be transposed into realms which entirely include $\mathfrak{P}_\kappa'(\mathfrak{o}', \mathfrak{x}'')$. If then the bodies $\mathfrak{P}_\kappa'(\mathfrak{G}', \mathfrak{x}'')$ entirely cover the manifold $\mathfrak{X}'$, this must also be true of the associated bodies $\mathfrak{Q}'_\kappa(\mathfrak{G}', \mathfrak{x}'')$. From this it follows further that if $\mathfrak{P}_\kappa(\mathfrak{G}', \mathfrak{o}'')$ entirely fills the realm $\mathfrak{X}'$, $\mathfrak{P}''_\kappa$, the same must be true of $\mathfrak{Q}_\kappa(\mathfrak{G}', \mathfrak{o}'')$. In this case the bodies $\mathfrak{P}_\kappa$ and $\mathfrak{Q}_\kappa$ both cover (fill up) the entire realm $\mathfrak{B}'$, $\mathfrak{P}''_\kappa$ and coincide the one with the other. See figure on succeeding page. We thus have *first*: If $N_\kappa = M_\kappa$, then also $Q_\kappa = P_\kappa$. If *secondly* $N_\kappa > M_\kappa$, it may be proved as follows that necessarily $Q_\kappa > P_\kappa$. For let $\mathfrak{l}$ be any point in $\mathfrak{X}'$, $\mathfrak{P}''_\kappa$ for which $\varphi_\kappa(\mathfrak{l})$ is as great as possible. Observe on the one hand that $S''(\mathfrak{D}''\mathfrak{l}'') \leqq \frac{1}{2}M_\kappa$ and on the other hand $\varphi_\kappa(\mathfrak{l}) = \frac{1}{2}N_\kappa$. Write $t_\kappa = \dfrac{N_\kappa - M_\kappa}{2M_\kappa}$, if this quantity $\leqq 1$; and otherwise put $t_\kappa = 1$, so that in every case $t_\kappa > 0$ and $\leqq 1$. Further put $\mathfrak{j}'' = t_\kappa \mathfrak{o}'' + (1 - t_\kappa)\mathfrak{l}''$, and note that there exists a point $\mathfrak{j} = \mathfrak{j}', \mathfrak{j}''$ in $\mathfrak{X}'$, $\mathfrak{j}''$ for which $S(\mathfrak{j}\mathfrak{l}) \leqq \frac{t_\kappa}{2}M_\kappa$. From this it follows, due to (3), that

$$\varphi_\kappa(\mathfrak{j}) \geqq \varphi_\kappa(\mathfrak{l}) - S(\mathfrak{j}\mathfrak{l}) \geqq \frac{1}{2}N_\kappa - \frac{t_\kappa}{2}M_\kappa,$$

or

$$\varphi_\kappa(\mathfrak{j}) \geqq \frac{1+t_\kappa}{2}M_\kappa.$$

From this it is seen that there exists a point such that the body $S(\mathfrak{j}\mathfrak{x}) \leqq \frac{t_\kappa}{2}M_\kappa$. This body we call $\cdot\mathfrak{P}(\mathfrak{j})$. And then the realms $\mathfrak{P}_\kappa(\mathfrak{g}', \mathfrak{o}'')$ have with one another no inner points in common. But at the same time we have in $\mathfrak{X}'$, $\mathfrak{j}''$ the point $\mathfrak{e} = \mathfrak{o} + \dfrac{1-t_\kappa}{t_\kappa}(\mathfrak{e} - \mathfrak{j})$ for which $\mathfrak{e}'' = \mathfrak{j}''$ so that $S(\mathfrak{o}\mathfrak{e}) \leqq \frac{1}{2}(1 - t_\kappa)M_\kappa$, and accordingly the body $\cdot\mathfrak{P}_\kappa(\mathfrak{e})$, that is $S(\mathfrak{e}\mathfrak{x}) \leqq \frac{t_\kappa}{2}M_\kappa$ lies entirely within $\mathfrak{P}_\kappa(\mathfrak{o})$. (See Fig. 104.) Next let $\mathfrak{x}''$ be an inner point of $\mathfrak{P}''$ in $\mathfrak{X}''$ and write $\mathfrak{y}'' - \mathfrak{l}'' = t_\kappa(\mathfrak{x}'' - \mathfrak{o}'')$. The systems (points) thus defined for y'' have the corresponding meaning for $\cdot\mathfrak{P}_\kappa(\mathfrak{e})$ as the systems $\mathfrak{x}''$ for $\cdot\mathfrak{P}_\kappa(\mathfrak{o})$. For such a system $\mathfrak{y}''$ we may denote by

$\cdot\mathfrak{P}_\kappa(\mathfrak{e}', \mathfrak{y}'')$ the assemblage of systems $\mathfrak{x}'$ for which $\mathfrak{x}', \mathfrak{y}''$ is a point out of $\cdot\mathfrak{P}_\kappa(\mathfrak{e})$; and translating the theorem of Art. 153 (2) from the manifold $\mathfrak{X}$ to $\mathfrak{X}'$ we find the volume of $\cdot\mathfrak{P}_\kappa(\mathfrak{H}', \mathfrak{y}'')$ in $\mathfrak{X}'$ to be $\geqq t_\kappa^{\mu_\kappa}\Pi'_\kappa(\mathfrak{x}'')$.

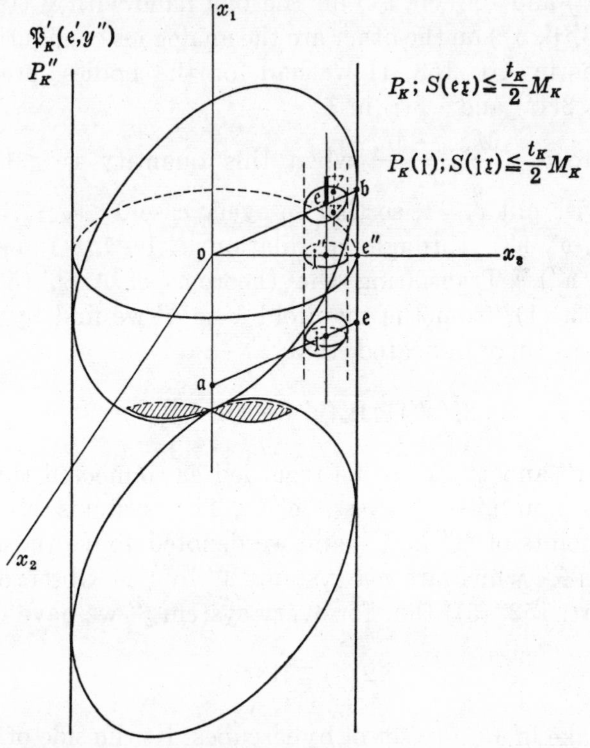

We choose a point $\mathfrak{e}$ such that

$$\varphi_\kappa(\mathfrak{e})=\frac{N_\kappa}{2}.$$

There exists a $\mathfrak{b}$ such that $S(\mathfrak{o}\mathfrak{b})\leqq\frac{M_\kappa}{2}$, therefore $\mathfrak{e}''$ is such that

$$S''(\mathfrak{o}'', \mathfrak{e}'')\leqq\frac{M_\kappa}{2}.$$

$$t_\kappa=\frac{N_\kappa-M_\kappa}{2M_\kappa}. \qquad j''=t_\kappa\mathfrak{o}''+(1-t_\kappa)\mathfrak{e}''. \qquad \frac{\text{segment } \mathfrak{o}''\mathfrak{j}''}{\text{segment } \mathfrak{j}''\mathfrak{e}''}=\frac{1-t_\kappa}{t_\kappa}.$$

Divide segment $\mathfrak{a}\mathfrak{e}$ in the same way so that

$$S(\mathfrak{j}\mathfrak{e})\leqq\frac{t_\kappa}{2}M_\kappa.$$

FIG. 104

On the other hand the systems $\mathfrak{y}''$ themselves are inner points of $\mathfrak{P}''$, and the remaining systems $\mathfrak{x}''$ which simultaneously are *not* systems $\mathfrak{y}''$ may be so designated by $\mathfrak{z}''$. With this stipulation for every system $\mathfrak{y}''$ the configurations $\mathfrak{P}'_\kappa(\mathfrak{o}'\mathfrak{y}'')$ and $\cdot\mathfrak{P}'_\kappa(\mathfrak{G}', \mathfrak{y}'')$ on the one hand with $\mathfrak{P}'_\kappa(\mathfrak{G}', \mathfrak{y}'')$ and $\cdot\mathfrak{P}'_\kappa(\mathfrak{j}', \mathfrak{y}'')$ on the other are the analogous configurations in $\mathfrak{X}'$ as in Art. 153, II we had for the bodies $\mathfrak{P}(\mathfrak{o})$ and $\cdot\mathfrak{P}(\mathfrak{o})$, $\mathfrak{P}(\mathfrak{G})$ and $\cdot\mathfrak{P}(\mathfrak{j})$ in $\mathfrak{X}$.

Write $\theta_\kappa = \dfrac{M_{\kappa+1} - M_\kappa}{M_\kappa}$ when this quantity is $\leqq 1$, and otherwise put $\theta_\kappa = 1$, so that in every case $0 < \theta_\kappa \leqq 1$. And let $\mathfrak{P}_\kappa(\mathfrak{o}', \mathfrak{y}'')$ through a dilation $\geqq 1 + \theta_\kappa : 1$ become $\mathfrak{Q}'_\kappa(\mathfrak{o}', \mathfrak{y}'')$. Translating the theorems of Arts. 153, (4) and 153, (1), from the manifold $\mathfrak{X}$ to $\mathfrak{X}'$ we find by using results as there indicated, that

$$\text{(4)} \qquad X'_\kappa(\mathfrak{y}'') \geqq \Pi'_\kappa(\mathfrak{y}'') + \theta_\kappa^{\mu_\kappa} t_\kappa^{\mu_\kappa} \Pi'_\kappa(\mathfrak{x}'')$$

where $\mathfrak{x}''$ and $\mathfrak{y}''$ are to be regarded as connected through the relation $\mathfrak{y}'' - \mathfrak{e}'' = t_\kappa(\mathfrak{x}'' - \mathfrak{o}'')$. The systems $\mathfrak{y}''$ were inner points of $\mathfrak{P}''_\kappa$ in $\mathfrak{X}''$; and we denoted above those systems in $\mathfrak{X}''$ which are *not* systems $\mathfrak{y}''$ by $\mathfrak{z}''$. Observe then (Cf. Art. 152, (5)) that for every system $\mathfrak{z}''$ we have

$$\text{(5)} \qquad X'_\kappa(\mathfrak{z}'') \geqq \Pi'_\kappa(\mathfrak{z}'').$$

Next take in $\mathfrak{X}''$ any set of hypercubes; let the side of these hypercubes be $t_\kappa \delta$ and apply (4) and (5) to all those systems $\mathfrak{y}''$ and $\mathfrak{z}''$ which enter as midpoints of hypercubes of this net. Form the systems $\mathfrak{x}''$. Then form the systems $\mathfrak{x}''$ which are connected with these systems $\mathfrak{y}''$ in (4) and have as inner points of $\mathfrak{P}''_\kappa$ precisely all the midpoints of hypercubes of a certain net in $\mathfrak{X}''$ with side δ. Add the inequalities (4) and (5) that are thus found.

If this result is multiplied by $(t_\kappa \delta)^{n-\mu_\kappa}$ and δ made to decrease toward zero, we have from Art. 151, II:

$$X_\kappa \geqq \Pi_\kappa + t_\kappa^n \theta_\kappa^{\mu_\kappa} \Pi_\kappa,$$

and from preceding results it follows that

$$\frac{Q_\kappa}{P_\kappa} \geqq 1 + t_\kappa^n \theta_\kappa^{\mu_\kappa} > 1.$$

Finally consider the case $\kappa = \lambda$. If the relation $N_\lambda = M_\lambda$, then $\mathfrak{P}_\lambda(\mathfrak{G})$ fills the entire manifold $\mathfrak{X}$. We therefore have $P_\lambda = 1$, and consequently also $Q_\lambda = P_\lambda$. If, however, $N_\lambda > M_\lambda$, then determine any point $\mathfrak{l}$ from which the least radial-distance from $\mathfrak{G}$, that is $\varphi_\lambda(\mathfrak{l})$, is $= \frac{1}{2}N_\lambda$. Further write $\theta_\lambda = \dfrac{N_\lambda - M_\lambda}{M_\lambda}$, when this quantity is $\leqq 1$, and in the other event put $\theta_\lambda = 1$ so that in all events $\theta_\lambda > 0$ and $\leqq 1$. Then on the one hand the body $S(\mathfrak{l}\mathfrak{x}) \leqq \dfrac{\theta_\lambda}{2} M_\lambda$ and the realm $\mathfrak{P}_\lambda(\mathfrak{G})$ have no inner point in common, and on the other hand $\mathfrak{Q}_\lambda(\mathfrak{o})$ exists out of $\mathfrak{P}_\lambda(\mathfrak{o})$ through a dilation in a ratio which is $\geqq 1 + \theta_\lambda : 1$. The application of the theorem in Art. 153, II (keeping sight of the final remark there given) leads to

$$X_\lambda \geqq \Pi_\lambda + \theta_\lambda^n \Pi_\lambda$$

and from this follows

$$\frac{Q_\lambda}{P_\lambda} \geqq 1 + \theta_\lambda^n > 1.$$

Thus it is seen that *a necessary and sufficient condition for the appearance of the equality sign in (1) is that the* λ *equations* $N_1 = M_1$, $N_2 = M_2$, $\cdots$, $N_\lambda = M_\lambda$ *must exist.*

The further development of these conditions leads at once to simple and interesting results.

III. Let us define λ bodies $\mathfrak{R}_1(\mathfrak{o})$, $\mathfrak{R}_2(\mathfrak{o})$, $\cdots$, $\mathfrak{R}_\lambda(\mathfrak{o})$ in the following way: First let $\mathfrak{R}_1(\mathfrak{o})$ denote the body $S(\mathfrak{o}\mathfrak{x}) \leqq \frac{1}{2}M_1$ and from $\mathfrak{R}_\kappa(\mathfrak{o})$ $(\kappa = 1, 2, \cdots, \lambda - 1)$ let the body $\mathfrak{R}_{\kappa+1}(\mathfrak{o})$ be derived by changing every point $\mathfrak{x}_\kappa'$, $\mathfrak{x}_\kappa''$ of the first realm into $\mathfrak{x}_\kappa'$, $\mathfrak{y}_\kappa''$, where $\mathfrak{y}_\kappa''$ is defined through the relation $\mathfrak{y}_\kappa'' - \mathfrak{o}_\kappa'' = \dfrac{M_{\kappa+1}}{M_\kappa}(\mathfrak{x}'' - \mathfrak{o}_\kappa'')$, that is in the same way as the body $\mathfrak{P}_{\kappa+1}(\mathfrak{o})$ was derived out of the body $\mathfrak{Q}_\kappa(\mathfrak{o})$ in Art. 152,

IV. In the end, $\mathfrak{R}_\lambda(\mathfrak{o})$ will have simply the following character: while $x_1, x_2, \cdots, x_n$ move in the body $S(\mathfrak{o}\mathfrak{x}) \leqq 1$, the realm $\mathfrak{R}_\lambda(\mathfrak{o})$ will be described with the coordinates $\frac{S_1}{2}x_1$, $\frac{S_2}{2}x_2, \cdots, \frac{S_n}{2}x_n$.

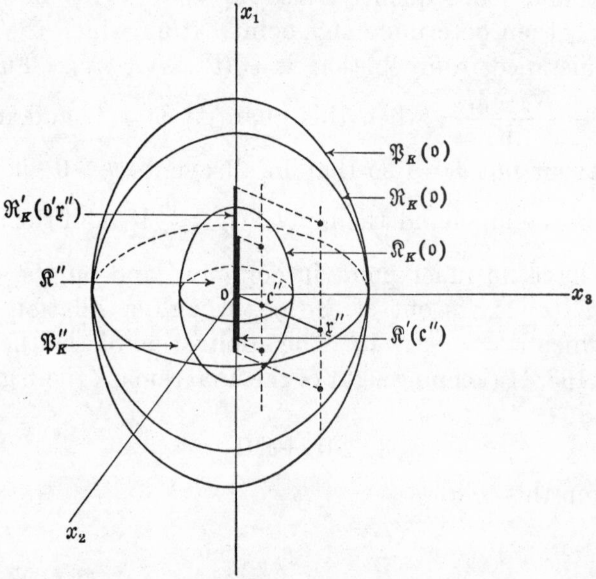

The points $\mathfrak{c}''$ of $\mathfrak{K}''$ and the points $\mathfrak{x}''$ of $\mathfrak{P}''_\kappa$ are related by the equations

$$\mathfrak{x}''-\mathfrak{o}''=\tfrac{1}{2}M_\kappa(\mathfrak{c}''-\mathfrak{o}'').$$

Let the points in $\mathfrak{R}'_\kappa(\mathfrak{o}', \mathfrak{x}'')$ be represented by $\mathfrak{x}'$ and the points in $\mathfrak{K}'(\mathfrak{c}'')$ by $\mathfrak{c}'$. Then $\mathfrak{K}'(\mathfrak{c}'')$ goes into $\mathfrak{R}_\kappa(\mathfrak{o}', \mathfrak{x}'')$ by means of the transformation

$$x'_1=\frac{S_1}{2}c'_1,$$
$$x'_2=\frac{S_2}{2}c'_2,$$
$$\cdots\cdots\cdots$$
$$x'_\kappa=\frac{S_\kappa}{2}c'_\kappa,$$

so that the volume of $\mathfrak{R}'(\mathfrak{o}', \mathfrak{x}'')$ in $\mathfrak{X}'$ is (see text)

$$\left(\frac{M_1}{2}\right)^{\nu_1}\cdots\left(\frac{M_{\nu_\kappa}}{2}\right)^{\nu_\kappa}J'(\mathfrak{c}'').$$

FIG. 105

Observe next that $\mathfrak{R}_1(\mathfrak{o})$ is identical with $\dot{\mathfrak{P}}_1(\mathfrak{o})$ and therefore $\mathfrak{R}_1(\mathfrak{G}_1', \mathfrak{o}_1'')$ is identical with $\mathfrak{P}_1(\mathfrak{G}_1', \mathfrak{o}_1'')$. And with this it is seen that the individual bodies $\mathfrak{R}_1(\mathfrak{g}_1', \mathfrak{o}_1'')$ are entirely distinct as to their inner points. Now if $N_1 = M_1$, then due to the observations in II, $\mathfrak{P}_1(\mathfrak{G}_1', \mathfrak{o}_1'')$ covers the entire realm $\mathfrak{X}_1'$, $\mathfrak{P}_1''$ and $\mathfrak{Q}_1(\mathfrak{G}_1', \mathfrak{o}_1'')$ covers $\mathfrak{P}_1(\mathfrak{G}_1', \mathfrak{o}_1'')$, that is $\mathfrak{R}_1(\mathfrak{G}_1', \mathfrak{o}_1'')$; and due to this $\mathfrak{P}_2(\mathfrak{G}_1', \mathfrak{o}_1'')$ covers $\mathfrak{R}_2(\mathfrak{G}_1', \mathfrak{o}'')$; while $\mathfrak{P}_2(\mathfrak{G}_2', \mathfrak{o}_2'')$ covers $\mathfrak{R}_2(\mathfrak{G}_2', \mathfrak{o}_2'')$. Due to this last fact the individual realms in $\mathfrak{R}_2(\mathfrak{G}_2', \mathfrak{o}_2'')$ are entirely different in their interior points. Again assume that $N_2 = M_2$; it follows from above that $\mathfrak{P}_2(\mathfrak{G}_2', \mathfrak{o}_2'')$ covers the entire realm $\mathfrak{X}_2'$, $\mathfrak{P}_2''$ and $\mathfrak{Q}_2(\mathfrak{G}_2', \mathfrak{o}_2'')$ is covered by $\mathfrak{P}_2(\mathfrak{G}_2', \mathfrak{o}_2'')$. If in addition $N_3 = M_3$ then $\mathfrak{Q}_2(\mathfrak{G}_2', \mathfrak{o}_2'')$ is covered by $\mathfrak{R}_2(\mathfrak{G}_2', \mathfrak{o}_2'')$. And from this we have $\mathfrak{P}_3(\mathfrak{G}_2', \mathfrak{o}'')$ covering $\mathfrak{R}_3(\mathfrak{G}_2', \mathfrak{o}'')$, etc. Through the continuation of this process we come to the final result that *if all the* λ *equations*

$$N_1 = M_1, \qquad N_2 = M_2, \qquad \cdots, \qquad N_\lambda = M_\lambda$$

exist, then $\mathfrak{R}_\lambda(\mathfrak{o})$ *is a remainder realm in* $\mathfrak{X}$, being of a special kind which we shall now establish more exactly. To this end let κ be any arbitrary one of the numbers $1, 2, \cdots, \lambda - 1$. We shall confine ourselves only to the distribution $\mathfrak{x} = \mathfrak{x}', \mathfrak{x}''$ that belongs to this value κ. For brevity put $m = \mu_\kappa$. Further let $\mathfrak{K}$ denote the body $S(\mathfrak{o}\mathfrak{x}) \leqq 1$, J its volume, $\mathfrak{K}''$ the assemblage of the systems $\mathfrak{x}''$ in the body $\mathfrak{K}$ and finally J'' the volume of $\mathfrak{K}''$ in $\mathfrak{X}''$. The systems $\mathfrak{x}''$ that appear in $\mathfrak{R}_\kappa(\mathfrak{o})$ and whose complex constitutes the realm $\mathfrak{P}_\kappa''$ is had from the formula

$$\mathfrak{x}'' - \mathfrak{o}'' = \tfrac{1}{2} M_\kappa (\mathfrak{c}'' - \mathfrak{o}''),$$

where $\mathfrak{c}''$ moves in $\mathfrak{K}''$. For a system $\mathfrak{c}''$ of $\mathfrak{K}''$ we are to understand by $\mathfrak{K}'(\mathfrak{c}'')$ the assemblage of those systems $\mathfrak{x}'$, for which $\mathfrak{x}'$, $\mathfrak{c}''$ appears as a point of $\mathfrak{K}$. $J'(\mathfrak{c}'')$ denotes the volume of $\mathfrak{K}'(\mathfrak{c}'')$ in $\mathfrak{X}'$. And further, for the system $\mathfrak{x}''$ that belongs here to $\mathfrak{c}''$ we are to understand by $\mathfrak{R}_\kappa'(\mathfrak{o}', \mathfrak{x}'')$ the assemblage of those systems $\mathfrak{x}'$, for which $\mathfrak{x}'$, $\mathfrak{x}''$ is a point of

$\mathfrak{R}_\kappa(\mathfrak{o})$. The volume of $\mathfrak{R}'_\kappa(\mathfrak{o}', \mathfrak{x}'')$ in $\mathfrak{X}'$ is expressed through

$$\begin{vmatrix} \frac{S_1}{2}, & 0, & \cdots, & 0 \\ 0, & \frac{S_2}{2}, & \cdots, & 0 \\ \cdots & \cdots & \cdots & \cdots \\ 0, & 0, & \cdots, & \frac{S_m}{2} \end{vmatrix} J'(\mathfrak{c}'') = \frac{1}{2^m} M_1^{\mathfrak{v}_1} M_2^{\mathfrak{v}_2} \cdots M_\kappa^{\mathfrak{v}_\kappa} J'(\mathfrak{c}'').$$

The equations

$$(6) \qquad N_1 = M_1, \qquad N_2 = M_2, \qquad \cdots, \qquad N_\kappa = M_\kappa$$

are presupposed. After what has been just shown the result of these κ equations is that the individual bodies $\mathfrak{R}_\kappa(\mathfrak{g}', \mathfrak{o}'')$ are different in their interior points and collectively they fill the entire realm $\mathfrak{X}'$, $\mathfrak{P}''_\kappa$. These conditions have the following significance: Every system $\mathfrak{x}''$ of inner points of $\mathfrak{P}''_\kappa$ presents in the assemblage $\mathfrak{R}'_\kappa(\mathfrak{o}', \mathfrak{x}'')$ a remainder realm in $\mathfrak{X}'$. For a remainder realm the volume $=1$. We thus find on the one hand $J'(\mathfrak{c}'')$ to be a constant $=J'(\mathfrak{o}'')$ for inner points of $\mathfrak{K}''$ and then from Art. 151, III is everywhere constant in the entire realm $\mathfrak{K}''$; and on the other hand we have

$$(7) \qquad M_1^{\mathfrak{v}_1} M_2^{\mathfrak{v}_2} \cdots M_\kappa^{\mathfrak{v}_\kappa} J'(\mathfrak{o}'') = 2^m.$$

The essence of the first of these conditions has been made clear in Art. 151, IV. In the case of (7) of that article its proof requires additionally what is found in Arts. 152 and 153.

If $J'(\mathfrak{c}'')$ is constant in $\mathfrak{K}''$, it follows from the considerations there given that a definite substitution (see (8) of Art. 151)

$$x_1 = y_1 + a_1^{(m+1)} x_{m+1} + \cdots + a_1^{(n)} x_n,$$
$$\cdots\cdots\cdots\cdots\cdots\cdots\cdots\cdots$$
$$x_m = y_m + a_m^{(m+1)} x_{m+1} + \cdots + a_m^{(n)} x_n,$$

always exists which is such that in $\mathfrak{K}$ the variables y_1, y_2,

$\cdots, y_m$ and $x_{m+1}, x_{m+2}, \cdots, x_n$ run completely independent of one another; that is to say that $\mathfrak{K}$ is had, if we take for all systems $x_{m+1}, x_{m+2}, \cdots, x_n$ all systems $\mathfrak{x}''$ of $\mathfrak{K}''$, and with

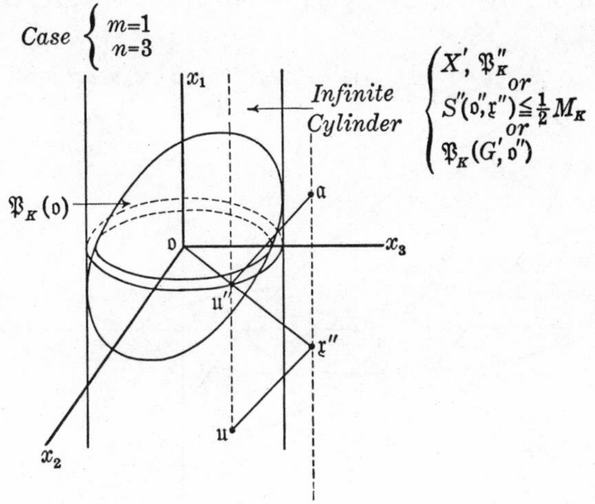

$\mathfrak{x}$ is any point outside the infinite cylinder. On the segment $\mathfrak{o}''\mathfrak{x}''$ we choose $\mathfrak{u}''$ so that

$$S''(\mathfrak{o}''\mathfrak{u}'') = \tfrac{1}{2}M_\kappa.$$

In $\mathfrak{X}'$, $\mathfrak{u}''$ we choose $\mathfrak{u}$ so that

$$S(\mathfrak{u}\mathfrak{x}) = S(\mathfrak{u}''\mathfrak{a}) = S''(\mathfrak{u}''\mathfrak{x}''),$$

where $\mathfrak{a}$ is a point on $\mathfrak{X}'$, $\mathfrak{x}''$ which gives a minimum distance from $\mathfrak{u}''$.

FIG. 106

each single one of these systems $x_{m+1}, x_{m+2}, \cdots, x_n$ we take for $y_1, y_2, \cdots, y_m$ all systems $\mathfrak{x}'$ out of $\mathfrak{K}'(\mathfrak{o}'')$. The fact that $J'(\mathfrak{c}'')$ is constant leads to the equation $J = J'(\mathfrak{o}'')J''$, where J'' is the volume of $\mathfrak{K}''$ in $\mathfrak{X}''$. The relation (7) indicates nothing else than that $\mathfrak{K}'(\mathfrak{o}'')$ is an extreme standard body in $\mathfrak{X}'$. It may be remarked further that this body here appears prepared (p. 614) for the coordinates $x_1, x_2, \cdots, x_m$.

The equations (6) carry with themselves still further results: As already seen in II we have always

$$S''(\mathfrak{o}'', \mathfrak{x}'') \leqq \varphi_\kappa(\mathfrak{x}).$$

Observe that here $N_i = M_i$ ($i = 1, 2, \cdots, \kappa$) and that here

$\mathfrak{X}'$, $\mathfrak{P}_\kappa'' = S''(\mathfrak{o}'', \mathfrak{x}'') \leqq \frac{1}{2}M_\kappa$ coincides with the realm that is expressed through $\mathfrak{P}_\kappa(\mathfrak{G}', \mathfrak{o}'')$. If for a point $\mathfrak{u}$ we have the equation $S''(\mathfrak{o}''\mathfrak{u}) = \frac{1}{2}M_\kappa$, we must have also $\varphi_\kappa(u) = \frac{1}{2}M_\kappa$. We cannot have $\varphi_\kappa(u) < \frac{1}{2}M_\kappa$. For N_κ is the greatest value

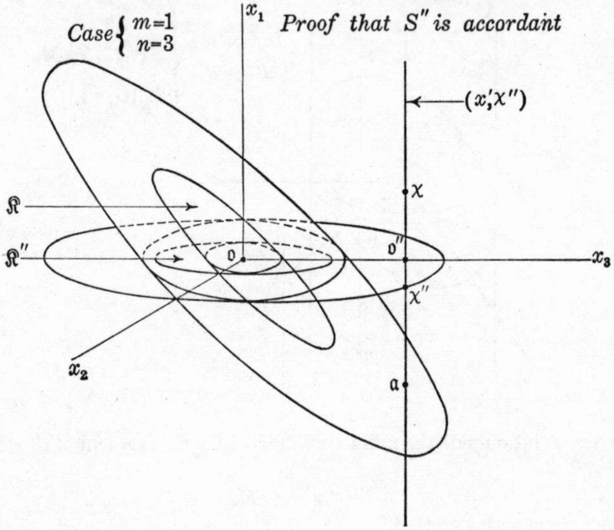

If we dilate the standard body until it is just touching the domain $(\mathfrak{X}', \mathfrak{x}'')$, and $\mathfrak{a}$ is a point of contact, we have

$$S''(\mathfrak{o}''\mathfrak{x}'') = S(\mathfrak{o}\mathfrak{a}).$$

And if the dilation was made in the ratio $r : 1$ we have

$$S''(\mathfrak{o}''\mathfrak{x}'') = r.$$

But we have also dilated $\mathfrak{K}''$ in the ratio $r : 1$, into a nowhere concave (if $\mathfrak{K}$ is nowhere concave) body with $\mathfrak{x}''$ on its boundary. Thus it is apparent that $\mathfrak{K}''$ is the standard body which defines S''. Since $\mathfrak{K}''$ is nowhere concave, S'' is accordant.

FIG. 107

of φ_κ in this interval, and here $M_\kappa = N_\kappa$. If on the other hand $\mathfrak{x}$ is any point without $\mathfrak{P}_\kappa(\mathfrak{G}', \mathfrak{o}'')$ we have for this point not only $\varphi_\kappa > \frac{1}{2}M_\kappa$, but also $S''(\mathfrak{o}''\mathfrak{x}'') > \frac{1}{2}M_\kappa$. We may accordingly find on the stretch $\mathfrak{o}''\mathfrak{x}''$ a definite point u'' in $\mathfrak{X}''$ for which $S''(\mathfrak{o}''\mathfrak{u}'') = \frac{1}{2}M_\kappa$, $S''(\mathfrak{u}''\mathfrak{x}'') = S''(\mathfrak{o}''\mathfrak{x}'') - \frac{1}{2}M_\kappa$ (See Fig. 106). And then we may determine a point $\mathfrak{u}$ in $\mathfrak{X}'$, $\mathfrak{u}''$ such that for it $S(\mathfrak{u}\mathfrak{x}) = S''(\mathfrak{u}''\mathfrak{x}'')$. We must also have from above $\varphi_\kappa(u)=\frac{1}{2}M_\kappa$. From this and from $\varphi_\kappa(\mathfrak{x})\leqq\varphi_\kappa(u)+S(u\mathfrak{x})$ we have

$$\varphi_\kappa(u)\leqq S''(\mathfrak{o}''\mathfrak{x}'')\cdots(ii).$$

From (i) and (ii) it is seen that for points without the realm $\mathfrak{P}_\kappa(\mathfrak{G}', \mathfrak{o}'')$, that is if $\varphi_\kappa(\mathfrak{x})>\frac{1}{2}M_\kappa$, we have always $\varphi_\kappa(\mathfrak{x})=S''(\mathfrak{o}''\mathfrak{x}'')$. In the above we have tacitly assumed that S'' is accordant. The Fig. 107 illustrating this property is given by Dr. Clemmer Mitchell, with additional remarks accompanying the figure.

We may write as in Art. 146

$$M_1=S_1=\cdots=S_{\mu_1}, \quad \cdots, \quad M_\lambda=S_{\mu_{\lambda-1}+1}, \quad \cdots, \quad S_{\mu_\lambda}.$$

Let $\mathfrak{p}_1, \cdots, \mathfrak{p}_n$ be a system of n lattice points in n independent directions from $\mathfrak{o}$, and with the radial-distances

$$S(\mathfrak{o}\mathfrak{p}_1)=S_1, \quad S(\mathfrak{o}\mathfrak{p}_2)=S_2, \quad \cdots, \quad S(\mathfrak{o}\mathfrak{p}_n)=S_n.$$

As in Art. 146, $\mathfrak{X}'$, $\mathfrak{o}''$ denotes the manifold laid through $\mathfrak{p}_1, \mathfrak{p}_2, \cdots, \mathfrak{p}_m$ and the values $\varphi_\kappa(\mathfrak{p}_{m+1}), \varphi_\kappa(\mathfrak{p}_{m+2}), \cdots, \varphi_\kappa(\mathfrak{p}_n)$ cannot be smaller than $S(\mathfrak{o}\mathfrak{p}_{m+1}), S(\mathfrak{o}\mathfrak{p}_{m+2}), \cdots, S(\mathfrak{o}\mathfrak{p}_n)$; and hence they are equal to these quantities. From this it follows that $S''(\mathfrak{o}''\mathfrak{p}''_{m+1})=S_{m+1}, \cdots, S''(\mathfrak{o}''\mathfrak{p}''_n)=S_n$; and it is seen that $\mathfrak{p}''_{m+1}, \cdots, \mathfrak{p}''_n$ are systems (points), being lattice points of the lattice $\mathfrak{G}$ in $\mathfrak{X}''$ which lie in $n-m$ independent directions from $\mathfrak{o}''$. On the other hand if $\mathfrak{q}''_{m+1}, \cdots, \mathfrak{q}''_n$ are any $n-m$ systems of this kind taken out of $\mathfrak{G}$ we may always in the manifold $\mathfrak{X}'$, $\mathfrak{q}''_{m+1}$, in the manifold $\mathfrak{X}'$, $\mathfrak{q}''_{m+2}, \cdots$, and in the manifold $\mathfrak{X}'$, $\mathfrak{q}''_n$ choose respectively lattice points $\mathfrak{q}_{m+1}, \mathfrak{q}_{m+2}, \cdots, \mathfrak{q}_n$ for which the radial-distances $\varphi_m(\mathfrak{q}_{m+1}), \cdots, \varphi_m(\mathfrak{q}_n)$ are offered through $S(\mathfrak{o}\mathfrak{q}_{m+1}), \cdots, S(\mathfrak{o}\mathfrak{q}_n)$. Further, since $\mathfrak{p}_1, \mathfrak{p}_2, \cdots, \mathfrak{p}_m, \mathfrak{q}_{m+1}, \cdots, \mathfrak{q}_n$ are lattice points in n independent directions from $\mathfrak{o}$, it is seen that $S''(\mathfrak{o}''\mathfrak{q}''_{m+1})\geqq S_{m+1}, \cdots, S''(\mathfrak{o}''\mathfrak{q}_n)\geqq S_n$. Thus it is seen that for the radial-distances $S''(\mathfrak{a}, \mathfrak{b})$ in $\mathfrak{X}''$ *the least system of independently directed radial-distances in the lattice* $\mathfrak{G}''$ *are the quantities* $S_{m+1}, \cdots, S_n$. Further observe also that the body

$S''(\mathfrak{o}''\mathfrak{x}'') \leqq 1$, and that is $\mathfrak{K}''$ as presented, *is prepared for the coordinates* $x_{m+1}, \cdots, x_n$.

From the equations (7) and $J = J'(\mathfrak{o}'')J''$ it follows from (1) that

$$M_{\kappa+1}^{v_{\kappa+1}} \cdots M_\lambda^{v_\lambda} J'' \leqq 2^{n-m},$$

and from the explanation of $M_{\kappa+1}, \cdots, M_\lambda$ just given it is necessary for the existence of the equality sign in (1) that we must have the additional condition that $\mathfrak{K}''$ be an *extreme standard body* in $\mathfrak{X}''$.

Observe that with the bodies $\mathfrak{K}'(\mathfrak{o}'')$ and $\mathfrak{K}''$ instead of λ the smaller numbers κ and $\lambda - \kappa$ appear, and further observe the nature of the case $\lambda = 1$ found at the beginning of this article. It then follows the

THEOREM. *Let* $v_1, v_2, \cdots, v_\lambda$ *be any positive integers whose sum* $= n$, *and put* $\mu_0 = 0$, $\mu_1 = v_1$, $\mu_2 = v_1 + v_2$, $\cdots$, $\mu_\lambda = v_1 + v_2 + \cdots + v_\lambda = n$; *further introduce any substitution*

$$(8)\quad \begin{cases} x_h = \dfrac{2y_h + a_h^{(\mu_\kappa+1)} y_{\mu_\kappa+1} + \cdots + a_h^{(n)} y_n}{M_\kappa}, \\ (h = \mu_{\kappa-1}+1, \quad \cdots, \quad \mu_\kappa; \qquad \kappa = 1, 2, \cdots, \lambda - 1), \\ x_h = \dfrac{2y_h}{M_\lambda} \qquad (h = \mu_{\lambda-1}+1, \cdots, \mu_\lambda), \end{cases}$$

with determinant $\dfrac{2^n}{M_1^{v_1} M_2^{v_2} \cdots M_\lambda^{v_\lambda}}$ *where* $0 < M_1 < M_2 < \cdots < M_\lambda$, *and where the quantities* M_κ *and* $a_h^{(\kappa)}$ *may be arbitrarily chosen; and for* $\kappa = 1, 2, \cdots, \lambda$ *let* $y_{\mu_{\kappa-1}+1}, y_{\mu_{\kappa-1}+2}, \cdots, y_{\mu_\kappa}$ *describe any fixed remainder realm* $\mathfrak{R}^{(\kappa)}$ *in the manifold of these variables. An extreme standard body* $\mathfrak{K}$ *is thus produced which is prepared for the special variables* $x_1, x_2, \cdots, x_n$; *and every extreme standard body thus prepared in* $x_1, x_2, \cdots, x_n$ *may be had in this manner and always only through an assumption regarding* λ *and the quantities* v_κ, M_κ, $a_h^{(\kappa)}$, $\mathfrak{R}^{(\kappa)}$.

Through this theorem the determination of all extreme standard bodies is reduced to *the finding of the remainder realms in the manifolds of n and of fewer variables.*

The remainder realm denoted here by $\mathfrak{R}^{(\kappa)}$ in its manifold of v_κ variables has not more than $2^{v_\kappa+1}-2$ essential tac-planes (*Stützebene*) (Cf. Art. 48, II). If through (8) we introduce the variables $x_1, x_2, \cdots, x_n$ into the equations of these planes and take one after the other every value $\kappa=1, 2, \cdots, \lambda$, we derive exactly all the essential tac-planes of the extreme standard realm. It is seen[1] that their number is (p. 170) $\leqq[(2^{v_1+2}-2)+\cdots+(2^{v_\lambda+1}-2)]$. And the aggregate of this last number is for $\lambda\geqq 1$ always $\leqq 2^{n+1}-2$. (See Art. 48, end.)

Further observe that if $\lambda>1$, there must necessarily appear rational directions in some of the above planes, since the equations do not really contain all the variables.

On the other hand, a realm $\mathfrak{R}^{(\kappa)}$ must contain *at least* $2v_\kappa$ tac-planes. If the realm $\mathfrak{K}$ is in particular a parallelopipedon, and therefore has only $2n$ essential tac-planes, then every realm $\mathfrak{R}^{(\kappa)}$ must of itself be a parallelopipedon.

If we note for the case $\lambda>1$ the remark just made above, and for $\lambda=1$ the presentation of Art. 55, II, we have the following theorem:

A parallelopipedon on whose boundary there are no rational directions can never offer an extreme standard body.

ART. 155. An Auxiliary Consideration Regarding Ovals. In Art. 151 (7) certain lemmas were indicated without sufficient proof. These lemmas are considered here in detail with complete proof, and this completes the results of the preceding article. We begin with a more exact consideration of the results that exist for the case $n=2$.

I. First recall the proof of a known property of continuous functions. Let $y(x)$ be a continuous function of x in the interval $a_0\leqq x\leqq a_1$; and let $y(a_0)=b_0$, $y(a_1)=b_1$, and $b_0<b_1$. Let b denote any given value such that $b_0\leqq b\leqq b_1$ and let a be the greatest lower limit (Art. 34) of all those values x in the interval $a_0\leqq x\leqq a_1$ for which $y(x)-b>0$. We cannot then have $y(a)-b>0$. For in that case we

[1] Minkowski, *Ges. Abhandl.*, II, pp. 120, 137, 166.

necessarily have $a > a_0$. This follows from the assumption $y(a) > b \geqq b_0 = y(a_0)$. And if we take a *smaller* value of x than a in $y(a) - b > 0$ due to the continuity of $y(x)$ at a toward smaller values of x, we meet with a contradiction of the concept of a lower limit. Similarly we cannot have $y(a) - b < 0$. For necessarily $a < a_1$. And due to the continuity of $y(x)$ at a toward greater values of x we meet a contradiction of a greater lower limit. Hence necessarily we must have $y(a) = b$.

If $y(x)$, a continuous function in the interval $a_0 \leqq x \leqq a_1$, continuously increases with x, then for every value of y within the interval $b_0 \leqq y \leqq b_1$ there is only *one* value x for which $y(x) = y$. Denote this value of x by $x(y)$. Then $x(y)$ is inversely a continuously increasing function with y in the interval $b_0 \leqq y \leqq b_1$ and it is seen that this function is *continuous* within this interval. For corresponding to an arbitrarily given change of the variable x from a value a corresponds a definite change of the function $y(x)$ from $y(a) = b$ on in an equal sense, and then there belongs to every smaller change of the variable y from b in this sense always a smaller change of $x(y)$ than the previous.

II. In this book certain concepts regarding manifolds of n variables have been introduced under the notation "nowhere concave bodies" and "volume." These expressions were chosen that in the case of any integer n the geometric visualization made possible in the case $n = 3$ might also be of value. However this fails if the investigation has to do with the case $n = 2$ and consequently here we must change the notation [1] to the words "oval" and "content."

Consider a manifold of two variables x, y. An *oval* in x, y (Cf. Art. 151) is to be defined as an assemblage of points x, y, 1°, which has in common with a straight line either *no* point, or *one* point, or a *stretch* of points, and 2°, which itself

[1] Brunn has given some interesting properties of the nowhere concave structures in two and three dimensions, *Über Ovale und Eiflächen*, München, 1887; *Über Curven ohne Wendepunkte*, "Habilitationsschrift," München, 1889. See also "Sitzungsber. d. math.-physik," *Classe der bayer. Akad. d. Wiss.*, 1894, Vol. 24, pp. 93–111. See also references at the end of Art. 156.

does not express only a *stretch* on a single point. As seen in Art. 151 the property 1° has for an assemblage of points the same significance as the following conditions: 3° that if two points belong to the assemblage of points, then every point of the stretch joining them also belongs to the assemblage; 4° that the assemblage is a closed one, and finally 5° that for the values of the coordinates x, y in the assemblage there exist upper as well as lower limits.

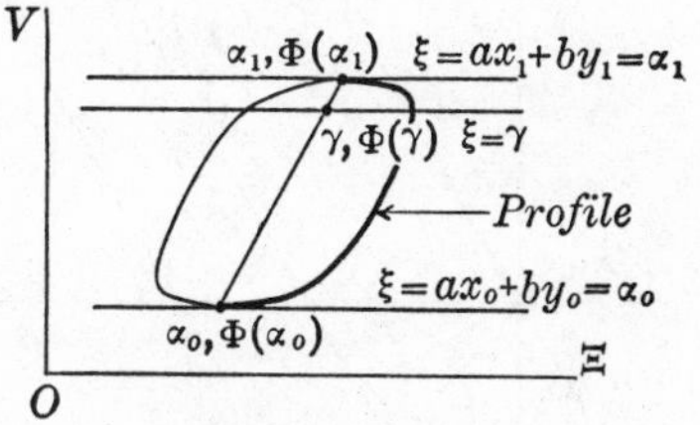

$$\left.\begin{array}{l}\xi = ax+by\\ v = cx+dy\end{array}\right\}, \qquad ad-bc=1.$$

FIG. 108

Let $\mathfrak{A}$ be an oval in x, y and let $J(\mathfrak{A})$ be its content in x, y. Further let ξ and v be two linear forms in x, y with a determinant $=1$. Due to 4° and 5° ξ has in $\mathfrak{A}$ a definite minimum α_0 and a definite maximum α_1 in $\mathfrak{A}$. Further v has on the line $\xi = \alpha_0$ in $\mathfrak{A}$ a maximum value, which call $\Phi(\alpha_0)$ and a maximum on the line $\xi = \alpha_1$ which call $\Phi(\alpha_1)$. The points of the stretch between the point $\xi = \alpha_0$, $v = \Phi(\alpha_0)$ and the point $\xi = \alpha_1$, $v = \Phi(\alpha_1)$ are expressed through

(1) $\xi = \gamma = (1-\tau)\alpha_0 + \tau\alpha_1, \qquad v = F(\gamma) = (1-\tau)\Phi(\alpha_0) + \tau\Phi(\alpha_1)$

for values $\tau \geqq 0$ and $\leqq 1$. Observe that on every line $\xi = \gamma$ (See Fig. 109) where $\gamma \geqq \alpha_0$ and $\leqq \alpha_1$ in $\mathfrak{A}$ there is a definite maximum of v which is denoted by $\Phi(\gamma)$. It is evident that we have always

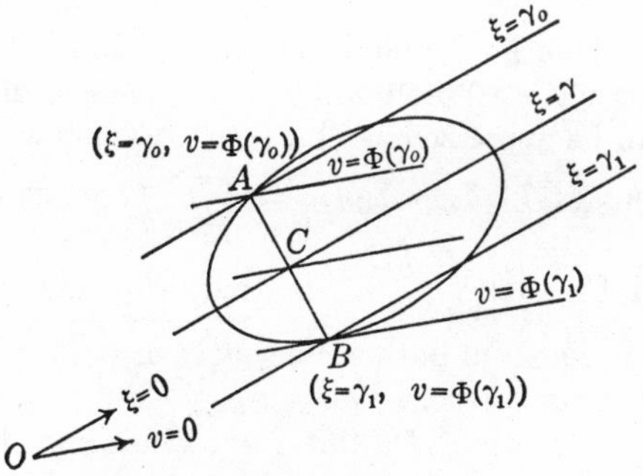

Oblique coordinates (ξ, v) of C are (if we use the relation $ad-bc=1$)

$$\left\{\gamma, \frac{\gamma_1-\gamma}{\gamma_1-\gamma_0}\Phi(\gamma_0)+\frac{\gamma-\gamma_0}{\gamma_1-\gamma_0}\Phi(\gamma_1)\right\}.$$

FIG. 109

(2) $$\Phi(\gamma) \geqq F(\gamma).$$

In particular it is seen that the minimum of the two values $\Phi(\alpha_0)$ and $\Phi(\alpha_1)$ is a *lower limit* for all values $\Phi(\gamma)$. The assemblage of points defined through $\alpha_0 \leqq \xi \leqq \alpha_1$, $v = \Phi(\xi)$ may be called the ξ-*profile* of $\mathfrak{A}$. This assemblage clearly does *not* depend upon the form v.

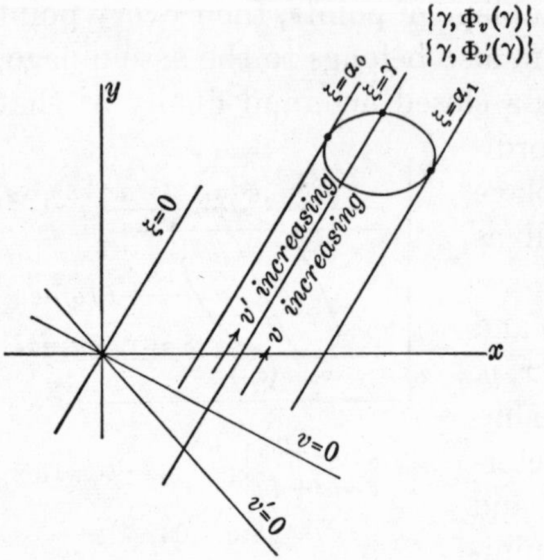

FIG. 110

Remark. The ξ-profile of the oval is independent of the linear form v so long as the determinant of ξ and v is greater than zero.

If $\xi = ax + by$, $v = cx + dy$, and $v' = c'x + d'y$ are three arbitrary linear expressions for which (Fig. 110)

$$\begin{vmatrix} a, & b \\ c, & d \end{vmatrix} > 0, \qquad \begin{vmatrix} a, & b \\ c', & d' \end{vmatrix} > 0, \qquad \begin{vmatrix} c, & d \\ c', & d' \end{vmatrix} \neq 0,$$

it then follows that points along $\xi = 0$ which yield $v < 0$ yield $v' < 0$, and points on $\xi = 0$ which yield $v > 0$ yield $v' > 0$. For, the coordinates of points on $\xi = 0$ can be expressed as $(kb, -ka)$. The value of v for any one of these points $k = \bar{k}$ is $\bar{k}bc - \bar{k}ad$ or $-\bar{k}\begin{vmatrix} a, & b \\ c, & d \end{vmatrix}$. The value of v' for the same point is $-\bar{k}\begin{vmatrix} a, & b \\ c', & d' \end{vmatrix}$. So that for points on $\xi = 0$, v and v' have the same sign and both are negative or both are positive according as k is positive or negative.

If we now consider the intersection of a line $\xi = \gamma$ with an oval, the maximum of v is yielded at the same extremity of this line-segment of the oval as is the maximum of v'.

The ξ-profile of the oval is then independent of the line $v = 0$, depending only upon the sign of the determinant $\begin{vmatrix} a, & b \\ c, & d \end{vmatrix}$ which was stipulated to be positive.

If we have $\alpha_0 \leqq \gamma_0 \leqq \gamma \leqq \gamma_1 \leqq \alpha_1$ then since the stretch from $\xi = \gamma_0$, $v = \Phi(\gamma_0)$ to $\xi = \gamma_1$, $v = \Phi(\gamma_1)$ lies entirely in $\mathfrak{A}$ due to the meaning of $\Phi(\gamma)$, we must always have (Figure 109).

$$\Phi(\gamma) \geqq \frac{\gamma_1-\gamma}{\gamma_1-\gamma_0}\Phi(\gamma_0)+\frac{\gamma-\gamma_0}{\gamma_1-\gamma_0}\Phi(\gamma_1). \tag{3}$$

The case (2) is a special case of (3), namely when $\alpha_1=\gamma_1$ and $\alpha_0=\gamma_0$. For writing $\gamma_1-\gamma=(\gamma_1-\gamma_0)(1-\tau)$, $\gamma-\gamma_0=(\gamma_1-\gamma_0)\tau$ the expression (3) becomes

$$\Phi(\gamma) \geqq (1-\tau)\Phi(\gamma_0)+\tau\Phi(\gamma_1) \tag{3'}$$

and the expression on the right is $F(\gamma)$ when $\gamma_0=\alpha_0$ and $\gamma_1=\alpha_1$.

We may next ask how far does the inequality (3) contribute to the definition of the function $\Phi(\xi)$. Denote the quotient $\dfrac{\Phi(\xi_1)-\Phi(\xi_0)}{\xi_1-\xi_0}$ by (ξ_0, ξ_1), where $\xi_0<\xi_1$. Observe that the inequality

$$\frac{\Phi(\gamma)-\Phi(\gamma_0)}{\gamma-\gamma_0} \geqq \frac{\Phi(\gamma_1)-\Phi(\gamma_0)}{\gamma_1-\gamma_0}$$

leads at once to

$$\Phi(\gamma) \geqq \frac{\gamma-\gamma_0}{\gamma_1-\gamma_0}\Phi(\gamma_1)+\frac{\gamma_1-\gamma}{\gamma_1-\gamma_0}\Phi(\gamma_0),$$

that is, the inequality $(\gamma_0, \gamma) \geqq (\gamma_0, \gamma_1)$ has the same significance as (3), as has also the inequality $(\gamma_0, \gamma_1) \geqq (\gamma, \gamma_1)$. And that is (3) has the same significance as either

$$(\gamma_0, \gamma) \geqq (\gamma_0, \gamma_1) \qquad \text{or} \qquad (\gamma_0, \gamma_1) \geqq (\gamma, \gamma_1),$$

where $\gamma_1>\gamma>\gamma_0$. From this it is seen that the function (ξ_0, ξ_1) never *increases* when either of the arguments ξ_0, ξ_1 increases.

Next observe that

$$\frac{\Phi(\gamma)-\Phi(\alpha_0)}{\gamma-\alpha_0} \geqq \frac{\Phi(\alpha_1)-\Phi(\alpha_0)}{\alpha_1-\alpha_0}$$

becomes at once

$$\Phi(\gamma) \geqq \frac{\gamma-\alpha_0}{\alpha_1-\alpha_0}\Phi(\alpha_1)+\frac{\alpha_1-\gamma}{\alpha_1-\alpha_0}\Phi(\alpha_0),$$

where the right-hand side is $F(\gamma)$, if we put

$$\alpha_1-\gamma=(\alpha_1-\alpha_0)(1-\tau), \qquad \gamma-\alpha_0=(\alpha_1-\alpha_0)\tau.$$

Hence (2) has the same significance as

$$(\alpha_0, \gamma) \geqq (\alpha_0, \alpha_1)$$

or

$$(\alpha_0, \alpha_1) \geqq (\gamma, \alpha_1),$$

where $\alpha_0<\gamma<\alpha_1$.

Consider next the inequalities

$$(\alpha_0, \gamma) \geqq (\alpha_0, \xi), \qquad (\xi_0, \alpha_1) \geqq (\gamma, \alpha_1)$$

where $\alpha_0<\xi_0<\gamma<\xi_1<\alpha_1$.
From

$$\frac{\Phi(\alpha_1)-\Phi(\alpha_0)}{\alpha_1-\alpha_0} \geqq \frac{\Phi(\alpha_1)-\Phi(\gamma)}{\alpha_1-\gamma}$$

we have

$$\Phi(\gamma) \geqq \frac{\gamma-\alpha_0}{\alpha_1-\alpha_0}\Phi(\alpha_1)+\frac{\alpha_1-\gamma}{\alpha_1-\alpha_0}\Phi(\alpha_0)=(1-\tau)\Phi(\alpha_0)+\tau\Phi(\alpha_1);$$

and if for some value of γ the left-hand side is equal to the right-hand side, τ is fixed. Hence if for *one* value of γ within the interval $\alpha_0 \cdots \alpha_1$ we have $\Phi(\gamma)=F(\gamma)$ then necessarily in the whole interval $\Phi(\xi)=F(\xi)$. And due to the fact that from the second relation $(\xi_1, \alpha_1) \geqq (\gamma, \alpha_1)$ we have

$$\Phi(\gamma)=\frac{\gamma-\alpha_0}{\xi_1-\alpha_0}\Phi(\xi_1)+\frac{\xi_1-\gamma}{\xi_1-\alpha_0}\Phi(\alpha_0)$$
$$=(1-\tau)\Phi(\alpha_0)+\tau\Phi(\xi_1)=F(\gamma)$$

so that the point ξ_1, $\Phi(\xi_1)$ lies on the line joining α_0, $\Phi(\alpha_0)$ and α_1, $\Phi(\alpha_1)$.

From the inequalities

$$(\alpha_0, \gamma) \geqq (\xi_0, \gamma) \geqq (\gamma, \alpha_1)$$

and

$$(\alpha_0, \gamma) \geqq (\gamma, \xi_1) \geqq (\gamma, \alpha_1)$$

it follows that $\Phi(\xi)$ is continuous on the position $\xi=\gamma$, which is arbitrary but completely *within* the interval $\alpha_0 \leqq \xi \leqq \alpha_1$.

Finally it is seen that if $(\xi_0, \xi_1) > 0$, then $\Phi(\xi_1) > \Phi(\xi_0)$, and $\Phi(\xi)$ in the interval $\alpha_0 \leqq \xi \leqq \xi_0$ continuously decreases from the second to the first limit, and as long as $(\xi_0, \xi_1) < 0$ that is also $\Phi(\xi_1) < \Phi(\xi_0)$, then in the interval $\xi_1 \leqq \xi \leqq \alpha_1$ the function $\Phi(\xi)$ continuously decreases. Accordingly it apperas that in the realm $\alpha_0 < \xi < \alpha_1$ the function $\Phi(\xi)$ appears as a nowhere increasing or as a nowhere decreasing function; or thirdly, the other possibility is that we can find two arguments γ_0, γ_1 such that $\Phi(\xi)$ in the intervals $\gamma_0 \geqq \xi \geqq \alpha_0$ and $\gamma_1 \leqq \xi \leqq \alpha_1$ continuously decreases from the first to the second limit. Since there exist a lower and an upper limit for the values of $\Phi(\xi)$, it is clear in each of these cases with the approach of the argument ξ in the realm $\alpha_0 < \xi < \alpha_1$ to the one or the other limit, in either case $\Phi(\xi)$ converges toward a definite quantity which may be denoted by $\Phi(\alpha_0+0)$ or $\Phi(\alpha_1-0)$. From (2) it then follows that

$$\Phi(\alpha_0+0) \geqq \Phi(\alpha_0), \qquad \Phi(\alpha_1-0) \geqq \Phi(\alpha_1).$$

If we take into account the fourth property above (4°) that an oval represents a closed assemblage of points, then the points $\xi=\alpha_0$, $v=\Phi(\alpha_0+0)$ and $\xi=\alpha_1$, $v=\Phi(\alpha_1-0)$ belong to $\mathfrak{A}$; and due to the meaning of $\Phi(\alpha_0)$ and $\Phi(\alpha_1)$ we can only have $\Phi(\alpha_0+0)=\Phi(\alpha_0)$ and $\Phi(\alpha_1-0)=\Phi(\alpha_1)$. With this it is seen that the function $\Phi(\xi)$ in the interval $\alpha_0 \leqq \xi \leqq \alpha_1$ is continuous on the *boundaries* and is therefore everywhere continuous in this interval.

To this may be added that from

$$(\alpha_0, \gamma) \geqq (\xi_0, \gamma) \geqq (\gamma, \alpha_1),$$

$$\frac{\Phi(\gamma)-\Phi(\alpha_0)}{\gamma-\alpha_0} \geqq \frac{\Phi(\gamma)-\Phi(\xi_0)}{\gamma-\xi_0} \geqq \frac{\Phi(\alpha_1)-\Phi(\gamma)}{\gamma-\alpha_1},$$

$$(\gamma-\xi_0)\underbrace{\frac{\Phi(\gamma)-\Phi(\alpha_0)}{\gamma-\alpha_0}}_{\text{finite}} \geqq \Phi(\gamma)-\Phi(\xi_0) \geqq \underbrace{\frac{\Phi(\alpha_1)-\Phi(\gamma)}{\gamma-\alpha_1}}_{\text{finite}}(\gamma-\xi_0),$$

we get continuity for approach from the left.

Similarly, from

$$(\alpha_0, \gamma) \geqq (\gamma, \xi_1) \geqq (\gamma, \alpha_1),$$

$$(\xi_1-\gamma)\underbrace{\frac{\Phi(\gamma)-\Phi(\alpha_0)}{\gamma-\alpha_0}}_{\text{finite}} \geqq \Phi(\xi_1)-\Phi(\gamma) \geqq \underbrace{\frac{\Phi(\alpha_1)-\Phi(\gamma)}{\alpha_1-\gamma}}_{\text{finite}}(\xi_1-\gamma),$$

we get continuity for approach from the right.

And further it is seen that if we have a function $\Phi(\xi)$ defined in an interval $\alpha_0 \leqq \xi \leqq \alpha_1$ which obeys the law as given in formula (3) for any three values γ_0, γ, γ_1 where $\gamma_0 < \gamma < \gamma_1$ and for which $\Phi(\alpha_0+0)$ is *not* $> \Phi(\alpha_0)$ and $\Phi(\alpha_1-0)$ is not $> \Phi(\alpha_1)$, then this function is seen to be continuous everywhere in its interval.

If we then write

$$\frac{\alpha_1-\xi}{\alpha_1-\alpha_0}\Phi(\alpha_0)+\frac{\xi-\alpha_0}{\alpha_1-\alpha_0}\Phi(\alpha_1)=F(\xi),$$

we have either everywhere $\Phi(\xi)=F(\xi)$; or on the other hand the assemblage of points defined through $\alpha_0 \leqq \xi \leqq \alpha_1$, $F(\xi) \leqq v \leqq \Phi(\xi)$ is an oval, due to the properties 5°, 4°, 3°, 2°. The assemblage of points given through $\alpha_0 \leqq \xi \leqq \alpha_1$, $v=\Phi(\xi)$ form in the first case a stretch on a straight line, and in the second case the ξ-profile of an oval.

Further, on every straight line $\xi=\gamma$ where $\gamma \geqq \alpha_0$ and $\leqq \alpha_1$ there exists in $\mathfrak{A}$ a definite minimum which may be denoted by $\varphi(\xi)$. The assemblage of points given through $\alpha_0 \leqq \xi \leqq \alpha_1$, $v=\varphi(\xi)$ is then the $(-\xi)$-profile of $\mathfrak{A}$. And the oval $\mathfrak{A}$ itself is completely laid through its ξ- and $(-\xi)$-profiles; that is, through the assemblage of points in which we have $\alpha_0 \leqq \xi \leqq \alpha_1$, $\varphi(\xi) \leqq v \leqq \Phi(\xi)$.

In (3) we may write $-\varphi$ for Φ and have corresponding in particular to the relation (2):

$$\varphi(\gamma) \leqq (1-\tau)\varphi(\alpha_0)+\tau\varphi(\alpha_1),$$

or

$$(4) \qquad -\varphi(\gamma) \geqq -(1-\tau)\varphi(\alpha_0)-\tau\varphi(\alpha_1)$$

for $\gamma=(1-\tau)\alpha_0+\tau(\alpha_1)$ and $\tau \geqq 0$ and $\leqq 1$. Observe further that the difference $\Phi(\xi)-\varphi(\xi)$, which may be denoted by $\overline{\varphi}(\xi)$, is continuous with $\Phi(\xi)$ and $\varphi(\xi)$ in the entire interval $\alpha_0 \leqq \xi \leqq \alpha_1$. Through the addition of (2) and (4) we have

$$\overline{\varphi}(\gamma) \geqq (1-\tau)\overline{\varphi}(\alpha_0)+\tau\overline{\varphi}(\alpha_1) \tag{5}$$

for $\gamma=(1-\tau)\alpha_0+\tau\alpha_1$ where $0 \leqq \tau \leqq 1$; and in (5) we have always the sign $=$ or the sign $>$ for all values $\gamma > \alpha_0$ and $\gamma < \alpha_1$. From this property 2° for every value γ which $> \alpha_0$ and $< \alpha_1$ we have always $\overline{\varphi}(\gamma) > 0$ while $\overline{\varphi}(\alpha_0)$ may also be zero, as may $\overline{\varphi}(\alpha_1)$.

Finally, due to the theorem in Art. 151, II, we have here the following expression:

$$J(\mathfrak{A}) = \int_{\alpha_0}^{\alpha_1} \overline{\varphi}(\xi) d\xi. \tag{6}$$

III. Let $\mathfrak{B}$ be a second oval in x, y and let $\mathfrak{J}(\mathfrak{B})$ be its content in x, y. Let β_0 be the minimum and β_1 the maximum of ξ in $\mathfrak{B}$ and finally let $\Psi(\xi)$, $\overline{\psi}(\xi)$ be the functions for $\mathfrak{B}$ which correspond to the functions $\Phi(\xi)$ and $\overline{\varphi}(\xi)$ for $\mathfrak{A}$. The ovals $\mathfrak{B}$ and $\mathfrak{A}$ are said to be *similarly stretched* (ähnlich gestreckt) *in the system of lines* $\xi=$constant if the relation

$$\frac{\overline{\psi}(\beta_0+\tau(\beta_1-\beta_0))}{\overline{\varphi}(\alpha_0+\tau(\alpha_1-\alpha_0))} = \frac{\beta_1-\beta_0}{\alpha_1-\alpha_0} \tag{7}$$

holds in the whole interval $0 \leqq \tau \leqq 1$. If further we have $\beta_1-\beta_0=\alpha_1-\alpha_0$, then we may say instead of *similarly stretched* the ovals are *equally stretched.* It is clear in these relations that ξ alone, and not also v, plays the rôle. From (6) it is seen, if the relation (7) holds, that

$$\mathfrak{J}(\mathfrak{B}) : \mathfrak{J}(\mathfrak{A}) = (\beta_1-\beta_0)^2 : (\alpha_1-\alpha_0)^2,$$

so that the ratio $\beta_1-\beta_0 : \alpha_1-\alpha_0$ also does *not* depend upon the coefficients of the special form ξ but upon the realms $\mathfrak{B}$ and $\mathfrak{A}$. If it is required that $\mathfrak{B}$ be derived from $\mathfrak{A}$ through a dilation or translation, then this may be done, if $J(\mathfrak{B}) \neq J(\mathfrak{A})$ only through a dilation in the ratio

$$\sqrt{J(\mathfrak{B})} : \sqrt{J(\mathfrak{A})},$$

and if $J(\mathfrak{B})=J(\mathfrak{A})$, only through a translation; and to this end it will be necessary and sufficient *first* that $\mathfrak{B}$ and $\mathfrak{A}$ are similarly stretched in the line system $\xi=$constant and *in addition* that in the interval $0\leqq\tau\leqq1$ we have fixedly

$$\frac{\Psi(\beta_0+\tau(\beta_1-\beta_0))-\Psi(\beta_0)}{\beta_1-\beta_0}=\frac{\Phi(\alpha_0+\tau(\alpha_1-\alpha_0))-\Phi(\alpha_0)}{\alpha_1-\alpha_0}.$$

We then have the following theorem:

If the ovals $\mathfrak{B}$ *and* $\mathfrak{A}$ *are similarly stretched in the line system* $\xi=$*constant, and if it is not possible to derive* $\mathfrak{B}$ *from* $\mathfrak{A}$ *through a dilation or translation, then a quantity c may always be derived such that in the line system* $\zeta=v-c\xi=$*constant, the two ovals are not similarly stretched.*

Case where $\Psi(\alpha_1)=\Phi(\alpha_1)$

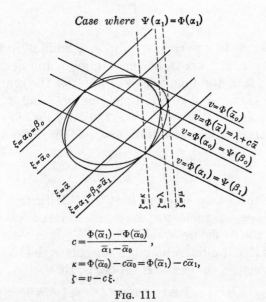

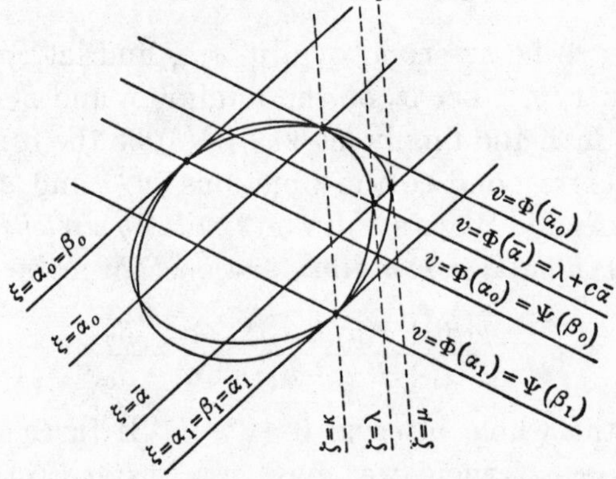

$$c=\frac{\Phi(\bar{\alpha}_1)-\Phi(\bar{\alpha}_0)}{\bar{\alpha}_1-\bar{\alpha}_0},$$
$$\kappa=\Phi(\bar{\alpha}_0)-c\bar{\alpha}_0=\Phi(\bar{\alpha}_1)-c\bar{\alpha}_1,$$
$$\zeta=v-c\xi.$$

FIG. 111

To prove this theorem it is clearly sufficient if it be proved for any oval derived from $\mathfrak{B}$ through a dilation or translation, and consequently it is permissible to make simply the assumptions $\beta_0=\alpha_0$, $\Psi(\beta_1)=\Phi(\alpha_0)$ and $\beta_1=\alpha_1$. In this case $\mathfrak{B}$ and $\mathfrak{A}$ will in particular be thought of as *equally stretched* in the line system $\xi=$constant, which carries with itself additionally $\mathfrak{J}(\mathfrak{B})=\mathfrak{J}(\mathfrak{A})$. And the function $\Psi(\xi)-\Phi(\xi)$ is now $=0$ for $\xi=\alpha_0$ besides being continuous in the entire interval $\alpha_0 \leqq \xi \leqq \alpha_1$ but by hypothesis this difference is constantly *not* $=0$. (See Fig. 111.) Two cases are now to be distinguished. *First,* let $\Psi(\alpha_1)-\Phi(\alpha_1)$ be *also* $=0$. We may then find any value $\gamma>\alpha_0$ and $<\alpha_1$ for which $\Phi(\gamma)-\Psi(\gamma)$ is different from zero.

Suppose for example that $\Psi(\gamma)>\Phi(\gamma)$; and let $\bar{\alpha}_0$ be the least upper limit of all values ξ in the interval $\alpha_0 \leqq \xi \leqq \gamma$ for which $\Psi(\xi)-\Phi(\xi) \leqq 0$, and let α_1 be the greatest lower limit of all values ξ in the realm $\gamma \leqq \xi \leqq \alpha_1$ for which $\Psi(\xi)-\Phi(\xi) \leqq 0$.

It is seen that $\bar{\alpha}_0<\gamma<\bar{\alpha}_1$ and (note remarks above in I) we have necessarily $\Psi(\bar{\alpha}_0)=\Phi(\bar{\alpha}_0)$ and $\Psi(\bar{\alpha}_1)=\Phi(\bar{\alpha}_1)$, while in the entire realm $\bar{\alpha}_0<\xi<\bar{\alpha}_1$ we have $\Phi(\xi)<\Psi(\xi)$. We accordingly introduce the quantity $c=\dfrac{\Phi(\alpha_1)-\Phi(\bar{\alpha}_0)}{\bar{\alpha}_1-\bar{\alpha}_0}$. Observe that the linear forms $\zeta=v-c\xi$ and $-\xi$ have the determinant 1 since the determinant of the linear forms ξ and v in x, y, is 1, so that the formula (6) is applicable.

Write $\Phi(\bar{\alpha}_0)-c\bar{\alpha}_0=\kappa$. Then from (3) we have

$$\Phi(\gamma)-c\gamma \geqq \frac{\bar{\alpha}_1-\gamma}{\bar{\alpha}_1-\bar{\alpha}_0}\Phi(\alpha_0)+\frac{\gamma-\bar{\alpha}_0}{\bar{\alpha}_1-\bar{\alpha}_0}\Phi(\alpha_1)=\frac{\Phi(\bar{\alpha}_1)-\Phi(\bar{\alpha}_0)}{\bar{\alpha}_1-\bar{\alpha}_0}\gamma,$$

so that

$$\Phi(\gamma)-c\gamma \geqq \frac{\bar{\alpha}_1}{\bar{\alpha}_1-\bar{\alpha}_0}\Phi(\bar{\alpha}_0)-\frac{\bar{\alpha}_0}{\bar{\alpha}_1-\bar{\alpha}_0}\Phi(\bar{\alpha}_1).$$

On the other hand

$$\kappa=\Phi(\bar{\alpha}_0)-c\bar{\alpha}_0=\frac{\bar{\alpha}_1}{\bar{\alpha}_1-\bar{\alpha}_0}\Phi(\bar{\alpha}_0)-\frac{\bar{\alpha}_0}{\bar{\alpha}_1-\bar{\alpha}_0}\Phi(\bar{\alpha}_1).$$

With this it is seen that

$$\Phi(\gamma)-c\gamma \geqq \kappa.$$

Further let λ be the *maximum* of ζ in $\mathfrak{A}$ where $\lambda \geqq \kappa$. Then if $\lambda>\kappa$, let $\xi=\bar{\alpha}$, $v=\lambda+c\bar{\alpha}$ be a point in $\mathfrak{A}$ in which we have this maximum of ζ. Again for brevity write (ξ_0, ξ_1)

for the quotient $\dfrac{\Phi(\xi_1)-\Phi(\xi_0)}{\xi_1-\xi_0}$, $\xi_1>\xi_0$. If then $\alpha_0\leqq\xi\leqq\overline{\alpha}_0$ it follows from $(\xi, \overline{\alpha})\geqq(\overline{\alpha}_0, \overline{\alpha}_1)$, or if $\overline{\alpha}_1\leqq\alpha_1$ it follows from $(\overline{\alpha}_0, \overline{\alpha}_1)\geqq(\overline{\alpha}_0, \xi)$ that $\Phi(\xi)-c\xi\leqq\kappa$. For if

$$\frac{\Phi(\overline{\alpha}_1)-\Phi(\overline{\alpha}_0)}{\overline{\alpha}_1-\overline{\alpha}_0}\geqq\frac{\Phi(\xi)-\Phi(\overline{\alpha}_0)}{\xi-\overline{\alpha}_0},$$

we have at once

$$\Phi(\xi)\leqq\frac{\overline{\alpha}_1-\xi}{\overline{\alpha}_1-\overline{\alpha}_0}\Phi(\alpha_0)+\frac{\xi-\overline{\alpha}_0}{\overline{\alpha}_1-\overline{\alpha}_0}\Phi(\overline{\alpha}_1);$$

and from this

$$\Phi(\xi)-c\xi\leqq\kappa.$$

Hence if $\lambda>\kappa$ for the point $\xi=\overline{\alpha}$, $\zeta=\lambda$ then necessarily $\overline{\alpha}_0<\overline{\alpha}=\xi<\overline{\alpha}_1$ and $v=\lambda+c\overline{\alpha}=\Phi(\overline{\alpha})$.

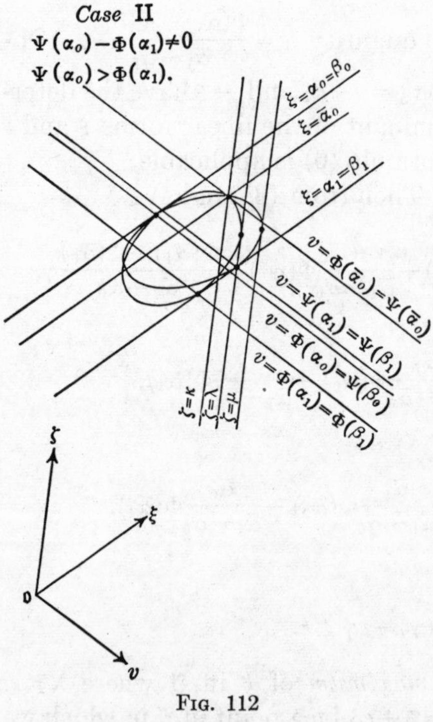

FIG. 112

Finally let μ denote the maximum of ζ in the oval $\mathfrak{B}$, then we have, if $\lambda>\kappa$ from $\Psi(\overline{\alpha})-c\overline{\alpha}>\Phi(\overline{\alpha})-c\overline{\alpha}$, and if $\lambda=\kappa$ from $\Psi(\gamma)-c\gamma>\Phi(\gamma)-c\gamma$, in every case $\mu>\lambda$. It is further seen precisely as in the case above for $\Phi(\xi)$, also for $\Psi(\xi)$, as long as $\alpha_0<\xi<\overline{\alpha}_0$ or $\overline{\alpha}_1\leqq\xi\leqq\alpha_1$, that always $\Psi(\xi)-c\xi\leqq\kappa$. Hence, due to the meaning of $\Psi(\xi)$ the function ζ can be $>\kappa$ in the oval $\mathfrak{B}$ only for such points for which $\overline{\alpha}_0<\xi<\overline{\alpha}_1$. Observe that this interval for ξ is the same here as it was found to be for $\mathfrak{A}$ above. In that case, however,

$\Phi(\xi)-c\xi \leqq \kappa$ while here $\Psi(\xi)-c\xi>\kappa$. And observe further that on the stretch which the line $\xi=\kappa=\lambda-(\lambda-\kappa)$ has in common with the oval $\mathfrak{A}$, the difference between the maximum and the minimum of $-\xi$ is at least $\bar{a}_1-\bar{a}_0$, since the two points $\xi=\bar{\alpha}_0$ and $\xi=\bar{\alpha}_1$ are points on this stretch. Note that for the line $\zeta=\mu-(\lambda-\kappa)$ in the oval $\mathfrak{B}$ the constant on the right $>\kappa$ so that ξ lies *within* the interval $\bar{\alpha}_0<\xi<\bar{\alpha}_1$. Hence the difference between the maximum and minimum of $-\xi$ in the oval $\mathfrak{B}$ on this line is less than $\bar{\alpha}_1-\bar{\alpha}_0$. Hence, here and that is for ξ within the interval just considered, the ovals $\mathfrak{A}$ and $\mathfrak{B}$ in the line-system $\zeta=$ constant *are not equally stretched.* See Fig. 112.

Secondly, let $\Psi(\alpha_1)-\Phi(\alpha_1)$ be different from zero and positive, say. Then denote by $\bar{\alpha}_0$ the least upper limit of all those values ξ in the interval $\alpha_0 \leqq \xi \leqq \alpha_1$ for which we have

$$\Psi(\xi)-\Phi(\xi) \leqq 0.$$

We then have necessarily

$$\Psi(\bar{\alpha}_0)-\Phi(\bar{\alpha}_0)=0,$$

and for every value $\xi>\bar{\alpha}_0$ and $\leqq \alpha_1$ then always

$$\Psi(\xi)>\Phi(\xi).$$

We may take here the value $c=\dfrac{\Phi(\alpha_1)-\Phi(\alpha_0)}{\bar{\alpha}_1-\bar{\alpha}_0}$, and write $\zeta=v-c\xi$, $\Phi(\bar{\alpha}_0)-c\bar{\alpha}_0=\kappa$. Again denote the maximum value of ζ in $\mathfrak{A}$ by λ, and let μ be this greatest value in $\mathfrak{B}$. Then through similar considerations as in the case above it is seen that $\kappa \leqq \lambda<\mu$, and that in $\mathfrak{B}$ so long as $\alpha_0 \leqq \xi \leqq \bar{\alpha}_0$, we always have $v \leqq \kappa$. It is then seen that the difference between the maximum and the minimum of $-\xi$ on the line $\zeta=\kappa=\lambda-(\lambda-\kappa)$ in $\mathfrak{A}$ is $\geqq \alpha_1-\bar{\alpha}_0$, while the corresponding difference on the line $\zeta=\mu-(\lambda-\kappa)=\kappa+(\mu-\lambda)$ in $\mathfrak{B}<\alpha_1 -\bar{\alpha}_0$; and accordingly $\mathfrak{B}$ and $\mathfrak{A}$ are *not* equally stretched in the line-system $\zeta=$ constant.

We may give the following expression to the theorem just proved:

If two ovals are found to be similarly stretched in every possible system of parallel lines, then always the one may be derived from the other through a dilation or a translation.

ART. 156. **Inequality among the Volumes of Three Parallel Sections of a Nowhere Concave Body.** Consider again a manifold of n variables $x_1, x_2, \cdots, x_n$. In it let $x=0$ and $x=1$ be equations of any two parallel planes where x represents any integral linear, not necessarily homogeneous, expression in $x_1, x_2, \cdots, x_n$. (Art. 22.) Further let t be an arbitrary variable in the interval of the values $\geqq 0$ and $\leqq 1$. Let $\mathfrak{C}$ be an assemblage of points lying wholly in the plane $x=1$, which has the property of having in common with any straight line either no point, or one point, or a stretch of points (Cf. Art. 151, 1°) and which also has interior (*inwendig*) (Art. 25) points. We shall use $\mathfrak{z}$ to denote an arbitrary point of $\mathfrak{C}$, and finally let c_h° and c_h' denote the *minimum* and the *maximum* of x_h in $\mathfrak{C}$. (Cf. Art. 151, 5° and 4°.)

Further let $\mathfrak{b}$ be a single point situated in the plane $x=0$. The union of all stretches $\mathfrak{b}\mathfrak{z}$ from $\mathfrak{b}$ to the individual points $\mathfrak{z}$ of $\mathfrak{C}$ represents then a special nowhere concave body. This body will be called a *cone* with $\mathfrak{b}$ as *vertex* and $\mathfrak{C}$ as *base* and it will be denoted by $\mathfrak{b}\mathfrak{C}$. The points of this cone in a plane $x=t$ are expressed in the form $(1-t)\mathfrak{b}+t\mathfrak{z}=t\mathfrak{z}+c$, where c is a constant $=(1-t)\mathfrak{b}$.

Next let $\mathfrak{B}$ be an assemblage of points situated in the plane $x=0$, which may be had *either* through a contraction of $\mathfrak{C}$ in the ratio $q:1$ where $q<1$, *or* through a translation, where in the latter case $q=1$. Let b° be the minimum and b' the maximum of x_h in $\mathfrak{B}$ so that in every case

$$(1) \qquad b_1'-b_1^\circ : c_1'-c_1^\circ = \cdots = b_n'-b_n^\circ : c_n'-c_n^\circ = q:1.$$

We shall now, if $q<1$, consider only the contraction from the point $\mathfrak{a}$ outward, where the coordinates of $\mathfrak{a}$ are determined through

$$b_h^\circ - a_h = q(c_h^\circ - a_h).$$

It is seen at once that this point lies in the plane $q(1-x)+x=0$; for writing for x_h the value a_h in

$$q+[\alpha_1 x_1+\alpha_2 x_2+\cdots+\alpha_n x_n](1-q)=0,$$

we have

$$q+[\alpha_1 b_1^\circ+\alpha_2 b_2^\circ+\cdots+\alpha_n b_n^\circ] \\ -q[\alpha_1 c_1^\circ+\alpha_2 c_2^\circ+\cdots+\alpha_n c_n^\circ]=q+0-q[1]=0,$$

where $x=\alpha_1 x_1+\alpha_2 x_2+\cdots+\alpha_n x_n$.

Observe that for the point $\mathfrak{a}$, we have $x<0$. The assemblage of all the points of the cone $\mathfrak{a}\mathfrak{C}$, for which $x\geqq 0$ is called the *truncated cone* with $\mathfrak{B}$ and $\mathfrak{C}$ the *bases*. This will be denoted by $\mathfrak{B}\mathfrak{C}$. This assemblage of points again represents a nowhere concave body. The points of $\mathfrak{B}$ belong to it in the plane $x=0$, and these points are expressed through

$$\mathfrak{y}=\mathfrak{a}+q(\mathfrak{z}-\mathfrak{a})=q\mathfrak{z}+\text{constant},$$

and, further, the points of the truncated cone $\mathfrak{B}\mathfrak{C}$ in an arbitrary plane $x=t$ may be expressed through $(1-t)\mathfrak{y}+t\mathfrak{z}$; and that is, writing for $\mathfrak{y}$ its value above,

$$(1-t)(\mathfrak{a}+q(\mathfrak{z}-\mathfrak{a}))+t\mathfrak{z}=((1-t)q-t)\mathfrak{z}+\text{constant}.$$

In the case of a translation $(q=1)$ we shall consider here only the translation, which leads from $\mathfrak{o}$ out to the point $\mathfrak{d}$ with coordinates $b_1^\circ-c_1^\circ, \cdots, b_n^\circ-c_n^\circ$, so that here the points of $\mathfrak{B}$ appear in the form $\mathfrak{y}=\mathfrak{z}+(\mathfrak{d}-\mathfrak{o})$. In this case the union of all the stretches $\mathfrak{y}\mathfrak{z}$, where $\mathfrak{y}$, a point of $\mathfrak{B}$, and $\mathfrak{z}$ of $\mathfrak{C}$ connected as just given, form a nowhere concave body which, indicated also by $\mathfrak{B}\mathfrak{C}$, is called a *cylinder* with $\mathfrak{B}$ and $\mathfrak{C}$ as bases. The points of this cylinder in a plane $x=t$ are expressed through

$$(1-t)\mathfrak{y}+t\mathfrak{z}=\mathfrak{z}+(1-t)(\delta-\mathfrak{o})=\mathfrak{z}+\text{constant}.$$

Next let $\mathfrak{L}$ denote the cone $\mathfrak{b}\mathfrak{C}$ or the truncated cone or the cylinder $\mathfrak{B}\mathfrak{C}$. Let x_n in the plane x have a coefficient that is different from zero, so that the points in a plane $x=t$ are determined through their $n-1$ coordinates $x_1, x_2, \cdots, x_{n-1}$. Let $\mathfrak{L}'(t)$ denote the assemblage of these systems $x_1, x_2, \cdots,$

x_{n-1} for the points of $\mathfrak{L}$ in the plane $x=t$, so that $\mathfrak{L}'(t)$ always represents a nowhere concave body in $x_1, x_2, \cdots, x_{n-1}$, with the single exception that in case of the cone $\mathfrak{L}'(0)$ where the system $x_1, x_2, \cdots, x_{n-1}$ stands for the vertex of the cone. Further let $L'(t)$ denote the volume of $\mathfrak{L}'(t)$ in $x_1, x_2, \cdots, x_{n-1}$. We then have in the case of a cone

$$L'(0)=0, \qquad L'(t)=t^{n-1}L'(1);$$

in the case of a truncated cone

$$L'(0)=q^{n-1}L'(1), \qquad L'(t)=((1-t)q+t)^{n-1}L'(1);$$

in the case of a cylinder

$$L'(0)=L'(1), \qquad L'(t)=L'(1).$$

In all three cases observe that

(2) $$\sqrt[n-1]{L'(t)}=(1-t)\sqrt[n-1]{L'(0)}+t\sqrt[n-1]{L'(1)}.$$

Next let $\mathfrak{K}$ be a second nowhere concave body which incloses $\mathfrak{L}$ but is not identical with $\mathfrak{L}$ and which lies entirely within the region of the planes $0 \leqq x \leqq 1$. Since the points of $\mathfrak{K}$ in the planes $x=0$ and $x=1$ appear as points of condensation of the other points of $\mathfrak{K}$ for which $0<x<1$, it is possible to find, due to these assumptions, a point $\mathfrak{k}$ in $\mathfrak{K}$ which does not belong to $\mathfrak{L}$ and also does not lie in $x=0$ or $x=1$. In the same plane $x=$constant in which $\mathfrak{k}$ lies suppose that $\mathfrak{l}$ is a point of $\mathfrak{L}$ such that the stretch $\mathfrak{kl}$ has besides $\mathfrak{l}$ no other point of $\mathfrak{L}$. We may then from above express $\mathfrak{l}$ in *one way* in the form $(1-t)\mathfrak{y}+t\mathfrak{z}$ where $\mathfrak{y}$ and $\mathfrak{z}$ are associated points of $\mathfrak{B}$ and $\mathfrak{C}$. (In the case of the cone we shall have to introduce for $\mathfrak{B}$ as for $\mathfrak{y}$ the vertex $\mathfrak{b}$ of the cone.) It is then seen that on the stretches $\mathfrak{yk}$ and $\mathfrak{kz}$ only the two points $\mathfrak{y}$ and $\mathfrak{z}$ belong to $\mathfrak{L}$; and it is then clear that the body $\mathfrak{K}$ in every plane $x=t$, where $t>0$ and <1, has other points besides those of $\mathfrak{L}$. If we give to $K'(t)$ the same meaning for $\mathfrak{K}$ as $L'(t)$ had above for $\mathfrak{L}$, and if in the manifold of the variables $x_1, x_2, \cdots, x_{n-1}$ we apply the theorem that if a nowhere concave body contains another such body the first has an essentially greater volume (Cf. Art. 151, II) we have for every value $t>0$ and <1 at all events the inequality

$$(3) \qquad K'(t)>L'(t).$$

After all this preparation we shall completely fill up the gaps which remained in the investigation relative to the establishing of the theorems given in Art. 151, IV.

I. Let $\mathfrak{K}$ be an arbitrary nowhere concave body in $x_1, x_2, \cdots, x_n$. Let b be the minimum, c the maximum of x_n in $\mathfrak{K}$. Then x_n takes every value $\geqq b$ and $\leqq c$ in $\mathfrak{K}$. If t takes a value $\geqq 0$ and $\leqq 1$, we shall understand by $\mathfrak{T}$ the assemblage of all points of $\mathfrak{K}$ in the plane $x_n=(1-t)b+tc$, and by $\mathfrak{T}'$ the assemblage of systems $x_1, x_2, \cdots, x_{n-1}$ for these points. Associated with $\mathfrak{T}$ there is (Art. 151, II) a definite volume in $x_1, x_2, \cdots, x_{n-1}$, which we shall denote by T'. Finally denote the quantities $\mathfrak{T}$, $\mathfrak{T}'$, T' for $t=0$ by $\mathfrak{B}$, $\mathfrak{B}'$, B. For a value $t>0$ and <1 the quantity $\mathfrak{T}'$ has always inner points and represents a nowhere concave body in $x_1, x_2, \cdots, x_{n-1}$. However, under certain conditions both B' and C' may be $=0$. From the general result in Art. 151, (4) it is seen that the function T' in the region $0<t<1$ with the approach of t to 0 cannot take a limit $>B'$, and with an approach of t to 1, T' cannot take a limit $>C'$.

It may be proved now that the following very important inequality always exists:

$$(4) \qquad \sqrt[n-1]{T'} \geqq (1-t)\sqrt[n-1]{B'}+t\sqrt[n-1]{C'}.$$

For $t=0$ and $t=1$, we have at once the sign $=$.

Suppose for a moment that (4) is already proved. If b^* and c^* are two values such that $b\leqq b^*\leqq c^*\leqq c$, then the assemblage $\mathfrak{K}^*$ of points out of $\mathfrak{K}$, for which we have $b^*\leqq x_n\leqq c^*$, always represents a nowhere concave body. If for each of these bodies (the most comprehensive of which is $\mathfrak{K}$ itself) all the inequalities like (4) are set up, and if we take into consideration the remark just made regarding the behavior of T' at $t=0$ and at $t=1$, then all these conditions taken together (observe in this connection Art. 155, II) lead to the following actuality:

The assemblage of systems t, u defined through

$$0 \leqq u \leqq \sqrt[n-1]{T'}, \qquad 0 \leqq t \leqq 1$$

forms an oval in t, u.

$$u \leqq \sqrt[n-1]{T'(t)}; \qquad t \geqq 0 \qquad \text{and} \qquad \leqq 1.$$

The t-profile of this oval consists of the systems

$$u = \sqrt[n-1]{T'}, \qquad 0 \leqq t \leqq 1.$$

The remark in Art. 155 (5) indicates that in the inequality (4) for the body $\mathfrak{K}$ either the sign = holds throughout or the sign > is to be taken for every value t which is >0 and <1. Further, due to Art. 155, II the function T' is continuous in x_n in the entire interval $b \leqq x_n \leqq c$ and from Art. 151, II it is seen that the volume of $\mathfrak{K}$ in $x_1, x_2, \cdots, x_n$ is equal to

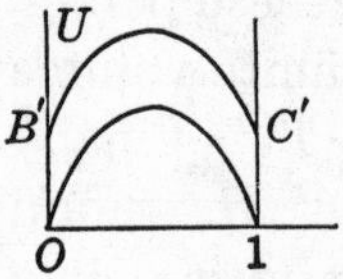

FIG. 113

(5) $$\int_b^c T' dx_n.$$

Assume that $B' \leqq C'$. First observe that if $B'=0$ and also $C'=0$, then the inequality (4) is evident with the sign > for every value $t>0$ and <1. Next let $B'=0$, but $C'>0$. Take any point $\mathfrak{b}$ of $\mathfrak{B}$, then from the nature of a nowhere concave body $\mathfrak{K}$ it must include the entire cone $\mathfrak{b}\mathfrak{C}$ within itself. From (2) and (3) it is seen that always $T' \geqq t^{n-1}C'$, and from this we have (4), and also it is seen that the sign = is to be taken always if $\mathfrak{K}$ coincides with the cone, in which case then B would consist of the one single point $\mathfrak{b}$. On the other hand it is evident here that for every value $t>0$ and <1 the sign > holds, if $\mathfrak{K}$ *does not represent a cone with the vertex in the plane* $x_n=b$ *and its base in* $x_n=c$. Now let $C' \geqq B' > 0$. Then besides the inequality (4) the following also will be proved:

(6) *In order that the equality sign may appear in (4) for a value $t>0$ and <1, it is above all necessary that the realm $\mathfrak{B}$ be derived from the realm $\mathfrak{C}$ through a dilation or a translation,*

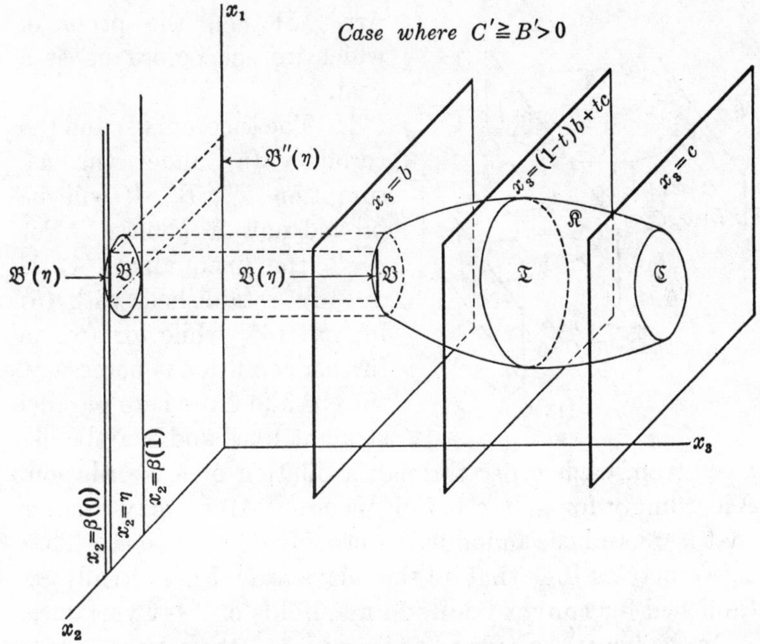

FIG. 114

or, what amounts to the same thing, that $\mathfrak{B}'$ be derived from $\mathfrak{C}'$ through a dilation or a tranlsation in the manifold x_1, x_2, $\cdots$, x_{n-1}.

From this first circumstance are to be had the complete conditions for the appearance of the limiting case in question, and that is of the equality sign. For if $\mathfrak{B}$ is derived from $\mathfrak{C}$ by a dilation or a translation, then $\mathfrak{K}$ as a nowhere concave body must include with $\mathfrak{B}$ and $\mathfrak{C}$ at the same time the entire truncated cone or the cylinder $\mathfrak{B}\mathfrak{C}$. From (2) and (3) it is seen if $\mathfrak{K}$ coincides with this realm $\mathfrak{B}C$, that then in (4) the equality sign enters for all values $t>0$ and <1; however, on the other hand if $\mathfrak{K}$ does not express a truncated cone or cylinder with the bases in the planes $x_n=b$ and

$x_n = c$, then for every value $t > 0$ and < 1 the sign $>$ is had in (4).

From these general theorems, if we take $C' = B'$ and put m in the place of $n-1$, follow at once the theorems of Art. 151 (7), the proof of which we set before us as a goal.

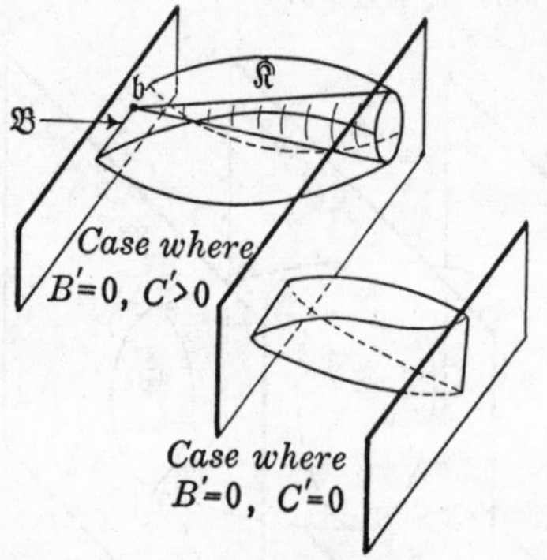

Fig. 115

II. The theorem (4) and the corollary (6) under the assumption $C' \geqq B' > 0$ will be proved now in general. For $n = 2$ the inequality (4) is already established with (5) in Art. 155, while for (6) no further condition is necessary, since $\mathfrak{B}$ and $\mathfrak{C}$ are here parallel straight lines and may be derived from each other through a dilation or a translation. Accordingly for the proof of theorem (4) we may assume that $n \geqq 3$ and use an inductive proof from $n-1$ to n. That is, we may assume that all the relations of I are already established for convex bodies in manifolds of $n-1$ variables.

As the body $\mathfrak{K}$ above was resolved into the realms $\mathfrak{T}$ with respect to the variable x_n, so here the assemblage $\mathfrak{T}'$ will be resolved further into partial assemblages with respect to x_{n-1}.

Since B' is assumed to be >0, $\mathfrak{B}'$ represents a nowhere concave body in $x_1, x_2, \cdots, x_{n-1}$. Denote by $\beta(0)$ the minimum, and by $\beta(1)$ the maximum of x_{n-1} in $\mathfrak{B}'$; and for every value $\eta \geqq \beta(0)$ and $\leqq \beta(1)$ we shall understand by $\mathfrak{B}(\eta)$ the assemblage of the points of $\mathfrak{B}$ for which $x_{n-1} = \eta$; and by $\mathfrak{B}'(\eta)$ the assemblage of the systems $x_1, x_2, \cdots, x_{n-1}$ for these points, and further by $\mathfrak{B}''(\eta)$ the assemblage of the systems $x_1, x_2, \cdots, x_{n-2}$ for them.

For every such system $\mathfrak{B}''(\eta)$ there exists a definite volume in $x_1, x_2, \cdots, x_{n-2}$ which we shall denote by $B''(\eta)$. This function $B''(\eta)$ is continuous in the entire interval

$\beta(0) \leqq \eta \leqq \beta(1)$ and for all values within this interval it is always positive. Due to (5) we have for the volume of $\mathfrak{B}'$ in $x_1, x_2, \cdots, x_{n-1}$ the equation

$$B' = \int_{\beta(0)}^{\beta(1)} B''(\eta) d\eta.$$

In general, write

$$\int_{(0)}^{\eta} B''(x_{n-1}) dx_{n-1} = \sigma_\eta B',$$

where η lies in the interval $\beta(0) \leqq \eta \leqq \beta(1)$. It is then seen that σ is a continuous and continually increasing function of η whose values vary from 0 to 1 when η goes through the above interval. Reciprocally, it is seen from Art. 155, I that corresponding to every value $\sigma \geqq 0$ and $\leqq 1$ there is always a completely determined value $\eta \geqq \beta(0)$ and $\leqq \beta(1)$, with which as upper limit the last integral is $= \sigma B'$. This value η shall be denoted by $\eta(\sigma)$. It also is a continuous function and continually increases from $\beta(0)$ to $\beta(1)$, when σ goes through the interval $0 \leqq \sigma \leqq 1$. It is seen that for every value $\sigma > 0$ and < 1 the differential quotient $\dfrac{d\eta(\sigma)}{d\sigma}$ has always a definite finite positive value which is had by observing that

$$B'(\bar{\sigma}_\eta - \sigma_\eta) = \int_\eta^{\bar{\eta}} B''(x_{n-1}) dx_{n-1},$$

or

(7) $$B' d\sigma = B''(\eta(\sigma))[\bar{\eta} - \eta] = B''(\eta(\sigma)) d\eta(\sigma).$$

Further, with respect to the realm $\mathfrak{C}$ we may give the same meaning to $\gamma(0)$, $\gamma(1)$, ζ; $\mathfrak{C}(\zeta)$, $\mathfrak{C}'(\zeta)$, $\mathfrak{C}''(\zeta)$, $C''(\zeta)$; σ_ζ, $\zeta(\sigma)$ as was given above for the quantities $\beta(0)$, $\beta(1)$, η; $\mathfrak{B}(\eta)$, $\mathfrak{B}'(\eta)$, $\mathfrak{B}''(\eta)$, $B''(\eta)$; σ_η, $\eta(\sigma)$ with respect to the realm $\mathfrak{B}$. Here also $\zeta(\sigma)$ is a continuous and continually increasing function of σ in the interval $0 \leqq \sigma \leqq 1$, and further $C''(\zeta)$ is a continuous function of ζ in the interval $\gamma(0) \leqq \zeta \leqq \gamma(1)$ and we have always

$$C''(\zeta(\sigma)) > 0$$

for every value $\sigma > 0$ and < 1. It also follows that

$$C''(\zeta(\sigma))\frac{d\zeta(\sigma)}{d\sigma} = C'. \tag{8}$$

Again let t take any definite value >0 and <1; and for a

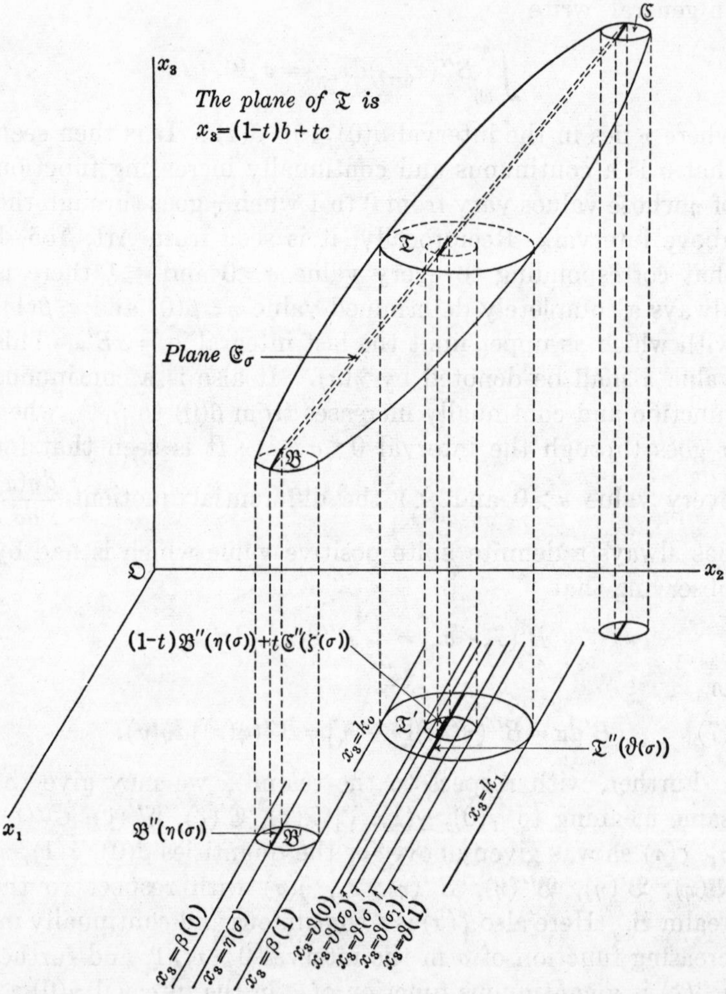

$$\mathfrak{T}' = \int_{k_0}^{k_1}\mathfrak{T}''(\vartheta(\sigma))d\vartheta \geqq \int_{\vartheta(0)}^{\vartheta(1)}\mathfrak{T}''(\vartheta)d\vartheta > \int_{\vartheta(\sigma_0)}^{\vartheta(\sigma_1)}\mathfrak{T}''(\vartheta(\sigma))d\vartheta = \int_{\sigma_0}^{\sigma_1}\mathfrak{T}''\vartheta(\sigma)\frac{d\vartheta}{d\sigma}d\sigma.$$

FIG. 116

value $\sigma \geqq 0$ and $\leqq 1$ consider the plane $\mathfrak{E}_\sigma$ which is expressed through the equation

$$\frac{x_{n-1}-\eta(\sigma)}{x_{n-1}-\zeta(\sigma)}=\frac{x_n-b}{x_n-c}.$$

Observe that for the points in this plane we always have x_{n-1} determined through x_n and in particular when $x_n=b$, then $x_{n-1}=\eta(\sigma)$, while for $x_n=c$, we have $x_{n-1}=\zeta(\sigma)$. With this it is seen that the plane $\mathfrak{E}_\sigma$ cuts out of $\mathfrak{B}$ and $\mathfrak{C}$ the realms $\mathfrak{B}(\eta(\sigma))$ and $\mathfrak{C}(\eta(\sigma))$, and further for the realm $\mathfrak{T}$ belonging to t those points of $\mathfrak{E}_\sigma$ are cut out for which

$$x_{n-1}=\theta=(1-t)\eta(\sigma)+t\zeta(\sigma)=\theta(\sigma). \tag{9}$$

The assemblage of these points cut out of $\mathfrak{T}$ by $\mathfrak{E}_\sigma$ will be denoted by $\mathfrak{T}(\theta))$, while the assemblage of the systems $x_1, x_2, \cdots, x_{n-2}$ in them is denoted by $\mathfrak{T}''(\theta)$, and the volume of $\mathfrak{T}''(\theta)$ in $x_1, x_2, \cdots, x_{n-2}$ is denoted by $T''(\theta)$. With $\eta(\sigma)$ and $\zeta(\sigma)$ the function $\theta(\sigma)$ defined through (9) is continuous and is a continually increasing function of σ for $0 \leqq \sigma \leqq 1$. Reciprocally there belongs to every value θ which is $\geqq \theta(0) = (1-\tau)\beta(0)+\tau\gamma(0)$ and $\leqq \theta(1)=(1-\tau)\beta(1)+\tau\gamma(1)$ a definite value $\sigma \geqq 0$ and $\leqq 1$, for which $\theta(\sigma)=\theta$. Further, for all values $\sigma>0$ and <1, the differential quotient (see Fig. 116)

$$\frac{d\theta(\sigma)}{d\sigma}=(1-\tau)\frac{d\eta(\sigma)}{d\sigma}+\tau\frac{d\zeta(\sigma)}{d\sigma} \tag{10}$$

is, see (7) and (8), a continuous and positive function of σ.

In $\mathfrak{T}'$ there exist for x_{n-1} all values $\geqq \theta(0)$ and $\leqq \theta(1)$ and therefore we have

$$T' \geqq \int_{\theta(0)}^{\theta(1)} T''(\theta)\,d\theta. \tag{11}$$

Let $\overline{\mathfrak{K}}_\sigma$ denote the assemblage of the systems $x_1, x_2, \cdots, x_{n-2}, x_n$ for the points of $\mathfrak{K}$ in the plane $\mathfrak{E}_\sigma$. For a value $\sigma>0$ and <1 the plane $\mathfrak{E}_\sigma$ clearly cuts the body $\mathfrak{K}$ so that $\mathfrak{K}_\sigma$ has inner points and is a nowhere concave body in $x_1, x_2, \cdots, x_{n-2}, x_n$. Assuming that the theorem expressed through (4) regarding nowhere concave bodies is already proved for manifolds of $n-1$ variables, the consideration of the intersections of $\bar{\mathfrak{K}}_\sigma$ with $x_n=b$, $x_n=c$ and $x_n=(1-\tau)b+\tau c$ leads to

$$(12)\qquad \sqrt[n-2]{T''(\theta(\sigma))} \geqq (1-\tau)\sqrt[n-2]{B''(\eta(\sigma))}+\tau\sqrt[n-2]{C''(\zeta(\sigma))}$$

for values of $\sigma>0$ and <1.

Observe next that if V, W, v, w are any four positive quantities, then

$$(13)\qquad f=\sqrt[n-1]{(V+W)^{n-2}(v+w)}-\sqrt[n-1]{V^{n-2}v}-\sqrt[n-1]{W^{n-2}w}\geqq 0.$$

If we put $V:W=v:w=q:1$, we have

$$f=\sqrt[n-1]{W^{n-2}w}[(q+1)-q-1]=0.$$

On the other hand, if $\frac{V}{v}\neq\frac{W}{w}$, say $\frac{V}{v}>\frac{W}{w}$, we have $\frac{V+W}{v+w}>\frac{W}{w}$; and it is seen that

$$(n-1)\frac{\partial f}{\partial w}=\left(\frac{V+W}{v+w}\right)^{\frac{n-2}{n-1}}-\left(\frac{W}{w}\right)^{\frac{n-2}{n-1}}>0,$$

since $n>2$. We may let w continually decrease until it reaches the value $\frac{W}{V}v$. It is seen that f simultaneously decreases until it takes the value zero. Hence this function was initially greater than zero. A similar result would of course have been obtained if we had assumed that $\frac{W}{w}>\frac{V}{v}$ and differentiated partially with regard to v.

In (13) make the substitutions

$$(14)\qquad \begin{aligned} V&=(1-\tau)\sqrt[n-2]{B''(\eta(\sigma))}, & W&=\tau\sqrt[n-2]{C''(\zeta(\sigma))},\\ v&=(1-\tau)\frac{d\eta(\sigma)}{d\sigma}, & w&=\tau\frac{d\zeta(\sigma)}{d\sigma},\end{aligned}$$

observe the inequality (12) and the relation (10), and we

have

$$(15)\quad \sqrt[n-1]{T''(\theta(\sigma))\frac{d\theta(\sigma)}{d\sigma}}$$
$$\geqq(1-\tau)\sqrt[n-1]{B''(\eta(\sigma))\frac{d\eta(\sigma)}{d\sigma}}+\tau\sqrt[n-1]{C''(\zeta(\sigma))\frac{d\zeta(\sigma)}{d\sigma}},$$

which, due to (7) and (8), becomes

$$(16)\qquad T''(\theta(\sigma))\frac{d\theta(\sigma)}{d\sigma}\geqq[(1-\tau)\sqrt[n-1]{B'}+\tau\sqrt[n-1]{C'}]^{n-1}$$

for $0<\sigma<1$.

Let σ_0 and σ_1 be any two values such that $0<\sigma_0<\sigma_1<1$, observe the nature of $\frac{d\theta(\sigma)}{d\sigma}$ from (10), and we have

$$\int_{\theta(\sigma_0)}^{\theta(\sigma_1)}T''(\theta)d\theta=\int_{\sigma_0}^{\sigma_1}T''(\theta(\sigma))\frac{d\theta(\sigma)}{d\sigma}d\sigma.$$

The integral on the left-hand side is, due to (11), $<T'$, and using the expression on the right in (16), it is seen that

$$T'>[(1-\tau)\sqrt[n-1]{B'}+\tau\sqrt[n-1]{C'}]^{n-1}(\sigma_1-\sigma_0).$$

Since σ_0 may approximate arbitrarily 0, and σ_1 may be arbitrarily near 1, we have thus derived the inequality (4), which was to be established.

III. It remains to establish more definitely the corollary (6) for $C'\geqq B'>0$ and $n\geqq3$. Assume in this connection that in the inequality (4) just established the equality sign holds true. In the inequality (13) established above for four positive quantities V, W, v, w, the limiting case $f=0$ can only enter if $V:W=v:w$. It is also seen that if a value $\sigma>0$ and <1 is such that the equality

$$(17)\qquad \sqrt[n-2]{B''(\eta(\sigma))}:\sqrt[n-2]{C''(\zeta(\sigma))}=\sqrt[n-1]{B'}:\sqrt[n-1]{C'}$$

does not hold, then, due to (7) and (8) for this same value of σ with the substitutions from (14) the equality $\frac{V}{W}=\frac{v}{w}$ also is *not* true, and we must accordingly have $f>0$ and hence also in (15) and (16) the sign $>$ must hold. Similarly it may be shown that if for a value $\sigma>0$ and <1 the difference of the left-hand side and the right-hand side of (12) is >0, then for this same value of σ the equality sign in (15) and (16) can *not* exist. For, using (14), we have from (12)

$$(12') \qquad T''(\theta(\sigma))>(V+W)^{n-2}.$$

If the equality sign existed in (15) so that

$$(15') \quad T''(\theta(\sigma))\frac{d\theta(\sigma)}{d\sigma}$$
$$=\left[(1-\tau)\sqrt[n-1]{B''(\eta(\sigma))\frac{d\eta(\sigma)}{d\sigma}}+\tau\sqrt[n-1]{C''(\zeta(\sigma))\frac{d\zeta(\sigma)}{d\sigma}}\right]^{n-1},$$

then observing that $\frac{d\theta(\sigma)}{d\sigma}=u+v$ and again using (14), it follows from (12′) and (15′) that

$$[V^{\frac{n-2}{n-1}}v^{\frac{1}{n-1}}+W^{\frac{n-2}{n-1}}w^{\frac{1}{n-1}}]^{n-1}>(V+W)^{n-2}(v+w),$$

which contradicts (13). Or, noting that here $\frac{V}{W}=\frac{v}{w}=q$, say, and writing $V=qW$, $v=qw$ in the above expression, it becomes

$$(1+q)^{n-1}W^{n-2}w>(1+q)^{n-1}W^{n-2}w.$$

If for any definite value of $\sigma=\rho>0$ and <1 the difference between the left and right hand sides of (16) is positive, and if δ is a smaller positive quantity than this difference, then, due to the continuity of the functions $T''(\theta(\sigma))$ and $\frac{d\theta(\sigma)}{d\sigma}$ in the realm $0<\sigma<1$ we may determine a definite interval $\rho_0\leqq\sigma\leqq\rho_1$ in this realm in which that difference is always $>\delta$, and then it is seen that T' is greater than

$$[(1-\tau)^{n-1}\sqrt{B'}+\tau^{n-1}\sqrt{C'}]^{n-1}$$

by at least $\delta(\rho_1-\rho_0)$, and therefore the equality sign in (4) cannot exist. We are assuming, however, that this equality sign does exist, and hence that assumption requires for $0<\sigma<1$ that the relation (17) always is true, as is also the equation

$$(18)\qquad \sqrt[n-2]{T''(\theta(\sigma))}=(1-\tau)\sqrt[n-2]{B''(\eta(\sigma))}+\tau\sqrt[n-2]{C''(\zeta(\sigma))}$$

is true always.

We must now digest the above results. From (17) in connection with (7) and (8) we have

$$\frac{1}{\sqrt[n-1]{B'}}\frac{d\eta(\sigma)}{d\sigma}=\frac{1}{\sqrt[n-1]{C'}}\frac{d\zeta(\sigma)}{d\sigma}$$

for $0<\sigma<1$. From this it follows at once, if $0<\sigma_0<\sigma<1$, that

$$\frac{\eta(\sigma)-\eta(\sigma_0)}{\sqrt[n-1]{B'}}=\frac{\zeta(\sigma)-\zeta(\sigma_0)}{\sqrt[n-1]{C'}}.$$

Due to the continuity of the functions $\eta(\sigma)$ and $\zeta(\sigma)$ in the entire interval $0\leqq\sigma\leqq1$, it is seen that if σ_0 decreases toward zero as a limit, then

$$(19)\qquad \frac{\eta(\sigma)-\beta(0)}{\sqrt[n-1]{B'}}=\frac{\zeta(\sigma)-\gamma(0)}{\sqrt[n-1]{C'}};$$

and further if σ converges toward 1, then

$$(20)\qquad \frac{\beta(1)-\beta(0)}{\sqrt[n-1]{B'}}=\frac{\gamma(1)-\gamma(0)}{\sqrt[n-1]{C'}}.$$

Consider next the equation (18). Let h be any one of the indices $1, 2, \cdots, n-2$ and let $\mathfrak{Q}_h(\mathfrak{B})$ be the assemblage of all systems x_h, x_{n-1} which appear in $\mathfrak{B}$. This assemblage, due to Arts. 155, II and 151, I, represents an oval in x_h, x_{n-1}. Note from above that $\beta(0)$ represents the smallest value of x_{n-1} in $\mathfrak{B}$, the greatest value of x_{n-1} being $\beta(1)$; and for a value $x_{n-1}=\eta(\sigma)\geqq\beta(0)$ and $\leqq\beta(1)$ denote by $\eta_h(\sigma)$ the least and by $\mathrm{H}_h(\sigma)$ the greatest value of x_h on the line $x_{n-1}=\eta(\sigma)$ in $\mathfrak{Q}_h(\mathfrak{B})$. Further observe that $\eta_h(\sigma)$ and $\mathrm{H}_h(\sigma)$ are continuous functions of $\eta(\sigma)$, and therefore also of σ. It is seen that $\eta_h(\sigma)$ presents the minimum, while $\mathrm{H}_h(\sigma)$ offers the maximum of x_h in the realm $\mathfrak{B}''(\eta(\sigma))$.

Let $\mathfrak{Q}_h(\mathfrak{C})$, $\zeta_h(\sigma)$, $\mathrm{Z}_h(\sigma)$ have for $\mathfrak{C}$ the meaning corresponding to $\mathfrak{Q}_h(\mathfrak{B})$, $\eta_h(\sigma)$, $\mathrm{H}_h(\sigma)$ for $\mathfrak{B}$. Suppose next that the corollary (6) is already proved for nowhere concave bodies in the manifold of $n-1$ variables; then, due to (18), this corollary is true in the case of each of the bodies $\overline{\mathfrak{K}}_\sigma$ for $0<\sigma<1$. That is, $\mathfrak{B}''(\eta(\sigma))$ is derived from $C''(\zeta(\sigma))$ from a dilation or translation in $x_1, x_2, \cdots, x_{n-2}$. We thus have for consideration a dilation in the ratio

$$\sqrt[n-2]{B''(\eta(\sigma))} : \sqrt[n-2]{C''(\zeta(\sigma))},$$

if this ratio is different from 1, and a translation if the ratio is $=1$. Due to (17) this ratio is the same as

$$\sqrt[n-1]{B'} : \sqrt[n-1]{C'}.$$

Writing the ratios at the beginning of this Art. 156 in the form $b'_h - b^\circ_h = q(c'_h - c^\circ_h)$, it is seen that

$$b'_h - qc'_h = b^\circ_h - qc^\circ_h \qquad (k=1, 2, \cdots, n-2)$$

or

$$b'_h - \frac{\sqrt[n-1]{B'}}{\sqrt[n-1]{C'}} c'_h = b^\circ_h - \frac{\sqrt[n-1]{B'}}{\sqrt[n-1]{C'}} c^\circ_h.$$

It is seen that the dilation or translation here may be expressed through the $n-2$ quantities

$$\frac{\zeta_h(\sigma)}{\sqrt[n-1]{C'}} - \frac{\eta_h(\sigma)}{\sqrt[n-1]{B'}} \qquad (h=1, 2, \cdots, n-2)$$

or through the maxima $\mathrm{H}_h(\sigma)$ and $\mathrm{Z}_h(\sigma)$ of x_h in $\mathfrak{B}''(\eta(\sigma))$ and $\mathfrak{C}''(\zeta(\sigma))$ and then from (1) we have

$$\frac{\mathrm{Z}_h(\sigma)}{\sqrt[n-1]{C'}} - \frac{\mathrm{H}_h(\sigma)}{\sqrt[n-1]{B'}} = \frac{\zeta_h(\sigma)}{\sqrt[n-1]{C'}} - \frac{\eta_h(\sigma)}{\sqrt[n-1]{B'}};$$

and that is,

$$(21) \qquad \frac{\mathrm{Z}_h(\sigma) - \zeta_h(\sigma)}{\sqrt[n-1]{C'}} = \frac{\mathrm{H}_h(\sigma) - \eta_h(\sigma)}{\sqrt[n-1]{B'}}$$

for $h=1, 2, \cdots, n-2$ and $0<\sigma<1$. Since all the functions that appear here are continuous in the entire realm, this relation also holds for $\sigma=0$ and $\sigma=1$. Observe that the equations (19) and (20) are free of the index h and when taken in connection with equation (21) for $0\leqq\sigma\leqq 1$, they indicate, if account is taken of the expressions introduced in Art. 155, III, the following: *The ovals* $\mathfrak{O}_h(\mathfrak{B})$ *and* $\mathfrak{O}_h(\mathfrak{C})$ *are similarly stretched in the line-system* $x_{n-1}=$ *constant.*

This result is essentially susceptible of extension. Let h be a definite one of the indices $1, 2, \cdots, n-2$ and let e be any constant. Instead of x_h, x_{n-1} introduce as new variables $x_h^*=-x_{n-1}$, $x_{n-1}^*=x_h-ex_{n-1}$, while the remaining variables remain unchanged. The volumes of $\mathfrak{B}'$, $\mathfrak{C}'$, $\mathfrak{T}'$ in $x_1, x_2, \cdots, x_{h-1}, x_h^*, x_{h+1}, \cdots, x_{n-2}, x_{n-1}^*$ are again B', C', T', since the determinant of the transformation is 1; and on the other hand the assemblages of the systems x_h^*, x_{n-1}^* in $\mathfrak{B}$ and $\mathfrak{C}$ are given again through the ovals $\mathfrak{O}_h(\mathfrak{B})$ and $\mathfrak{O}_h(\mathfrak{C})$ in terms of the coordinates x_h^*, x_{n-1}^*. This latter result, if the equality sign exists in (4), offers at once the further conclusion: *The ovals* $\mathfrak{O}_h(\mathfrak{B})$ *and* $\mathfrak{O}_h(\mathfrak{C})$ *are similarly stretched in every line system* $x_h-ex_{n-1}=$ *constant.* And further, the lemma of Art. 155, III shows that the oval $\mathfrak{O}_h(\mathfrak{B})$ is always derived from the oval $\mathfrak{O}_h(\mathfrak{C})$ through dilation or translation. Having regard to (19) it follows then always that

$$\frac{\zeta_h(\sigma)-\zeta_h(0)}{\sqrt[n-1]{C'}}=\frac{\eta_h(\sigma)-\eta_h(0)}{\sqrt[n-1]{B'}} \tag{22}$$

for $0\leqq\sigma\leqq 1$. (Cf. also (7) of Art. 155 et seq.) This relation that $\frac{\zeta_h(\sigma)}{\sqrt[n-1]{C'}}-\frac{\eta_h(\sigma)}{\sqrt[n-1]{B'}}$ is independent of σ with the additional result expressed in (19) that also $\frac{\zeta(\sigma)}{\sqrt[n-1]{C'}}-\frac{\eta(\sigma)}{\sqrt[n-1]{B'}}$ is independent of σ, shows that the dilation or translation in x_1, $x_2, \cdots, x_{n-2}, x_{n-1}$ through which for a $\sigma>0$ and <1 the realm $\mathfrak{B}'(\eta(\sigma))$ follows out of $\mathfrak{C}'(\zeta(\sigma))$, is for all values of σ one and the same dilation or translation. The fact that the systems $x_1, x_2, \cdots, x_{n-1}$ in $\mathfrak{B}'$, for which $x_{n-1} = \beta(0)$ or $= \beta(1)$, follows out of the collective assemblage $\mathfrak{B}'(\eta(\sigma))$, $0 < \sigma < 1$, without being a point of condensation of it—the same being true with respect to $\mathfrak{C}'$—shows that through the above dilation or translation the entire realm $\mathfrak{B}'$ is produced by the entire realm $\mathfrak{C}'$; and with this the corollary (6) is proved.

With these results following the remarks made at the conclusion of I, the proofs of the theorems of Art. 151, IV are completely demonstrated.

The service of having first derived the important inequality (4) is due to Brunn (see his monograph, *Über Ovale und Eiflächen*, p. 23, Art. 5). The presentation by Brunn has to do in particular with the case $n = 3$ and is of a more geometric nature, while here it is purely analytical. Fundamental in the present proof is the possibility of a conclusion from $n-1$ to n through the introduction of the inverse functions $\eta(\sigma)$ and $\zeta(\sigma)$ defined as the upper limits of integrals. The corollary (6), which is of especial importance for the deductions in Art. 151, IV, and for further application, is also indicated by Brunn for the case $n = 3$. Due to a remark by Minkowski regarding the necessity of a more rigorous proof of this corollary (Cf. above-mentioned monograph, pp. 24–5, Arts. 9 and 10) Brunn returned to this subject in an article "Exacte Grundlagen für eine Theorie der Ovale" (*Sitzungsberichte der bayer. Akad.*, mentioned above). The results found here are more general and simpler.

CHAPTER XVIII

DENSEST PLACEMENT OF CONGRUENT HOMOLOGOUS BODIES

ART. **157.** While the volume M^3J of a Minkowski M-parallelopiped (Art. 4) under certain conditions (Art. 5) reaches the upper limit 8, we have seen that only the inequality $M^3J \leqq 8$ is had for the three bodies which we treated in Chapt. I, namely the double cone, cylinder and octahedron. If by a variation of the coefficients $\lambda, \lambda', \cdots, \nu''$ in the forms ξ, η, ζ of Art. 10 there exists a maximal value of M^3J—and we shall show that there is—this maximal values lies in every case under 8. We may now consider the methods for the determination of this maximal value. In this procedure instead of fixing the lattice in x, y, z, and causing to vary the coordinate system of the ξ, η, ζ of Art. 10 or that of φ, ψ, ζ of Art. 11 and with these the M bodies expressed through them by changes of $\lambda, \lambda', \cdots, \nu''$, it is more advantageous to hold fixed the ξ, η, ζ system or the φ, ψ, ζ system, and to vary the corresponding lattice in x, y, z. This last lattice is to be determined in such a way that for it M^3J is a maximum. However, since

$$M^3J = \frac{M^3}{|\Delta|}\int\int\int d\xi\, d\eta\, d\zeta \qquad \text{or} \qquad \frac{M^3}{|\Delta|}\int\int\int d\varphi\, d\psi\, d\zeta$$

where the triple integral is to be taken over the standard body, and since further the volume of the standard body in the φ, ψ, ζ or ξ, η, ζ coordinates remains constant during the variations which we are proposing, the question is entirely regarding the maximum of $\dfrac{M^3}{|\Delta|}$.

In the equations

$$\begin{aligned} \xi &= \lambda x + \lambda' y + \lambda'' z, \\ \eta &= \mu x + \mu' y + \mu'' z, \\ \eta &= \nu x + \nu' y + \nu'' z, \end{aligned} \qquad \Delta = \begin{vmatrix} \lambda, & \lambda', & \lambda'' \\ \mu, & \mu', & \mu'' \\ \nu, & \nu', & \nu'' \end{vmatrix},$$

let all the quantities $\lambda, \lambda', \cdots, \nu''$ be multiplied by a constant quantity τ. The M-body belonging to the given standard body in the new lattice that has been thus formed is generated out of the M-body of the original lattice through a dilation in the ratio $\tau : 1$ and will therefore have belonging to the parameter no longer the previous value M but the value $\tau M = M^*$. At the same time Δ becomes $\Delta^* = \tau^3\Delta$, so that

$$\frac{M^{*3}}{|\Delta^*|} = \frac{M^3}{|\Delta|}.$$

It is thus shown that the quotient $\frac{M^3}{|\Delta|}$, upon which the whole question before us rests, does not change its value.

Accordingly we may give to τ the special value $\tau = \frac{1}{M}$, so that $M^* = 1$. Our problem then becomes:

Derive the conditions and the value of the maximum of $\frac{1}{|\Delta^*|}$ *and that is the minimum of* $|\Delta^*|$.

For simplicity for the quantities $\tau\lambda, \tau\lambda', \cdots, \tau\nu'', \Delta^*$ we shall now retain the old notations $\lambda, \lambda', \cdots, \nu'', \Delta$ and observe that $|\Delta|$ is the volume of the parallelopiped $\mathfrak{G}$, that is, $0 \leqq x < 1$, $0 \leqq y < 1$, $0 \leqq z < 1$, is identically

$$\iiint d\xi\, d\eta\, d\zeta$$

or

$$\iiint d\varphi\, d\psi\, d\zeta = |\Delta| \iiint dx\, dy\, dz = |\Delta|.$$

The parallelopiped $\mathfrak{G}$ we shall in the sequel designate as the *fundamental parallelopiped* in the coordinates x, y, z.

We may now express our problem as follows:

In a fixed system of coordinates ξ, η, ζ or φ, ψ, ξ with the origin O a convex body $\mathfrak{K}$ is given with center at O; a lattice in x, y, z, with origin O is to be found which offers besides O no lattice point in the interior of $\mathfrak{K}$ and has a fundamental parallelopiped $\mathfrak{G}$ of smallest possible volume; and that is *otherwise expressed, this lattice in x, y, z is to be as dense as possible. By dense we mean that the lattice points are to be as close together as possible.*

This may be expressed as follows: If we construct about the origin as center an $\frac{M}{2}$ body (in the ratio $1 : \frac{1}{2}$ to the given M-body) and consider this body shoved parallel to itself to every lattice point as center, then the question resolves itself into the one that follows:

There are given an infinite number of congruent convex bodies with centers. They are to be shoved parallel to themselves and arranged in space in such a way that no two intersect while the centers of the bodies form a three dimensional lattice. How is this arrangement of the bodies to be made in order that the space that is not filled by them shall be as small as possible?

Briefly the question is regarding the densest lattice-formed placement of homologous congruent bodies with centers. By homologous (with respect to a lattice) we are to understand in general such structures that arise the one from the other through translations with regard to integral values of the lattice coordinates.

It is clear above all that with such a densest placement of the bodies, each of the bodies must abut against certain others and will accordingly have the character of an $\frac{M}{2}$ body (or step). We shall next show that each of the bodies in a perfectly definite manner and following a definite sequence must abut the neighboring bodies.

ART. **158. Relative Density of Two Lattices.** For the treatment of the preceding theorems additional lemmas regarding linear substitutions with integral coefficients are necessary. These we may now give with emphasis upon their geometric aspect.

Let a lattice in x, y, z be given and take from it any three lattice points $A=(p_1, q_1, r_1)$, $B=(p_2, q_2, r_2)$, $C=(p_3, q_3, r_3)$, which are different from the origin and which do not lie in a plane which passes through the origin.

We accordingly have

$$D=\begin{vmatrix} p_1, & p_2, & p_3 \\ q_1, & q_2, & q_3 \\ r_1, & r_2, & r_3 \end{vmatrix} \neq 0.$$

Making basal the tetrahedron $OABC$ as fundamental tetrahedron we build a new system of coordinates in X, Y, Z, which are connected with the system of the x, y, z through the equations of transformations

$$\begin{aligned} x&=p_1X+p_2Y+p_3Z, \\ y&=q_1X+q_2Y+q_3Z, \\ z&=r_1X+r_2Y+r_3Z. \end{aligned}$$

By means of these equations we may express X, Y, Z through x, y, z in the forms

$$\begin{aligned} X&=P_1x+Q_1y+R_1z, \\ Y&=P_2x+Q_2y+R_2z, \\ Z&=P_3x+Q_3y+R_3z, \end{aligned}$$

where

$$\begin{vmatrix} P_1, & Q_1, & R_1 \\ P_2, & Q_2, & R_2 \\ P_3, & Q_3, & R_3 \end{vmatrix} = \frac{1}{D}.$$

It is clear that every lattice point in X, Y, Z is at the same time a lattice point in x, y, z. If further it is required that every lattice point x, y, z offer integral values for X, Y, Z, then in particular the three points

$$(x, y, z)=(1, 0, 0), \quad (0, 1, 0), \quad (0, 0, 1)$$

must offer integral X, Y, Z coordinates; and putting these values for P_1, Q_1, $\cdots$, R_3 in the last written determinant, it is seen that $D=\pm 1$. Reciprocally if $D=\pm 1$, then integral values of x, y, z offer integral values in X, Y, Z and vice versa. In this case the fundamental parallelopiped in X, Y, Z defined through

$$0 \leqq X < 1, \qquad 0 \leqq Y < 1, \qquad 0 \leqq Z < 1$$

may serve equally as well for the construction of the lattice

x, y, z as the fundamental parallelopiped in x, y, z. This latter parallelopiped is defined through $0 \leqq x < 1$, $0 \leqq y < 1$, $0 \leqq z < 1$. Hence when $D = \pm 1$, either of the parallelopipeds just mentioned may be taken as fundamental parallelopiped for the lattice in x, y, z.

Let D be an arbitrary integer that is different from ± 1. It may be proved then that $|D|$ *is equal to the number of lattice points of* (x, y, z) *that belong to the fundamental parallelopiped* $\mathfrak{G}$ *of* X, Y, Z. Note first that $|D|$ is identical with the volume of $\mathfrak{G}$ computed in the x, y, z coordinates. For it is clear that

$$\iiint\limits_{(\mathfrak{G})} dx\, dy\, dz = \left|\frac{d(x, y, z)}{d(X, Y, Z)}\right| \iiint\limits_{(\mathfrak{G})} dX\, dY\, dZ = |D|.$$

About the origin in the lattice (x, y, z) erect a large cube with the vertices $(\pm\Omega, \pm\Omega, \pm\Omega)$ where Ω is an integer at our disposal. This cube contains $(2\Omega+1)^3$ lattice points in x, y, z and has a volume $8\Omega^3$. Consider next the lattice points of (X, Y, Z) that are situated in this cube. About each of these lattice points as center construct a parallelopiped which is homologous to the fundamental parallelopiped. Next let d be an integer such that for all points x, y, z of the fundamental parallelopiped $\mathfrak{G}$ we have $|x| \leqq d$, $|y| \leqq d$, $|z| \leqq d$. Then $\mathfrak{G}$ may be inscribed entirely within a cube with sides parallel to the x, y, z axes and edge $= 2d$, the center being the origin. We take $\Omega > d$. Observe that the last constructed body out of parallelopipeds homologous to $\mathfrak{G}$ which have centers as the lattice points (X, Y, Z) in the cube with vertices $\{\pm(\Omega+d), \pm(\Omega+d), \pm(\Omega+d)\}$ lies entirely within the cube with edge $2(\Omega+\delta)$ and contains the cube with vertices $\{\pm(\Omega-d), \pm(\Omega-d), \pm(\Omega-d)\}$. If V denotes the volume of this body, it follows that

$$8(\Omega-d)^3 \leqq V \leqq 8(\Omega+d)^3.$$

Next observe that this body of volume V consists—due to the meaning found above of $|D|$—of exactly $V/|D|$ regions or domains that are homologous to the fundamental parallelopiped 𝔊. If N is the number of lattice points (x, y, z) in 𝔊, then the number of lattice points (x, y, z) in the body in question is $\frac{V}{|D|}N$ and these lattice points are found among $(2\Omega+2d+1)^3$ lattice points of the cube with vertices $(\pm\Omega+d, \pm\Omega+d, \pm\Omega+d)$ and contains all the lattice points of the cube with vertices $\{\pm(\Omega-d), \pm(\Omega-d), \pm(\Omega-d)\}$. It follows that

$$(2\Omega-2d+1)^3 \leqq \frac{V}{|D|}N \leqq (2\Omega+2d+1)^3.$$

For V substitute the inequalities found above and we have the inequality

$$\left(\frac{2\Omega-2d+1}{2(\Omega+d)}\right)^3 \leqq \frac{N}{|D|} \leqq \left(\frac{2\Omega+2d+1}{2(\Omega-d)}\right)^3.$$

By causing Ω to become indefinitely large, it is seen that $N=|D|$. The quotient $\frac{1}{|D|}=\frac{1}{N}$ is called the *relative density* of the lattice (X, Y, Z) to the lattice (x, y, z).

ART. 159. **Adaption[1] of a Lattice of Numbers with Respect to a Lattice that Contains It.** We shall now consider the case where $|D|>1$, and that is where the lattices in x, y, z and in X, Y, Z do not coincide. Among all the parallelopipeda for the lattice in x, y, z we shall seek a special one derived in the following unique way that has reference to the fundamental parallelopiped 𝔊 in X, Y, Z.

We shall first derive the analogous problem for two dimensional lattices. In a two dimensional lattice in x, y, we take two lattice points that are different from the origin and do not lie in a straight line with the origin, say

$$A=(p_1, q_1), \qquad B=(p_2, q_2),$$

where consequently

$$\begin{vmatrix} p_1, & p_2 \\ q_1, & q_2 \end{vmatrix} \neq 0. \qquad \text{(See Fig. 117.)}$$

[1] Word coined by Minkowski in this connection.

We enlarge the triangle OAB to a parallelogram $OAEB$ and assume that the area $|p_1q_2-p_2q_1|>1$. It is seen that this parallelogram contains besides its vertices other lattice points. We shall construct by means of this parallelogram another parallelogram which contains no lattice points save its vertices. To this end on the stretch OA we seek the lattice point A_1 which lies nearest O. This may be possibly A itself. We then lay off lattice points on OA. Then from

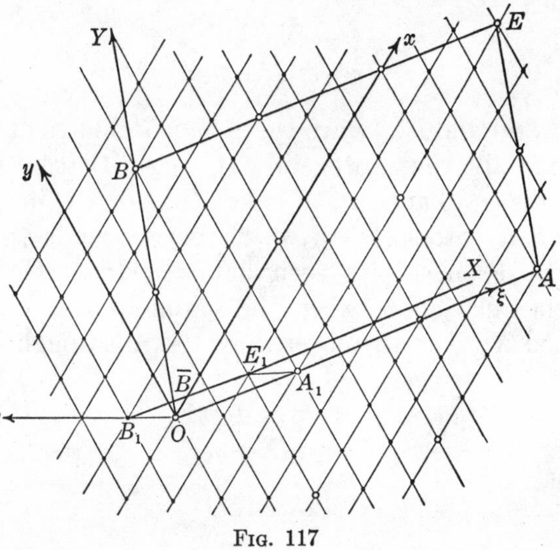

FIG. 117

the lattice points not on OA but within $OAEB$ find the one that lies as near as possible to OA and draw a straight line through it parallel to OA. On this line lay off equidistant lattice points like OA and let B_1 be the first lattice point that falls outside of $OAEB$ and to the left of OY. It is seen that the parallelogram $OA_1E_1B_1$ contains no lattice points other than its vertices.

We may next form a new lattice in the coordinates ξ, η by means of the points O, A_1, B_1 if we take as their coordinates $\xi, \eta=0, 0; 1, 0; 0, 1$. The lattice in ξ, η coincides completely with the lattice in x, y, and if a_1, b_1 and a_2, b_2 are the x, y coordinates of A_1 and B_1, the two lattices are connected by the equations of transformation

$$x=a_1\xi+a_2\eta,\quad y=b_1\xi+b_2\eta, \qquad \text{where} \quad \begin{vmatrix} a_1, & a_2 \\ b_1, & b_2 \end{vmatrix} = \pm 1.$$

On the other hand consider a lattice in X, Y derived from the lattice points O, A, B by writing for these points the coordinates $X, Y=0, 0; 1, 0; 0, 1$. It is seen that this lattice in X, Y is connected with the one in ξ, η through the equations

$$\xi=l_1X+l_2Y,$$
$$\eta=m_1X+m_2Y,$$

where l_1, m_1 and l_2, m_2 are the ξ, η coordinates of A and B and are at all events integers. It is clear that for the point A we have $l_1>0$ and $m_1=0$. For the point ζ, in which the stretch B_1E_1 intersects OB, we have $\eta=1$, while $\xi=l_2/m_2\geqq 0$ and <0. From this it is seen that $0\leqq l_2<m_2$. On the other hand the relation between the variables x, y on the one hand and X, Y on the other is expressed through the equations

$$x=p_1X+p_2Y,$$
$$y=q_1X+q_2Y,$$

so that from above it follows that

$$\begin{vmatrix} p_1, & p_2 \\ q_1, & q_2 \end{vmatrix} = \begin{vmatrix} a_1, & a_2 \\ b_1, & b_2 \end{vmatrix} . \begin{vmatrix} l_1, & l_2 \\ 0, & m_2 \end{vmatrix},$$

where $0<l_1$, and $0\leqq l_2<m_2$.

This process for determining a fundamental parallelogram $OA_1E_1B_1$ for the lattice x, y from the fundamental parallelogram $OAEB$ of a lattice in X, Y that is contained in the lattice x, y, we shall call the *adaption* [1] of the lattice in x, y with respect to the lattice in X, Y which is contained in x, y where $OAEB$ has been taken as the fundamental parallelogram of X, Y. The results of this process may be expressed as follows:

[1] Minkowski, *Dioph. Approx.*, p. 92.

THEOREM. *Every integral binary substitution with non-vanishing determinant may be compounded of two such substitutions of which the first has a determinant* $=\pm 1$, *while the second has a determinant in which the terms of the principal diagonal are all positive, the term below this diagonal is zero, while the term above this diagonal is a number which is not negative and is smaller than the term directly under it of the principal diagonal.*

An exact analogue may be derived for three dimensional lattices. Returning to the notations of the previous article, we consider the fundamental parallelepiped $\mathfrak{G}$ defined through

$$0 \leqq X < 1, \qquad 0 \leqq Y < 1, \qquad 0 \leqq Z < 1$$

and having as edges OA, OB, OC. Observe the plane OAB which is a side of the parallelepiped. Determine in this plane the lattice points A_1, B_1 and the parallelogram $OA_1E_1B_1$ precisely as in the above case of a two dimensional lattice. Using $OA_1E_1B_1$ as a fundamental parallelogram we construct a lattice with the coordinates ξ, η and such that the parallelogram is defined through $0 \leqq \xi < 1$, $0 \leqq \eta < 1$, the sides A_1E_1 and B_1E_1 being counted as being sides of the adjacent parallelograms of the net. Next, of all lattice points x, y, z of $\mathfrak{G}$ choose the one, say C_1, which is nearest the plane OAB. Through C_1 draw a plane parallel to the plane OAB and in this plane construct a net of parallelograms homologous to $OA_1E_1B_1$ by sliding O into C_1 and holding the sides OA_1 and OB_1 parallel to the $O\xi$ and$O\eta$ axes respectively. The parallelepiped whose face cuts the

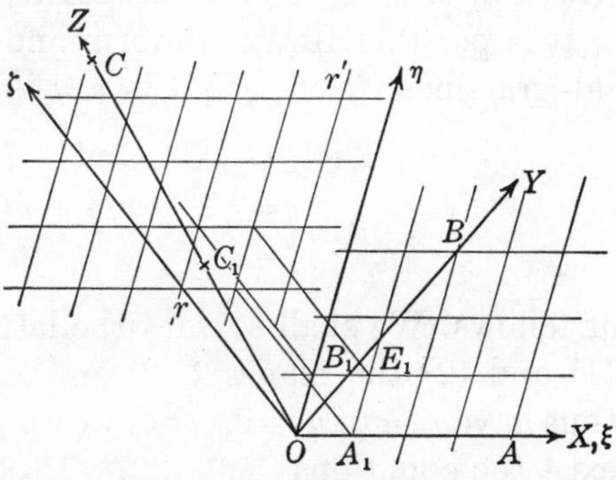

FIG. 118

OZ axis in the point $\bar{C}$ and with side OC_1 may be taken as the fundamental parallelogram in ξ, η, ζ. If a_1, b_1, c_1; a_2, b_2, c_2; a_3, b_3, c_3 are the x, y, z coordinates of the three points A_1, B_1, C_1, the relations among the ξ, η, ζ and the x, y, z coordinates are expressed through the equations

$$(1)\qquad \begin{cases} x=a_1\xi+a_2\eta+a_3\zeta, \\ y=b_1\xi+b_2\eta+b_3\zeta, \\ z=c_1\xi+c_2\eta+c_3\zeta, \end{cases} \qquad \text{where} \qquad \begin{vmatrix} a_1, & a_2, & a_3 \\ b_1, & b_2, & b_3 \\ c_1, & c_2, & c_3 \end{vmatrix} = \pm 1.$$

The ξ, ζ, η coordinates are connected with the X, Y, Z coordinates, which were determined through the fundamental tetrahedron $OABC$, by the equations

$$(2)\qquad \begin{cases} \xi=l_1X+l_2Y+l_3Z, \\ \eta=m_1X+m_2Y+m_3Z, \\ \zeta=n_1X+n_2Y+n_3Z, \end{cases}$$

where l_1, m_1, $\cdots$, n_3 are necessarily integers.

It is possible always to form and only in one way three integral linear forms ξ, η, ζ in x, y, z, so that

$$\begin{aligned} \xi &= l_1X+\ l_2Y+\ l_3Z, \\ \eta &= \qquad\quad m_2Y+m_3Z, \\ \zeta &= \qquad\qquad\qquad n_3Z, \end{aligned}$$

as follows: We shall so vary the lattice in x, y, z that using (1) and (2) the planes $\zeta=0$ and $Z=0$ are identical. We thus have $n_1=0$, $n_2=0$. For every point of this plane there exist the equations

$$\begin{aligned} \xi &= l_1X+l_2Y, \\ \eta &= m_1X+m_2Y. \end{aligned}$$

As shown above for a two dimensional lattice we have here $m_1=0$, $0<l_1$, $0\leqq l_2<m_2$. Observe that $\dfrac{O\bar{C}}{OC}=\dfrac{OC_1}{[\zeta]_{z=1}}=\dfrac{1}{n_3}$.

Hence the coordinates of $\bar{C}$ are $\xi=\dfrac{l_3}{n_3}$, $\eta=\dfrac{m_3}{n_3}$, $\zeta=1$.

Observing the position of $\bar{C}$ in the fundamental (ξ, η, ζ) parallelopiped, it is seen that $0\leqq l_3<n_3$, $0\leqq m_3<n_3$. Due to

the original equations of the previous article namely,

$$x = p_1X + p_2Y + p_3Z,$$
$$y = q_1X + q_2Y + q_3Z,$$
$$z = r_1X + r_2Y + r_3Z,$$

it is seen that

$$\begin{vmatrix} p_1, & p_2, & p_3 \\ q_1, & q_2, & q_3 \\ r_1, & r_2, & r_3 \end{vmatrix} = \begin{vmatrix} a_1, & a_2, & a_3 \\ b_1, & b_2, & b_3 \\ c_1, & c_2, & c_3 \end{vmatrix} \begin{vmatrix} l_1, & l_2, & l_3 \\ 0, & m_2, & m_3 \\ 0, & 0, & n_3 \end{vmatrix}$$

where the elements of the determinants are all integers and

$$0 < l_1; \qquad 0 \leqq l_2 < m_2; \qquad 0 \leqq l_3 < n_3; \qquad 0 \leqq m_3 < n_3.$$

In an analogous manner as in the case of a two dimensional lattice we shall call the introduction of the special lattice coordinates ξ, η, ζ for the lattice in x, y, z having regard to the lattice in X, Y, Z (which is contained in the lattice in x, y, z) the adaptation of the lattice in x, y, z with respect to the lattice in X, Y, Z. The parallelopiped $O(A_1B_1C_1)$ may be regarded as the adapted fundamental parallelopiped.

This geometrical process may be expressed as follows:

THEOREM. *Every integral linear ternary substitution with non-vanishing determinant may be compounded of two such substitutions of which the one has a determinant* $=\pm 1$ *while the second has only positive numbers in its principal diagonal. The elements below this principal diagonal are all zero, while above the elements are non-negative and of these the elements of a vertical column are all less than the corresponding element of the principal diagonal that stands in the same vertical column.*

ART. **160. Triple Steps.** Returning to the problem of the densest placement of congruent lattice-formed convex bodies in space we may show that this thickest placement can only enter if each individual one of the bodies (each step as we say) not only abuts on one but on three different steps and in fact in such a way that its mid-point does not lie in the same plane with the three mid-points of the steps that abut it.

To prove this, consider in the lattice of x, y, z about the origin O as center a given M-body whose boundary contains only one pair of lattice points A, A_0 and choose on the outside of this body any two lattice points B, C which do not lie on the same plane with OA. We then adapt the given x, y, z lattice with respect to the lattice constructed from $OABC$ as fundamental tetrahedron and we thus obtain a fundamental tetrahedron $OA_1B_1C_1$ for the given lattice where A and A_1 coincide. Next we transform the lattice of x, y, z by means of a unimodular substitution so that the new lattice contains the parallelopiped with sides OA_1, OB_1, OC_1 as fundamental parallelopiped. We may then decrease in a continuous manner the volume of this last parallelopiped by letting B_1 approach O along the side OB_1 and having C_1 slide along OC_1 towards O. The unit length in the x, y, z coordinates are correspondingly decreased so that OA_1, OB_1, OC_1 do not cease to form a parallelopiped system of lattice points. This process is continued until new lattice points enter on the boundary of the M-body. We saw in Art. 5 that, J being the volume of a fixed convex body, then always $M^3J \leqq 8$. And this shows the necessity of new lattice points appearing on the boundary of the M-body due to the above contraction.

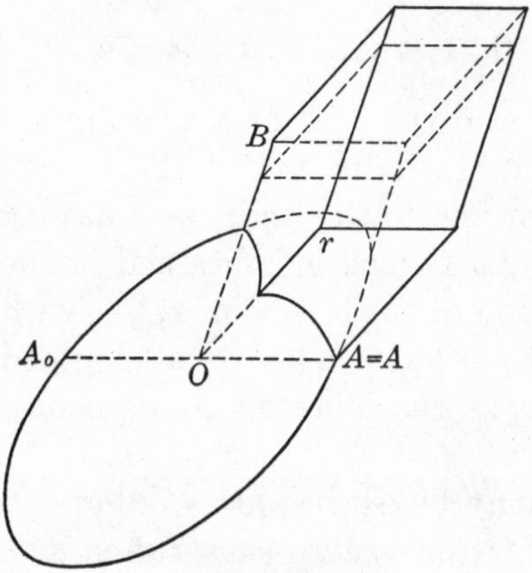

FIG. 119

There now appear on the boundary of the M-body at least two lattice points that do not lie on a straight line through O. These we again denote by A and B and the two symmetric points with respect to O are indicated by

A_0 and B_0. If these are the only lattice points on the surface of the M-body or if there are only others that lie in the plane OAB, we take another lattice point that lies without the M-body and not on the OAB plane. Denote this point by C. By means of the tetrahedron $OABC$ we again derive by the process of adaptation a fundamental tetrahedron $OA_1B_1C_1$ for the given lattice of x, y, z where the plane OA_1B_1 coincides with the plane OAB. Then by sliding the point C_1 along OC_1 towards O we decrease the volume of $OA_1B_1C_1$ producing thereby a continuous variation of the lattice until new lattice points appear on the boundary of the M-body. These new lattice points will not lie in the plane OAB since the two dimensional lattice was not changed through the variation made in the three dimensional lattice.

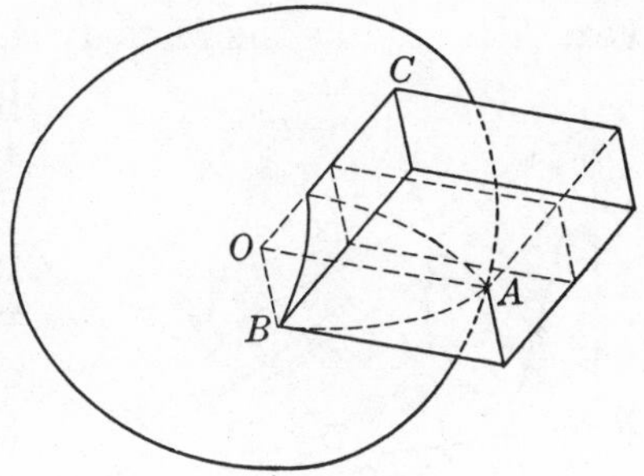

FIG. 120

It is clear that the given M-body, if a densest placement of the associated homologous $\frac{M}{2}$-body is to be brought about, must contain at least three pairs of oppositely situated lattice points that do not lie in the same plane. For otherwise through a corresponding change of the lattice we may affect a decrease of the volume of the fundamental parallelopiped of this lattice. It is thus seen that each of the $\frac{M}{2}$ bodies abuts on at least three such neighboring steps where the center of a step does not lie in the same plane with the three centers of the three neighboring steps. Steps of this character are called *triple steps*. The study of such steps is not only important for further treatment of the problem of the densest placement of homologous bodies but also for certain applications to the theory of algebraic numbers.

ART. 161. Lattice-Octahedra. Let six lattice points be on the boundary of a given M-body whose center is the origin, and let these six points be A, A_0; B, B_0; C, C_0 arranged in pairs symmetric with respect to the origin. These six lattice points determine as vertices an octahedron which lies within the M-body. This body by hypotheses is convex. Hence like the M-body the octahedron has no interior lattice points save the origin. However, on the boundary of the octahedron there may be lattice points besides the vertices. If D is such a point and lies for example on the face ABC of the octahedron and not on the edge AB, we have in $AA_0BB_0DD_0$ (where D_0 is symmetric to D with respect to the origin) an octahedron whose vertices are also lattice points on the boundary of the M-body, and whose volume is less than that of $AA_0BB_0CC_0$. If then we form all possible octahedra out of every three pairs of diametrically opposite lattice points that are found on the boundary of the M-body, whose number is finite, and choose the one that has the smallest possible volume, it is clear that the boundary of such an octahedron contains besides its vertices no other lattice points.

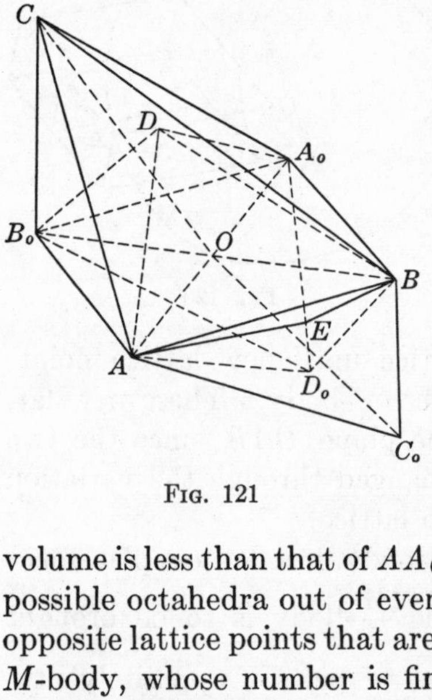

FIG. 121

An octahedron which has the origin as center and lattice points as vertices and besides these no other lattice points, is called a *lattice octahedron.*[1] It is clear that there always exists at least *one* lattice octahedron whose vertices lie on the boundary of the M-body under consideration.

Let $AA_0BB_0CC_0$ be any lattice octahedron in the lattice, of x, y, z. Corresponding to $OABC$ as fundamental tetrahedron we introduce coordinates X, Y, Z so that in X, Y, Z

[1] Minkowski, *Dioph. Appr.*, p. 97.

we have $A=(1, 0, 0)$, $B=(0, 1, 0)$, $C=(0, 0, 1)$. The domain of the octahedron in question is then defined through

$$(1) \qquad |X|+|Y|+|Z|\leqq 1.$$

Starting with this octahedron, or the lattice in X, Y, Z we may derive a special lattice in x, y, z as follows. From the tetrahedron $OABC$ we shall introduce a fundamental tetrahedron $OA_1B_1C_1$ for the lattice in x, y, z as in Art. 159. For the points A_1, B_1 we may take directly the points A, B. For observe the parallelogram $OAEB$ in the above figure; since the triangle AEB is homologous in the lattice with the triangle B_0OA_0 it contains besides its vertices no other lattice points. Now let the coordinates ξ, η, ζ belong to the fundamental tetrahedron $OA_1B_1C_1$ where the lattice in ξ, η, ζ coincides with the lattice in x, y, z; and let l, m, n be the ξ, η, ζ coordinates of C, where as in Art. 159 we have

$$(2) \qquad 0\leqq l<n, \qquad 0\leqq m<n.$$

The equations of transformation which connect the coordinate systems of the ξ, η, ζ and the X, Y, Z with one another have the form

$$\begin{aligned} \xi &= X + lZ, \\ \eta &= Y+mZ, \\ \zeta &= nZ, \end{aligned}$$

and accordingly having reference to (1) above the octahedron $AA_0BB_0CC_0$ is expressed in terms of ξ, η, ζ through the inequality

$$(3) \qquad |\xi-(l/n)\zeta|+|\eta-(m/n)\zeta|+|\zeta/n|\leqq 1.$$

The question now is how must the coefficients l, m, n be further chosen that $AA_0BB_0CC_0$ be a lattice octahedron, or in other words that the inequality (3) admit besides the solutions

$$(4) \qquad (\xi, \eta, \zeta)=(0, 0, 0),\ (\pm 1, 0, 0),\ (0, \pm 1, 0),\ (l, m, n),\ (-l, -m, -n)$$

no further integral solutions.

In this connection several cases are to be considered separately. First if $n=1$ we have from (2) $l=0$, $m=0$ and therefore $\xi=X$, $\eta=Y$, $\zeta=Z$ and accordingly $AA_0BB_0CC_0$ is a lattice octahedron in ξ, η, ζ.

Suppose next that $n>1$ and is an *odd* integer say $=2t+1 \geqq 3$; then due to (2) we have at all events $0 \leqq l \leqq 2t$, $0 \leqq m \leqq 2t$. In (3) write for ζ the value l, and for ξ the value 0 or 1, according as $l \leqq t$ or $\geqq t+1$, and similarly for η the value 0 or 1 according as $m \leqq t$ or $\geqq t+1$. In each of these cases we have

$$\left| \xi - \frac{l}{2t+1}\zeta \right| \leqq \frac{t}{2t+1}; \quad \left| \eta - \frac{m}{2t+1}\zeta \right| \leqq \frac{t}{2t+1};$$
$$\left| \frac{\zeta}{2t+1} \right| = \frac{1}{2t+1},$$

which values satisfy the inequality (3). Accordingly we have in one octahedron a lattice point with the coordinates $\xi=0$ or 1, $\eta=0$ or 1, $\zeta=1$, points which coincide with none of the points (4). Hence $AA_0BB_0CC_0$ would not be a lattice octahedron in the coordinates ξ, η, ζ. If finally n is an even integer $=2t \geqq 2$, then necessarily we must have $0 \leqq l \leqq 2t-1, 0 \leqq m \leqq 2t-1$. In (3) put $\zeta=1$ and $\xi=0$ or $=1$. according as $l \leqq t$ or $>t$ and $\eta=0$ or $=1$, according as $m \leqq t$ or $>t$. Then in all cases, except the case $l=m=t$, we have

$$\left| \xi - \frac{l}{2t}\zeta \right| + \left| \eta - \frac{m}{2t}\zeta \right| + \left| \frac{\zeta}{2t} \right| \leqq \frac{t-1}{2t} + \frac{t}{2t} + \frac{1}{2t} = 1,$$

and we thus find lattice points with coordinates $\xi=0, 1$; $\eta=0, 1$; $\zeta=1$ in the octahedron $AA_0BB_0CC_0$ which are identical with none of the points (4); and from this it again follows that $AA_0BB_0CC_0$ is no lattice octahedron.

On the other hand in the exceptional case $l=m=t$, the inequality (3) takes the form

$$\left| \xi - \frac{1}{2}\zeta \right| + \left| \eta - \frac{1}{2}\zeta \right| + \left| \frac{\zeta}{2t} \right| \leqq 1;$$

and if finally $t=1=l=m$ and $n=2$, then the solutions (4) are the only integral solutions of the inequality (3).

With this we have arrived at the result that a relation between the lattice in ξ, η, ζ and the lattice in X, Y, Z belonging to the lattice octahedron $AA_0BB_0CC_0$ (and that is the fundamental tetrahedron $OABC$) is had necessarily *either* through

(5) $$\xi = X, \qquad \eta = Y, \qquad \zeta = Z,$$

or through

(6) $$\xi = X + Z, \qquad \eta = Y + Z, \qquad \zeta = 2Z.$$

In the first case we shall say that the lattice octahedron in question is one of the *first kind*, in the second case it is one of the *second kind*. We observe that in the case of a lattice octahedron of the first kind the lattice in X, Y, Z coincides completely with the lattice in x, y, z; and the original lattice may be completely derived from the vertices A, B, C of the octahedron and the origin O. In the case of a lattice octahedron of the second kind, however, the lattice points (ξ, η, ζ) not only fall on all the lattice points of X, Y, Z but also, due to the relations $X = \xi - \frac{\zeta}{2}$, $Y = \eta - \frac{\zeta}{2}$, $Z = \frac{\zeta}{2}$, they fall on all those additional points whose X, Y, Z coordinates are odd multiples of $\frac{1}{2}$. Thus it is seen that the lattice in ξ, η, ζ not only includes all the lattice points in X, Y, Z but in addition also the points which are had from the latter points by a translation of the origin to the point $(X, Y, Z) = (\frac{1}{2}, \frac{1}{2}, \frac{1}{2})$, and that is the centers of the parallelopipeds in X, Y, Z.

If x_1, y_1, z_1; x_2, y_2, z_2; x_3, y_3, z_3 are the coordinates of three vertices of a lattice octahedron which do not lie in a plane with the origin, which lattice octahedron has the origin as center, then the absolute value of the determinant

$$\begin{vmatrix} x_1, & x_2, & x_3 \\ y_1, & y_2, & y_3 \\ z_1, & z_2, & z_3 \end{vmatrix}$$

is four-thirds times the volume of the lattice octahedron.

Due to the derivation of the (X, Y, Z) lattice from the (ξ, η, ζ) lattice or from the (x, y, z) lattice by means of equations (5) and (6) this determinant has the value 1 in the case of an octahedron of the first kind, while for one of the second kind it is

$$\begin{vmatrix} 1, & 0, & 1 \\ 0, & 1, & 1 \\ 0, & 0, & 2 \end{vmatrix} = 2.$$

From this determinant it is seen that the three values $x_1+x_2+x_3$, $y_1+y_2+y_3$, $z_1+z_2+z_3$ are all even integers, a circumstance which in the sequel is often used as a criterion as to whether a lattice octahedron is one of the first or the second kind. As is seen in the sequel a distinction must be made regarding the two kinds of lattice octahedra in the analytic treatment of the problem of the densest placement of homologous bodies in space.

ART. 162. **The Analytic Formulation of the Conditions for the Densest Lattice Formed Placement of Congruent Bodies in Space.** As at the beginning of the previous article, let A, A_0, B, B_0, C, C_0 be the vertices of a lattice octahedron that is contained in a given M-body, $\mathfrak{K}$, say. We take $OABC$ as the fundamental tetrahedron with coordinates X, Y, Z so that

$$A=(1, 0, 0), \qquad B=(0, 1, 0), \qquad C=(0, 0, 1),$$

and let the given M-body be taken with reference to these coordinates. Its domain, as in Art. 3, may be expressed by an inequality

$$F(X, Y, Z) \leqq 1,$$

where $F(X, Y, Z)$ is a function of X, Y, Z which satisfies the functional equations

$$F(0, 0, 0)=0; \quad F(tX, tY, tZ)=tF(X, Y, Z), \quad t>0;$$
$$F(-X, -Y, -Z)=F(X, Y, Z),$$

and also the functional equation

$$F(X_1, Y_1, Z_1)+F(X_2, Y_2, Z_2) \geqq F(X_1+X_2, Y_1+Y_2, Z_1+Z_2).$$

Since the points A, B, C lie on the boundary of $\mathfrak{K}$, we also have

$$(1)\quad F(1, 0, 0)=1, \qquad F(0, 1, 0)=1, \qquad F(0, 0, 1)=1.$$

The condition that no lattice points other than the origin lie within $\mathfrak{K}$ offers for the function F the following limitations: In case the lattice octahedron is of the first kind we have for every integral system of values (l, m, n) that is different from $(0, 0, 0)$ the inequality

$$(2)\qquad F(l, m, n) \geqq 1;$$

and if the lattice octahedron is of the second kind, we must have besides the inequalities (1) for every integral system of values (l, m, n) the further inequality

$$(3)\qquad F(l+\tfrac{1}{2}, m+\tfrac{1}{2}, n+\tfrac{1}{2}) \geqq 1.$$

Through the equations (1), (2) and (3) the condition that the body $F(X, Y, Z) \leqq 1$ be an M-body is completely satisfied.

The infinite number of inequalities (2) and (3) may be reduced through the equations (1) to a finite number of such equations. In the case of the lattice octahedron of the first kind the inequalities (2) reduce to the following:

$$(4)\quad F(\pm 1, \pm 1, 0) \geqq 1, \qquad F(\pm 1, 0, \pm 1) \geqq 1, \qquad F(0, \pm 1, \pm 1) \geqq 1;$$

$$(5)\qquad F(\pm 1, \pm 1, \pm 1) \geqq 1;$$

$$(6)\quad F(\pm 1, \pm 1, \pm 2) \geqq 1, \qquad F(\pm 1, \pm 2, \pm 1) \geqq 1, \qquad F(\pm 2, \pm 1, \pm 1) \geqq 1.$$

If equations (1) together with (4), (5) and (6) are satisfied, then the inequality (2) is true for every arbitrary integral system of values (l, m, n) that is different from $(0, 0, 0)$.

Proof. Suppose in spite of the existence of the equations (1) and the inequalities (4), (5) and (6) that for some lattice point $D(X=l, Y=m, Z=n)$, which is different from the lattice points indicated in (1), (4), (5) and (6) and from $(0, 0, 0)$

we had

$$F(l, m, n) < 1. \tag{7}$$

Without making any essential limitations we may assume that $0 \leqq l \leqq m \leqq n$, and then at all events $n \geqq 2$ and (l, m, n) is different from $(1, 1, 2)$.

Consider the octahedron $AA_0BB_0DD_0$, where D_0 is the point symmetric to D with respect to 0. The domain of this octahedron (Art. 161) is given through the inequality

$$\left| X - \frac{l}{n} Z \right| + \left| Y - \frac{m}{n} Z \right| + \left| \frac{Z}{n} \right| \leqq 1. \tag{8}$$

We observe (see (1), (4), (5), (6)) that the inequality (8)

for $(0, 0, 1)$ is $\dfrac{l}{n} + \dfrac{m}{n} + \dfrac{1}{n} \leqq 1,$

for $(0, 1, 1)$ is $\dfrac{l + 1 - m + 1}{n} \leqq 1,$

for $(1, 1, 1)$ is $\dfrac{1 - l + 1 - m + 1}{n} \leqq 1,$

and for $(1, 1, 2)$ is $\dfrac{1 - l + 1 - m + 2}{n} \leqq 1.$

The assumptions made here regarding l, m, n require that the inequality (8) be satisfied by at least one of the systems of values

$$(X, Y, Z) = (0, 0, 1),\ (0, 1, 1),\ (1, 1, 1),\ (1, 1, 2).$$

Let such a lattice point, say $E(X_0, Y_0, Z_0)$, lie in the octahedron $AA_0BB_0DD_0$ and without the plane AA_0BB_0 since in this plane $Z = 0$. Since the points D, D_0 lie within the body $\mathfrak{K}$ due to the assumption (7), it follows also that E lies within $\mathfrak{K}$ and hence we have

$$F(X_0, Y_0, Z_0) < 1.$$

This, however, is in contradiction with one of the equations or inequalities (1), (4), (5), (6). With this follows the inadmissibility of our assumption and the correctness of the assertion preceding it. This in greater detail is considered in Arts. 173.

If $AA_0BB_0CC_0$ is a lattice octahedron of the second kind, the method of procedure is somewhat simpler. *In this case all the inequalities (2) and (3), if use is made of the equations (1), may be replaced by the following inequalities*

$$(9) \qquad F(\pm\tfrac{1}{2}, \pm\tfrac{1}{2}, \pm\tfrac{1}{2}) \geqq 1,$$

or what is the same thing by

$$(10) \qquad F(\pm 1, \pm 1, \pm 1) \geqq 2.$$

In fact from the inequalities (10) we may derive the inequalities (4), (5) and (6). Note that (5) follows of itself. The general rule for accordant functions, if use is made of (10) and (6), shows that

$$F(1, 1, 0) \geqq F(1, 1, 1) - F(0, 0, 1) \geqq 1.$$

The remaining inequalities in (4) are had from

$$F(1, 1, 2) \geqq F(1, 1, 1) - F(0, 0, -1) \geqq 1,$$

as are also the remaining inequalities in (6). Further assuming (9) and (1) and proceeding as in the case of the octahedra of the first kind, we may derive all the inequalities (2). Next turning our attention to (3), assume that there is a system of values consisting of the half of three odd integers, say $\frac{1}{2}(2l+1)$, $\frac{1}{2}(2m+1)$, $\frac{1}{2}(2n+1)$, which notwithstanding the existence of (1) and (9), nevertheless satisfy the inequality

$$(11) \qquad F(l+\tfrac{1}{2}, m+\tfrac{1}{2}, n+\tfrac{1}{2}) < 1.$$

We may assume without making any essential limitation that

$$0 < l+\tfrac{1}{2} \leqq m+\tfrac{1}{2} \leqq n+\tfrac{1}{2},$$

so that at all events $n+\frac{1}{2} \geqq 3/2$.

If D is the lattice point with coordinates $X = l+\frac{1}{2}$, $Y = m+\frac{1}{2}$, $Z = n+\frac{1}{2}$ and D_0 the point symmetric to D with respect to the origin, then the octahedron $AA_0BB_0CC_0$ is defined through the inequality (Art. 161),

$$\left| X - \frac{2l+1}{2n+1} Z \right| + \left| Y - \frac{2m+1}{2n+1} Z \right| + \left| \frac{2Z}{2n+1} \right| \leqq 1.$$

Since this inequality is satisfied by $(X, Y, Z) = (\frac{1}{2}, \frac{1}{2}, \frac{1}{2})$, the lattice point E, say, in the (ξ, η, ζ) lattice lies in the octahedron in question and not in the plane AA_0BB_0.

Since on the other hand D, D_0, due to the assumption (11), lies within the body $\mathfrak{K}$, the point E must also lie within this body. This contradicts the inequality (9). And it is thus shown that all the inequalities (3) are a consequence of (1) and (9).

The problem of the densest lattice-formed placement of bodies which are arranged congruent to the body $\mathfrak{K}$ and homologous in space may be expressed analytically in the following manner:

On the boundary of a convex body $\mathfrak{K}$ which has its center at the origin and which, in a system of coordinates ξ, η, ζ with O as the origin, is expressed through the inequality $\varphi(\xi, \eta, \zeta) \leqq 1$, three points $(\xi, \eta, \zeta) = (\lambda, \mu, \nu), (\lambda', \mu', \nu'), (\lambda'', \mu'', \nu'')$ are taken which do not lie in a plane with the origin. From these three points and O we derive a lattice in X, Y, Z, which with the system in ξ, η, ζ is connected through the equations of transformations

$$\xi = \lambda X + \lambda' Y + \lambda'' Z,$$
$$\eta = \mu X + \mu' Y + \mu'' Z,$$
$$\zeta = \nu X + \nu' Y + \nu'' Z.$$

We next write $\varphi(\xi, \eta, \zeta) = F(X, Y, Z)$, and assume either that the inequalities (4), (5), (6) or the inequalities (9) are satisfied; in the first case we have to form the absolute value of the determinant

$$\begin{vmatrix} \lambda, & \lambda', & \lambda'' \\ \mu, & \mu', & \mu'' \\ \nu, & \nu', & \nu'' \end{vmatrix},$$

while in the second case we have to form one half of this absolute value and this function of the lattice we have to minimize through a proper choice of the quantities λ, μ, $\cdots$, ν''.

With this the way is outlined for the solution of our problem for any special given case. Such cases are given in the sequel.

ART. **163. Densest Placement of Spheres.** On the boundary of a sphere $\mathfrak{K}$ with origin at O we take any three points A, B, C which do not lie in the same plane with O and we introduce having $OABC$ as fundamental tetrahedron the coordinates X, Y, Z. In this system of coordinates the domain of $\mathfrak{K}$ is given through an inequality

$$(1)\quad F^2(X, Y, Z) = X^2 + Y^2 + Z^2 + 2a'YZ + 2b'ZX + 2c'XY \leqq 1.$$

For the sphere the case is at once excluded that the lattice octahedron of the points A, B, C, A_0, B_0, C_0 is one of the second kind; in other words that the inequalities (9) of the preceding case exist. This would mean here that

$$(2)\qquad F^2\left(\frac{1}{2}, \frac{1}{2}, \frac{1}{2}\right) = \frac{3 \pm 2a' \pm 2b' \pm 2c'}{4} \geqq 1,$$

where always the three signs are to be taken such that their product $= +1$.

Now observe that two of these signs may be chosen arbitrarily and accordingly we may take the three signs such that of the expressions $\pm 2a'$, $\pm 2b'$, $\pm 2c'$—if they are arranged so as to be in a non-decreasing order—the first two are negative. For such a combination the left-hand side of (2) is clearly $\leqq \frac{3}{4}$ which is a contradiction to one of the inequalities of (2).

With this it is shown that the lattice octahedron in question is necessarily one of the first kind and our problem consists now in so choosing the points A, B, C (or, what amounts to the same thing, the coefficients a', b', c' in (1)) that the volume of the tetrahedron $OABC$ be a minimum while all the inequalities (4), (5) and (6) of the preceding article are satisfied.

We shall first show that for the existence of a minimum of the volume in question certain of the inequalities just mentioned must necessarily be satisfied with the sign of equality. In fact the existence of the finite number of inequalities (4), (5) and (6) carries with it the existence of the infinite number of inequalities (2) of the preceding article. If then by a continuous change of the coefficients a', b', c' the system of inequalities (2) of the preceding article cease to exist, then one of the inequalities (4), (5), (6) must lose its import. Suppose at the beginning in these inequalities (4), (5), (6) the sign $>$ everywhere exists. By holding fixed the points A, B we cause the point C to vary along a curve on the boundary of the sphere $\mathfrak{K}$ in a continuous manner towards the plane OAB and causing at the same time a corresponding variation of the lattice in X, Y, Z so that it never loses its character as a lattice. We thus bring about a continual decrease in the volume of $OABC$. We continue this process and hold the inequalities (2) of the preceding article unchanged until the equality sign appears in one of the inequalities (4), (5), (6). The lattice point P of the associated inequality then becomes a lattice point on the boundary of $\mathfrak{K}$. And this must happen before the volume of $OABC$ becomes one eighth of the volume of $\mathfrak{K}$ (Art. 5). The point P can belong to none of the inequalities (6) of the preceding article. For suppose for example we had $F(1, 1, 2)=1$. The points $(-1, 0, 0)$, $(0, -1, 0)$, $(1, 1, 2)$ with their symmetric points with respect to the origin would form a lattice octahedron of the second kind in $\mathfrak{K}$, since the determinant $=2$, which was excluded. Hence the equality sign must enter in one of the inequalities (4) or (5).

I. We shall first exclude the case that now or by further variations to be considered later of the lattice any one of the inequalities (5) of the preceding Article is satisfied by an equality sign.

Observe that the point P does not lie in the $Z=0$ plane; for the two dimensional lattice in this plane is not effected through the variation in question of the entire X, Y, Z lattice. Hence the point P is to be sought alone among the points $(0, \pm 1, \pm 1)$, $(\pm 1, 0, \pm 1)$, since instead of the point P the point P_0 symmetric to it with respect to the origin may be taken. Since further the notation for X and Y may be interchanged, and as Y may be replaced by $-Y$, we may take for P the point $(0, -1, 1)$. Since this point lies on the surface of the sphere we have on the one hand $F^2(0, -1, 1) = 1$, and on the other hand $F^2(0, -1, 1) = 2 - 2a'$; and consequently $2a' = 1$. At the same time it is seen that $F^2(0, 1, 1) = 2 + 2a' = 3$. It follows that if the point $(0, -1, 1)$ lies on the surface of $\mathfrak{K}$, the point $(0, 1, 1)$ lies without it.

If besides P and $P_0 = (0, 1, -1)$ there are no further lattice points on the surface of $\mathfrak{K}$, we shall move, and thereby diminish the volume of $OABC$, the segment of line PC which is parallel and equal to OB, and keeping it parallel with itself cause it to approach nearer the plane OAB. At the same time its two end points are caused to remain on the surface of the sphere. Simultaneously we vary in a corresponding manner the entire lattice until on the surface of $\mathfrak{K}$ there enter lattice points that appear in the inequalities (4), (5) and (6). Since the lattice points in (6) have been already considered and since the point $(0, 1, 1)$ lies without the sphere while those points of (5) for the time being are excluded, there remain only the points $(\pm 1, 0, \pm 1)$ to be considered. As eventually X may be replaced by $-X$, we may assume that now the points $Q = (1, 0, -1)$ and $Q_0 = (-1, 0, 1)$ have entered on the surface of the sphere. It then follows that $F^2(1, 0, -1) = 1$, and as above $2b' = 1$. At the same time we have $F^2(1, 0, 1) = 2 + 2b' = 3$ and accordingly the point $(1, 0, 1)$ lies necessarily outside the sphere. There are now five lattice points on the surface of the sphere.

If there are no other such points, we may further diminish the volume of $OABC$ in that the plane OAC is held fixed as also the points A, C, Q on it. The length P_0B which is parallel to OC is made to approach OC while P_0 and B are kept on the surface of the sphere, there being made a simultaneous variation of the entire lattice, and this is kept up until lattice points of (4) enter on the surface of $\mathfrak{K}$. Among these last there remain only the points $(\pm 1, \pm 1, 0)$. And of these the lattice point $(1, 1, 0)$ is to be excluded, because it with the points $P = (0, -1, 1)$ and $Q_0 = (-1, 0, 1)$ forms the three vertices of a lattice octahedron of the second kind. Hence there remain necessarily the lattice points $R = (-1, 1, 0)$ and $R_0 = (1, -1, 0)$ on the surface of the sphere. We accordingly have $F^2(-1, 1, 0) = 1$, and as above $2c' = 1$. It is thus seen in the case of the densest placement of spheres, as has been shown through an assumption of the existence of all the inequalities (5) with signs of inequality (no equality sign being permitted), that there must enter three pairs of lattice points on the surface of the sphere. And these arise from equality signs appearing in the inequalities (4). These are the points

$$A = (1, 0, 0), \qquad B = (0, 1, 0), \qquad C = (0, 0, 1),$$
$$P = (0, -1, 1), \qquad Q = (1, 0, -1), \qquad R = (-1, 1, 0)$$

and the symmetric points with respect to the origin. This system of the six pairs of lattice points is indicated through a vector-tetrahedron. See Fig. 123.

II. We have to consider next the case where any one of the lattice points $(\pm 1, \pm 1, \pm 1)$ of the inequalities (5) of the preceding article is allowed to enter on the surface of the sphere $\mathfrak{K}$.

It may be shown that only one pair of such points can fall on the boundary of $\mathfrak{K}$. For suppose that $T = (1, 1, 1)$, $T_0 = (-1, -1, -1)$ is a pair of such points. This supposition carries with it no restriction, since the coordinate axes and their directions may be interchanged.

If $F^2(1, 1, 1) = 1 = F^2(-1, -1, -1)$, then the other points of the lattice $(\pm 1, +1, \pm 1)$ must lie necessarily without the sphere since these points are had by increasing the line stretches TA, TB, TC, T_0A_0, T_0B_0, T_0C_0 by their own lengths

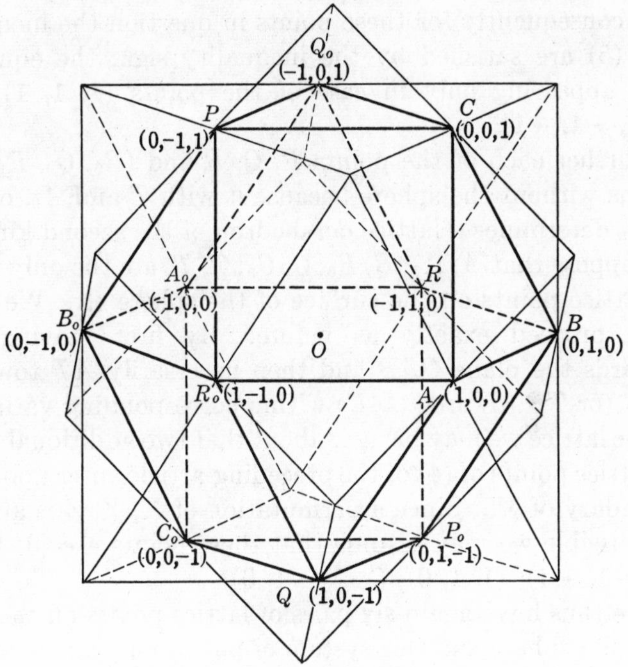

FIG. 122

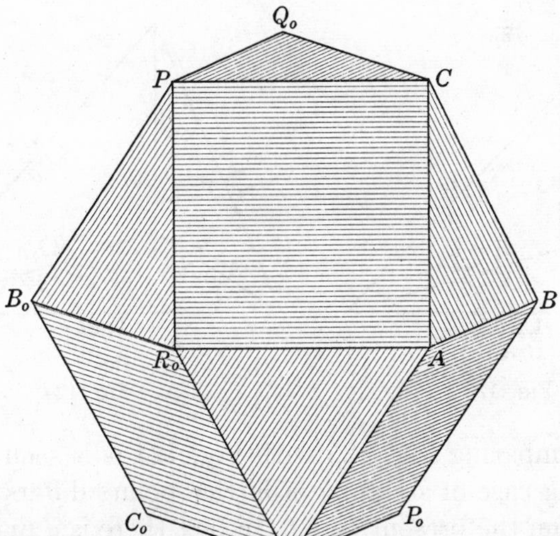

FIG. 122a

and consequently for these points in question the inequalities (5) are satisfied by the inequality sign, the equality sign appearing only in case of the points (1, 1, 1) and (−1, −1, −1).

Further each of the points P, Q, R and (P_0, Q_0, R_0) remains without the sphere because it with T and A_0, or B_0, or C_0 determines a lattice octahedron of the second kind.

Suppose that A, A_0; B, B_0; C, C_0; T, T_0 are the only pairs of lattice points on the surface of the sphere $\mathfrak{K}$. We may then proceed exactly as before. By first moving CT towards the plane OAB and then necessarily AT towards OBC (or TB towards OAC) with a corresponding variation of the lattice we may bring it about that two additional pairs of lattice points of (4) of the preceding article enter upon the boundary of $\mathfrak{K}$. Since a permutation of X, Y, Z is always permissible we may assume that these points are (0, 1, 1), (0, −1, −1), (1, 1, 0), (−1, −1, 0).

We thus have again six pairs of lattice points on the surface of a sphere and this system of points may again be put into evidence through a vector tetrahedron.

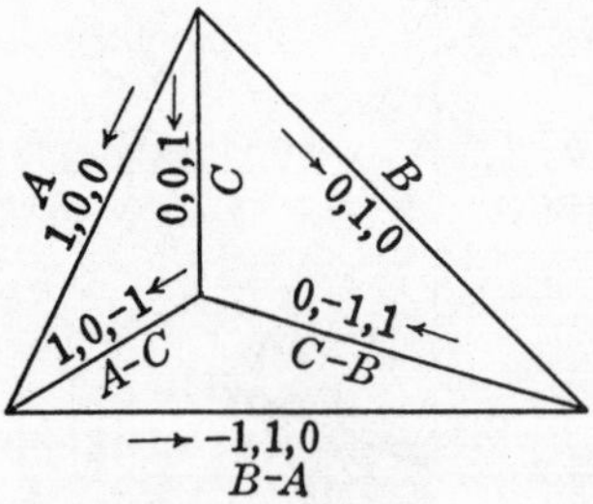

Fig. 123

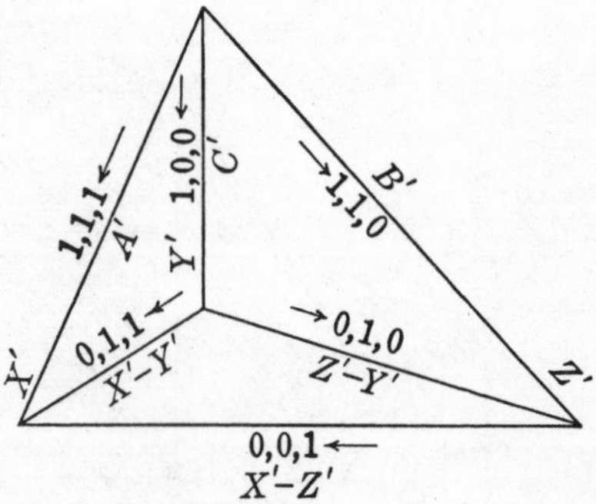

Fig. 124

By comparing Fig. 123 with Fig. 124 it is seen that the preceding case of six pairs of lattice points differs unessentially from the present case. In fact there is a unimodular substitution $X = Z'$, $Y = Y' - Z'$, $Z = X' - Y'$ through which the six lattice points $(X', Y', Z') = (1, 1, 1)$, $(1, 1, 0)$, $(1, 0, 0)$,

(0, −1, 0), (0, 1, 1), (0, 0, −1) of the second case are transformed into the six lattice points $(X, Y, Z) = (1, 0, 0)$, (0, 1, 0), (0, 0, 1), (0, −1, 1), (1, 0, −1), (−1, 1, 0) of the first case. Observe that

$$\begin{aligned} A_0 &= A+B+C, & A &= C_0, \\ B_0 &= A+B, & B &= B_0 - C_0, \\ C_0 &= A, & C &= A_0 - B_0. \end{aligned}$$

It is thus shown as densest placement of equal spheres in a three dimensional space that there is essentially only *one* definitely determined such placement; and since every other placement may be transformed into this by a continual decreasing of the volume of the fundamental parallelopiped, such a placement remaining finally alone must be the densest.

This placement is such that every sphere abuts neighboring spheres in the twelve vertices of a cubooctahedron, a body which as seen in Fig. 122 exists through intersection of a cube with a regular octahedron. The figure is seen to have 12 vertices and 14 sides or faces. The spheres are arranged in layers, in which a plane net of congruent equilateral triangles exists through joining the centers of any two abutting spheres. The layers rest upon one another in such a way that the spheres of every individual layer penetrate into the gaps made by two neighboring spheres as deep as possible and besides every layer may be transposed into the two neighboring layers through two opposite translations.

Making use of this fact we may determine the ratio of the volumes of the space occupied by (included in) the spheres placed so as to be as dense as possible to the entire space. In the following article it is seen that $M^3 < \frac{6\sqrt{D}}{\pi}$, where for the case in question $D = \frac{1}{2}$. This makes the ratio of the volume of the space in question that is filled by the spheres to the volume of all space $= \frac{\pi\sqrt{2}}{6} : 1$.

The observations made in this article are true with slight modification not only for the densest lattice formed placement of spheres but also for the densest lattice formed placement of arbitrary congruent and homologous ellipsoids. We have only to take in the place of the sphere $\mathfrak{K}$ a general ellipsoid as standard body of radial distances F and the whole treatment is the same practically word for word as in the preceding case

We also find that the volume of the space occupied by homologous ellipsoids in densest lattice formed placement is to that of the entire space as $\frac{\pi\sqrt{2}}{6} : 1$.

The picture which the ellipsoids present in this connection is had from that of spheres placed so as to be as dense as possible through an affine transformation of the kind which takes the sphere $\mathfrak{K}$ into the given ellipse.

ART. 164. **Arithmetical Consequences.** The result found above may be interpreted arithmetically. Take a positive definite ternary quadratic form

$$f(x, y, z) = ax^2 + by^2 + cz^2 + 2a'yz + 2b'zx + 2c'xy$$

with the determinant

$$D = \begin{vmatrix} a, & c', & b' \\ c', & b, & a' \\ b', & a', & c \end{vmatrix}.$$

Here a, $ab - c'^2$, D are necessarily positive and these conditions also characterize $f(x, y, z)$ fully as a positive form.

Without leaving the realm of the real the form f may be written as follows:

$$(1) \quad f(x, y, z) = \left(\sqrt{a}x + \frac{c'}{\sqrt{a}}y + \frac{b'}{\sqrt{a}}z\right)^2$$
$$+ \left(\sqrt{\frac{ab - c'^2}{a}}y + \frac{aa' - b'c'}{\sqrt{a}\sqrt{ab - c'^2}}z\right)^2 + \left(\sqrt{\frac{D}{ab - c'^2}}z\right)^2.$$

Writing

$$(2)\qquad \begin{cases} \xi = \sqrt{a}x + \dfrac{c'}{\sqrt{a}}y + \dfrac{b'}{\sqrt{a}}z, \\ \eta = \qquad \sqrt{\dfrac{ab-c'^2}{a}}y + \dfrac{aa'-b'c'}{\sqrt{a}\sqrt{ab-c'^2}}z, \\ \zeta = \qquad\qquad \sqrt{\dfrac{D}{ab-c'^2}}z, \end{cases}$$

we have

$$f(x, y, z) = \xi^2 + \eta^2 + \zeta^2,$$

where ξ, η, ζ are the usual rectangular coordinates.

Consider next the sphere defined through the inequality

$$\xi^2 + \eta^2 + \zeta^2 \leqq 1$$

with the origin as center. The volume of this sphere is $\frac{4}{3}\pi$ in the ξ, η, ζ coordinates; in the x, y, z coordinates, as defined above, it is

$$J = \int\int\int dx\, dy\, dz = \frac{d(x, y, z)}{d(\xi, \eta, \zeta)}\int d\xi\, d\eta\, d\zeta = \frac{4\pi}{3\sqrt{D}}\cdot$$

The associated M-sphere in respect to the lattice of x, y, z, and defined through the inequality

$$\xi^2 + \eta^2 + \zeta^2 \leqq M^2,$$

has in the x, y, z coordinates the volume $M^3J = \dfrac{4\pi}{3\sqrt{D}}M^3$. We saw (Art. 5) that $M^3J \leqq 8$. Hence here there exists the inequality $M \leqq \sqrt[3]{\dfrac{6}{\pi}}\sqrt{D}$. Since M^2 is the least value which $f(x, y, z)$ can take for integral values of the argument that are not all zero it is seen that we have in $\sqrt[3]{\dfrac{36}{\pi^2}D}$ an upper limit for this "minimum" of the form f. However, it may be shown as follows that a value of $\dfrac{M^2}{\sqrt[3]{D}}$ may be found by a variation of the coefficients $a, b, \cdots, c'$, where the form f remains always positive and for which this value $<\sqrt[3]{\frac{36}{\pi^2}}$.

The results of Art. 163 permit us to determine this maximum of $\frac{M^2}{\sqrt[3]{D}}$. For from (2) above it is seen that $\sqrt{D}$ calculated in the ξ, η, ζ coordinates is identical with the volume of the fundamental parallelopiped for the x, y, z lattice. We found, however, in Art. 163 where $M=1$, that by varying the lattice of x, y, z the minimum of the volume in question is had if the M-sphere in the x, y, z coordinates has the form

$$x^2+y^2+z^2+yz+zx+xy=1.$$

The minimum of D has then the value

$$D_{\min}=\begin{vmatrix} 1, & \frac{1}{2}, & \frac{1}{2} \\ \frac{1}{2}, & 1, & \frac{1}{2} \\ \frac{1}{2}, & \frac{1}{2}, & 1 \end{vmatrix}=\frac{1}{2}.$$

Hence the maximum of $\frac{M^2}{\sqrt[3]{D}}$ is $=\sqrt[3]{2}$ and consequently $M^2 \leqq \sqrt[3]{2D}$.

With this we have derived the following theorem:

Every positive definite ternary quadratic form with the determinant $D>0$ by a suitable choice of integral values of the variables, which do not all simultaneously vanish, may be made to have a value $\leqq \sqrt[3]{2D}$. The equality sign appears here only if the form is arithmetically equivalent with the form

$$\sqrt[3]{2D}(x^2+y^2+z^2+yz+zx+xy)=\sqrt[3]{2D}.$$

ART. **165. Application to the Theory of Equivalence of the Ternary Quadratic Forms.** From the results of Arts. 163 and 164 regarding the densest lattice-formed placement of ellipsoids we may develop in a few lines the whole theory of the arithmetical equivalence of positive ternary quadratic forms. The fundamental theorems of such forms were first given by Gauss [1] and Seeber [2] and later and in simpler form through geometric considerations by Dirichlet.[3] These developments preceding those of Minkowski are presented, however, in a formal way.

We shall now prove the following theorem of Gauss:

If an arbitrary positive definite ternary quadratic form

$$f(x, y, z) = ax^2 + by^2 + cz^2 + 2a'yz + 2b'zx + 2c'xy \tag{1}$$

with determinant $D > 0$ is given, an arithmetically equivalent form

$$g(X, Y, Z) = AX^2 + BY^2 + CZ^2 + 2A'YZ + 2B'XZ + 2C'XY \tag{2}$$

may always be found, such that $ABC \leqq 2D$.

To prove this theorem observe that $f(x, y, z) \leqq t^2$, where t is a positive parameter, represents the realm (or domain) of an ellipsoid whose center is the origin. By taking t sufficiently small this ellipsoid contains no other lattice point save the origin. This t is caused to increase until for $t = M_1$, say, a lattice point appears on the surface of the ellipsoid. Denote this point by $P_1 = (l_1, m_1, n_1)$. We again increase t until for $t = M_2$ a lattice point $P_2 = (l_2, m_2, n_2)$ appears on the surface of a dilated ellipsoid which lattice point is not on the line OP_1. Finally we dilate this second ellipsoid until for $t = M_3$ a lattice point appears on the boundary of a third ellipsoid. This lattice point $P_3 = (l_3, m_3, n_3)$ must not lie in the plane OP_1P_2. Observe that $M_3 \geqq M_2 \geqq M_1$. Taking $OP_1P_2P_3$ as a fundamental tetrahedron we form a lattice in X, Y, Z. This lattice is connected with the lattice in x, y, z through the equations of transformation

$$\begin{aligned} x &= l_1X + l_2Y + l_3Z, \\ y &= m_1X + m_2Y + m_3Z, \\ z &= n_1X + n_2Y + n_3Z, \end{aligned} \tag{3}$$

[1] *Gott. gel. Anz.* 1831 (*Ges. Werke*, II, p. 188).

[2] *Untersuchungen über die Eigenschaften der pos. tern. qu. Formen.* Freiburg i. Br. 1831.

[3] *Crelle's Journal*, Vol. 40, p. 209. *Werke*, Vol. II, p. 27.

See also Hermite, *Crelle's Journal*, Vol. 40, p. 173; Vol. 79, p. 17; *Oeuvres*, T. I, p. 94; T. III, p. 190. Selling, *Crelle's Journal*, Bd. 77, p. 143.

with determinant

$$E=\begin{vmatrix} l_1, & l_2, & l_3 \\ m_1, & m_2, & m_3 \\ n_1, & n_2, & n_3 \end{vmatrix}.$$

These equations take the form $f(x, y, z)$ into a form

$$(4)\quad g(X, Y, Z)=AX^2+BY^2+CZ^2+2A'ZY \\ +2B'ZX+2C'XY$$

with a determinant $D^*=E^2D$, where

$$(5)\qquad \begin{aligned} A&=g(1, 0, 0)=f(l_1, m_1, n_1)=M_1^2, \\ B&=g(0, 1, 0)=f(l_2, m_2, n_2)=M_2^2, \\ C&=g(0, 0, 1)=f(l_3, m_3, n_3)=M_3^2, \end{aligned}$$

and this last form is such a one whose existence is predicated in the theorem above.

To prove this following the analogy of (1) in Art. 164 write $g(X, Y, Z)$ in the form

$$(6)\quad g(X, Y, Z)=\left(\sqrt{A}X+\frac{C'}{\sqrt{A}}Y+\frac{B'}{\sqrt{A}}Z\right)^2 \\ +\left(\sqrt{\frac{AB-C'^2}{A}}Y+\frac{AA'-B'C'}{\sqrt{A}\sqrt{AB-C'^2}}Z\right)^2 \\ +\left(\sqrt{\frac{D^*}{AB-C'^2}}Z\right)^2.$$

Denoting the linear forms within the brackets by Ξ, Η, Ζ, the above expression is

$$g(X, Y, Z)=\Xi^2+\mathrm{H}^2+\mathrm{Z}^2.$$

Consider next the domain

$$(7)\qquad h(X, Y, Z)=\frac{\Xi^2}{A}+\frac{\mathrm{H}}{B}+\frac{\mathrm{Z}}{C}\leq 1$$

and in it the variables X, Y, Z expressed through x, y, z. Writing $Y=Z=0$, $X=1$, it is seen that $\mathrm{H}=0=\mathrm{Z}$ and $\Xi=A$, so that the point P_1 lies on the surface of the ellipsoid expressed through (7). It is further seen that within this ellipsoid save O there is no other lattice point in x, y, z. This may be proved as follows: In the first place for every lattice point (x, y, z) which lies on the line through OP_1 without O, so that $X \geqq 0$, $Y=0=Z$, it is clear that $h(X, Y, Z) \geqq 1$; observe further, due to the definition of M_1 and M_2, there is no lattice point in x, y, z situated between the ellipsoids $f(x, y, z) \leqq M_1^2$ and $f(x, y, z) \leqq M_2^2$. Consequently for lattice points without the line OP_1 and on the plane OP_1P_2, so that $Y \gtrless 0$, $Z=0$, we have $g(X, Y, Z) \geqq B$, and since $B \geqq A$, it follows that $h(X, Y, Z) \geqq 1$. Finally for every lattice point without the plane OP_1P_2, so that $Z \gtrless 0$, we have $g(X, Y, Z) \geqq C$, and since $C \geqq B \geqq A$, it again follows that $h(X, Y, Z) \geqq 1$. Having references to the theorem at the end of Art. 163 concerning the densest lattice-formed placement of homologous ellipsoids, we note that the volume J of the ellipsoid (7) necessarily satisfies the inequality

(8)
$$\frac{J}{8} \leqq \frac{\pi\sqrt{2}}{6}.$$

On the other hand

$$J = \left| \frac{d(x, y, z)}{d(\Xi, \mathrm{H}, \mathrm{Z})} \right| \int\!\!\int\!\!\int d\Xi\, d\mathrm{H}\, d\mathrm{Z},$$

where the triple integral taken over (7) is $\frac{4}{3}\pi\sqrt{ABC}$.

Observing that

$$\frac{d(x, y, z)}{d(\Xi, \mathrm{H}, \mathrm{Z})} = \frac{\dfrac{d(x, y, z)}{d(X, Y, Z)}}{\dfrac{d(\Xi, \mathrm{H}, \mathrm{Z})}{d(X, Y, Z)}},$$

and that

$$\frac{d(x, y, z)}{d(X, Y, Z)} = E, \qquad \frac{d(\Xi, \mathrm{H}, \mathrm{Z})}{d(X, Y, Z)} = E\sqrt{D}$$

it is seen that

$$J = \frac{4\pi}{3}\sqrt{\frac{ABC}{D}}.$$

This compared with (8) shows that

(9)
$$ABC \leqq 2D.$$

Further by equating coefficients of Y^2 and Z^2 in (4) and (6) and noting that A, $AB-C'^2$ are both positive (see beginning of Art. 164), it is seen that

$$B \geqq \frac{AB-C'^2}{A}, \qquad C \geqq \frac{D^*}{AB-C'^2}.$$

These two expressions multiplied show that $ABC \geqq D^* = E^2D$. This compared with (9) indicates that the integer $E = \pm 1$. Noting the definition of E, it follows that the forms $g(X, Y, Z)$ and $f(x, y, z)$ are arithmetically equivalent. This in connection with (9) proves the theorem cited at the beginning of the article.

Making use of the transformation (2) of Art. 164 and considering ξ, η, ζ as the usual rectangular coordinates in space the fundamental parallelopiped in x, y, z being a completely general parallelopiped has a volume $=\sqrt{D}$. From (5) it is seen that $\sqrt{A}$, $\sqrt{B}$, $\sqrt{C}$ are in the usual sense the lengths OP_1, OP_2 and OP_3, and the Gaussian theorem of this article expressed geometrically is:

An arbitrary parallelopiped lattice always may be arranged with respect to a fundamental parallelopiped in which the product of the lengths of the three sides is not greater than the $\sqrt{2}$ *times the volume of the fundamental parallelopiped.*

The problem of the densest lattice formed placement of spheres may be extended to a space of arbitrary many dimensions and occupies in general a central position in the arithmetical theory of positive quadratic forms as shown in particular in Minkowski's paper on the Realm of Discontinuity for Arithmetical Discontinuity. See Chapt. XX.

See references in the *Gött. Nachr., Math.-Phys. Kl.*, 1904, p. 330.

ART. **166. Correction of an Error found in Minkowski's *Collected Works*, Vol. II, p. 34.** (By Dr. Paul Pepper.) Let

$$\phi = -\xi + \eta + \zeta, \quad \chi = \xi - \eta + \zeta, \quad \psi = \xi + \eta - \zeta, \quad \omega = -\xi - \eta - \zeta,$$

be three linear forms in ξ, η, ζ, where

$$\phi + \chi + \psi + \omega \equiv 0.$$

The inequalities

$$\phi \leqq \tfrac{1}{4}, \qquad \chi \leqq \tfrac{1}{4}, \qquad \psi \leqq \tfrac{1}{4}, \qquad \omega \leqq \tfrac{1}{4}$$

define the tetrahedron with vertices

(1) $A: (\tfrac{1}{4}, \tfrac{1}{4}, \tfrac{1}{4})$; $B: (-\tfrac{1}{4}, -\tfrac{1}{4}, \tfrac{1}{4})$;
$C: (-\tfrac{1}{4}, \tfrac{1}{4}, -\tfrac{1}{4})$; $D: (\tfrac{1}{4}, -\tfrac{1}{4}, -\tfrac{1}{4})$

referred to the ξ, η, and ζ axes. This tetrahedron is denoted by $\mathfrak{K}$; the reflection of $\mathfrak{K}$ through the origin, namely the tetrahedron with vertices at A', B', C', and D', where the coordinates of A' are the negatives of those of A, etc., is denoted by $\mathfrak{K}'$.

Let the tac-plane [1] function for $\mathfrak{K}$ be $H(\lambda, \mu, \nu)$ where $H(\lambda, \mu, \nu) \equiv \max(\lambda\xi + \mu\eta + \nu\zeta)$ for points of $\mathfrak{K}$. Then $H(-\lambda, -\mu, -\nu) \equiv \max(-\lambda\xi, -\mu\eta, -\nu\zeta)$ is the tac-plane function of $\mathfrak{K}'$.

One defines $\mathfrak{K}$ to be the convex body which has

$$H(\lambda, \mu, \nu) \equiv \tfrac{1}{2}[H(\lambda, \mu, \nu) + H(-\lambda, -\mu, -\nu)]$$

as its tac-plane function. Under this definition we shall derive equations of the essential tac-planes of $\mathfrak{K}$.

From (1) and the inequalities which define $\mathfrak{K}$, one derives the relations

$$\phi \geqq -\tfrac{3}{4}, \qquad \chi \geqq -\tfrac{3}{4}, \qquad \psi \geqq -\tfrac{3}{4}, \qquad \omega \geqq -\tfrac{3}{4}$$

for points of $\mathfrak{K}$, and the corresponding inequalities

$$\phi \leqq \tfrac{3}{4}, \qquad \chi \leqq \tfrac{3}{4}, \qquad \psi \leqq \tfrac{3}{4}, \qquad \omega \leqq \tfrac{3}{4}$$

for points of $\mathfrak{K}'$. This means that all points of $\mathfrak{K}'$ lie toward the origin from each of the planes $\phi = \tfrac{3}{4}$, $\chi = \tfrac{3}{4}$, $\psi = \tfrac{3}{4}$, $\omega = \tfrac{3}{4}$. The points D', C', B', A' are in these respective planes so that they are actually tac-planes of $\mathfrak{K}'$. If

[1] By a *tac-plane* of a convex body is meant a plane which touches the body but does not separate the body in such a way that the open half planes each contain points of the body. It is the type of plane which L. L. Dines, *Bull. Am. Math. Soc.*, Vol. 42, p. 355, terms *a supporting plane* as employed in connection with much more general points sets. The German used by Minkowski is *Stützebene*. The *tac-plane function* is by definition that function $H(\lambda, \mu, \nu)$ for which $\xi\lambda + \eta\mu + \zeta\nu = H(\lambda, \mu, \nu)$ are all tac-planes. (See Art. 168.)

$e_i = \pm 1$, then $H(e_1, e_2, e_3) = \frac{1}{4}$ and $H(-e_1, -e_2, -e_3) = \frac{3}{4}$, or $H(e_1, e_2, e_3) = \frac{3}{4}$ and $H(-e_1, -e_2, -e_3) = \frac{1}{4}$ according as $e_1e_2e_3 = 1$, or $e_1e_2e_3 = -1$, since $\max(\lambda\xi, \mu\eta, \nu\zeta)$ must occur for a vertex of $\mathfrak{K}$. Then $H(e_1, e_2, e_3) = \frac{1}{2}$ so that $\mathfrak{K}$ has

$$\phi = \pm\tfrac{1}{2}, \qquad \chi = \pm\tfrac{1}{2}, \qquad \psi = \pm\tfrac{1}{2}, \qquad \omega = \pm\tfrac{1}{2}$$

as tac-planes.

The inequalities

$$|\phi| \leqq \tfrac{1}{2}, \qquad |\chi| \leqq \tfrac{1}{2}, \qquad |\psi| \leqq \tfrac{1}{2}, \qquad |\omega| \leqq \tfrac{1}{2}$$

define the octahedron $\mathfrak{K}^*$ with vertices $(\pm\frac{1}{2}, 0, 0)$, $(0, \pm\frac{1}{2}, 0)$, $(0, 0, \pm\frac{1}{2})$ in coordinates ξ, η, ζ. This octahedron can be defined equally as well by the inequality

$$|\xi| + |\eta| + |\zeta| \leqq \tfrac{1}{2}.$$

Let $H^*(\lambda, \mu, \nu)$ be the tac-plane function for K^*. Then $H^*(\lambda, \mu, \nu) \neq H(\lambda, \mu, \nu)$, for one would have in particular $H^*(1, 0, 0) = H(1, 0, 0) = \frac{1}{2}[H(1, 0, 0) + H(-1, 0, 0)]$. But $H^*(1, 0, 0) = \frac{1}{2}$ since $(\frac{1}{2}, 0, 0)$ is the point of K^* for which ξ is a maximum. On the other hand, from an inspection of the coordinates of the vertices of $\mathfrak{K}$ and $\mathfrak{K}'$ one can see that the maximum of ξ in each of these bodies is $\frac{1}{4}$, so that $H(1, 0, 0) = \frac{1}{2}(\frac{1}{4} + \frac{1}{4}) = \frac{1}{4}$. Thus $H(1, 0, 0) \neq H^*(1, 0, 0)$ and H and H^* are different functions.

From the definition of the tac-plane function, it follows that $1 \cdot \xi + 0 \cdot \eta + 0 \cdot \zeta = H(1, 0, 0)$ or, what is the same,

$$\xi = \tfrac{1}{4}$$

is a tac-plane of say $K = \frac{1}{2}(\mathfrak{K} + \mathfrak{K}')$. Similarly,

$$\xi = -\tfrac{1}{4}, \qquad \eta = \pm\tfrac{1}{4}, \qquad \zeta = \pm\tfrac{1}{4}$$

are all tac-planes of K. As each of these intersects K^*, they, together with the planes forming the surface of the octahedron, bound K. Thus K is *contained in* the 14 faced polyhedron K^{**} defined by the inequalities

$$|\xi| + |\eta| + |\zeta| \leqq \tfrac{1}{2}, \qquad |\xi| \leqq \tfrac{1}{4}, \qquad |\eta| \leqq \tfrac{1}{4}, \qquad |\zeta| \leqq \tfrac{1}{4}.$$

The question remains whether K and $\mathfrak{K}^{**}$ are identical. This will be answered in the affirmative by demonstrating that every vertex of the convex polyhedron $\mathfrak{K}^{**}$ is a point of the convex body K which it contains.

To demonstrate that a vertex of $\mathfrak{K}^{**}$ is a point of K, one needs merely to show that a tac-plane of $\mathfrak{K}^{**}$ which touches at only the vertex in question, also touches the body K.

If one sets $\xi=\pm\frac{1}{4}$ in the inequalities which define $\mathfrak{K}^{**}$ one has

$$|\eta|+|\zeta|\leqq\tfrac{1}{4}$$

as the cross section of $\mathfrak{K}^{**}$ in the planes $\xi=\pm\frac{1}{4}$. The vertices in these planes are $(\pm\frac{1}{4}, \frac{1}{4}, 0)$, $(\pm\frac{1}{4}, -\frac{1}{4}, 0)$, $(\pm\frac{1}{4}, 0, \frac{1}{4})$, $(\pm\frac{1}{4}, 0, -\frac{1}{4})$. Similarly, the remaining vertices (there are 12 in all) can be found by considering the cross sections in the planes $\eta=\pm\frac{1}{4}$, of $\zeta=\pm\frac{1}{4}$. They are $(0, \pm\frac{1}{4}, \frac{1}{4})$, $(0, \pm\frac{1}{4}, -\frac{1}{4})$.

Let (ξ_i, η_i, ζ_i) $(i=1, 2, \cdots, 12)$ be the coordinates of the i-th vertex. Choose $\lambda_i=4\xi_i$, $\mu_i=4\eta_i$, $\nu_i=4\zeta_i$; then λ_i, μ_i, $\nu_i=\pm1$ or 0 according as $\zeta_i=\pm\frac{1}{4}$ or 0, etc.

The equations

$$\xi\lambda_i+\eta\mu_i+\zeta\nu_i=\tfrac{1}{2} \qquad (i=1, 2, \cdots, 12)$$

are of 12 planes, the i-th of which passes through the i-th vertex, and no other of the 12 vertices, *of which all lie on the same side of this plane as the origin.* Since $\mathfrak{K}^{**}$ is a polyhedron, this requires that every point of $\mathfrak{K}^{**}$ except this i-th vertex lie on the side of the plane toward the origin. This plane, then touching $\mathfrak{K}^{**}$ at a point, but not separating points of $\mathfrak{K}^{**}$ from one another fulfills the definition of a tac-plane to $\mathfrak{K}^{**}$; and $H^{**}(\lambda_i, \mu_i, \nu_i)=\frac{1}{2}$. *But this plane has the additional property of touching* $\mathfrak{K}^{**}$ *at only the one point* (ξ_i, η_i, ζ_i).

On the other hand,

$$\begin{aligned} H(\lambda_i, \mu_i, \nu_i) &= \tfrac{1}{2}[H(\lambda_i, \mu_i, \nu_i)+H'(\lambda_i, \mu_i, \nu_i)] \\ &= \tfrac{1}{2}[\text{max in } \mathfrak{K} \text{ of } (\xi\lambda_i+\eta\mu_i+\zeta\nu_i) \\ &\qquad +\text{max in } \mathfrak{K} \text{ of } (-\xi\lambda_i-\eta\mu_i-\zeta\nu_i) \\ &= \tfrac{1}{2}(\tfrac{1}{2}+\tfrac{1}{2})=1/2. \end{aligned}$$

Hence $\xi\lambda_i+\eta\mu_i+\zeta\nu_i=\frac{1}{2}$ are tac-planes of K, which body is *contained in* $\mathfrak{K}^{**}$, a polyhedron. But the only points of K^{**} in these planes are the vertices of $\mathfrak{K}^{**}$, hence, they must also be points of K. From this it follows that $K\equiv\mathfrak{K}^{**}$.

By taking the average of two tac-plane functions as its tac-plane function we derive a new convex body. Minkowski defines this as equivalent to finding the locus of all midpoints of line segments that originate in the body having the first tac-plane function and terminating in the body with the second tac-plane function. An example is found in the following article.

ART. 167. **Theorem.** *If $\mathfrak{K}$ is a tetrahedron with the origin in its interior and if $\mathfrak{K}'$ is the tetrahedron which is obtained from $\mathfrak{K}$ by a reflection through the origin, then the locus of midpoints of all line segments which originate in $\mathfrak{K}$ and terminate in $\mathfrak{K}'$ is a 14 faced convex polyhedron symmetric about the origin.*

It suffices to show that among the midpoints of all line segments which join a vertex of $\mathfrak{K}$ to a vertex of $\mathfrak{K}'$ there are 12 points of such a nature that they are the vertices of a 14 faced *convex polydedron* which contains in its *interior* any other such midpoints as may exist, and that these 12 points are symmetric in pairs about the origin.

Let the coordinates in (x_1, x_2, x_3) of the 4 vertices of $\mathfrak{K}$ be A_1: (a_{11}, a_{12}, a_{13}), A_2: (a_{21}, a_{22}, a_{23}), A_3: (a_{31}, a_{32}, a_{33}), and A_4: (a_{41}, a_{42}, a_{43}), and the origin $(0, 0, 0)$, *interior* to $\mathfrak{K}$. One can introduce an oblique coordinate system by means of the linear transformation

$$\begin{aligned} 2x_1&=a_{11}y_1+a_{21}y_2+a_{31}y_3,\\ 2x_2&=a_{12}y_1+a_{22}y_2+a_{32}y_3, \qquad \text{det. } |a_{ij}|\neq 0.\\ 2x_3&=a_{13}y_1+a_{23}y_2+a_{33}y_3, \end{aligned}$$

The determinant is not zero since the origin is in the *interior* and hence not coplanar with A_1, A_2, and A_3.

Then the vertices have new coordinates as indicated A_1: $(2, 0, 0)$; A_2: $(0, 2, 0)$; and A_3: $(0, 0, 2)$. That the origin be in the interior of $\mathfrak{K}$ requires that the coordinates of A_4

be all negative. For suppose y_1 were positive or zero for A_4, then the tetrahedron would lie so that y_1 would be positive or zero for every point of the tetrahedron. Then the origin could not be an *interior* point. Similarly, y_2 and y_3 must be negative for A_4. Conversely, if all three coordinates of A_4 are negative, then the origin is in the interior of $\mathfrak{K}$. Then set A_4: $(-2d_1, -2d_2, -2d_3)$ where d_1, d_2, and d_3 are three positive constants.

The vertices of $\mathfrak{K}$ and $\mathfrak{K}'$ are then

$$A_1: (2, 0, 0), \quad A_2: (0, 2, 0), \quad A_3: (0, 0, 2), \quad A_4: (-2d_1, -2d_2, -2d_3);$$

$$A_1': (-2, 0, 0), \quad A_2': (0, -2, 0), \quad A_3': (0, 0, -2), \quad A_4': (2d_1, 2d_2, 2d_3).$$

Denote by $B_{ij} \equiv B_{ji}'$ the midpoint of the line segment A_iA_j'. Observe that B_{ii} $(i=1, 2, 3, 4)$ are coincident with the origin. The other B_{ij} are:

$$B_{12}: (1, -1, 0); \quad B_{13}: (1, 0, -1); \quad B_{12}': (-1, 1, 0); \quad B_{23}: (0, 1, -1); \quad B_{13}': (-1, 0, 1);$$

$$B_{23}': (0, -1, 1); \quad B_{14}: (1+d_1, d_2, d_3); \quad B_{24}: (d_1, 1+d_2, d_3); \quad B_{34}: (d_1, d_2, 1+d_3);$$

$$B_{14}': (-1-d_1, -d_2, -d_3); \quad B_{24}': (-d_1, -1-d_2, -d_3); \quad B_{34}': (-d_1, -d_2, -1-d_3).$$

It is seen that B_{hk} and B_{hk}' are symmetric to each other with respect to the origin for any pair of numbers h and k. Since $B_{ij} \equiv B_{ji}'$ one uses the form in which the first subscript is less than the second.

By differencing the coordinates one can see that the four points B_{13}' $(\equiv B_{31})$, B_{12}' $(\equiv B_{21})$, B_{34}, and B_{24} are the vertices of a parallelogram (see figure). The plane of the parallelogram is at once seen to be that plane of the pencil

$$k(y_2+y_3-1)+m(y_1+1)=0$$

which passes through B_{34}; that is, the plane

$$-(d_1+1)(y_2+y_3-1)+(d_2+d_3)(y_1+1)=0.$$

A direct substitution of the coordinates of B_{24} shows that it is also in the plane (it was seen, however, above by differencing the coordinates of the four points, that not only are they coplanar but form a parallelogram). All other points listed above make the left side of the equation posi-

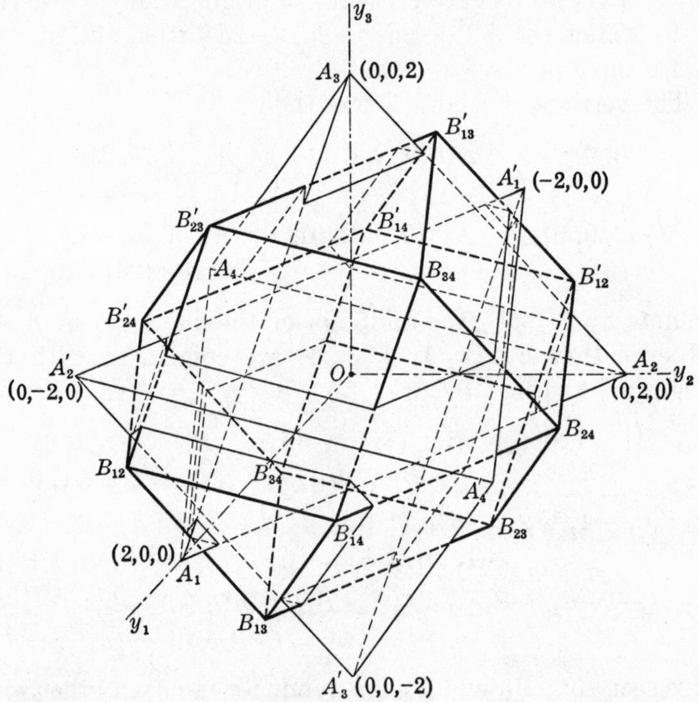

The points A_1, A_2, A_3, A_4 are the vertices of $\mathfrak{K}$; A'_1, A'_2, A'_3, A'_4 are those of $\mathfrak{K}'$. B_{ij} is the midpoint of the segment $A_iA'_j$; hence $B_{ij}=B'_{ji}$ if by B'_{ji} one denotes the midpoint of A'_jA_i. The points B_{ij} constitute the set of vertices of a 14-faced convex polyhedron. Minkowski called such a polyhedron a "cubo-octahedron" since it is the portion of an octahedron which is contained in a cube.

FIG. 125

tive, as does also the origin, hence all are on the same side of the plane as the origin.

The plane of the face symmetric to this one about the origin is

$$(d_1+1)(y_2+y_3+1)-(d_2+d_3)(y_1-1)=0.$$

From these two equations one can obtain by cyclic permutation of the subscripts 1, 2, and 3, the equations of the planes of the other parallelogrammatic faces. For example,

$$-(d_2+1)(y_3+y_1-1)+(d_3+d_1)(y_2+1)=0$$

passes through the points B_{12}, B'_{23} ($\equiv B_{32}$), B_{14}, B_{34}.

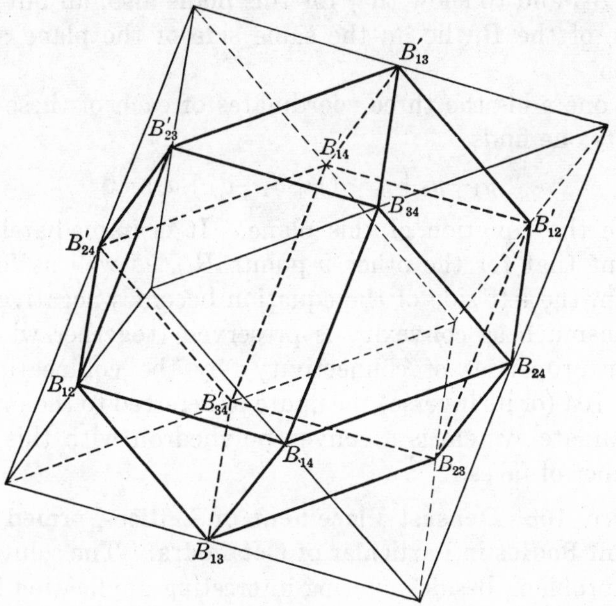

FIG. 125a

The plane in which lies the triangle with vertices B'_{13} ($=B_{31}$), B'_{23} ($=B_{32}$), and B_{34} can be determined as the plane of the pencil

$$k(y_1+y_2+1)+m(y_3-1)=0$$

which passes through B_3; namely the plane

$$d_3(y_1+y_2+1)-(d_1+d_2+1)(y_3-1)=0.$$

The plane opposite this with respect to the origin is

$$-d_3(y_1+y_2-1)+(d_1+d_2+1)(y_3+1)=0.$$

From these two equations one can obtain the equations of the planes of 4 other triangular faces by cyclic permutation of the subscripts. It is readily verified as before that all of the points B_{ij} which are not in these planes lie on the same side of them as the origin, and that only three of the points lie in any one of these last planes.

It remains to determine the equation of the plane of B_{14}, B_{24}, B_{34} and to show that for this plane also, all but these three of the B_{ij} lie on the same side of the plane as the origin.

If one adds the three coordinates of each of these three points one finds

$$y_1+y_2+y_3-(1+d_1+d_2+d_3)=0$$

to be the equation of this plane. It is immediately apparent that for the other 9 points B_{ij}, as well as for the origin, the left side of the equation becomes negative.

Inasmuch as convexity is preserved (together with the other properties of connectivity) by the collineation on page 704 (or its inverse) the figure as referred to the original coordinate system is a convex polyhedron with this same number of faces.

ART. **168. Densest Placement of Lattice-Formed Congruent Bodies in Particular of Octahedra.** The solution of this problem, besides offering interesting application in the theory of algebraic numbers, has significance also in the structure of crystals, molecular dynamics, etc. (See also remarks in the introduction.) The densest placement of octahedra also offers a solution of the simultaneous approximation of two quantities through rational numbers with equal denominators. (See p. 742.)

In order to reduce the problem to the case of bodies which have centers, Minkowski introduced the notion of the *tac-plane function.*[1] Let $\overline{\mathfrak{K}}$ be an arbitrary convex body and J its volume. Let ξ, η, ζ be rectangular coordinates with a point 0 within the interior of $\overline{\mathfrak{K}}$ as the origin of coordinates.

[1] *Ges. Abhandl.*, Vol. II, pp. 4 and 230.

If λ, μ, ν are any fixed values, the linear expression $\lambda\xi+\mu\eta+\nu\zeta$ for the points ξ, η, ζ in the entire domain of $\bar{\mathfrak{K}}$ has a greatest value, which is denoted by $\bar{H}(\lambda, \mu, \nu)$. This function $\bar{H}(\lambda, \mu, \nu)$ of the three real arguments λ, μ, ν clearly satisfies the following four conditions

$$(1) \qquad \bar{H}(0, 0, 0)=0, \qquad \bar{H}(\lambda, \mu, \nu)>0,$$

$$(2) \quad \bar{H}(t\lambda, t\mu, t\nu)=t\bar{H}(\lambda, \mu, \nu), \quad \text{if} \quad \lambda, \mu, \nu\neq 0, 0, 0;\ t>0.$$

If λ_1, μ_1, ν_1 and λ_2, μ_2, ν_2 are any two systems of values in $\bar{\mathfrak{K}}$, there is always a point ξ, μ, ζ for which

$$(\lambda_1+\lambda_2)\xi+(\mu_1+\mu_2)\eta+(\nu_1+\nu_2)\zeta=\bar{H}(\lambda_1+\lambda_2, \mu_1+\mu_2, \nu_1+\nu_2);$$

and since for this point we clearly have $\lambda_1\zeta+\mu_1\eta+\nu_1\zeta \leqq \bar{H}(\lambda_1, \mu_1, \nu_1)$ and $\lambda_2\xi+\mu_2\eta+\nu_2\zeta \leqq \bar{H}(\lambda_1, \mu_2, \nu_2)$, it follows always that

$$(3) \quad \bar{H}(\lambda_1+\lambda_2, \mu_1+\mu_2, \nu_1+\nu_2) \leqq \bar{H}(\lambda_1, \mu_1, \nu_1)+\bar{H}(\lambda_2, \mu_2, \nu_2).$$

The greatest value of $-(\lambda\xi+\mu\eta+\nu\zeta)$ in $\bar{\mathfrak{K}}$ is

$$\bar{H}(-\lambda, -\mu, -\nu)$$

and consequently in $\bar{\mathfrak{K}}$ we have always

$$-\bar{H}(-\lambda, -\mu, -\nu) \leqq \lambda\xi+\mu\eta+\nu\zeta \leqq \bar{H}(\lambda, \mu, \nu).$$

Hence since $\bar{\mathfrak{K}}$ does not lie entirely in a plane and if λ, μ, $\nu\neq 0, 0, 0$; we must have always

$$(4) \qquad \bar{H}(\lambda, \mu, \nu)+\bar{H}(-\lambda, -\mu, -\nu)>0.$$

Hence if $\bar{H}(\lambda, \mu, \nu)$ *is an arbitrary real function of three real arguments* λ, μ, ν *which satisfies all the conditions (1) to (4) inclusive, we may denote the domain of points* ξ, η, ζ *which is defined through the inequalities*

$$(3) \qquad \lambda\xi+\mu\eta+\nu\zeta \leqq \bar{H}(\lambda, \mu, \nu)$$

for all possible systems of values λ, μ, ν, *as a convex body.*

ART. **169.** If P is a point ξ, η, ζ, we denote the point $-\xi$, $-\eta$, $-\zeta$ as the *opposed* point and indicate it by P_0. The opposed points of all the points of $\bar{\mathfrak{K}}$ constitute the convex body $\bar{K}_0$ with the tac-plane function

$$\bar{H}_0(\lambda, \mu, \nu) = \bar{H}(-\lambda, -\mu, -\nu)$$

and $\bar{\mathfrak{K}}_0$ is the *image* of $\bar{\mathfrak{K}}$ with respect to the point 0. The function $\frac{1}{2}[\bar{H}'(\lambda, \mu, \nu) + \bar{H}(-\lambda, -\mu, -\nu)]$ forms the tac-plane function for a certain convex body, which we denote by $\frac{1}{2}(\bar{\mathfrak{K}} + \bar{\mathfrak{K}}_0)$. This body is the domain of all such points which in any way enter as the midpoints of stretches (lines) connecting a point of $\bar{\mathfrak{K}}$ with a point of $\bar{\mathfrak{K}}_0$. To be observed is the fact that if $\bar{\mathfrak{K}}$ has a center, then both $\bar{\mathfrak{K}}_0$ and $\frac{1}{2}(\bar{\mathfrak{K}} + \bar{\mathfrak{K}}_0)$ exist merely through translations of $\bar{\mathfrak{K}}$. Questions relative to accordant (einhellig) radial distances are thus reduced to the consideration of symmetric (wechselseitig) radial distances as were defined in Arts. 15 and 16.

We let [1]

$$\begin{aligned} \xi &= \alpha_1 x + \alpha_2 y + \alpha_3 z, \\ \eta &= \beta_1 x + \beta_2 y + \beta_3 z, \\ \zeta &= \gamma_1 x + \gamma_2 y + \gamma_3 z, \end{aligned} \tag{1}$$

be an arbitrary linear substitution with real coefficients and a determinant different from zero whose absolute value is denoted by Δ. Observe that Δ computed in the ξ-, η-, and ζ-coordinates is identical with the volume of the parallelopiped

$$0 \leqq x < 1, \qquad 0 \leqq y < 1, \qquad 0 \leqq z < 1$$

(which in Art. 157 was called the fundamental parallelopiped). This is indicated in the formula

$$\iiint d\xi\, d\eta\, d\zeta = \Delta \iiint dx\, dy\, dz = \Delta.$$

The lattice in x, y, z is denoted by (G), and any point of the lattice by G (Gitterpunkt). Through a parallel sliding of the fundamental parallelopiped from 0 to every individual point of the lattice there is a gapless filling of space. With the parallel sliding we shall assume that the nowhere concave body $\bar{\mathfrak{K}}$ is such that the like bodies, say $\bar{\mathfrak{K}}_G$, about

[1] The constants $\alpha_1, \alpha_2, \cdots, \gamma_3$ are written in the place of $\lambda, \lambda', \cdots, \nu''$ of Art. 157.

each point G are separated, and that is they abut one another at most on the boundaries. To this end it is sufficient that the initial domain $\bar{\mathfrak{K}}$ penetrates into no other of the domains $\bar{\mathfrak{K}}_G$. If then G is an arbitrary lattice point different from 0, there is a plane which separates $\bar{\mathfrak{K}}$ from $\bar{\mathfrak{K}}_G$ such that the points common to these two domains (in case they touch) lie entirely in the plane while for all other points $\bar{\mathfrak{K}}$ lies on the one side of the plane and $\bar{\mathfrak{K}}_G$ on the other. Accordingly if λ, μ, ν are the direction cosines of the perpendicular from 0 to this plane, then the plane has a distance from 0 which is $\geqq \bar{H}(\lambda, \mu, \nu)$ while its distance from G is $\geqq \bar{H}(-\lambda, -\mu, -\nu)$. Hence the parallel plane through G has a distance from 0 which is

$$\geqq \bar{H}(\lambda, \mu, \nu) + \bar{H}(-\lambda, -\mu, -\nu).$$

Hence the lattice point G lies without or on the boundary of the body $\mathfrak{K} = \bar{\mathfrak{K}} + \bar{\mathfrak{K}}_0$, which exists through a dilation of the body $\frac{1}{2}(\bar{\mathfrak{K}} + \bar{\mathfrak{K}}_0)$ from the center 0 in the ratio 2 : 1. With this we have in particular the following:

From a convex body $\bar{\mathfrak{K}}$ there exist through the translations of a lattice (G) entirely separated bodies then and only then, when the corresponding condition exists for the convex body $\frac{1}{2}(\bar{\mathfrak{K}} + \bar{\mathfrak{K}}_0)$ with center which is derived from $\bar{\mathfrak{K}}$. Minkowski, *Ges. Abhandl.*, II, p. 5.

ART. **170.** We denote the boundary of $\mathfrak{K} = \bar{\mathfrak{K}} + \bar{\mathfrak{K}}_0$ by $\mathfrak{F}$ and a function $\varphi(\xi, \eta, \zeta)$ is defined for arbitrary real arguments, if we stipulate that $\varphi(\xi, \eta, \zeta) = 1$ for all points ξ, η, ζ on the surface $\mathfrak{F}$ and further that

$$\varphi(t\xi, t\eta, t\zeta) = t\varphi(\xi, \eta, \zeta)$$

for positive values of t, and also that $\varphi(0, 0, 0) = 0$. That $\mathfrak{K}$ is a convex body is found in the general functional inequality

$$\varphi(\xi_1 + \xi_2, \eta_1 + \eta_2, \zeta_1 + \zeta_2) \leqq \varphi(\xi_1, \eta_1, \zeta_1) + \varphi(\xi_2, \eta_2, \zeta_2);$$

and that $\mathfrak{K}$ has a center at 0 finds expression in

$$\varphi(-\xi, -\eta, -\zeta) = \varphi(\xi, \eta, \zeta).$$

Due to the substitution (1) of Art. 169 we put

$$\varphi(\xi, \eta, \zeta) = f(x, y, z).$$

In order that all the bodies $\overline{\mathfrak{K}}_G$ lie separated for every integral system x, y, z that is different from 0, 0, 0, we must have

$$(1) \qquad f(x, y, z) \leqq 1.$$

Observe that the ratio of the space filled up by bodies $\overline{\mathfrak{K}}_G$ to the entire space is $= J : \Delta$ where J is the volume of $\overline{\mathfrak{K}}$ and Δ that of the fundamental parallelopiped, and it is clear that the bodies $\overline{\mathfrak{K}}_G$ fill up space, if each of them has a volume $J = \Delta$; however, the volume of $\frac{1}{2}(\overline{\mathfrak{K}} + \overline{\mathfrak{K}}_0)$ is always greater than $\overline{\mathfrak{K}}$, if $\overline{\mathfrak{K}}$ is a body without a center.[1] It is clear that the filling up of space without gaps by means of the bodies $\overline{\mathfrak{K}}$ requires necessarily that $\overline{\mathfrak{K}}$ be a body with a center.

Our problem now is *so to choose the coefficients* $\alpha_1, \alpha_2, \cdots, \gamma_3$ *of the substitution (1) of Art. 169, that the absolute value of* Δ *be as small as possible while at the same time all the inequalities (1) just written be satisfied.* (See also Arts. 157 and 162.)

ART. **171.** As in Art. 159 we take three lattice points A_1, B_1, C_1 of (G) and by means of them we derive three points A, B, C and the adapted parallelogram $O(ABC)$. Here we shall take x, y, z as integral linear functions of X, Y, Z with a determinant $= \pm 1$ so that the lattice points of (G) in x, y, z are identical with those of X, Y, Z. If further x, y, z are any integral linear forms in $\bar{x}, \bar{y}, \bar{z}$ with a determinant $\neq 0$, it is always possible and only in one way (Art. 159) to form three integral forms X, Y, Z in x, y, z with a determinant $= \pm 1$, so that the following relations

$$\begin{aligned} X &= a_1\bar{x} + a_2\bar{y} + a_3\bar{z}, \\ Y &= \qquad\quad b_2\bar{y} + b_3\bar{z}, \\ Z &= \qquad\qquad\qquad c_3\bar{z}, \end{aligned}$$

[1] Minkowski, *Ges. Abhandl.*, Vol. II, p. 261.

exist. These relations are such that $a_1>0$, $b_2>0$, $b_3>0$; $0\leqq\frac{a_2}{b_2}, \frac{a_3}{b_3}, \frac{b_3}{c_3}<1$. The introduction of the variables X, Y, Z in the place of x, y, z we call the *adaption* of the lattice (G) with regard to the parallelepiped $O(ABC)$ and we denote $O(ABC)$ as the *adapted* fundamental parallelepiped.

Observe that the variables X, Y, Z here take the place of ξ, η, ζ or Art. 159, while $\bar{x}$, $\bar{y}$, $\bar{z}$ here take the place of X, Y, Z there.

ART. **172.** We shall now continue the treatment of lattice octahedra of Art. 159. Let A, B, C and their opposed points A_0, B_0, C_0 with respect to O lie on the surface $\mathfrak{F}$, and with these six points which do not lie in a plane let $\mathfrak{K}$ as a convex body contain the entire domain of the octahedron $ABCA_0B_0C_0$, the six points being the vertices and its center O. This octahedron which contains besides O and its vertices no other lattice points we called (Art. 159) a *lattice octahedron.* And we ask how from such an octahedron may we derive the entire lattice (G).

Associated with every point $P=(x, y, z)$ of space there belong definite values $\bar{x}$, $\bar{y}$, $\bar{z}$ so that the vector OP is connected with the vectors OA, OB, and OC through a relation

$$OP=\bar{x}OA+\bar{y}OB+\bar{z}OC.$$

The domain of the octahedron is defined through

$$|\bar{x}|+|\bar{y}|+|\bar{z}|\leqq 1. \tag{1}$$

We introduce the adaption of the lattice (G) with respect to the parallelepiped $O(ABC)$. Let $O(ABC)$ be the adapted fundamental parallelepiped and let X, Y, Z be the new lattice coordinates for which the relations

$$\begin{aligned} X&=a_1\bar{x}+a_2\bar{y}+a_3\bar{z},\\ Y&=\qquad\quad\; b_2\bar{y}+b_3\bar{z},\\ Z&=\qquad\qquad\qquad c_3\bar{z}, \end{aligned} \tag{2}$$

exist, where the constants have values as defined in the

previous article. Observe that the lattice points of (G) are precisely the same as the integral systems in X, Y, Z. For A, B, C we have the values

$$X, Y, Z = a_1, 0, 0; \qquad a_2, b_2, 0; \qquad a_3, b_3, c_3.$$

The inequality (1) takes the form

$$(3) \qquad \left|X - \frac{a_1}{c_1}Z\right| + \left|Y - \frac{b_1}{c_1}Z\right| + \left|\frac{Z}{c_1}\right| \leqq 1,$$

see Art. 161, and as in that article the only solutions of (2) are first

$$X = \bar{x}, \qquad Y = \bar{y}, \qquad Z = \bar{z},$$

and the original lattice (G) in x, y, z is identical with the lattice in $\bar{x}$, $\bar{y}$, $\bar{z}$. In this case we denoted (Art. 159) the octahedron $Oct(ABC)$ as a *lattice octahedron of the first kind.* Note that its determinant in $\bar{x}$, $\bar{y}$, $\bar{z}$ is 1. The original lattice (G) in x, y, z is identical with the lattice in $\bar{x}$, $\bar{y}$, $\bar{z}$. In the second case we have

$$X = \bar{x} + \bar{z}, \qquad Y = \bar{y} + \bar{z}, \qquad Z = 2\bar{z}$$

and here integral values of X, Y, Z exist if $\bar{x}$, $\bar{y}$, $\bar{z}$ are integers and further also if $\bar{x} - \frac{1}{2}$, $\bar{y} - \frac{1}{2}$, $\bar{z} - \frac{1}{2}$ are integers. In this case the octahedron $Oct(ABC)$ is said to be of the *second kind.* Its determinant $= 2$. In particular the point C' with coordinates $\bar{x} = \frac{1}{2}$, $\bar{y} = \frac{1}{2}$, $\bar{z} = \frac{1}{2}$ which is the center of the parallelopiped $O(ABC)$ is a point of the lattice x, y, z. The original lattice (G) consists here on the one hand of the lattice in $\bar{x}$, $\bar{y}$, $\bar{z}$ and on the other hand of the points which are had through a translation of this lattice from O to C'. The volume of the parallelopiped $O(ABC)$ is here $= \frac{1}{2}$ that of the octahedron of the second kind.

The following criteria are useful for the characterization of octahedra of the first and second kinds (see Art. 161):

If $x_1, y_1, z_1; x_2, y_2, z_2; x_3, y_3, z_3$ are the coordinates of three lattice points A, B, C, then the octahedron with the vertices A, B, C, A_1, B_1, C_1 is a lattice octahedron of the first kind if the determinant

$$D=\begin{vmatrix} x_1, & y_1, & z_1 \\ x_2, & y_2, & z_2 \\ x_3, & y_3, & z_3 \end{vmatrix}=\pm 1;$$

while it is one of the second kind if $D=\pm 2$ and if in addition

$$\frac{x_1+x_2+x_3}{2}, \qquad \frac{y_1+y_2+y_3}{2}, \qquad \frac{z_1+z_2+z_3}{2}$$

are equal to integers.

ART. **173.** In (3) of the preceding article take $0 \leqq a_3 \leqq b_3 \leqq c_3$ and $c_3 \geqq 2$ and note that the left-hand side of that expression becomes <1 for at least one of the systems $X, Y, Z=0, 0, 1; 0, 1, 1; 1, 1, 1$, unless $c_3=2d+1$ and $a_3, b_3=d, d; d, d+1; d+1, d$ or $c_3=2d$ and also $a_3, b_3=d-1, d; d, d+1; d, d$. Note that the left-hand side of (3) has in this latter case for $X, Y, Z=1, 1, 2$, the value $\frac{4}{2d+1}$ (<1 for $c_3>3$) or $\frac{4}{2d}$ (<1 for $c_3>4$) or $\frac{2}{2d}$ (<1 for $c_3>2$). Hence among the four systems of values $0, 0, 1; 0, 1, 1; 1, 1, 1; 1, 1, 2$ for X, Y, Z, there is always one for which the left-hand side of (3) is <1 except for the following eight lattice points

$$a_3, b_3, c_3=0, 1, 2; \quad 1, 1, 2; \quad 1, 2, 2; \quad 1, 1, 3; \quad 1, 2, 3; \quad 2, 2, 3; \quad 1, 2, 4; \quad 2, 3, 4.$$

This discussion is continued in Arts. 179, 182.

ART. **174.** We assume that no lattice point save O lies within $\mathfrak{K}$, however on the boundary $\mathfrak{F}$ of $\mathfrak{K}$ we assume that the three lattice points A, B and C are situated. Accordingly we change the notation to conform with that of Art. 162 and put the function defined in Art. 170 in the form

$$\varphi(\xi, \eta, \zeta)=f(x, y, z)=F(X, Y, Z)$$

so that in the coordinates X, Y, Z we have

(1) $\quad A=(1, 0, 0), \qquad B=(0, 1, 0), \qquad C=(0, 0, 1).$

The general theory as developed in Art. 162 is at once applicable here. In particular it is to be noted that besides the relations (1) the inequalities

(2) $F(\pm 1, \pm 1, 0) \geqq 1, \quad F(\pm 1, 0, \pm 1) \geqq 1, \quad F(0, \pm 1, \pm 1) \geqq 1,$

(3) $F(\pm 1, \pm 1, \pm 1) \geqq 1,$

(4) $F(\pm 1, \pm 1, \pm 2) \geqq 1, \quad F(\pm 1, \pm 2, \pm 1) \geqq 1, \quad F(\pm 2, \pm 1, \pm 1) \geqq 1$

are sufficient to assure the existence of all inequalities

(I) $F(X, Y, Z) \geqq 1, \qquad (X, Y, Z) \neq 0, 0, 0$

for all other integral systems of X, Y, Z. (Art. 162.)

With this we have the theorem:

If Oct(ABC) is a lattice octahedron of the first kind the conditions (1), (2), (3) and (4) carry with them the collectivity of the infinite many inequalities (I).

On the other hand if *Oct(ABC)* is a lattice octahedron of the *second kind* we need besides the relations (1) only the inequalities

(5) $F(\pm\tfrac{1}{2}, \pm\tfrac{1}{2}, \pm\tfrac{1}{2}) \geqq 1.$

And this gives rise to the second theorem:

If Oct(ABC) is a lattice octahedron of the second kind the equations (1) and the inequalities (5) are sufficient to assure the inequalities (I) as well as the inequalities

(II) $F(X+\tfrac{1}{2}, Y+\tfrac{1}{2}, Z+\tfrac{1}{2}) \geqq 1$

for all integral systems of values of X, Y, Z. (Art. 162.)

ART. **175.** To Art. 173 we may now add the following: If $P=(a, b, c)$ is a lattice point, where $0 \leqq a \leqq b \leqq c$, and $c \geqq 2$, and further if (a, b, c) is not one of the eight systems of values 0, 1, 2; 1, 1, 2; 1, 2, 2; 1, 1, 3; 1, 2, 3; 2, 2, 3; 1, 2, 4; 2, 3, 4; then we find that at least *one* of the lattice points 0, 0, 1; 0, 1, 1; 1, 1, 1; 1, 1, 2 is situated on the *interior* of the *Oct(ABC)* and *cannot* be on the boundary of $\mathfrak{K}$ with the result therefore that

$$F(a, b, c) > 1.$$

These eight systems are left for further consideration in Art. 179.

ART. **176.** Our problem is (Art. 162, end) to minimize the determinant Δ which may be regarded as a function of the nine variables $\lambda, \mu, \cdots, \nu''$ and this is done as in Art. 163 by a variation of the lattice (G) in x, y, z. Observe that this lattice is the same for integral values of X, Y, Z, there being a linear set of relations among these variables with determinant $= \pm 1$ and the x, y, z coordinates. Further we hold the points A, B, C on the surface $\mathfrak{F}$ and observing that $J \leqq \Delta$ we may as in Arts. 163 *for an Octahedron of the first kind* so vary the positions A, B, C on $\mathfrak{F}$ that three new points $R = (0, 1, -1)$, $S = (-1, 0, 1)$, $T = (1, -1, 0)$ with their opposites $R_1 = (0, -1, 1)$, $S_1 = (1, 0, -1)$, $T_1 = (-1, 1, 0)$ appear on this surface $\mathfrak{F}$.

Observe that if the points A, B, C, R, S, T all lie on $\mathfrak{F}$, then from the relations

$$\begin{aligned} F(1, 1, 2) + F(-1, 0, 1) + F(0, -1, 1) &\geqq 4F(0, 0, 1), \\ F(1, -1, 2) + F(-1, 1, 0) &\geqq 2F(0, 0, 1), \\ F(-1, -1, 2) + F(1, -1, 0) &\geqq 2F(0, -1, 1), \\ F(1, 1, 1) + F(-1, 0, 1) + F(0, -1, 1) &\geqq 3F(0, 0, 1) \end{aligned}$$

it is seen that of the inequalities (2), (3), (4) of Art. 174 it remains only to consider whether the following

$$F(-1, 1, 1) \geqq 1, \qquad F(1, -1, 1) \geqq 1, \qquad F(1, 1, -1) \geqq 1$$

are satisfied. If, however, for example $F(1, 1, -1) = 1$, we should have in $0, 0, 1; 1, -1, 0; 1, 1, -1$ three lattice points on $\mathfrak{F}$, which determine a lattice octahedron of the second kind. Hence for the time being in these three inequalities the sign $>$ must be required.

ART. **177.** We consider next the case where $Oct(ABC)$ is a *lattice octahedron of the second kind* and that is the case where equations (1) and the inequalities (5) of Art. 174 exist.

Note for example that if $F(\frac{1}{2}, \frac{1}{2}, \frac{1}{2}) \geqq 1$, then also $F(1, 1, 1) \geqq 2$, and since $F(1, 1, 0)+F(0, 0, 1) \geqq F(1, 1, 1)$, it follows that $F(1, 1, 0) \geqq 1$. And in general it is seen that one of the points $(\pm\frac{1}{2}, \pm\frac{1}{2}, \pm\frac{1}{2})$ is caused to fall on the surface $\mathfrak{F}$ as soon as any of the lattice points. Hence as in Art. 162 this is had by varying the points A, B, C and that is the variables $\lambda, \mu, \cdots, \nu''$ in such a way that Δ continuously decreases. Noting always that $J \leqq \Delta$ we may bring it about that three of the inequalities $F(\pm\frac{1}{2}, \pm\frac{1}{2}, \pm\frac{1}{2}) \leqq$ become equalities thus causing three points, say $L=(-\frac{1}{2}, \frac{1}{2}, \frac{1}{2})$, $M=(\frac{1}{2}, -\frac{1}{2}, \frac{1}{2})$, $N=(\frac{1}{2}, \frac{1}{2}, -\frac{1}{2})$, to be on the surface $\mathfrak{F}$. Next observe that the substitution

$$X^*=Y+Z, \qquad Y^*=X+Z, \qquad Z^*=X+Y,$$

with determinant $=2$, offer for A, B, C, L, M, N and the lattice point $(\frac{1}{2}, \frac{1}{2}, \frac{1}{2})$ the new coordinates

$$\begin{aligned} X^*, Y^*, Z^* &= (0, 1, 1) \text{ for } B+C; \\ &\quad (1, 0, 1) \text{ for } A+C; \quad (1, 1, 0) \text{ for } A+B; \\ &= (1, 0, 0) \text{ for } M+N; \\ &\quad (0, 1, 0) \text{ for } L+N; \quad (0, 0, 1) \text{ for } L+M; \\ &= (1, 1, 1) \text{ for } L+M+N. \end{aligned}$$

The original lattice (G) for all points of the octahedron of the second kind is identical with the lattice in X^*, Y^*, Z^* so that it remains to see only that the point $X^*, Y^*, Z^* = (1, 1, 1)$ does *not* lie on the interior of $\mathfrak{K}$.

ART. **178.** Through the considerations of the two preceding articles we have come to the following results. *In order to find the minimum (or the different existing minima) of Δ for a given convex body $\mathfrak{K}$, it is sufficient to consider such arrangements of the lattice (G) where the following points*

(I) $1, 0, 0;\ 0, 1, 0;\ 0, 0, 1;\ 0, 1, -1;\ -1, 0, 1;\ 1, -1, 0$

fall on the boundary of $\mathfrak{K}=\overline{\mathfrak{K}}+\overline{\mathfrak{K}}_0$ while the points $-1, 1, 1$; $1, -1, 1$; $1, 1, -1$ fall on the outside of $\mathfrak{K}$; or, where the points

(II) $1, 0, 0;\ 0, 1, 0;\ 0, 0, 1;\ 0, 1, 1;\ 1, 0, 1;\ 1, 1, 0$

fall on the boundary of $\mathfrak{K}$ *and the point 1, 1, 1 outside; or, where the points*

(III) 1, 0, 0; 0, 1, 0; 0, 0, 1; 0, 1, 1; 1, 0, 1;
1, 1, 0 *and* 1, 1, 1

all fall on this boundary.

It is possible, in certain cases where straight line stretches appear on the boundary of $\mathfrak{K}$, that besides one of the above arrangements of the lattice (G) which offers a minimum of Δ, there are other arrangements of (G) and not of the above character which are had through a continual variation without change of the value of Δ. These would then in a similar

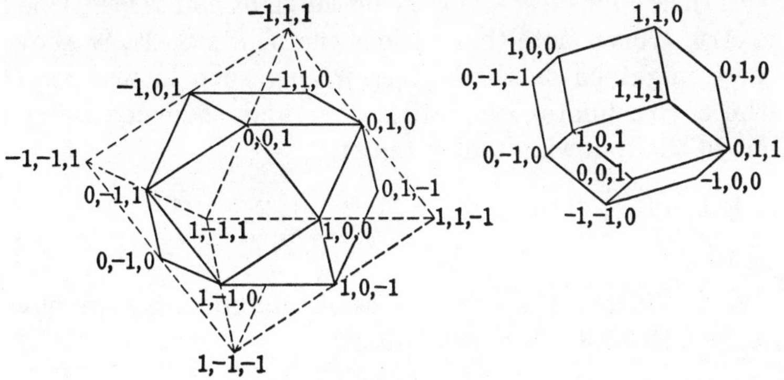

FIG. 126

manner determine densest lattice-formed placements for the fundamental body $\mathfrak{K}$. The six lattice points found in (I) above and their opposites with respect to 0 form the corners of a cubo-octahedron. The seven points given in (III) and their opposites form the vertices of a so-called rhombo-dodecahedron.

ART. 179. **Further Conditions for a Densest Placement.** The quantity Δ is a function of the nine variables α_1, α_2, $\cdots$, γ_3 which serve for the fixing of a lattice. For the establishing of a minimum of this function we have assumed as satisfied in the preceding article six or seven equations. And this leaves three or two further equations for the characterization of Δ. These we shall next derive.

For the case (I) of the preceding article we are advancing that the points (observe change in lettering)

$$\begin{array}{cccccc} \mathfrak{L} & \mathfrak{M} & \mathfrak{N} & \mathfrak{R} & \mathfrak{S} & \mathfrak{T} \\ 1,0,0; & 0,1,0; & 0,0,1; & 0,1,-1; & -1,0,1; & 1,-1,0 \end{array}$$

lie on the surface $\mathfrak{F}$ of $\mathfrak{K}$ and that the points $-1, 1, 1$; $1, -1, 1$; $1, 1, -1$ lie without $\mathfrak{K}$. Observe that $\mathfrak{M}-\mathfrak{N}=\mathfrak{R}$; $\mathfrak{N}-\mathfrak{L}=\mathfrak{S}$; $\mathfrak{L}-\mathfrak{M}=\mathfrak{T}$. We further assume that there are no three lattice points on $\mathfrak{F}$ which determine a lattice octahedron of the second kind. The question now is: Can there be other lattice points on $\mathfrak{F}$ other than the six just written with their opposites? Observing the eight points mentioned in Art. 173 we note that besides the points $\mathfrak{L}$, $\mathfrak{M}$, $\mathfrak{N}$ above there might be on the surface $\mathfrak{F}$ only such lattice points whose coordinates neglecting sign and sequence offered one of the following ten systems:

$$0,1,1;\quad 1,1,1;\quad 0,1,2;\quad 1,1,2;\quad 1,2,2;\quad 1,1,3;$$
$$1,2,3;\quad 2,2,3;\quad 1,2,4;\quad 2,3,4.$$

Due to the accordant properties of the function F we have at once the following inequalities:

$$F\left(\substack{2\\-2}, 3, \pm 4\right)+F(-1,1,0)+F(-1,0,0) \geqq 4F\left(\substack{0\\-1}, 1, \pm 1\right),$$

$$F\left(-1, \substack{2\\-2}, \pm 4\right)+F(1,-1,0)+F(0,-1,0) \geqq 4F\left(0, \substack{0\\-1}, \pm 1\right),$$

$$F(a,b,c)+aF(-1,0,1)+bF(0,-1,1) \geqq (a+b+c)F(0,0,1),$$
$$(a, b, c=2,2,3;\quad 1,2,3;\quad 1,1,3;\quad 1,2,2;\quad 1,1,2),$$

$$F\left(\substack{2\\-1}, -2, 3\right)+F(1,-1,0) \geqq 3F\left(\substack{1\\0}, -1, 1\right),$$

$$F(-2,-2,3)+F(-1,0,0)+F(0,-1,0) \geqq 3F(-1,-1,1),$$

$$F(1, -2, 3)+F(1, -1, 0)+F(1, 0, 0) \geqq 3F(1, -1, 1),$$
$$F(-1, 2, 3)+2F(0, -1, 1)+F(1, 0, 0) \geqq 5F(0, 0, 1),$$
$$F(-1, 1, 3)+F(1, -1, 0) \geqq 3F(0, 0, 1),$$
$$F(-1, 2, 2)+F(-1, 0, 0) \geqq 2F(-1, 1, 1),$$
$$F(1, -2, 2)+F(1, 0, 0) \geqq 2F(1, -1, 1),$$
$$F(1, -1, 2)+F(1, -1, 0) \geqq 2F(1, -1, 1),$$
$$F(0, 1, 2)+F(0, -1, 1) \geqq 3F(0, 0, 1).$$

Due to the above inequalities and others which may be derived from them by permuting the variables, it is seen that many of the ten systems under consideration may be discarded, since evidently they lie without the body $\mathfrak{K}$.

It remains to inquire into the position on $\mathfrak{F}$ of only those lattice points whose coordinates neglecting their sequence are

$$-1, -1, 3; \quad -1, -1, 2; \quad 0, -1, 2; \quad 1, 1, 1; \quad 0, 1, 1.$$

If, however, we observe in Art. 161, end, the criteria for lattice octahedra of the second kind, we note that such are offered by the following systems

$$\begin{array}{lll} 0, 0, -1; & 1, -1, 0; & -1, -1, 3, \\ 1, 0, 0; & 0, 1, 0; & -1, -1, 2, \\ 1, 0, 0; & -1, 1, 0; & 0, -1, 2, \\ -1, 0, 0; & 0, -1, 1; & 1, 1, 1, \\ 1, -1, 0; & 1, 0, -1; & 0, 1, 1. \end{array}$$

With this it is shown that besides the six lattice points $\mathfrak{L}, \mathfrak{M}, \mathfrak{N}, \mathfrak{R}, \mathfrak{S}, \mathfrak{T}$ and their opposites no other lattice points are found on $\mathfrak{F}$.

ART. **180.** Through each of the points $\mathfrak{L}, \mathfrak{M}, \mathfrak{N}, \mathfrak{R}, \mathfrak{S}, \mathfrak{T}$ we draw a tac-plane to $\mathfrak{K}$. Let the equations of these planes be

$$(1) \quad \begin{cases} L = X+\lambda_2 Y+\lambda_3 Z = 1; & \mathfrak{L}=1, 0, 0, \\ M = \mu_1 X+ Y+\mu_3 Z = 1; & \mathfrak{M}=0, 1, 0, \\ N = \nu_1 X+\nu_2 Y+ Z = 1; & \mathfrak{N}=0, 0, 1, \\ R = (\rho_2-\rho_1)X+\rho_2 Y+(1-\rho_2)Z = 1; & \mathfrak{R}=0, 1, -1, \\ S = -(1-\sigma_3)X+(\sigma_3-\sigma_2)Y+\sigma_3 Z = 1; & \mathfrak{S}=-1, 0, 1, \\ T = \tau_1 X-(1-\tau_1)Y+(\tau_1-\tau_3)Z = 1; & \mathfrak{T}=1, -1, 0. \end{cases}$$

Each of the expressions L, M, N, R, S, T lies in the entire region of $\mathfrak{K}$. in the interval $\geqq 1$ and $\leqq 1$. The form L has for the six lattice points on $\mathfrak{K}$ the values

$$1, \quad \lambda_2, \quad \lambda_3, \quad \lambda_2-\lambda_3, \quad -1+\lambda_3, \quad 1-\lambda_3$$

and consequently λ_2, λ_3 are both $\geqq 0$ and $\leqq 1$. The form R takes the following values for these six points:

$$\rho_2-\rho_1, \quad \rho_2, \quad -1+\rho_2, \quad 1, \quad -1+\rho_1, \quad -\rho_1.$$

Consequently ρ_2 and ρ_1 are both $\geqq 0$ and $\leqq 1$. The same is true of $\mu_3, \mu_1; \nu_1, \nu_2; \sigma_3, \sigma_2; \tau_1, \tau_3$.

We shall next vary the lattice (G) by transferring the points $\mathfrak{L}, \mathfrak{M}, \mathfrak{N}$ so that their new positions with respect to the old coordinate system X, Y, Z are

$$1+\epsilon X_1, \ \epsilon Y_1, \ \epsilon Z_1; \quad \epsilon X_2, \ 1+\epsilon Y_2, \ \epsilon Z_2; \quad \epsilon X_3, \ \epsilon Y_3, \ 1+\epsilon Z_3,$$

where ϵ is a *positive* parameter. We shall indicate the values of the forms $L, M, \cdots, T$ for the systems X_i, Y_i, Z_i by the suffix i. Then to hold the points $\mathfrak{L}, \mathfrak{M}, \mathfrak{N}, \mathfrak{R}, \mathfrak{S}, \mathfrak{T}$ on their respective tac-planes or on the other side of these tac-planes from the origin, we must have

$$(1) \quad L_1 \geqq 0, \quad M_2 \geqq 0, \quad N_3 \geqq 0, \quad R_2-R_3 \geqq 0, \quad -S_1+S_3 \geqq 0, \quad T_1-T_2 \geqq 0.$$

With these conditions presupposed, it is seen that no lattice point may enter into the interior of $\mathfrak{K}$ so long as ϵ does not exceed a certain limit. The value of the determinant Δ with this variation of $\mathfrak{L}, \mathfrak{M}, \mathfrak{N}$ becomes

$$\Delta(\epsilon) = \begin{vmatrix} 1+\epsilon X_1, & \epsilon Y_1, & \epsilon Z_1 \\ \epsilon X_2, & 1+\epsilon Y_2, & \epsilon Z_2 \\ \epsilon X_3, & \epsilon Y_3, & 1+\epsilon Z_3 \end{vmatrix}.$$

Hence with the above transformations

$$\Delta(\epsilon) = \Delta(0)[1+\epsilon(X_1+Y_2+Z_3)+\epsilon^2(\ \ )]$$

it follows that smaller values may be derived for Δ unless the inequality $X_1+Y_2+Z_3 \geqq 0$ is a necessary consequence of the inequalities (1). Hence for the existence of a minimum of Δ, the left-hand side of the inequality just written must be a homogeneous linear combination of the left-hand sides of the six inequalities in (1) with non-negative coefficients, and that is

$$X_1+Y_2+Z_3=c_1L_1+c_2M_2+c_3N_3+c_4(R_2-R_3)\\ +c_5(-S_1+S_3)+c_6(T_1-T_2),$$

where $c_1, \cdots, c_6$ are positive constants. Observing the suffixes on either side of this equation we have, for example,

$$X_1=c_1L_1-c_5S_1+c_6T_1,$$

or omitting the suffixes and using a different notation for the constants we have, after proceeding in the same way for Y_2 and Z_3, the relations

$$\text{(A)}\qquad \begin{aligned} X&=lL-sS+tT,\\ Y&=rR+mM-tT,\\ Z&=-rR+sS+nN, \end{aligned}$$

where l, m, n, r, s, t are non-negative factors.

These are three additional equations of other than the inequalities (1) which must be satisfied in order that Δ be a minimum.

If for L, S, T, R, M, N their values in terms of X, Y, Z are written and the coefficients of these variables on either side of their respective equations be equated, there are here in fact *nine* equations to be satisfied. These are considered later in Art. 187.

ART. **181.** We consider next case (II) of Art. 178. Here the points

$\mathfrak{L}$	$\mathfrak{M}$	$\mathfrak{N}$	$\mathfrak{R}$	$\mathfrak{S}$	$\mathfrak{T}$
1, 0, 0;	0, 1, 0;	0, 0, 1;	0, 1, 1;	1, 0, 1;	1, 1, 0

lie on the surface $\mathfrak{F}$ while the point (1, 1, 1) falls on the outside of $\mathfrak{K}$. The points $\mathfrak{R}, \mathfrak{S}, \mathfrak{T}$ here are of course different from those of Art. 179. Observe that $\mathfrak{N}+\mathfrak{M}=\mathfrak{R}$, $\mathfrak{L}+\mathfrak{N}=\mathfrak{S}$, $\mathfrak{L}+\mathfrak{M}=\mathfrak{T}$. Through each of the points $\mathfrak{L}, \mathfrak{M}, \mathfrak{N}, \mathfrak{R}, \mathfrak{S}, \mathfrak{T}$

of $\mathfrak{K}$ we lay tac-planes to $\mathfrak{K}$. Let their equations be

$$(1)\quad \begin{cases} L= \quad X-\lambda_2 Y-\lambda_3 Z=1, \\ M=-\mu_1 X+\quad Y-\mu_3 Z=1, \\ N=-\nu_1 X-\nu_2 Y+\quad Z=1, \\ R=-\rho_1 X+\rho_2 Y+(1-\rho_2)Z=1, \\ S=(1-\sigma_3)X-\sigma_2 Y+\sigma_3 Z=1, \\ T=\tau_1 X+(1-\tau_1)Y-\tau_3 Z-1. \end{cases}$$

In the body $\mathfrak{K}$ the expressions L, M, N, R, S, T are all $\geqq -1$ and $\leqq 1$. The form L has for the six lattice points $\mathfrak{L}$, $\mathfrak{M}$, $\mathfrak{N}$, $\mathfrak{R}$, $\mathfrak{S}$, $\mathfrak{T}$ the values

$$1, \quad -\lambda_2, \quad -\lambda_3, \quad -\lambda_2-\lambda_3, \quad 1-\lambda_3, \quad 1-\lambda_2.$$

It follows that $0\leqq\lambda_2\leqq 1$, $0\leqq\lambda_3\leqq 1$ and $\lambda_2+\lambda_3\leqq 1$. Similarly the form R becomes for these six points

$$-\rho_1, \quad \rho_2, \quad 1-\rho_2, \quad 1, \quad -\rho_1+1-\rho_2, \quad -\rho_1+\rho_2.$$

We therefore have $0\leqq\rho_2\leqq 1$ and

$$\begin{cases} \text{either } 0\leqq\rho_1\leqq 1; \\ \text{or } 0\leqq -\rho_1 \text{ and } -\rho_1\leqq\rho_2,\ -\rho_1\leqq 1-\rho_2. \end{cases}$$

Corresponding conditions exist for μ_3, μ_1; ν_1, ν_2; σ_3, σ_2; τ_1, τ_2. We now vary $\mathfrak{L}$, $\mathfrak{M}$, $\mathfrak{N}$ in such a way that their new positions with respect to the old coordinate system X, Y, Z become

$$1+\epsilon X_1, \quad \epsilon Y_1, \quad \epsilon Z_1; \qquad \epsilon X_2, \quad 1+\epsilon Y_2, \quad \epsilon Z_2;$$
$$\epsilon X_3, \quad \epsilon Y_3, \quad 1+\epsilon Z_3,$$

where ϵ is a parameter. And further each of the six points $\mathfrak{L}$, $\mathfrak{M}$, $\mathfrak{N}$, $\mathfrak{R}$, $\mathfrak{S}$, $\mathfrak{T}$ is required to remain on its respective tac-planes.

We accordingly have the equations $L_1=0$, $M_2=0$, $N_3=0$, $R_2+R_3=0$, $S_1+S_3=0$, $T_1+T_2=0$ for the respective systems X_i, Y_i, Z_i. Now in case no other lattice point save $\mathfrak{L}$, $\mathfrak{M}$, $\mathfrak{N}$, $\mathfrak{R}$, $\mathfrak{S}$, $\mathfrak{T}$ is on the surface $\mathfrak{F}$, then after the variation with sufficiently small values of $|\epsilon|$ of the lattice there appear no other lattice points on $\mathfrak{K}$. Similar considerations as in the preceding article show that for *the existence of a minimum of* Δ, *the following three equations must exist:*

$$\text{(B)}\qquad \begin{aligned} X&=lL+sS+tT,\\ Y&=rR+mM+tT,\\ Z&=rR+sS+nN, \end{aligned}$$

where l, m, n, r, s, t *are constant factors.*

These equations are considered later in Art. 188.

ART. **182.** Even though there are other lattice points on $\mathfrak{F}$ besides the points $\mathfrak{L}, \mathfrak{M}, \mathfrak{N}, \mathfrak{R}, \mathfrak{S}, \mathfrak{T}$, it will now be shown that the forms L, M, N, R, S, T may be so chosen that during the variation in question with sufficiently small $|\epsilon|$ no lattice point enters the interior of $\mathfrak{K}$ and we again find for the existence of a minimum of Δ that the equations (B) are necessary. We have to consider further the points mentioned in Art. 173, namely,

0, 1, 2; 1, 1, 2; 1, 2, 2; 1, 1, 3; 1, 2, 3;
2, 2, 3; 1, 2, 4; 2, 3, 4.

For this purpose we note the following inequalities and those that are derived from them through a permutation of the variables:

$$F\left(\begin{matrix}3\\-1\end{matrix}, \begin{matrix}2\\-2\end{matrix}, \pm 4\right)+F(1, 1, 0)+F(0, 1, 0) \geqq 4F\left(\begin{matrix}1\\0\end{matrix}, \begin{matrix}1\\0\end{matrix}, \pm 1\right),$$

$$F\left(\begin{matrix}2\\-1\end{matrix}, \begin{matrix}2\\-1\end{matrix}, \pm 3\right)+F(1, 1, 0) \geqq 3F\left(\begin{matrix}1\\0\end{matrix}, \begin{matrix}1\\0\end{matrix}, \pm 1\right),$$

$$F(-a, -b, c)+aF(1, 0, 1)+bF(0, 1, 1) \geqq (a+b+c)F(0, 0, 1).$$

where $(-a, -b, c=-1, -2, 3; -1, -2, 2; -1, -1, 2)$,

$$F(-2, 2, 3)+2F(-1, -1, 0)+3F(-1, 0, -1) \geqq 7F(-1, 0, 0),$$

$$F(1, 2, 3)+F(1, 1, 0)+F(1, 0, 0) \geqq 3F(1, 1, 1),$$

$$F(1, -1, 3)+F(0, 1, 1)+F(-1, 0, 0) \geqq 4F(0, 0, 1),$$

$$F(1, 2, 2)+F(1, 0, 0) \geqq 2F(1, 1, 1),$$

$$F(-1, 2, 2)+\tfrac{1}{2}F(1, 1, 0)+\tfrac{1}{2}F(1, 0, 1) \geqq \tfrac{5}{2}F(0, 1, 1),$$

$$F(1, 1, 2)+F(1, 1, 0) \geqq 2F(1, 1, 1),$$

$$F(0, -1, 2)+F(0, 1, 1) \geqq 3F(0, 0, 1).$$

After a study of the above inequalities it still remains questionable as to whether or not those lattice points lie on $\mathfrak{F}$, whose coordinates, neglecting the sequence, offer one of the following systems:

$$-1, 1, 2; \quad 0, 1, 2; \quad -1, 1, 1; \quad 0, -1, 1.$$

These we now consider:

If $F(-1, 1, 2) = 1 = F(1, -1, -2)$ the point $L = (1, 0, 0)$ lies within the triangle $\mathfrak{U}_0$, $\mathfrak{S}$, $\mathfrak{T}$, and from (B) $L = X$, necessarily, and we may choose $S = L$ and $T = L$. See Fig. 129. It then follows since $L_1 = 0$ that $X_1 = 0$; and then from the relations $T_1 + T_2 = L_1 + L_2 = 0$, $S_1 + S_3 = L_1 + L_3 = 0$, it is seen that $X_2 = 0$, $X_3 = 0$. The body $\mathfrak{K}$ lies entirely in the region $-1 \leqq X \leqq 1$ and the lattice points which are situated in the bounding planes $X = \pm 1$ remain by the proposed variation in these planes. At the same time as an additional lattice point on $\mathfrak{F}$ there appears in the plane $X = 0$ the point $(0, 1, 2)$. We may further choose $M = R$ in (B). Equating the coefficients of Y on either side of these two expressions, we have $\rho_2 = 1$, so that $R = M = Y$ so that the lattice point in question does not fall on the interior of $\mathfrak{K}$.

If $F(0, 2, 3) = 1$, it is seen by writing 0, 1, 2 in N that $-\nu_2 + 2 \leqq 1$, so that $\nu_2 = 1$; and as $\nu_1 + \nu_2 \leqq 1$, it follows that $\nu_1 = 0$. We then have $N = \pm Y + Z$. We may then choose $S = N$, $T = -N$ and reach the required result.

If $F(-1, 1, 1) = 1$, we again see that $L = X$ and in the $X = 0$ plane are found on $\mathfrak{F}$ the points 0, 2, 1 (Fig. 133); 0, 1, 2 (Fig. 131); 0, -1, 1 (Fig. 130).

The presence of $-\mathfrak{U} = (1, -1, 2)$ and $\mathfrak{T} = (1, 1, 0)$ on $\mathfrak{F}$ requires that $\mathfrak{F}$ contain

$$\frac{T - U}{2} = (1, 0, 1) \qquad \text{and} \qquad \frac{\mathfrak{T} + \mathfrak{U}}{2} = (-1, 0, 1).$$

As regards the lattice points $(0, 1, 2)$, $(0, 2, 1)$ and $(0, -1, 1)$ only the first can be on $\mathfrak{F}$ at the same time as $(-1, 1, 2)$. In this connection Minkowski (*Ges. Abhandl.*, Vol. II,

p. 32) is in error. For *first*, the coordinates of (0, −1, 1) in $N=-Y+Z$ give $N=2$. Since $N=1$ is a tac-plane, the point (0, −1, 1) is not on $\mathfrak{F}$. *Secondly*, if (0, 2, 1) were on $\mathfrak{F}$ at the same time as $\mathfrak{M}$, $\mathfrak{N}$ and $\mathfrak{R}$, the cross section of $\mathfrak{K}$ in the plane $X=0$ would be forced into the parallelogram with vertices at (0, 2, 1), (0, 0, 1), (0, −2, −1) and (0, 0, −1).

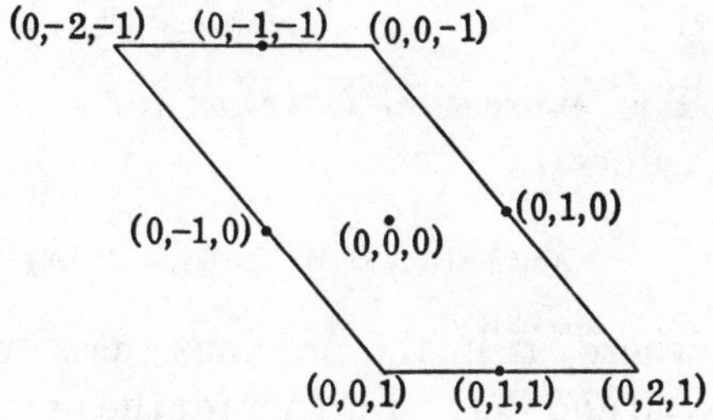

FIG. 127

On the other hand every point on the line joining $\mathfrak{S}$ and $\mathfrak{U}$ is a point of $\mathfrak{K}$ and in particular the mid-point $\dfrac{\mathfrak{S}+\mathfrak{U}}{2}=(0, \tfrac{1}{2}, \tfrac{3}{2})$, a point outside the parallelogram in question. Thus the presence of both (−1, 1, 2) (Fig. 129) and (0, 2, 1) on $\mathfrak{F}$ is also impossible.

Thirdly, if (0, 1, 2) is on $\mathfrak{F}$ then for this point $R=\rho_2+2-2\rho_2\leqq 1$ so that $\rho_2=1$, and one has necessarily $R\equiv Y$. Since M is in $Y=1$ one can set $R=M=Y$.

If $F(1, -1, -1)=F(-1, 1, 1)=1$, we again find that $L=X$ and that the point (0, 1, 2) lies on $\mathfrak{F}$. See Fig. 131.

If $F(-1, 1, 1)=1$, we have $\mu_3=0=\nu_2$. We again have $L=X$. The intersection of $X=0$ with $\mathfrak{K}$ gives the quadrilateral with vertices ±1, ±1. Fig. 130. We may choose $R=N$ and the points 0, 0, 1; 0, 1, 1; 0, −1, 1 remain in the plane $N=1$.

If two points such as 1, −1, 0 and −1, 0, 1 are simultaneously on $\mathfrak{F}$, it follows that $L=X$ and we may proceed as in the case $F(-1, 1, 1)=1$.

ART. **183.** We consider finally the case (III) of Art. 178. Here the seven lattice points

$\mathfrak{L}$	$\mathfrak{M}$	$\mathfrak{N}$	$\mathfrak{R}$	$\mathfrak{S}$	$\mathfrak{T}$	$\mathfrak{Q}$
1, 0, 0;	0, 1, 0;	0, 0, 1;	0, 1, 1;	1, 0, 1;	1, 1, 0;	1, 1, 1

are situated on the surface $\mathfrak{F}$. We shall use the same notations for the tac-planes drawn through the first six points as in Art. 181, and take as equation of the tac-plane through $\mathfrak{Q}$

$$Q = k_1X + k_2Y + k_3Z.$$

The expression Q takes for the seven lattice points the values

$$k_1,\ k_2,\ k_3,\ k_2+k_3,\ k_1+k_3,\ k_1+k_2,\ k_1+k_2+k_3=1,$$

where, as in the previous cases, we have here k_1, k_2, k_3 all $\geqq 0$ and $\leqq 1$. Further for the point $\mathfrak{Q}$ the value of $R = 1-\rho_1$ so that necessarily $0 \leqq \rho_1 \leqq 1$ with analogous values for σ_2 and τ_3.

We next change the points $\mathfrak{L}$, $\mathfrak{M}$, $\mathfrak{N}$ into the new positions

$$1+\epsilon X_1,\quad \epsilon Y_1,\quad \epsilon Z_1;\qquad \epsilon X_2,\quad 1+\epsilon Y_2,\quad \epsilon Z_2;$$
$$\epsilon X_3,\quad \epsilon Y_3,\quad 1+\epsilon Z_3,$$

and require that all the points $\mathfrak{L}$, $\mathfrak{M}$, $\mathfrak{N}$, $\mathfrak{Q}$, $\mathfrak{R}$, $\mathfrak{S}$, $\mathfrak{T}$ remain in their respective tac-planes. This imposes the conditions $L_1=0$, $M_2=0$, $N_3=0$, $Q_1+Q_2+Q_3=0$, $R_2+R_3=0$, $S_1+S_3=0$, $T_1+T_2=0$. Considerations as in Arts. 180 and 181 show that we may keep ϵ in absolute value sufficiently small that with the variation in question no lattice point penetrates into the interior of $\mathfrak{K}$. As further necessary conditions for the existence of a minimum of Δ we must necessarily have the three following equations:

$$\text{(C)}\qquad \begin{aligned} X &= lL+sS+tT+qQ,\\ Y &= rR+mM+tT+qQ,\\ Z &= rR+sS+nN+qQ, \end{aligned}$$

where l, m, n, q, r, s, t are constant factors.

The conditions already derived are then sufficient for a minimum value of Δ provided the above seven lattice points and their opposites are the only ones on $\mathfrak{F}$. Further it is shown below that these conditions remain sufficient even when there are additional lattice points on $\mathfrak{F}$ when the tac-planes L, M, N, Q, R, S, T have been suitably chosen.

By a similar treatment of the inequalities as in Art. 182, we have besides the points already treated still further lattice points 1, 2, 3; 1, 2, 2; 1, 1, 2 and the systems which exist from these through permutation of the coordinates remaining for consideration. By means of the substitution

$$X^* = -X, \qquad Y^* = Y - X, \qquad Z^* = Z - X$$

the systems of values in X, Y, Z, namely (see also Art. 182)

$$1,0,0;\quad 0,1,0;\quad 0,0,1;\quad 0,1,1;\quad 1,0,1;\quad 1,1,0;$$
$$1,1,1;\quad 1,2,3;\quad 1,2,2;\quad 1,1,2;\quad -1,1,0;\quad 0,-1,1,$$

are transformed into the following systems in X^*, Y^*, Z^*:

$$-1,-1,-1;\quad 0,1,0;\quad 0,0,1;\quad 0,1,1;\quad -1,-1,0;$$
$$-1,0,-1;\quad -1,0,0$$

with the additional systems

$-1, 1, 2$ (Fig. 132); $\quad -1, 1, 1$; $\quad -1, 0, 1$ (Fig. 132);
$1, 2, 1$; $\quad 0, -1, 1$ (Fig. 129),

and these additional systems remain to be treated as potential lattice points on $\mathfrak{F}$ in a similar manner as the systems $-1, 1, 2$; $-1, 1, 1$; $0, -1, 1$, etc. were treated in Art. 182.

The question is raised regarding certain new possibilities for example that two lattice points say $1, -1, 0$ and $1, 1, 2$ simultaneously appear on $\mathfrak{F}$. That these points be on $\mathfrak{F}$ we must necessarily have

$$\lambda_2 = 0, \qquad \mu_1 = 0, \qquad \nu_1 + \nu_2 = 1, \qquad k_3 = 0;$$

and at all events we may set up the relation

$$l_0 L + m_0 M + n_0 N = q_0 Q,$$

where the constants l_0, m_0, n_0, q_0 are not all zero. Since the roles of the pairs L, M and N, Q as well as the elements in each pair are interchangeable, we may assume that $|l_0|$, $|m_0|$, $|n_0|$ are all $\leqq |q_0|$. By substituting the points 1, 1, 1 and 0, 0, -1 respectively in the above equation we have $l_0(1-\lambda_3) + m_0(1-\mu_3) = q_0$; $l_0\lambda_3 + m_0\mu_3 = n_0$. If $\lambda_3 = 0$, we have $L = X$, a case already considered in Art. 182. We shall consequently take $\lambda_3 > 0$ and also $\mu_3 > 0$. The equations just written then show that l_0, m_0 and further n_0 have the same sign as q_0 and we may take

$$l_0 + m_0 = n_0 + q_0 = 1.$$

By putting $l_0 = n_0\nu_1 + q_0 k_1$, $m_0 = n_0\nu_2 + q_0 k_2$, we may choose

$$T = l_0 L + m_0 M = -n_0 N + q_0 Q.$$

It is then seen that $T=1$ is a tac-plane of $\mathfrak{K}$ through the point $\mathfrak{T}$. We shall now introduce the variations

$$\mathfrak{L} = (1+X_1,\ Y_1,\ Z_1), \qquad \mathfrak{M} = (X_2,\ 1+Y_2,\ Z_2),$$
$$\mathfrak{N} = (X_3,\ Y_3,\ 1+Z_3).$$

Observing that $\mathfrak{R} = 0, 1, -1$; $\mathfrak{M} = 0, 1, 0$; and $\mathfrak{N}_0 = 0, 0, 1$, we note that $R = M + N_0$ and have the further variations

$$\begin{aligned}
\mathfrak{R} &= (X_2+X_3,\ 1+Y_2+Y_3,\ 1+Z_2+Z_3),\\
\mathfrak{S} &= (1+X_1+X_3,\ Y_1+Y_3,\ 1+Z_1+Z_3),\\
\mathfrak{T} &= (1+X_1+X_2,\ 1+Y_1+Y_2,\ Z_1+Z_2).
\end{aligned}$$

The restrictions above are to be made, namely

$$L_1 = 0, \quad M_2 = 0, \quad N_3 = 0, \quad R_2 + R_3 = 0, \quad S_1 + S_3 = 0,$$
$$T_1 + T_2 = 0, \quad Q_1 + Q_2 + Q_3 = 0.$$

Imposing these variations on $T = l_0 L + m_0 M = 1$ it is seen that

$$\begin{aligned}
T(\mathfrak{T}) &= l_0[1+X_1+X_2-\lambda_3(Z_1+Z_2)]\\
&\quad + m_0[1+Y_1+Y_2-\mu_3(Z_1+Z_2)] = l_0(1+L_2)+m_0(1+M_1)\\
&= l_0+m_0+l_0L_2+m_0M_1 = 1.
\end{aligned}$$

It follows that

$$l_0 L_2 + m_0 M_1 = 0.$$

On the other hand

$$\begin{aligned}
T(\mathfrak{T}) &= -n_0[-\nu_1(1+X_1+X_2)-\nu_2(1+Y_1+Y_2)+Z_1+Z_2]\\
&\quad + q_0[k_1(1+X_1+X_2)+k_2(1+Y_1+Y_2)]\\
&= -n_0(-\nu_1-\nu_2+N_1+N_2)+q_0(k_1+k_2+Q_1+Q_2)\\
&= n_0 - n_0(N_1+N_2)+q_0(Q_1+Q_2)\\
&= 1 - n_0(N_1+N_2+N_3) - q_0Q_3 = 1
\end{aligned}$$

or

$$-n_0(N_1+N_2+N_3)-q_0Q_3=0.$$

Hence on the one hand L_2 and M_1 can not be two values different from zero with the same sign and likewise on the other hand $N_1+N_2+N_3$ and Q_3 are not two values different from zero with the same sign.

Finally observe that for the point 1, -1, 0 the above variation gives $L=1-\epsilon L_2$, $-M=1-\epsilon M_1$, so that at least one of these quantities becomes >1; while for the point 1, 1, 2 the same variation gives $N=1+\epsilon(N_1+N_2+N_3)$, $Q=1+\epsilon Q_3$ so that one of these quantities becomes >1.

ART. **184. Thickest Placement of Octahedra.** Let

(1) $\varphi=-\xi+\eta+\zeta,\qquad \chi=\xi-\eta+\zeta,$
$$\psi=\xi+\eta-\zeta,\qquad \omega=-\xi-\eta-\zeta$$

so that

(2) $$\varphi+\chi+\psi+\omega=0;$$

and consider the octahedron

$$|\xi|+|\eta|+|\zeta|=\tfrac{1}{2}$$

with vertices $(\pm\frac{1}{2}, 0, 0)$, $(0, \pm\frac{1}{2}, 0)$, $(0, 0, \pm\frac{1}{2})$. The volume of this octahedron $\frac{1}{2}(\overline{\mathfrak{K}}+\overline{\mathfrak{K}}_0)=\frac{1}{6}$. We next make the substitutions

$$\xi=\alpha_1X+\alpha_2Y+\alpha_3Z,$$
$$\eta=\beta_1X+\beta_2Y+\beta_3Z,$$
$$\zeta=\gamma_1X+\gamma_2Y+\gamma_3Z,$$

with determinant $\Delta\neq0$. The question is regarding the minimum of the absolute value of Δ while of the lattice points in X, Y, Z only the origin lies within $\mathfrak{K}$.

We may make application of the preceding rules neglecting the case that appears at the end of the preceding article, a case that does not enter here. It is seen that the six or the seven tac-planes to $\mathfrak{K}$, namely L, M, N, R, S, T, and Q, may always be taken as the faces of the octahedron under the assumption that each of the forms L, M, $\cdots$ coincides with one of the expressions $\pm\varphi$, $\pm\chi$, $\pm\psi$, $\pm\omega$.

Art. **185.** We shall anticipate the general method of procedure by treating a special case. Let the conditions of case II exist and put $\omega = Z$. The intersection of $\mathfrak{K}$ by the plane $Z = 0$ gives a six-sided figure (see Fig. 128) with $\mathfrak{O}$ as center and having its diagonals parallel to its sides. The lattice points $\mathfrak{L} = (1, 0, 0)$, $\mathfrak{M} = (0, 1, 0)$, $\mathfrak{T} = (1, 1, 0)$ lie on the sides of this six-sided

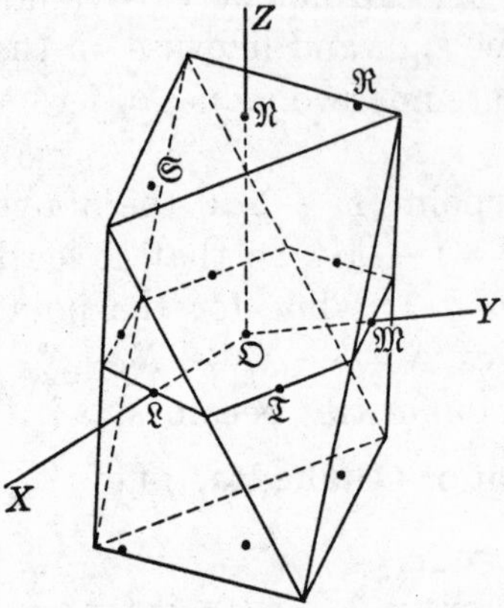

Fig. 128

Fig. 128. We may assume that the expressions L, M, T taken in any sequence coincide with $\pm\varphi$, $\pm\chi$, $\pm\psi$, for if two of the points $\mathfrak{L}$, $\mathfrak{M}$, $\mathfrak{T}$ lie on the same side of the six-sided figure, they and their three opposite points constitute the six vertices of this figure.

The equation (2) of the preceding article having regard to the expressions (1) of Art. 181 gives $\mu_1 = 1 - \tau_1$, $\lambda_2 = \tau_1$ and the equations (B) for $N = R = S = Z$ give $\tau_1 = \frac{1}{2}$, $\lambda_3 + \mu_3 - \tau_3 = 1$. And the three lattice points $\mathfrak{L} = (1, 0, 0)$, $\mathfrak{M} = (0, 1, 0)$, $\mathfrak{T} = (1, 1, 0)$ with their opposites are the midpoints of the sides of the six-sided figure.

Writing $L = X - \frac{1}{2}Y - \lambda_3 Z$, $M = -\frac{1}{2}X + Y - \nu_3 Z$, $T = \frac{1}{2}X + \frac{1}{2}Y - \tau_3 Z$, we have

$$\Delta = \begin{vmatrix} 1, & -\frac{1}{2}, & -\lambda_3 \\ -\frac{1}{2}, & 1, & -\mu_3 \\ \frac{1}{2}, & \frac{1}{2}, & -\tau_3 \end{vmatrix} = \frac{1}{2}\begin{vmatrix} 1, & -\frac{1}{2}, & -\lambda_3 \\ 0, & \frac{3}{2}, & -\mu_3 - \tau_3 \\ 0, & \frac{3}{2}, & -2\tau_3 + \lambda_3 \end{vmatrix}$$

$$= \frac{1}{2}\begin{vmatrix} \frac{3}{2}, & -\mu_3 - \tau_3 \\ 0, & -\tau_3 + \mu_3 + \lambda_3 \end{vmatrix} = \frac{1}{2}\cdot\frac{3}{2} \qquad (\text{since } \mu_3 + \lambda_3 - \tau_3 = 1).$$

If we change the points $\mathfrak{L}$, $\mathfrak{M}$, $\mathfrak{N}$ to the positions (for the derivation of this variation see following article)

$$1+\epsilon, \quad \epsilon, \quad \epsilon; \qquad -\epsilon, \quad 1-\epsilon, \quad -\epsilon; \qquad -\epsilon, \quad -2\epsilon, \quad 1$$

(where ϵ is positive) it may be shown that none of these points enter the interior of $\mathfrak{K}$ while Δ becomes $\Delta(1 \mid \epsilon^2)$. Consequently here there is no minimum of Δ. To show that the points in the new positions lie without $\mathfrak{K}$, put $\mathfrak{L}=(1+\epsilon,\ \epsilon,\ \epsilon)$; $\mathfrak{M}=(-\epsilon,\ 1-\epsilon,\ -\epsilon)$; $\mathfrak{N}=(-\epsilon,\ -2\epsilon,\ 1)$; $\mathfrak{R}=(L+M+N)=(-2\epsilon, 1-3\epsilon, 1-\epsilon)$; $\mathfrak{S}=(L+N)=(1,\ -\epsilon,\ 1+\epsilon)$; $\mathfrak{T}=(L+M)=(1,\ 1,\ 0)$ and test to see which of these points lie in the respective tac-planes.

It is seen that $L(\mathfrak{L})=1+\epsilon-\frac{1}{2}\epsilon-\frac{1}{2}\epsilon=1$ and remains in the plane $L=1$. The same is true of $M(\mathfrak{M})$, $N(\mathfrak{N})$, $R(\mathfrak{R})$, $T(\mathfrak{T})$. However, S is beyond the plane $N=1$ (away from 0) since $Z=1+\epsilon$ and $\epsilon>0$.

ART. **186.** We may give the above problem another setting (different from that of Minkowski) and derive the required variation. To the relations

$$L=X-\tfrac{1}{2}Y-\tfrac{1}{2}Z,$$
$$M=-\tfrac{1}{2}X+Y-\tfrac{1}{2}Z,$$
$$T=\tfrac{1}{2}X+\tfrac{1}{2}Y$$

we may add

$$N=Z, \qquad S=-M, \qquad R=-L$$

and apply the conditions

1) $L_1=0=X_1-\frac{1}{2}Y_1-\frac{1}{2}Z_1,$

2) $M_2=0=-\frac{1}{2}X_2+Y_2-\frac{1}{2}Z_2,$

3) $N_3=0=Z_3,$

4) $R_2+R_3=0=-\frac{1}{2}X_2+\frac{1}{2}Y_2+\frac{1}{2}Z_2-X_3+\frac{1}{2}Y_3,$

5) $S_1+S_2=0=\frac{1}{2}X_1-Y_1+\frac{1}{2}Z_1+\frac{1}{2}X_3-Y_3,$

6) $T_1+T_2=0=\frac{1}{2}X_1+\frac{1}{2}Y_1+\frac{1}{2}X_2+\frac{1}{2}Y_2.$

In the six by nine matrix of these equations the determinant whose terms are factors of X_1, Y_1, and Y_3 is not zero so that we may express the other six quantities in terms of these three, thus having at once $Z_3=0$, $Z_1=2X_1-Y_1$, $X_3=-3X_1+3Y_1+2Y_3$. The equations (4), (5), (6) offer

$$-X_2+2Y_2-Z_2=0,$$
$$-2X_2+Y_2+Z_2=-6X_1+6Y_1+5Y_3=k, \quad \text{say},$$
$$X_2+Y_2=-X_1-Y_1=m, \quad \text{say},$$

with determinant $=6$, or derived therefrom

$$X_2=\tfrac{1}{2}X_1-\tfrac{3}{2}Y_1+\tfrac{5}{6}Y_3,$$
$$Y_2=-\tfrac{3}{2}X_1+\tfrac{1}{2}Y_1+\tfrac{5}{6}Y_3,$$
$$Z_2=-\tfrac{7}{2}X_1+\tfrac{5}{2}Y_1+\tfrac{5}{2}Y_3.$$

To do away with fractional coefficients choose $X_1=2\epsilon_1$, $Y_1=2\epsilon_2$, $Y_3=6\epsilon_3$ and the above expressions become

$$X_3=-6\epsilon_1+6\epsilon_2+12\epsilon_3,$$
$$Z_1=4\epsilon_1-2\epsilon_2,$$
$$X_2=\epsilon_1-3\epsilon_2-5\epsilon_3,$$
$$Y_2=-3\epsilon_1+\epsilon_2+5\epsilon_3,$$
$$Z_2=-7\epsilon_1+5\epsilon_2+15\epsilon_3,$$
$$Z_3=0.$$

The determinant of L, M, N, namely

$$\begin{vmatrix} 1+X_1, & Y_1, & Z_1 \\ X_2, & 1+Y_2, & Z_2 \\ X_3, & Y_3, & 1+Z_3 \end{vmatrix},$$

becomes here

$$\begin{vmatrix} 1+2\epsilon_1, & 2\epsilon_2, & 4\epsilon_1-2\epsilon_3 \\ \epsilon_1-3\epsilon_2-5\epsilon_3, & 1-3\epsilon_1+\epsilon_2+5\epsilon_3, & -7\epsilon_1+5\epsilon_2+15\epsilon_3 \\ -6\epsilon_1+6\epsilon_2+12\epsilon_3, & 6\epsilon_3, & 1 \end{vmatrix}.$$

The expansion of this determinant offers a linear expression in the ϵ's, and accordingly we may so choose them that the determinant has a decreasing value. For example, put $\epsilon_1=\epsilon$, $\epsilon_2=0$, $\epsilon_3=0$, and the determinant becomes

$$\begin{vmatrix} 1+2\epsilon, & 0, & 4\epsilon \\ \epsilon, & 1-3\epsilon, & -7\epsilon \\ -6\epsilon, & 0, & 1 \end{vmatrix} = (1-3\epsilon)(1+2\epsilon+24\epsilon^2)=1-\epsilon+(\epsilon^2),$$

and there is no minimum.

ART. **187.** After the treatment of the above special case and by methods which show the general way of procedure we shall next take up the considerations of the case I of Arts. 178 and 180.

Observe here that the points 1, 0, 0; 0, 1, 0; 0, 0, 1; 0, 1, −1; −1, 0, 1; −1, 0, 1; 1, −1, 0 lie upon the surface F, while the points −1, 1, 1; 1, −1, 1; 1, 1, −1 lie without $\mathfrak{R}$. Since only the four pairs of values $\pm\varphi$, $\pm\chi$, $\pm\psi$, $\pm\omega$ may be regarded for the six expressions L, M, N, R, S, T in (1) of Art. 180, either any three must coincide or the equality of any two must occur twice where either of the signs ± 1 may be used. Certain of the equalities are of themselves excluded. It is evident for example that $L = X + \lambda_2 Y + \lambda_3 Z$ cannot equal $-M = -\mu_1 X - Y - \mu_3 Z$; for we would then have $\mu_1 = -1$, $\lambda_2 = -1$ and neither of these quantities lies within the limit $\geqq 0$ and $\leqq 1$. The assumption $L = R = (\rho_2 - \rho_1)X + \rho_2 Y - (1-\rho_2)Z$ leads to $\rho_2 - \rho_1 = 1$, $\rho_2 = \lambda_2$, $-(1-\rho_2) = \lambda_3$, so that $\rho_1 = 0$, $\rho_2 = 1$, $\lambda_2 = 1$, $\lambda_3 = 0$ and $L = X + Y$. The section of $\mathfrak{R}$ by the plane $X + Y = 0$ is a six-sided figure with two pairs of lattice points on the rim, say N, N_0; T, T_0. Through a general variation of either N or T we may decrease the value of Δ.

Consider the figure of the tetrahedron made of the vectors 1, 0, 0; 0, 1, 0; 0, 0, 1; 0, 1, −1; −1, 0, 1; 1, −1, 0, and observe how the roles of the individual vectors may be changed.

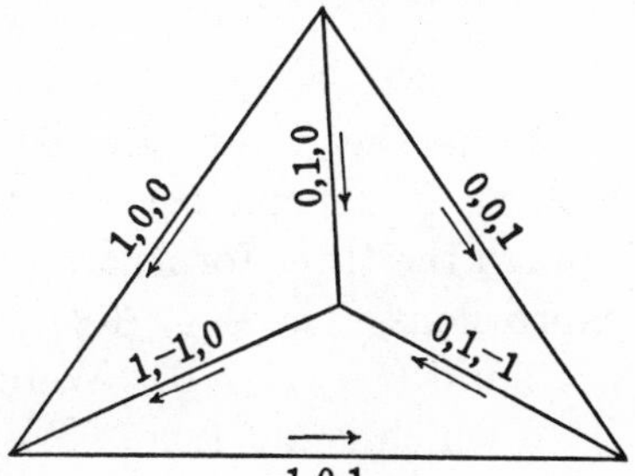

FIG. 128a

It is clear that we may exclude the equality for any two of the expressions $\pm L, \cdots, \pm T$ in case the associated systems $\mathfrak{L}$, $\mathfrak{L}_0$; $\cdots$; $\mathfrak{T}$, $\mathfrak{T}_0$ correspond to two such vectors in the tetrahedron which with their directions at a vertex include each other or if they are found on oppositely situated sides.

We accordingly have to discuss only the following assumptions:

(1) $L = M = N$. It follows that $\nu_1 = \mu_1 = 1$, $\lambda_2 = \nu_2 = 1$, $\lambda_3 = \mu_3 = 1$, $L = X + Y + Z$. Writing $X + Y + Z = \omega$, we have

conditions similar to those of the preceding article where $\omega = Z$ and it was seen that Δ is not a minimum.

(2) $L = M$, $R = -S$. From $L = M$, we at once have $\mu_1 = 1 = \lambda_2$, $\lambda_3 = \mu_3$; and from $R = -S$, it is seen that $\rho_2 - \rho_1 = 1 - \sigma_3$, $\rho_2 = \sigma_2 - \sigma_3$, $1 - \rho_2 = \sigma_3$ so that $\sigma_2 = 1$, $\rho_1 = 0$.

We accordingly have $R = -S = \rho_2(X+Y) - (1-\rho_2)Z$. Using the formula for Z found in (A) of Art. 180 we have

$$Z = -rR + sS + nN = -(r+s)R + nN.$$

In this equality write the expressions for R and N from above and equate the coefficients of X and Y on either side of the resulting identity. We thus have

$$(r+s)\rho_2 - n\nu_1 = 0,$$
$$(r+s)\rho_2 - n\nu_2 = 0.$$

In these two equations if ν_1 were $= \nu_2$, then is

$$N = \nu_1(X+Y) + Z.$$

It is then seen that the determinant of L, R, N is zero making a dependence among these three quantities although the three forms are to be regarded as three different expressions $\pm\varphi$, $\pm\chi$, $\pm\psi$, $\pm\omega$. It therefore follows that $n = 0$ and $(r+s)\rho_2 = 0$. Were $r+s = 0$, it would follow that $Z = 0$ which is not true. We accordingly must have $\rho_2 = 0$, so that $R = -Z$, a case similar to the one of the preceding article which showed that Δ was *not* a minimum.

(3) $L = N$, $R = -S$. Here it is seen that

$$N = X + \nu_2 Y + Z,$$
$$R = \rho_2(X+Y) - (1-\rho_2)Z;$$

and the equation above for Z, namely $Z = -rR + sS + nN$, requires either that $N = X + Y + Z$ or $R = -Z$. These two cases have already been considered and do not offer minimum values of Δ.

From the above considerations it is seen that no minimum of Δ may be found in case I.

ART. **188.** We may consider in the second place the results attending (II) Arts. 178, 181, where the points 1, 0, 0; 0, 1, 0; 0, 0, 1; 0, 1, 1; 1, 0, 1; 1, 1, 0 lie on F and the point 1, 1, 1 lies outside of $\mathfrak{K}$. Due to the conditions restricting the coefficients in the expressions in (1) of Art. 181 we cannot have $L=M$. The assumption $L=-M$ leads to $L=X-Y$ and may be treated essentially as the special case introduced in Art. 185. It is seen that we cannot have $L=R$. $L=-S$ and $L=-T$ are not possible. The assumption $R=-S$ leads to $R=-X+Y$.

Having regard to the fact that the roles of the three pairs L, R; M, S; N, T may be exchanged, the following different cases remain to be discussed:

(1) $R=S=N$.

Here

$$\begin{aligned} R&=-\rho_1X+\rho_2Y+(1-\rho_2)Z,\\ S&=(1-\sigma_3)X-\sigma_2Y+\sigma_3Z,\\ N&=-\nu_1X-\nu_2Y+Z. \end{aligned}$$

Equating the coefficients of the variables, we have $1-\rho_2=\sigma_3=1$, $\rho_2=-\sigma_2=-\nu_2$, $-\rho_1=1-\sigma_3=-\nu_1$. It follows that $\rho_2=-\sigma_2=-\nu_2=0$ and $\rho_1=0=\nu_1=1-\sigma_3$. These values give $N=Z$, a case treated above.

(2) The relation $R=S=T$ offers

$$\begin{aligned} -\rho_1&=1-\sigma_3=\tau_1,\\ \rho_2&=-\sigma_2=1-\tau_1,\\ 1-\rho_2&=\sigma_3=-\tau_3. \end{aligned}$$

From these we have $\rho_2=\frac{1}{2}$, $\rho_1=-\frac{1}{2}$; $\sigma_3=\frac{1}{2}$, $\sigma_2=-\frac{1}{2}$; $\tau_1=\frac{1}{2}$, $\tau_3=-\frac{1}{2}$. We accordingly have $R=\frac{1}{2}(X+Y+Z)=S=T$. The relations (B) of Art. 181 offer for X the equality

$$\begin{aligned} X&=lL+sS+tT\\ &=l(X-\lambda_2Y-\lambda_3Z)+(s+t)\tfrac{1}{2}(X+Y+Z), \end{aligned}$$

where $l\neq 0$. Equating the coefficients of Y and Z on either side of this expression, it is seen that

$$l(-\lambda_2)+\frac{s+t}{2}=0, \qquad l(-\lambda_3)+\frac{s+t}{2}=0.$$

It follows that $\lambda_2=\lambda_3$. Similarly it is seen that $\nu_1=\nu_2$ and $\mu_1=\mu_3$. From (2) of Art. 184 we have $\pm L\pm M\pm N=R$. Of these relations the two cases

$$1^\circ \quad R=L+M+N \quad \text{and}$$
$$2^\circ \quad -R=L+M+N \quad \text{appear permissible.}$$

The first case offers $\nu_1=\mu_1=\frac{1}{4}=\lambda_2$ so that

$$\begin{aligned} L&=X-\tfrac{1}{4}Y-\tfrac{1}{4}Z,\\ M&=-\tfrac{1}{4}X+Y-\tfrac{1}{4}Z,\\ N&=-\tfrac{1}{4}X-\tfrac{1}{4}Y+Z. \end{aligned}$$

Introducing variations as in Art. 185 we have $\mathfrak{L}=(1,\epsilon,-\epsilon)$, $\mathfrak{M}=(\epsilon,1,-\epsilon)$, $\mathfrak{N}=(0,0,1)$, $\mathfrak{R}=(\epsilon,1,1-\epsilon)$, $\mathfrak{S}=(1,\epsilon,1-\epsilon)$, $\mathfrak{T}=(1+\epsilon,1+\epsilon,-2\epsilon)$. It is seen further that

$$L(\mathfrak{L})=1=M(\mathfrak{M})=N(\mathfrak{N})=R(\mathfrak{R})=S(\mathfrak{S})=T(\mathfrak{T}),$$

so that the six points in their new positions remain on their respective tac-planes and are therefore not on the interior of $\mathfrak{K}$. The determinant of $\mathfrak{L}$, $\mathfrak{M}$ and $\mathfrak{N}$ is

$$\begin{vmatrix} 1, & \epsilon, & -\epsilon \\ \epsilon, & 1, & -\epsilon \\ 0, & 0, & 1 \end{vmatrix} = 1-\epsilon^2,$$

so that Δ becomes $\Delta(1-\epsilon^2)$ and there is no minimum.

Using the second case above, it is seen that $\lambda_2=\frac{3}{4}=\mu_1=\nu_1$ and a similar procedure in this case shows that Δ has no minimum value.

(3) $R=-L$, $S=-M$. We have

$$\begin{aligned} L&=X-\lambda_2Y-(1-\lambda_2)Z,\\ M&=-\mu_1X+Y-(1-\mu_1)Z. \end{aligned}$$

For the point 1, 1, 1 it is seen that both M and L are zero and consequently $N\neq 0$ since in L, M, N we have three of the expressions $\pm\varphi$, $\pm\chi$, $\pm\psi$, $\pm\omega$. We therefore must have $\nu_1+\nu_2<1$, since the initial condition was $\nu_1+\nu_2 \gtreqless 1$ for these quantities. Hence N is also different from $-T$ and we must have $T=\pm L\pm M\pm M$. Since the point 1, 1, 1 does not lie in the interior of $\mathfrak{K}$, it follows that $\nu_1 = 0 = \nu_2$ and consequently $N = Z$.

(4) $R = -L$, $S = N$. It follows that

$$-R = X - \lambda_2 Y - (1-\lambda_2)Z,$$
$$N = -\nu_2 Y + Z,$$

and the third equation in (B) of Art. 181, namely, $Z = rR + sS + nN$, becomes $Z = N$.

(5) $R = M$, $S = L$. We then have

$$M = -\mu_1 X + Y, \qquad L = X - \lambda_2 Y,$$

and from the first of the equations (B), namely, $X = lL + sS + tT$, it would follow that either $L = X$ or $T = \tau_1 X + (1-\tau_1)Y$. If the latter were true, it is seen that the determinant of L, M, T is zero, while these forms, being three of the expressions $\pm\varphi$, $\pm\chi$, $\pm\psi$, $\pm\omega$, cannot be linearly dependent.

(6) $R = M$, $S = -N$. We have here

$$R = -\mu_1 X + Y, \qquad N = -\nu_2 Y + Z$$

and the equation named under (4) for Z would require that $N = Z$, or $R = Y$.

(7) $R = S$, $T = -N$. We accordingly have

$$N = -\nu_1 X - (1-\nu_1)Y + Z,$$
$$R = \rho_2(X+Y) + (1-\rho_2)Z; \qquad \rho_2 \leqq \tfrac{1}{2}.$$

From the relation for Z, it is seen that either $R = Z$ or $N = -\frac{1}{2}X - \frac{1}{2}Y + Z$. In the latter case the equations (B) and the relation $R = \pm L \pm M \pm N$ lead to the expressions

$$L = X - \tfrac{1}{4}Y - \tfrac{1}{8}Z, \qquad M = -\tfrac{1}{4}X + Y - \tfrac{1}{8}Z,$$
$$R = S = \tfrac{1}{4}X + \tfrac{1}{4}Y + \tfrac{3}{4}Z.$$

As previously done we may derive a variation in the position of the points $\mathfrak{L}$, $\mathfrak{M}$, $\mathfrak{N}$, namely

$$1-\tfrac{1}{2}\epsilon, \quad -\tfrac{3}{2}\epsilon, \quad -\epsilon; \qquad -\tfrac{3}{2}\epsilon, \quad 1-\tfrac{1}{2}\epsilon, \quad -\epsilon; \qquad \epsilon, \quad \epsilon, \quad 1+\epsilon$$

such that with sufficiently small absolute values of ϵ, no lattice point lies in the interior of $\mathfrak{K}$, while Δ becomes $\Delta(1-\epsilon^2)$. Consequently here Δ is not a minimum.

(8) $R=S$, $T=L$. We have here

$$S=\rho_2(X+Y)+(1-\rho_2)Z, \qquad L=X-\lambda_3 Z,$$

and from $X=lL+sS+tT$ it follows necessarily that $L=X$ or $S=Z$.

It has thus been shown through the above results that in case II no minimum of Δ is to be found.

ART. **189.** It remains finally to consider the case III and use the relations of Art. 183. Here the points 1, 0, 0; 0, 1, 0; 0, 0, 1; 0, 1, 1; 1, 0, 1; 1, 1, 0; and 1, 1, 1 lie on the surface F.

The assumption $R=S$, since in this case $\rho_1 \geqq 0$ and $\sigma_2 \geqq 0$, has as a consequence $R=Z$. Observe that the roles of the four points $\mathfrak{L}$, $\mathfrak{M}$, $\mathfrak{N}$, $\mathfrak{Q}_0$ being interchangeable, we may limit ourselves to the following discussion. We may further assume that L, M, N, $-Q$ are identical with $\pm\varphi$, $\pm\chi$, $\pm\psi$, $\pm\omega$. It remains to consider the following:

(1) $L=-R$, $M=-S$, $N=-T$. It is observed that for the point 1, 1, 1 we have $L=O=M=N$. This is impossible since for this point a relation (2), Art. 184 makes $Q(1, 1, 1)=0$, whereas in fact it is $=k_1+k_2+k_3=1$.

(2) $L=S$, $M=R$, $N=-T$. We have here

$$L=X-\lambda_2 Y, \quad M=-\mu_1 X+Y, \quad N=-\nu_1 X-(1-\nu_1)Y+Z;$$

and from $Q=\pm L\pm M\pm N$, it is seen that $k_3=1$, $k_1=0$, $k_2=0$ and $Q=Z$.

(3) $L=S$, $M=T$, $N=R$. We then have

$$L=X-\lambda_2 Y, \qquad M=Y-\mu_3 Z, \qquad N=-\nu_1 X+Z.$$

If the point 0, 1, -1 lies on F, we would have $M=Y$ so that the exceptional case treated at the end of Art. 183 does not come into question here. From $Q=\pm L\pm M\pm N$, and that is

$$\pm(X-\lambda_2 Y)\pm(Y-\mu_3 Z)\pm(-\nu_1 X+Z)=k_1 X+k_2 Y+k_3 Z,$$

it is seen that the positive signs must be used so that

$$1-\nu_1=k_1, \qquad 1-\lambda_2=k_2, \qquad 1-\mu_3=k_3$$

and therefore

$$(1-\nu_1)+(1-\lambda_2)+(1-\mu_3)=1.$$

Using the relation $X=lL+sS+tT+qQ$, and that is

$$X=(s+l)(X-\lambda_2 Y)+t(Y-\mu_3 Z)+qQ,$$

we have

$$1=(s+l)+k_1 q,$$
$$0=-(s+l)\lambda_2+t+k_2 q,$$
$$0=-\mu_3 t+k_3 q.$$

It follows that

$$\lambda_2(1-k_1 q)=t+k_2 q,$$

$$\lambda_2(1-k_1 q)=\frac{k_3 q}{\mu_3}+k_2 q.$$

Writing for k_1, k_2, k_3 their values from above, it is seen that

$$\lambda_2[1+(1-\nu_1)q]=\frac{1-\mu_3}{\mu_3}q+(1-\lambda_2)q$$

or

a) $$\lambda_2\mu_3+\nu_1\lambda_2\mu_3=q.$$

Using the further relations

$$Y=rR+mM+tT+qQ,$$
$$Z=rR+sS+nN+qQ$$

we may derive the similar relations

b) $$\nu_1\mu_3+\nu_1\lambda_2\mu_3=q,$$

c) $$\lambda_2\nu_1+\nu_1\lambda_2\mu_3=q.$$

It follows from *a*), *b*), *c*) that

$$\lambda_2=\mu_3=\nu_1.$$

We accordingly have here for the forms φ, χ, ψ, ω the following expressions:

$$\varphi=X-\tfrac{2}{3}Y, \quad \chi=Y-\tfrac{2}{3}Z, \quad \psi=Z-\tfrac{2}{3}X, \quad \omega=-\tfrac{1}{3}X-\tfrac{1}{3}Y-\tfrac{1}{3}Z.$$

Further since $\varphi=-\xi+\eta+\zeta$, $\chi=\xi-\eta+\zeta$, $\psi=\xi+\eta-\zeta$ and the determinant of these three forms being $=4$, it is seen that

$$\Delta=\frac{1}{4}\left(1-\frac{8}{27}\right)=\frac{19}{108}.$$

In this the only remaining case, Δ is in fact a minimum.

See also Minkowski, *Dioph. Approx.*, p. 105.

ART. **190.** Note that in the above expressions the forms φ, χ, ψ may be cyclically interchanged, while ω retains its form. We accordingly may summarize the result as follows: An infinite number of octahedra being given which are congruent and lie parallel to the octahedron

$$|\xi|+|\eta|+|\zeta|\leqq\tfrac{1}{2},$$

we may find eight kinds of densest lattice-formed placements. These placements are had if $\pm\xi$, $\pm\eta$, $\pm\zeta$ or $\pm\xi$, $\pm\zeta$, $\pm\eta$ are taken in any manner with such signs whose product $=+1$, where

$$\xi=\frac{\chi+\psi}{2}=-\frac{2}{6}X+\frac{3}{6}Y+\frac{1}{6}Z,$$

$$\eta=\frac{\varphi+\psi}{2}=\frac{1}{6}X-\frac{2}{6}Y+\frac{3}{6}Z,$$

$$\zeta=\frac{\varphi+\chi}{2}=\frac{3}{6}X+\frac{1}{6}Y-\frac{2}{6}Z,$$

$$\Delta\text{ being }=\frac{19}{108}.$$

ART. **191.** The formula for J, Art. 157, is here

$$J=\frac{1}{\Delta}\int\int\int d\xi\,d\eta\,d\zeta,$$

where the triple integral to be taken over the octahedron $=\frac{1}{6}$. Hence $J=\frac{108}{19}\cdot\frac{1}{6}=\frac{18}{19}$. From this it is seen that the ratio of space filled by the octahedra is to the space filled by the gaps (i.e. the unoccupied space) as 18 : 1 (See Minkowski, *Ges. Abh.*, Vol. I, p. 354) and instead of the inequality $M^3J \leqq 8$ of Art. 6 we may employ the formula

$$M^3J \leqq 8 \cdot \frac{18}{19}.$$

And we now have $M \leqq \sqrt[3]{6 \cdot \frac{18}{19}\Delta}$ instead of $\leqq \sqrt[3]{6 \cdot \Delta}$. (See *Dioph. App.*, p. 104.) And this means of course that $|\xi|+|\eta|+|\zeta|$ and therefore also the absolute value of each of the four expressions

$$-\xi+\eta+\zeta, \qquad \xi-\eta+\zeta, \qquad \xi+\eta-\zeta, \qquad -\xi-\eta-\zeta$$

is $\leqq \sqrt[3]{\frac{108}{19}\Delta}$. Instead of the ($\leqq$) sign that appears here, we may use the sign $<$, if ξ, η, ζ are not such that $\pm\xi$, $\pm\eta$, $\pm\zeta$ with any signs and taken in any sequence may be transformed through a linear integral substitution with determinant $=\pm 1$ into the expressions

$$-\frac{2}{6}X+\frac{3}{6}Y+\frac{1}{6}Z, \qquad \frac{1}{6}X-\frac{2}{6}Y+\frac{3}{6}Z, \qquad \frac{3}{6}X+\frac{1}{6}Y-\frac{2}{6}Z.$$

ART. **192.** Again let ξ, η, ζ be three linear forms in x, y, z with arbitrary real coefficients and a determinant whose absolute value Δ is $\neq 0$. (Cf. Art. 202.) Write

$$\varphi=\omega_1=\xi+\zeta, \qquad \chi=\omega_2=-\xi+\zeta,$$
$$\chi=\omega_3=\eta-\zeta, \qquad \omega=\omega_4=-\eta-\zeta,$$

so that

$$\omega_1+\omega_2+\omega_3+\omega_4=0$$

and the absolute value of the determinant of ω_1, ω_2, ω_3 $=|-2|=2$. Making application of the theorem of the preceding article it is seen that it is possible to find integral values of x, y, z, that are not all simultaneous zero, for which $|\xi|+|\zeta|$ and $|\eta|+|\zeta|$ are both $\leqq \sqrt[3]{\frac{54}{19}\Delta}$. Noting that the arithmetical mean of positive quantities is $\geqq$ their geometrical mean, it follows that

$$\frac{|\xi^2\zeta|}{4} \leqq \left(\frac{2|\xi/2|+|\zeta|}{3}\right)^3, \qquad \frac{|\eta^2\zeta|}{4} \leqq \left(\frac{2|\eta/2|+|\zeta|}{3}\right)^3;$$

and from this it follows further that

$$|\xi^2\zeta| \leqq \frac{8}{19}\Delta, \qquad |\eta^2\zeta| \leqq \frac{8}{19}\Delta.$$

(Minkowski, Vol. I, p. 355; Vol. II, p. 41).

It must be observed in the limiting case, for which alone in the last theorem the sign $=$ is necessary, that the system x, y, z in question may be found always such that for these values neither $\xi = \pm 2\zeta$ nor $\eta = \pm 2\zeta$ and accordingly in the further inequalities the sign $=$ may be done away with.

If we put

$$\xi = x - az, \qquad \eta = y - bz, \qquad \zeta = \frac{z}{t}$$

where a, b are any two real quantities and t is a positive parameter $> \frac{54}{19}$, we observe that $\Delta = \frac{1}{t}$. It follows that

$$|\xi^2\zeta| \leqq \frac{8}{19}\cdot\frac{1}{t} \text{ or } \xi^2 \leqq \frac{8}{19}\frac{1}{t\zeta} \text{ or } \xi \leqq \sqrt{\frac{8}{19}}\frac{1}{z^{1/2}} \text{ so that}$$

$$|x - az| \leqq \sqrt{\frac{8}{19}}\frac{1}{z^{1/2}} \qquad \text{or} \qquad \left|\frac{x}{z} - a\right| \leqq \sqrt{\frac{8}{19}}\cdot\frac{1}{z^{3/2}}$$

and also

$$\left|\frac{y}{z} - b\right| \leqq \sqrt{\frac{8}{19}}\cdot\frac{1}{z^{3/2}}.$$

If we choose $t > \frac{54}{19}$, the equality sign may be discarded. (Minkowski, Vol. II, p. 41.) If in the above we put $\zeta = z/t^3$ and observe that $\Delta = 1/t^3$, we come to the same results. (Minkowski, Vol. I, p. 355, note also Vol. I, p. 292.)

Observe that $\sqrt{\frac{8}{19}}$ is smaller than $\frac{2}{3}$. With this we see that if a and b are any real quantities, we may derive integral values for x, y, z such that simultaneously $z > 0$ while $|x - az|$, $|y - bz|$ are both arbitrarily small and

$$\left|\frac{x}{z} - a\right| < \frac{2}{3}\frac{1}{z^{3/2}}, \qquad \left|\frac{y}{z} - b\right| < \frac{2}{3}\frac{1}{z^{3/2}}.$$

With this it is seen that *two real quantities a and b may be made to approach as near as we wish in value to the two fractions $\frac{x}{z}$ and $\frac{y}{z}$ that have the same denominator.*

ART. **193. Inaccuracy in a Statement Made by Lord Kelvin.** In his *Baltimore Lectures*, Appendix H, p. 618 ff., Lord Kelvin treats the densest lattice formed placement of congruent and parallel situated convex bodies and makes the assumption that in such a densest placement *there appear four bodies mutually touching one another.* These conditions in fact are had in the case I (see Art. 178 in the case of spheres for example) for bodies which are situated about the four points 0, 0, 0; 1, 0, 0; 0, 1, 0; 0, 0, 1. This is true also in case III (for example with octahedra) with bodies about the four points 0, 0, 0; 1, 0, 0; 1, 1, 0; 1, 1, 1. Minkowski (*Ges. Abhandl.*, Vol. II, p. 41) finds that the assumption is not true in the case II.

The exceptional case II appears, for example, if the polyhedron is bounded by the twelve sides

$$\begin{aligned} X-\delta Y-\delta Z&=\pm\tfrac{1}{2},\\ -\delta X+Y-\delta Z&=\pm\tfrac{1}{2},\\ -\delta X-\delta Y+Z&=\pm\tfrac{1}{2},\\ \epsilon X+\tfrac{1}{2}Y+\tfrac{1}{2}Z&=\pm\tfrac{1}{2},\\ \tfrac{1}{2}X+\epsilon Y+\tfrac{1}{2}Z&=\pm\tfrac{1}{2},\\ \tfrac{1}{2}X+\tfrac{1}{2}Y+\epsilon Z&=\pm\tfrac{1}{2}, \end{aligned}$$

where $0<\delta<\frac{1}{2}$, $0<\epsilon<\frac{1}{2}$ furnishes the basal body. It is seen that this polyhedron through a parallel sliding from the origin to all the lattice points X, Y, Z forms a system of bodies in densest lattice formed placement.

An article by Prof. Frederick T. Lewis of the Harvard Medical School (*Science*, Vol. 86, pp. 609 ff.) on "The Shapes of Compressed Spheres" is of particular interest. See also Sir D'Arcy Thompson, *Growth and Form*, p. 339; and remarks by the author on "Densest Placement of Homologous Bodies," *Science*, Vol. 87, pp. 320 ff.

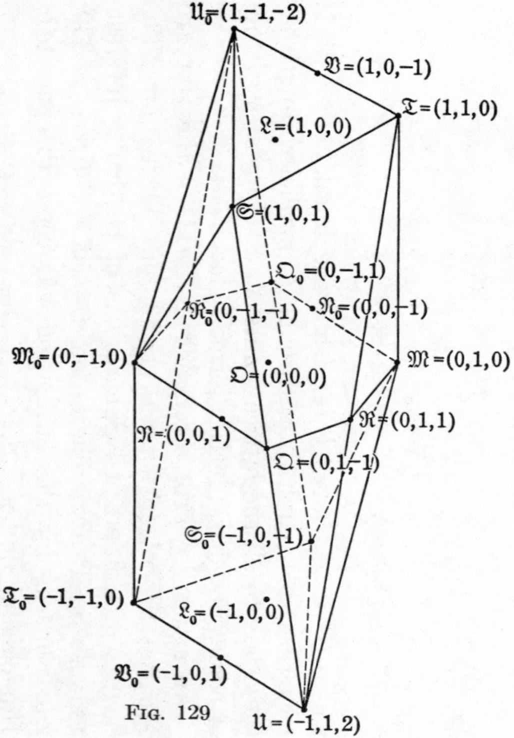

FIG. 129

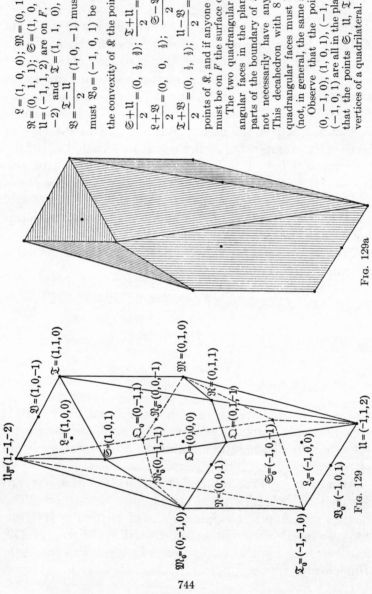

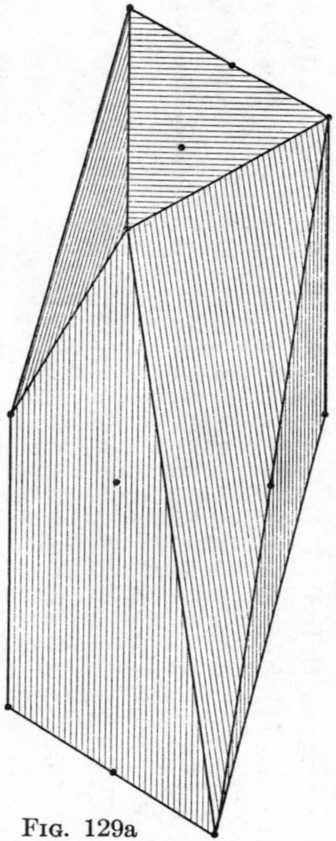

FIG. 129a

$\mathfrak{L}=(1, 0, 0)$; $\mathfrak{M}=(0, 1, 0)$; $\mathfrak{N}=(0, 0, 1)$; $\mathfrak{R}=(0, 1, 1)$; $\mathfrak{S}=(1, 0, 1)$; $\mathfrak{T}=(1, 1, 0)$; $\mathfrak{U}=(-1, 1, 2)$ are on F. With $\mathfrak{U}_0=(1, -1, -2)$ and $\mathfrak{T}=(1, 1, 0)$, the lattice point $\mathfrak{V}=\dfrac{\mathfrak{T}-\mathfrak{U}}{2}=(1, 0, -1)$ must be on F. So also must $\mathfrak{V}_0=(-1, 0, 1)$ be on F. Then from the convexity of $\mathfrak{K}$ the points $\dfrac{\mathfrak{L}+\mathfrak{U}}{2}=(0, \tfrac{1}{2}, 1)$; $\dfrac{\mathfrak{S}+\mathfrak{U}}{2}=(0, \tfrac{1}{2}, \tfrac{3}{2})$; $\dfrac{\mathfrak{T}+\mathfrak{U}}{2}=(0, 1, 1)=\mathfrak{R}$; and $\dfrac{\mathfrak{L}+\mathfrak{V}}{2}=(0, 0, \tfrac{1}{2})$; $\dfrac{\mathfrak{S}-\mathfrak{V}}{2}=(0, 0, 1)=\mathfrak{N}$; $\dfrac{\mathfrak{T}+\mathfrak{V}}{2}=(0, \tfrac{1}{2}, \tfrac{1}{2})$; $\dfrac{\mathfrak{U}-\mathfrak{V}}{2}=(0, \tfrac{1}{2}, \tfrac{1}{2})$ must be points of $\mathfrak{K}$, and if anyone is a lattice point, it must be on F the surface of $\mathfrak{K}$.

The two quadrangular faces and the triangular faces in the planes $X=x$ must be parts of the boundary of $\mathfrak{K}$ although $\mathfrak{K}$ does not necessarily have any polygonal faces. This decahedron with 8 triangular and 2 quadrangular faces must be contained in $\mathfrak{K}$ (not, in general, the same as $\mathfrak{K}$).

Observe that the points $(-1, -1, 0)$, $(0, -1, 0)$, $(1, 0, 1)$, $(-1, 1, 2)$, $(0, 0, 1)$ and $(-1, 0, 1)$ are all in the plane $Y-Z=-1$ and that the points $\mathfrak{S}$, $\mathfrak{U}$, $\mathfrak{T}_0$ and $\mathfrak{M}_0$ are the vertices of a quadrilateral.

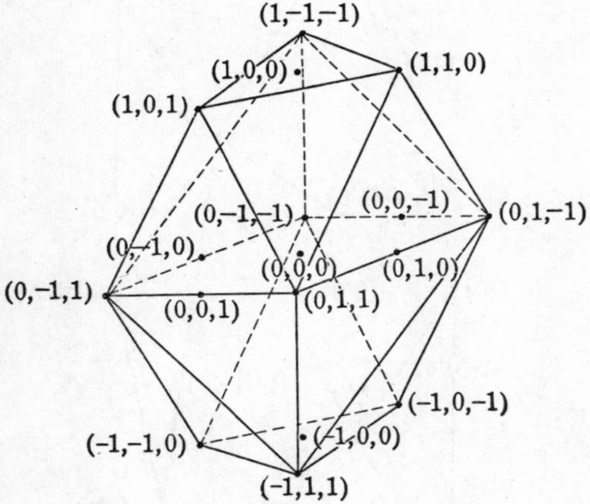

FIG. 130

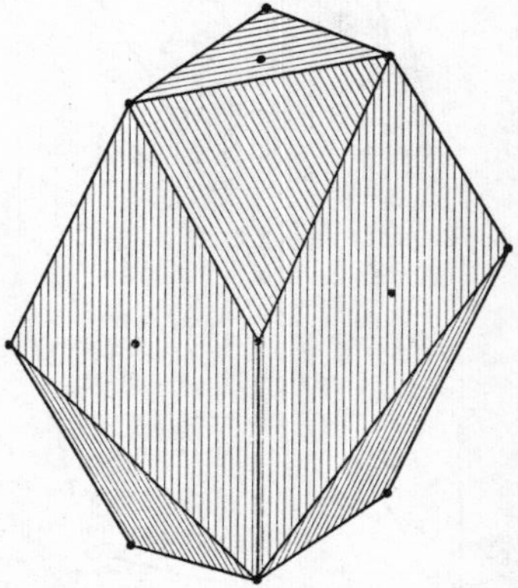
FIG. 130a

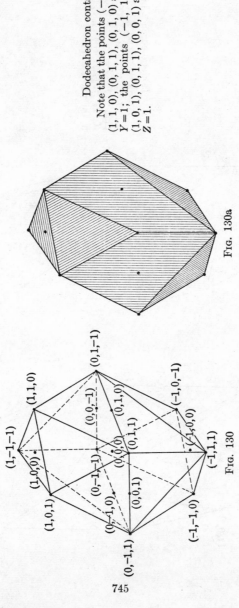

Dodecahedron contained in $\mathfrak{R}$.

Note that the points $(-1, 1, 1)$, $(0, 1, -1)$, $(1, 1, 0)$, $(0, 1, 1)$, $(0, 1, 0)$ are all in the plane $Y=1$; the points $(-1, 1, 1)$, $(0, -1, 1)$, $(1, 0, 1)$, $(0, 1, 1)$, $(0, 0, 1)$ are all in the plane $Z=1$.

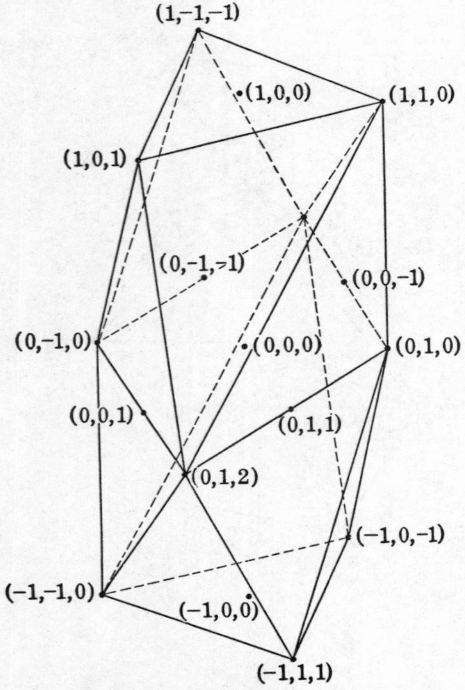

FIG. 131

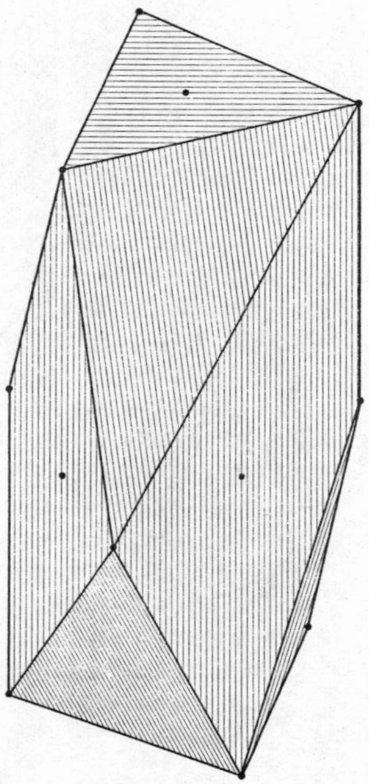

FIG. 131a

Dodecahedron contained in $\mathfrak{K}$.

Note that the points (0, −1, 0), (−1, −1, 0), (0, 1, 2), (0, 0, 1), (1, 0, 1) are all in the plane $Y-Z=1$; the points (−1, 1, 1), (0, 1, 2), (1, 1, 0), (0, 1, 0), (0, 1, 1) are all in the plane $Y=1$.

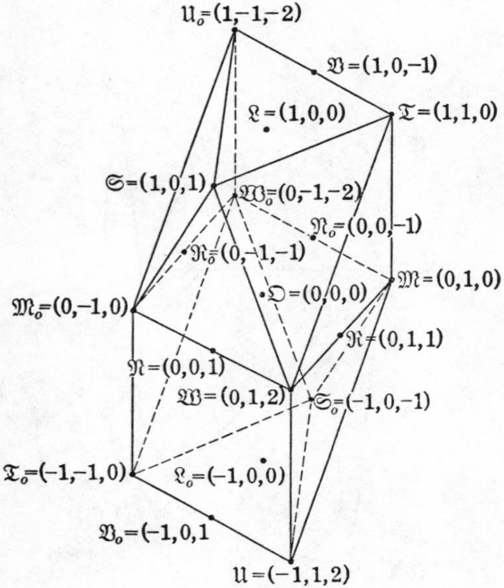

FIG. 132

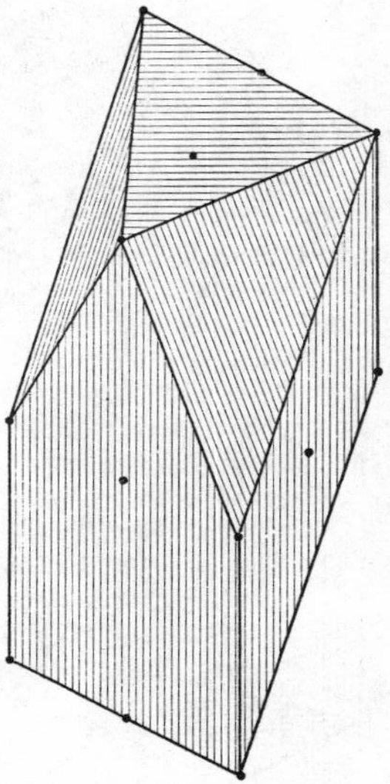

FIG. 132a

This decahedron with 2 pentagonal, 2 parallelogrammatic and 6 triangular faces is contained in $\mathfrak{K}$. The pentagons are in the planes $-Y+Z=\pm 1$, the parallelograms in $Y=\pm 1$, and two of the triangles in $X=\pm 1$. These 6 faces are all parts of $\mathfrak{F}$. $\mathfrak{K}$ is in turn contained in the parallelepiped defined by these 6 planes. The points $\mathfrak{L}$, $\mathfrak{M}$, $\mathfrak{N}$, $\mathfrak{R}$, $\mathfrak{S}$, $\mathfrak{T}$, $\mathfrak{U}=(-1, 1, 2)$, $\mathfrak{V}=(1, 0, -1)$, $\mathfrak{W}=(0, 1, 2)$ lie as indicated in the figure above.

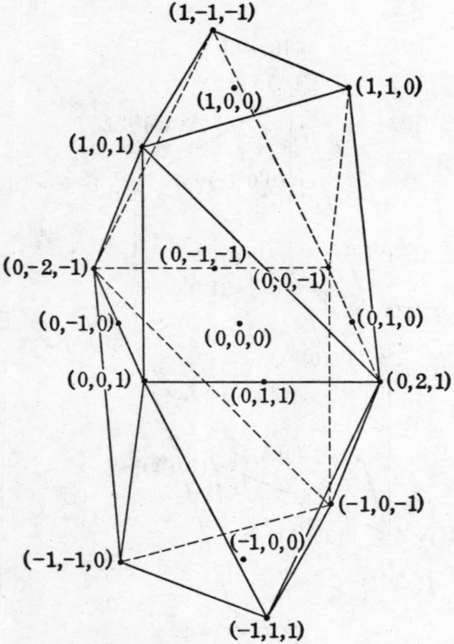

FIG. 133

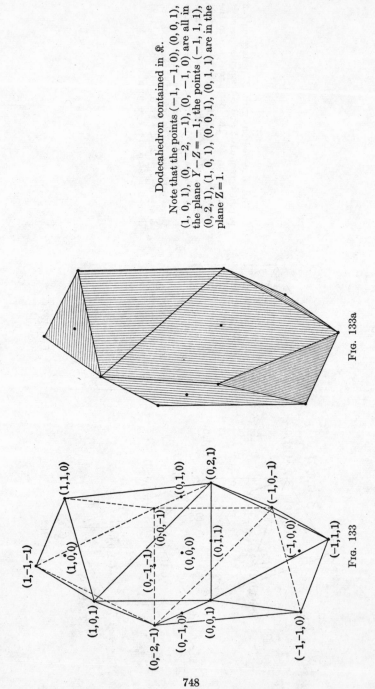

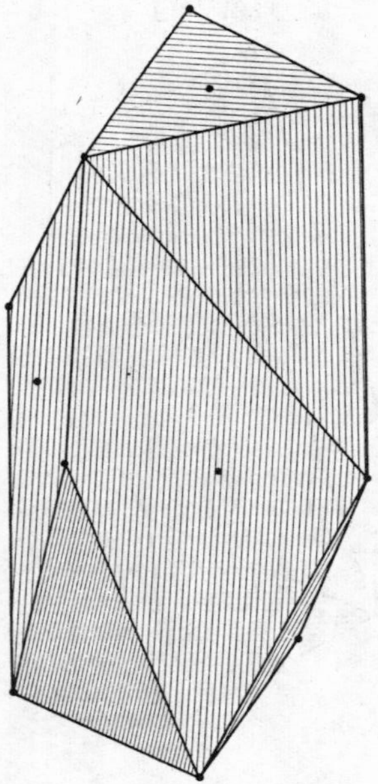

FIG. 133a

Dodecahedron contained in $\mathfrak{K}$.

Note that the points $(-1, -1, 0)$, $(0, 0, 1)$, $(1, 0, 1)$, $(0, -2, -1)$, $(0, -1, 0)$ are all in the plane $Y-Z=-1$; the points $(-1, 1, 1)$, $(0, 2, 1)$, $(1, 0, 1)$, $(0, 0, 1)$, $(0, 1, 1)$ are in the plane $Z=1$.

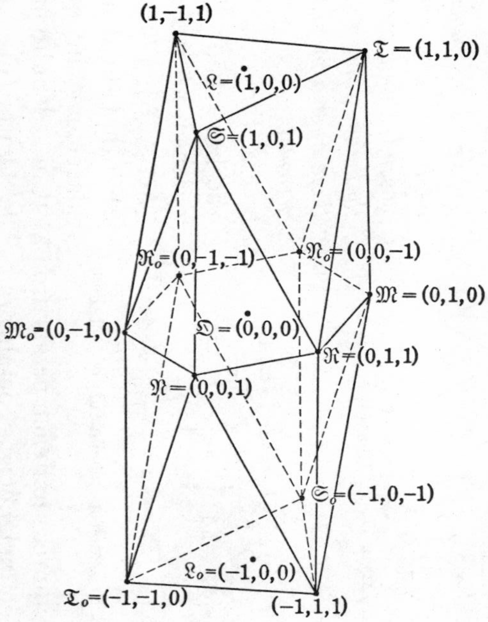

FIG. 134

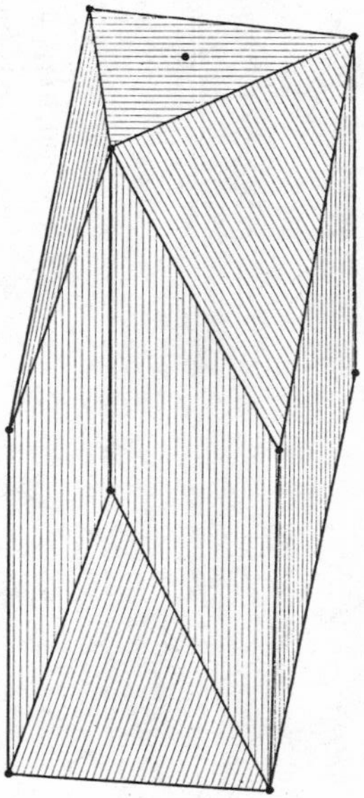

FIG. 134a

14-faced figure contained in 𝔎.

CHAPTER XIX

MISCELLANY

In this chapter are found notes, theorems, etc. enunciated, though not proved, by Minkowski. This with the other chapters of the present work, we believe, completes all that was published by Minkowski on the Geometry of Numbers.

ART. **194.** We consider an arbitrary convex body given in a three dimensional space. *Let there be an infinite number of congruent and parallel placed bodies so situated that their centers of gravity form a system of points arranged in order of parallelopipeds, i.e., lattice points, where no two of the bodies intersect. Under what conditions may these bodies be arranged so as to be as dense as possible, and that is, that the gaps among them offer a minimum volume?*

For the case that the basal body is an octahedron we saw (Arts. 163, 189, 190, 191) that the densest placement in question requires that each octahedron abut in a definite order fourteen neighboring octahedra. The figure (Fig. 135)

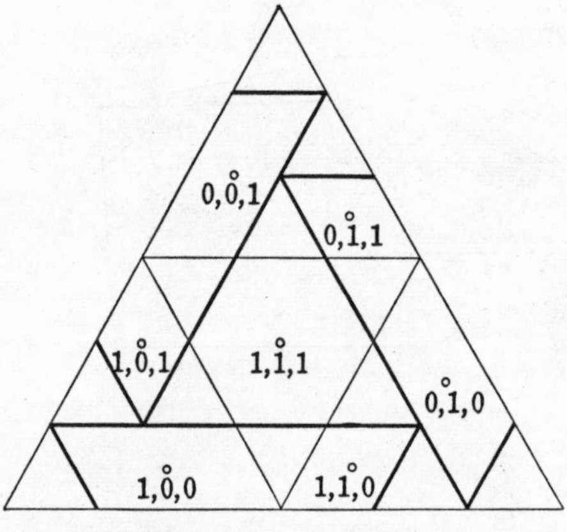

$$\varphi=-\xi+\eta+\zeta,\quad \chi=\xi-\eta+\zeta,\quad \psi=\xi+\eta-\zeta,$$
$$\omega=\xi+\eta+\zeta,$$

(1) $\varphi+\chi+\psi+\omega=0$, Det. $(\xi,\eta,\zeta)=\Delta\neq 0$;

(2) $|\varphi|,\ |\chi|,\ |\psi|,\ |\omega|\leqq\sqrt[3]{\frac{108}{19}}\Delta.$ (Art. 191.)

(3) $\pm(x-az)\pm\frac{z}{t}=1,\qquad \pm(y-bz)\pm\frac{z}{t}=1;$

(4) $\left|\frac{x}{z}-a\right|$ and $\left|\frac{y}{z}-b\right|<\sqrt{\frac{8}{19}}\frac{1}{z^{3/2}},$

$$\left(\sqrt{\frac{8}{19}}=0.648\cdots\right).$$

FIG. 135. Densest placement of octahedra.

laid out on a plane presents the half net of one of the octahedra and presents the seven parts with center in which the octahedron abuts on the neighboring octahedra. The minimum of space occupied by the gaps between the octahedra stands to that occupied by the octahedra in the ratio as 1 : 18 (Art. 191) when the placement is densest.

This result admits the following purely arithmetical statement: *If φ, χ, ψ, ω are any four linear forms with arbitrary real coefficients whose sum is identically zero and where any three have a determinant $=\pm 4\Delta$ (where $\Delta>0$), we may always find such integers x, y, z which are not all simultaneously zero which make $|\varphi|$, $|\chi|$, $|\psi|$, $|\omega|$ each* $\leqq\sqrt[3]{\frac{108}{19}}\Delta$. (See Art. 198.) A noteworthy application of this result is the following:

Let a, b be two arbitrary real quantities and t a positive parameter, then the eight planes

$$\pm(x-az)\pm\frac{z}{t}=1, \qquad \pm(y-bz)\pm\frac{z}{t}=1$$

determine an octahedron. And when t is taken arbitrarily large, we have the following:

Two arbitrary real quantities a and b may be made to approach as near as we wish in value the two fractions x/z and y/z, that have the same denominator and at the same time in such a way that

$$\left|\frac{x}{z}-a\right|<\sqrt{\frac{8}{19}}\frac{1}{z^{3/2}}, \qquad \left|\frac{y}{z}-b\right|<\sqrt{\frac{8}{19}}\frac{1}{z^{3/2}}.$$

Observe that

$$\sqrt{\frac{8}{19}}=.648<\frac{2}{3}.$$

ART. 195. **Approximation of Numbers in Complex Realms.** Let ξ, η be two linear forms with complex variables and complex coefficients, namely

$$(1)\qquad \begin{cases} \xi=(\alpha+i\alpha')(x+ix')+(\beta+i\beta')(y+iy'), \\ \eta=(\gamma+i\gamma')(x+ix')+(\delta+i\delta')(y+iy'), \end{cases}$$

with determinant

$$(2) \qquad \begin{vmatrix} x_1+ix_1', & x_2+ix_2' \\ y_1+iy_1', & y_2+iy_2' \end{vmatrix} = \text{Det. } (\xi, \eta) = \Delta \neq 0,$$

or

$$(3) \qquad \begin{aligned} \xi &= \lambda e^{i\varphi}[X+iX'+\rho(Y+iY')], \\ \eta &= \mu e^{i\psi}[\sigma[X+iX']+Y+iY']. \end{aligned}$$

It may be proved that (*Dioph. Approx.*, p. 218)

$$(4) \qquad |\xi|, \ |\eta| < \sqrt{\frac{\sqrt{3}+1}{\sqrt{6}}\,|\Delta|}$$

for integral values of the variables that are not simultaneously $=0, 0$. We may next ask: How may we transfer the theorems regarding the approximation of a real quantity through numbers of a natural realm of rationality to the realms of the complex quantities? We shall consider here the approximations in the realm of the third root of unity or the fourth root of unity. The conditions are essentially simpler in the realm of the third root of unity where the theorems are very similar to those for real quantities. We shall here merely touch upon the more complicated relations in the realm of the fourth root of unity.

Let ξ, η be two linear forms with arbitrary complex coefficients and two complex variables $x+ix'$, $y+iy'$ and a determinant $\Delta \neq 0$. We shall direct our attention to those "extreme" pairs of numbers $x+ix'$, $y+iy' \neq 0, 0$ in the real $\mathfrak{R}(i)$ in which there does not exist a pair of numbers of the same kind for which both $|\xi|$ and $|\eta|$ have smaller values. We may multiply the two numbers of a pair with one and the same unit $-1, \pm i$ and have an *associated* pair of numbers (see *Alg. Nos.*, Vol. I, Art. 91), which we do not regard as different from the original pair. All existing extreme pairs may now be arranged in a chain with respect to the magnitude of $|\xi|$ (and at the same time of $|\eta|$). Two neighboring pairs of the chain together are easy a priori to characterize. For the associated determinant (2) is either

(*A*) a unit ± 1, $\pm i$, or (B) equal to $(1+i)$ multiplied into a unit (Fig. 136). (*Dioph. Approx.*, p. 208.)

We use these two pairs as the vertical rows of the matrix of a substitution to be applied to ξ, η and thereby we have for ξ, η the expressions where $|\rho|$ and $|\sigma|$ in formula (3) are both $\leqq 1$. If the second pair is replaced by an associate pair and then i by $-i$, we may cause ρ to fall in the octant (marked in heavy lines) of the unit circle, while $\dfrac{1}{\rho}$ falls in the conjugate octant without this circle. The two cases

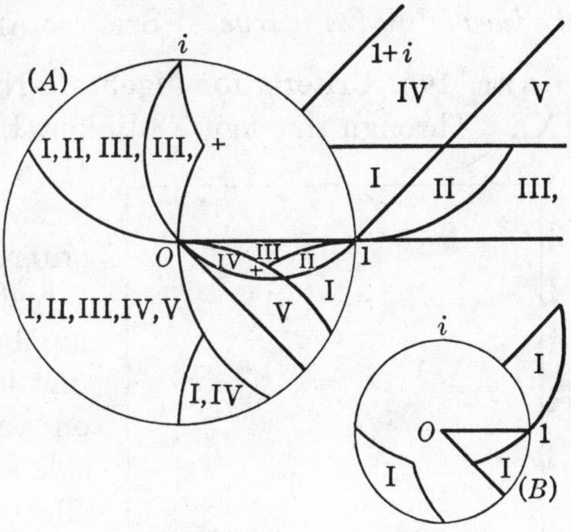

(1) $$\xi=(\alpha+i\alpha')(x+ix')+(\beta+i\beta')(y+iy'),$$
$$\eta=(\gamma+i\gamma')(x+ix')+(\delta+i\delta')(y+iy'),$$
$$\text{Det. }(\xi,\eta)=\Delta,$$

(2) $$\begin{vmatrix} x_1+ix_1', & x_2+ix_2' \\ y_1+iy_1', & y_2+iy_2' \end{vmatrix},$$

(3) $$\xi=\lambda e^{i}\varphi(X+iX'+\rho(Y+iY')),$$
$$\eta=\mu e^{i}\psi(\sigma(X+iX')+Y+iY'),$$

(4) $$|\xi|,\quad |\eta| \leqq \sqrt{\frac{\sqrt{3}+1}{\sqrt{6}}|\Delta|}=\sqrt{\frac{\sqrt{2}\Delta}{3-\sqrt{3}}}.$$

(See Minkowski, *Dioph. Approx.*, p. 216.)

FIG. 136

(A) and (B) are to be distinguished: In (A) each octant is divided through certain circles of radius 1 or $\dfrac{1}{\sqrt{2}}$ into five parts which are indicated in the figure, numbered I, $\cdots$, V. If ρ falls in a definite one of these parts then σ falls only into those portions of the unit circle that are marked in lighter lines in which the same number is entered. The smallest value of the absolute value of the determinant $|1-\rho\sigma|$ is had when ρ, σ correspond to the sharp vertices of the figure that are indicated by small crosses. In the case (B) we find that ρ can fall only in the heavy lined region (I) and σ then only in the light region (I). From this we have the very important result:

We may always write in the forms, ξ, η *for* $x+ix'$, $y+iy'$ *such integers of the realm* $\Re(i)$ *which are not both zero, that the inequality* (*4*) *is true.* (See also Art. 204.)

ART. **196. Criteria for Algebraic Numbers** (See Chapter IX). Through this figure Minkowski (*Ges. Abhandl.*, Vol. II, p. 51) wished to derive a new method for the known criterion of Lagrange for a real quadratic irrational number. In a square of unit length with the y-axis on the left-hand vertical side a continuous *halving* is effected on this side so that successively all points are had whose ordinate is a dyadic number, i.e., a rational number which has a power of 2 as a denominator. The associated intervals may be called the partial *points* on the y-axis. To every interval or partial point that appears on the y-axis there exists an interval or rational partial point on the x-axis, which axis is the lower line in the square. To the end-values $y=0$, $y=1$ on the y-axis, there correspond end-values $x=0$, $x=1$ on the x-axis. And further as often as an interval $a\cdots b$ is *halved* on the y-axis there exist between the end points $x=a/b$, $x=a'/b'$, on the x-axis a new partial point $x=\dfrac{a+a'}{b+b'}$, where a, b are relatively prime as are also b, b'. Thus on the horizontal side of the square there enter as partial points successively all points with rational abscissae and the arrangement of simultaneously constructed abscissae and ordinates offers the picture of a continuous increasing func-

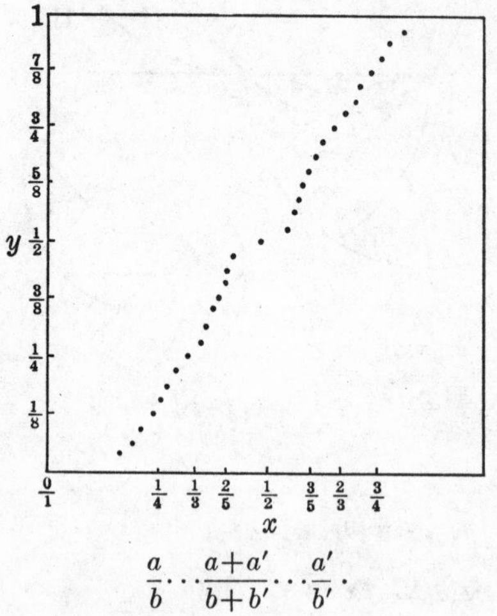

x quadratic irrational number, y rational and not dyadic.
$y=?(x)$:
x rational, y dyadic.

FIG. 137

tion[1] $y = ?(x)$ *first* for all rational values of x and *then* extended through the requirement of continuity to arbitrary real arguments in the interval $0 \leqq x \leqq 1$, while at the same time y traverses this interval at pleasure.

If then x is a quadratic irrational number and consequently leads to a periodic development of a continued fraction, there corresponds from it for the value $y = ?(x)$ a periodic dualistic development through which y is seen to be rational. From this we have the theorems:

If x is a quadratic irrational *number, then y is rational but not purely dyadic. If x is* rational, *then y is purely dyadic. And these theories are completely reversible.*

ART. **197. Criterion for the Real Cubic Irrational Numbers.** The figure shows a generalization of the above

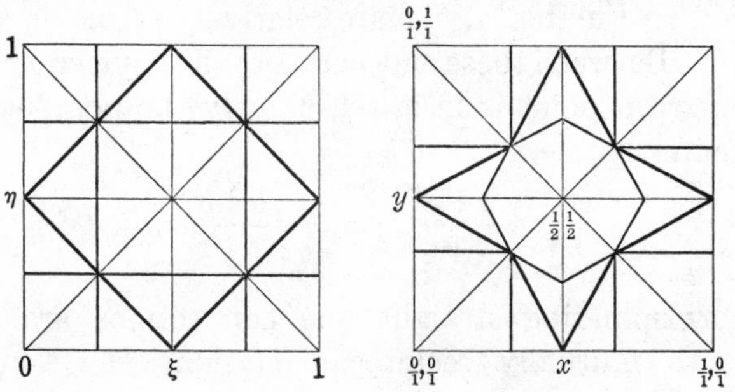

$$\frac{a}{c}, \quad \frac{b}{c} \cdots \frac{a+a'}{c+c'}, \quad \frac{b+b'}{c+c'} \cdots \frac{a'}{c'}, \quad \frac{b'}{c'},$$

(1) $$\xi = \varphi(x, y), \quad \eta = \psi(x, y).$$

x, y are independent numbers in a cubic realm ξ, η rational; none of the numbers ξ, η, $\xi - \eta$, $\xi + \eta$ is dyadic.

FIG. 138

theorems to cubic irrationalities, which Louis Kollros developed in a thesis (Zurich, 1904). On the one hand we have a square in which ξ, η have values situated between the limits 0 and 1. The square is divided first by the diagonal $\xi = \eta$ into two rectangular isosceles triangles and

[1] The question mark is employed as an interrogation of the function that connects x and y.

then each of these is divided into two rectangular isosceles triangles by drawing a perpendicular from the vertex to the mid-point of the hypotenuse. On the other hand and simultaneously a second square in which x, y likewise are situated within the limits 0 and 1 undergoes a certain associated step by step division into triangles as follows:

We first place the two squares so that the coordinates of the four vertices of the first square in ξ, η will correspond to the four vertices of the second square in x, y, the diagonal $x=y$ in the second square corresponding to $\xi=\eta$ in the first. We then proceed as follows: Where in the first square a hypotenuse was halved and a straight line connection introduced, in the second square we denote the end-points of the associated stretch by the coordinates x, $y=a/c$, b/c; a'/c', b'/c', where a/c, b/c are relatively prime as are also a'/c', b'/c'. Further a, b, c are relatively prime as are also a', b', c'. Between these end-points of the associated stretch a new partial point is inserted, namely the point with the coordinates

$$x=\frac{a+a'}{c+c'}, \qquad y=\frac{b+b'}{c+c'}.$$

The corresponding straight line connections are drawn. Thus two mutually reciprocal relations (1) $\xi=\varphi(x, y)$, $\eta=\psi(x, y)$ are uniquely determined, first for all rational x, y and dyadic ξ, η, and then through the requirement of continuity for arbitrary arguments and values of the function within the limits 0 to 1. From the above considerations Kollros found the following theorems whose correctness, proved by numerous examples, seems plausible. They are, however, questioned in an essential point by Minkowski. The two theorems are:

If 1, x, y are three independent numbers in a real cubic realm, then ξ, η are rational and none of the quantities ξ, η, $\xi+\eta$, $\xi-\eta$ is purely dyadic.

If x, y belong to a quadratic realm without both being rational, then ξ, η are rational and one of the quantities ξ, η,

$\xi+\eta$, $\xi-\eta$ is purely dyadic. If x, y are both rational, then ξ, η are purely dyadic. These theorems are completely reciprocal.

If we take $y=x^2$, we may derive from the above a complete criterion that x is a real cubic irrational number. It is to be emphasized in particular that these theorems seem to be applicable for all cubic realms and not only for those with a negative discriminant in which only *one* fundamental unit is present. (See Minkowski, *Ges. Abhandl.*, Bd. II, pp. 51, 52.)

ART. 198. **New Theorems on the Approximation of Quantities by Means of Rational Numbers.**[1] In many of his classic memoirs on the theory of numbers Hermite has investigated the minima of algebraic forms for integral values of the variables. Such investigations have led to certain approximations, the *algebraic character* of which has been put into evidence. But for the most part from the inequalities that have been obtained there still remains a great difficulty in determining the *most narrow* limits for the inequalities and the *extreme* forms to which in each case these limits are connected. The *precise* limits are given below for certain particularly simple cases.

THEOREM. *Let φ, χ, ψ, ω be four linear forms in three variables x, y, z with any real coefficients such that we have*

$$\varphi+\chi+\psi+\omega=0.$$

Suppose that the determinant of three of the forms is always different from zero and denote the absolute value by $4D$. There always exist three integers x, y, z which are not simultaneously zero such that each of the four forms φ, χ, ψ, ω is in absolute value less than

$$\sqrt{\frac{4D}{1-\left(\frac{2}{3}\right)^3}}=d=\sqrt[3]{\frac{108D}{19}}. \qquad \text{(See Art. 195.)}$$

[1] Minkowski, *Ges. Abhandl.*, Vol. I, pp. 353 ff. This paper was first printed in the *Bulletin des Sciences Mathématiques*, 2 Série, t. XXV, pp. 72–76.

The limit d is here precise. In general, we may always find integers x, y, z such that the absolute values of φ, χ, ψ, ω are all $<d$, but there is an exception where it is impossible to satisfy this condition, namely, when there exists a linear substitution with integral coefficients and a determinant $=\pm 1$, which neglecting the order transforms the forms φ, χ, ψ, ω, into

$$d(X-\tfrac{2}{3}Y),\quad d(Y-\tfrac{2}{3}Z),\quad d(-\tfrac{2}{3}X+Z),\quad -\tfrac{1}{3}d(X+Y+Z).$$

See Minkowski, *Diophantische Approximationene*, p. 105; *Ges. Abhandl.*, Vol. II, pp. 39 ff. See also Art. 189.

ART. **199.** The above theorem is susceptible of an interesting geometric application which may possibly find application in crystallography: Consider a system of octahedra parallel placed among one another and in a manner such that no two have a part in common and such that their centers of gravity form a parallelopiped net of points such as is considered in the structure of crystals. All the octahedra may then be derived from any one of them by the same system of translations. There is then a situation where the gaps created between the octahedra will occupy the smallest possible space or, what is the same thing, that the space occupied by the octahedra will be as great as possible. It is the situation where each of the octahedra has at least points in common with fourteen other octahedra (see Fig. 135). The space then occupied by the octahedra is in the ratio to the space left free by these bodies as 18 : 1. (Art. 191.) I have shown in *Science*, Vol. 87, pp. 320 ff., how this may be possible in cytology (theory of cells, in biology, botany, etc.).

ART. **200.** Let ξ, η, ζ be three forms in x, y, z with real coefficients and a determinant $=\pm D$, where $D\neq 0$. We may then take the theorem of Art. 191

$$\varphi=-\xi+\eta+\zeta,\quad \chi=\xi-\eta+\zeta,\quad \psi=\xi+\eta-\zeta,\quad \omega=-\xi-\eta-\zeta.$$

There then exist integers x, y, z that are not all simultaneously *zero and are such that*

$$|\xi|+|\eta|+|\zeta|\leqq\sqrt[3]{\frac{108D}{19}}.$$

In the restricted case where the sign = enters we may always bring it about that we do not have $|\xi|=|\eta|=|\zeta|$. We may then conclude also that

$$|\xi\eta\zeta|<\frac{4}{19}D.$$

It may also be observed that in this last inequality the factor 4/19 may be replaced by a smaller number.

ART. **201.** Observe also that we may take in Art. 192

$$\frac{\varphi}{\sqrt[3]{2}},\ \frac{\chi}{\sqrt[3]{2}},\ \frac{\psi}{\sqrt[3]{2}},\ \frac{\omega}{\sqrt[3]{2}}=\xi+\zeta,\quad -\xi+\zeta,\quad \eta-\zeta,\quad -\eta-\zeta,$$

and that there exist integers x, y, z that are not simultaneously zero and are such that we have

$$|\xi|+|\zeta|\leqq\sqrt[3]{\frac{54}{19}},\qquad |\eta|+|\zeta|\leqq\sqrt[3]{\frac{54}{19}}.$$

In the limiting case where one of the equality signs is taken, it may always be done in such a way that we never have $\pm\xi=\zeta$ nor $\pm\eta=\zeta$. Making use of the inequalities (see Art. 192)

$$\left|\left(\frac{\xi}{2}\right)^2\zeta\right|\leqq\left(\frac{2\left|\frac{\xi}{2}\right|+\zeta}{3}\right)^3,\qquad \left|\left(\frac{\eta}{2}\right)^2\zeta\right|\leqq\left(\frac{2\left|\frac{\eta}{2}\right|+\zeta}{3}\right)^3$$

we find

$$|\xi^2\zeta|<\frac{8}{19}D,\qquad |\eta^2\zeta|<\frac{8}{19}D.$$

In these last inequalities the limit is no longer precise.

ART. **202.** Let a, b, be any two real quantities. In the inequalities of the preceding article take (see Art. 192)

$$\xi=x-az,\qquad \eta=y-bz,\qquad \zeta=\frac{z}{t^3},$$

where t is a positive parameter. It is seen that we may find integers x, y, z (where z is positive) such that $x-az$, $y-bz$ are in absolute value less than any given quantity and that *in this approximation we have simultaneously*

$$\left|\frac{x}{z}-a\right|<\sqrt{\frac{8}{19}}\frac{1}{z^{3/2}}\,; \qquad \left|\frac{y}{z}-b\right|<\sqrt{\frac{8}{19}}\frac{1}{z^{3/2}}\,.$$

The constant $\sqrt{\frac{8}{19}}=.648\cdots$ which appears here is less than $\frac{2}{3}$.

ART. **203.** THEOREM. *Let* $\xi=\alpha x+\beta y$, $\eta=\gamma x+\delta y$ *be two linear forms with complex coefficients and let* $D=|\alpha\delta-\beta\gamma|>0$. *We may always find in the realm* $\Re(i)$, *where* $i=\sqrt{-1}$, *complex integers* x, y *different from 0, 0 such that*

$$|\xi|\leqq\sqrt{\frac{\sqrt{3}+1}{\sqrt{6}}D}, \qquad |\eta|\leqq\sqrt{\frac{\sqrt{3}+1}{\sqrt{6}}D}. \qquad \text{(See Art. 195.)}$$

The limit $d=\sqrt{\frac{\sqrt{3}+1}{\sqrt{6}}D}$ given here is *precise.*

In general, we will also have complex integers x, $y\neq 0$, 0 such that $|\xi|<d$, $|\eta|<d$. But there is a single case where it is impossible to satisfy these inequalities: it is when there exists a substitution

$$x=pX+rY, \qquad y=qX+sY,$$

where p, q, r, s are integers in the realm $\Re(i)$ (the determinant $ps-qr$ being $=\pm 1$ or $\pm i$) and are such that by this substitution the forms ξ, η are transformed into [1]

$$\lambda d\left\{X+\left[\frac{1}{2}-i\left(1-\frac{\sqrt{3}}{2}\right)\right]Y\right\}, \qquad \mu d\left\{\left[\frac{i}{2}+\left(1-\frac{\sqrt{3}}{2}\right)\right]X+Y\right\}$$

where the absolute values of the quantities λ and μ are $=1$.

ART. **204.** THEOREM. *Let* $\xi=\alpha x+\beta y$, $\eta=\gamma x+\delta y$ *be two linear forms with any complex coefficients and let*

$$D=|\alpha\delta-\beta\gamma|>0.$$

[1] See Minkowski, *Dioph. Approx.*, pp. 217 ff.

It is always possible to find in the realm $\Re(\omega)$, where

$$\omega=\frac{-1+\sqrt{-3}}{2},$$

complex integers x, y different from 0, 0 such that $|\xi|\leqq\sqrt{D}$, $|\eta|\leqq\sqrt{D}$.

The limit $d=\sqrt{D}$ is here *precise.* In general, there will also be integers x, $y\neq 0$, 0 such that $|\xi|$ and $|\eta|$ are $<d$, except in the case where in the realm $\Re(\omega)$ there exists a linear substitution with integral coefficients and a determinant equal to a unit of the realm through which ξ, η, neglecting the order, are changed into λdX, $\mu d(\tau X+Y)$ where λ, μ are quantities whose absolute value is equal to 1 and where τ is any complex quantity.

It is of interest to note that of those corresponding theorems the one $\Re(\omega)$ is much more simple than $\Re(i)$.

ART. **205.** Let a be any complex quantity. If we put

$$\xi=x-ay, \qquad \eta=y/t^2,$$

t being any real parameter >1, we see that in the realm $\Re(\omega)$ [but *not* in the realm $\Re(i)$] *there are always complex integers x, y such that*

$$0<|y|\leqq t, \qquad |x-ay|<\frac{1}{t}.$$

from which we further conclude that

$$|(x-ay)y|<1.$$

CHAPTER XX

NEW THEORY OF QUADRATIC FORMS. REGION OF DISCONTINUITY FOR ARITHMETICAL EQUIVALENCE

ART. **206. Introduction.** The following problem is proposed: A system of n linear forms $\xi_1, \xi_2, \cdots, \xi_n$ in n variables $x_1, x_2, \cdots, x_n$ with arbitrary real coefficients

$$\frac{\partial \xi_h}{\partial x_k} = \alpha_{hk} \qquad (h, k = 1, 2, \cdots, n),$$

with a determinant different from zero, is said to be *arithmetical equivalent* to a second such system $\eta_1, \eta_2, \cdots, \eta_n$, if each of the two systems may be transformed into the other through linear homogeneous substitutions with integral coefficients.

In somewhat different form this is the notion of modular systems as given in Chapter VIII of the first volume of my *Foundations of the Theory of Algebraic Numbers* where due credit is given to Kronecker with references to his work. This theory contains the underlying principles of much of his work on *Allgemeine Arithmetik*.

Two linear forms $\sum_{h=1}^{h=\mu} m_h x_h$, $\sum_{k=1}^{k=\nu} m'_k x'_k$ are defined as being equivalent when the one can be transformed into the other by the integral substitutions

$$x_h = \sum_k c_{hk} x'_k,$$

$$x'_k = \sum_h c'_{kh} x_h \quad (h = 1, 2, \cdots, \mu;\ k = 1, 2, \cdots, \nu),$$

in which the c's and c''s are rational integers. Hence the necessary and sufficient conditions for the equivalence of the two given forms are expressed through the equations

$$m_h = \sum_k c'_{kh} m'_k,$$

$$m'_k = \sum_h c_{hk} m_h \quad (h=1, 2, \cdots, \mu; k=1, 2, \cdots, \nu).$$

And this implies the equivalence of the two modular systems

$$(m_1, m_2, \cdots, m_\mu) \sim (m'_1, m'_2, \cdots, m'_\nu).$$

ART. **207.** Minkowski sets up a manifold A of the n^2 real parameters α_{hk} of the preceding article. In this realm he constructs a second realm B in which each complete union (class) of systems equivalent among one another is represented *by a point*, and if the point comes to lie in the interior of the realm, this union is represented only by a single point. For example if $n=3$, there exist the quantities a_{11}, a_{22}, a_{33}, a_{12}, a_{13}, a_{23} where $a_{ij}=a_{ji}$; and in general where $n=n$, there are $\frac{n(n+1)}{2}$ such quantities which in this manifold are regarded as the *coordinates* of a point.

The above problem may be at once reduced to a corresponding problem in positive quadratic forms. We form out of $\xi_1, \xi_2, \cdots, \xi_n$ the sum of squares

$$\xi_1^2 + \xi_2^2 + \cdots + \xi_n^2 = f.$$

It is a positive quadratic form

$$f = f(x_1, x_2, \cdots, x_n) = \sum a_{hk} x_h x_k \quad (h, k=1, 2, \cdots, n)$$

of the n variables $x_1, x_2, \cdots, x_n$ with the coefficients

$$\frac{1}{2}\frac{\partial^2 f}{\partial x_h \partial x_k} = a_{hk} = \alpha_{1h}\alpha_{1k} + \alpha_{2h}\alpha_{2k} + \cdots + \alpha_{nh}\alpha_{nk} \quad (h, k=1, 2, \cdots, n).$$

Encyklopädie der math. Wiss., Vol. I, p. 327 et seq.

We consider next the $n(n+1)/2$ manifold A of the $n(n+1)/2$ arbitrary variable real parameters a_{hk}. To each point $f=(a_{hk})$ of this manifold A for which the form f turns out to be essentially positive, there corresponds, due to the equations just written, an $n(n-1)/2$ dimensional realm A(f) of the points (α_{hk}) in the manifold A. We transfer the concept of arithmetical equivalence and class to the positive quadratic forms, and *we seek in a manifold* A *a region* B *in which each class of quadratic forms is represented through a point, and if the class falls in the interior of* B, *it is represented through one single point.*

The realms A(f) form for all points f situated in B the required realm of discontinuity B in the manifold A.

It will be proved that *the region of discontinuity* B *for the arithmetical equivalence of the positive quadratic forms may be constructed in such a way that in the manifold* A *it represents a convex cone bound by a finite number of planes with the origin represented through* $f=0$ *as vertex.* (See Art. 224.)

Through this theorem the theory of arithmetical equivalence for the positive quadratic forms in n variables is put on the same plane as the theory of ternary quadratic forms through the treatise of Dirichlet: *Ueber die Reduction der positiven quadratischen Formen mit drei unbestimmten ganzen Zahlen.* That part of the region of discontinuity B which corresponds to the forms f with a determinant $\leqq 1$, has a finite volume. For $n=2$ this volume is essentially the non-Euclidean area of the fundamental region of the elliptic[1] modular function $J(\omega)$. The general derivation of this volume is effected here by means of those principles upon which Dirichlet founded the calculation of the numbers of classes of the integral binary quadratic forms, and in fact the analytic element in these principles comes to light in its purest sense in the application which is made in this chapter.

With the volume there are connected certain asymptotic laws with respect to the forms with integral coefficients. On the other hand the value of the volume makes possible a conclusion regarding the densest filling up of the n-dimensional space through congruent spheres.

[1] See Klein, *Vorlesungen ueber die Theorie der elliptischen Modulfunctionen*, See Vol. 1, Chap. 1, where many references are given: see in particular Chap. V. p. 141 et seq.

Art. **208.** In his paper *Ueber die positiven quadratischen Formen und ueber Kettenbruchaehnliche Algorithmen* (see Arts. 75–82 of the present work) Minkowski gave the following more or less historical statement regarding quadratic forms. There exists, he says, the problem of characterizing a union of equivalent forms, a class, completely through invariants. This problem was first completely solved for binary forms through the investigations of Kronecker.

This problem admits solution in another sense. If we are able to separate one form out of the innumerable many forms of a class through definite conditions, such a so called reduced form in a certain measure presents a complete invariantive system of the class. The expression of this system can be derived however from any given form of the class and in each case through a certain particular method of procedure, which method requires only a limited number of arithmetical operations. In this way Lagrange (*Oeuvres*, T. III, p. 695) conceived the theory of the binary quadratic forms and brought it to a brilliant conclusion. His results regarding definite forms were shapened by Legendre (*Theorie des Nombres*, 3me ed., T. I, § VIII) in such a way that the possibility of generalization was put in evidence.

From the fifth section of Gauss's *Disquisitiones Arithmeticae*, Seeber ("Untersuchungen ueber die Eigenschaften der positiven ternaeren quadratischen Formen," Freiburg i. B., 1831) was inspired to study the analogous question regarding ternary definite forms. His extremely laborious but fruitful work found suitable valuation in a highly remarkable paper by Gauss (*Werke*, Bd. II, S. 188) that originated therefrom. Namely, this paper is doubly noteworthy: In the first place through the indication of the geometric equivalent of a class of positive quadratic forms through systems of points arranged regularly as parallelopipeds (see introduction to the chapter "Ueber die positiven quadratischen Formen," etc.) and in the second place through a peculiar identity by means of which an important limit, found through induction by Seeber, directly appears for the coefficients of his reduced forms.

The cumbrous methods and the complicated proofs by Seeber prompted Dirichlet (*Werke*, Bd. II, S. 21), for whom the not simple was always a sign of the imperfect, to a fundamentally new treatment by which he attained an extraordinary clearness through the geometric presentation indicated by Gauss but only in outline.

The great advance made by Dirichlet consisted in the fact that he did not operate with difficult numerical expressions on the inequalities through which Seeber had defined reduced forms but with their well known innate meaning which consisted in making the reduced forms dependent upon certain least distances in the associated point system.

The same, as simple as essential principle though in a purely arithmetical setting was followed by Hermite (*Oeuvres*, T. I, pp. 100–163) in his letters to Jacobi touching number theory. They appear in the same volume (No. 40, 1850) of Crelle's Journal in which Dirichlet's work appears more in detail than in a previous paper published by him in the Monatsbericht of the Berlin Academy (in 1848).

The researches of Hermite have to do with forms in an arbitrary number of variables. They begin with the exhibition of the fundamental theorem of reduction. It is seen that the least quantity ($\neq 0$) expressible through a positive quadratic form in n variables by means of integers in its ratio to the nth root of the determinant of the form never exceeds a definite value. And this value depends only upon n the number of dimensions. These investigations of Hermite present themselves as an uninterrupted evidence of the fruitfulness of this theorem in almost every chapter of the theory of numbers, to mention only the application to continued fractions, complex units and the approximate solution of equations.

In particular it is proved from this theorem with ease and in many ways that the number of classes is finite. To show this in the particular case where the coefficients are integers and the determinant a fixed integer a method of procedure is indicated according to which it is sufficient to separate out of each class only a finite number of forms and not just one single form. A valuable extension of this is furnished by Camille Jordan ("Memoire sur l'equivalence des formes," *Journal de l'École Polytechnique*, T. XXIX, Cat. 48, 1880, p. 111). He proved that (under certain conditions at least) a limit depending only upon the number of variables exists for the maximal number of forms that are separated from a class, if the substitutions through which the separated forms are transformed into themselves or equivalent forms, can be previously assigned under a limited number of variables.

New points of view were opened by Korkine and Zolotareff (*Mathematische Annalen*, Bd. 6, 1873, S. 366 and Bd. 11, 1877, S. 242). They determined completely those particular forms, the so-called *extreme* forms, up to five variables for which the ratio named in the fundamental theorem of Hermite (of the minimum that may be reached through integers to the nth root of the determinant) is a maximum. (See Art. 228.) In his paper *Ueber die positiven quadratischen Formen und ueber Kettenbruchahnliche Algorithmen* (see Chap. VIII of the present work) Minkowski tried in particular to fill up certain gaps that were seen to exist in the theory of positive quadratic forms.

The character inherent in the original binary reduced forms of Lagrange is lost in the case of the previously introduced reduced forms in a greater number of variables, in that Lagrange's reduced forms were defined through a series of linear inequalities in the coefficients.

It was noted above that in an $n(n+1)/2$ manifold every quadratic form in n variables could be represented by a point with the values of the coefficients as coordinates. Minkowski regarded it of great theoretical importance that here also we are in a position out of this manifold by means of a limited number of plane $(n(n+1)/2-1)$ply manifolds to bound a connected region in which (the limits being only partially included) every point represents a class of positive forms and in which each class appears once and only once. Such a region is divided through the $(n(n+1)/2-1)$ply manifolds of all forms which have a fixed positive but in other respects arbitrary determinant into two parts. It will be seen that one of them has at the origin a finite content. The expression of this content is given here in general. This content is connected with interesting mean valued theorems in the theory of numbers.

The transposition of any given form into a reduced form must be possible of execution through exclusive application of a limited number of a priori designated operations: and the initial form should be each time the standard only in regard to the sequence and repetition of the operations. It is possible here to meet the warranted requirement.

By the help also of a geometric method of expression carried over to forms with more than three variables it is possible to present the fundamental theorem of Hermite regarding the minimum of a positive quadratic form not only in a certain sense as evident but also to make more restricted the limits required in this theorem and in the extensions of it in contrast to the limits that had been previously used. Thus new and important applications of this theorem become possible.

ART. 209. **Character of the Positive Quadratic Forms.** Let $f(x_1, x_2, \cdots, x_n)=\Sigma a_{hk}x_h x_k$ $(h, k=1, 2, \cdots, n)$ be a quadratic form of the n variables $x_1, x_2, \cdots, x_n$ with real coefficients a_{hk}. We put $a_{kh}=a_{hk}$ for $h<k$. The following results have been derived in Art. 148. The determinant of the νth order derived from the $h_1, h_2, \cdots, h_\nu$ horizontal row and the $k_1, k_2, \cdots, k_\nu$ vertical column of the quadratic scheme of the a_{hk} $(h, k=1, 2, \cdots, n)$ was denoted by

$$D\begin{pmatrix} h_1, h_2, \cdots, h_\nu \\ k_1, k_2, \cdots, k_\nu \end{pmatrix}.$$

For example

$$D\begin{pmatrix} 1, 5, 6, \;\; 7, \;\; 8 \\ 2, 7, 9, 11, 13 \end{pmatrix} \qquad \text{in} \qquad D_n = \begin{vmatrix} a_{11}, \cdots, a_{1n} \\ \cdots\cdots\cdots\cdots \\ a_{n1}, \cdots, a_{nn} \end{vmatrix}$$

is

$$\begin{vmatrix} a_{1,2}, & a_{1,7}, & a_{1,9}, & a_{1,11}, & a_{1,13} \\ a_{5,2}, & a_{5,7}, & a_{5,9}, & a_{5,11}, & a_{5,13} \\ a_{6,2}, & \multicolumn{3}{c}{\cdots\cdots\cdots\cdots\cdots,} & a_{6,13} \\ a_{7,2}, & \multicolumn{3}{c}{\cdots\cdots\cdots\cdots\cdots,} & a_{7,13} \\ a_{8,2}, & \multicolumn{3}{c}{\cdots\cdots\cdots\cdots\cdots,} & a_{8,13} \end{vmatrix}.$$

It was proved that for $f=f(x_1, x_2, \cdots, x_n)$, to be an essentially positive quadratic form it was sufficient and necessary that the n determinants $D\begin{pmatrix}1, 2, \cdots, h\\1, 2, \cdots, h\end{pmatrix}=D_h$ for $h=1, 2, \cdots, n$ be all positive. The last of these quantities, namely D_n is the determinant of the form f, whose value is denoted by $D(f)$. Changing somewhat the notation of Art. 148, we use the notation of Minkowski in his paper which constitutes this chapter and put

$$D_1=1, \qquad \frac{D_h}{D_{h-1}}=q_h \qquad (h=1, 2, \cdots, n);$$

$$\frac{D\begin{pmatrix}1, 2, \cdots, h-1, h\\1, 2, \cdots, h-1, k\end{pmatrix}}{D\begin{pmatrix}1, 2, \cdots, h-1, h\\1, 2, \cdots, h-1, h\end{pmatrix}}=\gamma_{h,k} \quad \begin{pmatrix}h=1, 2, \cdots, n-1\\k=h+1, \cdots, n\end{pmatrix}.$$

It is then seen that all the quantities q_h are *positive* and the identical relation

(1) $$f=q_1\zeta_1^2+q_2\zeta_2^2+\cdots+q_n\zeta_n^2$$

exists, where

(2) $$\begin{aligned} \zeta_1&=x_1+\gamma_{12}x_2+\cdots+\gamma_{1n}x_n, \\ \zeta_2&=x_2+\gamma_{22}x_2+\cdots+\gamma_{2n}x_n, \\ &\cdots\cdots\cdots\cdots\cdots\cdots\cdots\cdots, \\ \zeta_n&= \qquad\qquad\qquad\quad x_n; \end{aligned}$$

and this puts in evidence the *character of f* as a positive form.

By equating the coefficients of $x_1^2, x_2^2, \cdots, x_n^2$ on either side of (1), it is seen that

(3) $$a_{11}=q_1, \quad a_{22}\geqq q_2, \quad \cdots, \quad a_{nn}\geqq q_n;$$

and through multiplication of these inequalities it follows that

$$a_{11}a_{22}\cdots a_{nn} \geqq D(f). \tag{4}$$

If L is a given positive quantity and if it is required that f be $\leqq L$ it follows from (1) that

$$|\zeta_n| \leqq \sqrt{\frac{L}{q_n}}, \qquad |\zeta_{n-1}| \leqq \sqrt{\frac{L}{q_{n-1}}}, \qquad \cdots, \qquad |\zeta_1| \leqq \sqrt{\frac{L}{q_1}};$$

and due to these inequalities and the expressions (2) it is seen that there is only a finite number of different systems $x_n, x_{n-1}, \cdots, x_2, x_1$ that satisfy the given requirement.

Accordingly we have the theorem: *A positive quadratic form f for only a finite number of integral systems of the variables can take values that do not exceed a given limit.*

ART. 210. **Arrangement in an n-Dimensional Manifold.** If $a_1, a_2, \cdots, a_n$ and $b_1, b_2, \cdots, b_n$ are two different systems each of n quantities and if $a_1 = b_1$, $a_2 = b_2$, $\cdots$, $a_{l-1} = b_{l-1}$, $a_l > b_l$, where l is one of the numbers $1, 2, \cdots, n$, we say that the first system is *higher*, the second *lower* than the other and in the lth place. Suppose that we have given an indefinitely large number of systems $S(a_1, a_2, \cdots, a_n)$, with the following property: If $a_1, a_2, \cdots, a_n$ is an arbitrary system selected out of the given systems and if l is any arbitrary one of the numbers $1, 2, \cdots, n$, then among all those systems $b_1, b_2, \cdots, b_n$ present which are exactly in the lth place lower than the first system we assume that for the quantities b there are only a finite number of different values.

LEMMA. *If then starting with an arbitrary system S of the given systems we form as far as possible a series of systems $S, S^{(1)}, S^{(2)}, \cdots$, so that each following system is lower than the preceding, then such a series must end after a finite number of steps.* And further *after a finite number of steps there exists a system, than which we have no lower in the given indefinitely large number of systems and which accordingly represents the lowest system of those given.*

To prove this observe that for $n=1$ the assertion is evident. Next let $n>1$. Take for an initial system $S(a_1, a_2, \cdots, a_n)$ and consider all systems $a_1, b_2, \cdots, b_n$ of the given number of systems which have the first element a_1 in common with the initial system. The systems $b_2, \cdots, b_n$ consisting of $n-1$ elements offer similar properties as we assumed for the systems in n elements. If then we assume the theorem set for proof in n elements as already proved when for n we write $n-1$ elements, we have a series $S, S^{(1)}, S^{(2)}, \cdots$ continuing with only a finite number of terms such that the first element remains unchanged and each time there appears a lowering on the second to the nth place. Since on the other hand a lowering (depression) exactly on the first place by hypothesis can appear only a finite number of times the theorem to be proved is at once clear for systems of n terms.

ART. 211. **Least Forms in a Class.** Two forms

$$f=\sum a_{hk}x_h x_k, \qquad g=\sum b_{hk}y_h y_k \quad (h, k=1, 2, \cdots, n)$$

are then and only then equivalent if f goes over into g through an integral transformation with a determinant $=\pm 1$. If

$$(5) \qquad a_{11}=b_{11}, \quad a_{22}=b_{22}, \quad \cdots, \quad a_{nn}=b_{nn},$$

then f and g are said to be *equally* placed. If however

$$(6) \qquad a_{11}=b_{11}, \quad \cdots, \quad a_{l-1,\, l-1}=b_{l-1,\, l-1}, \quad a_{ll}>b_{ll},$$

where l may take any of the values $1, 2, \cdots, n$, then f is placed *higher* than g and g is placed *lower* than f and in fact higher or lower on the lth place. Let

$$(7) \qquad x_h=s_{h1}y_1+s_{h2}y_2+\cdots+s_{hn}y_n \qquad (h=1, 2, \cdots, n)$$

be an integral substitution with determinant ± 1 which takes f into g. Then it may be proved that

$$b_{kk}=f(s_{1k}, s_{2k}, \cdots, s_{nk}) \qquad (k=1, 2, \cdots, n).$$

For write

$$x_h = \sum_t s_{ht} y_t, \qquad x_k = \sum_r s_{kr} y_r$$

in $f(x_1, x_2, \cdots, x_n) = \sum a_{hk} x_h x_k$ $(h, k = 1, 2, \cdots, n)$, and we have

$$f(x_1, x_2, \cdots, x_n) = \sum_{t,\, r} (\sum_{h,\, k} a_{hk} s_{ht} s_{kr}) y_t y_r;$$

and putting

$$b_{tr} = \sum a_{hk} s_{ht} s_{kr} = b_{tr}, \qquad b_{tt} = \sum a_{hk} s_{ht} s_{kt} = f(s_{1t}, \cdots, s_{nt}).$$

Q.E.D.

If g is on the lth place lower than f, it follows that

$$f(s_{11}, \cdots, s_{n1}) = a_{11}, \cdots,$$

(8) $$f(s_{1,\, l-1}, \cdots, s_{n,\, l-1}) = a_{l-1,\, l-1},$$

$$f(s_{1l}, \cdots, s_{nl}) = a_{ll}.$$

Further *the matrix formed out of the l first vertical rows of the substitution* (7), *namely*

(9) $$\| s_{hk} \| \qquad (h = 1, 2, \cdots, n;\ k = 1, 2, \cdots, l)$$

is unimodular, and that is the greatest common divisor of all the determinants of the lth order that may be formed out of this matrix is $=1$; otherwise the determinant of (7) when expanded by the Lagrange method in terms of these determinants of the lth order would not be $=\pm 1$.

Accordingly it is easy to determine *whether there exists in the class of f a form g which is lower than f.* For we take for l one after the other each of the values $1, 2, \cdots, n$ and each time consider the system of conditions (8). We saw above that there was only a finite number of integers s_{hk} $(k \leqq l)$ which satisfy these conditions.

If the matrix (9) is unimodular for one of the systems of solution in question we may add $n-l$ further rows of integral coefficients s_{hk} $(k = l-1, \cdots, n)$ so that the determinant of the then existing quadratic scheme is $=\pm 1$ and the associated substitution (7) transforms f into a lower form g at the lth place. *And thus are had in every case for* b_{ll} *only a finite number of different values.*

Due to the lemma in the preceding article *we may derive in every class* f *such a form* g than which there is no lower form in the class and which we accordingly call a *lowest* form of the class. *All forms equivalent to their equally placed forms are simultaneously lowest forms of the class.*

If the form f goes into an *equally placed* form through the substitution (7), the n equations

$$f(s_{11}, s_{21}, \cdots, s_{n1}) = a_{11},$$
$$\cdots\cdots\cdots\cdots\cdots$$
$$f(s_{1n}, s_{2n}, \cdots, s_{nn}) = a_{nn}$$

must exist. These are satisfied by only a finite number of integral systems s_{hk} and accordingly *there exist only a finite number of integral substitutions with a determinant* ± 1 *through which a form goes into an equally placed form. In particular it is seen that every positive form may be transformed into itself by only a finite number of integral substitutions.* Every form f is transformed into equally placed forms by the 2^n substitutions

$$(10) \qquad x_1 = \pm y_1, \quad x_2 = \pm y_2, \quad \cdots, \quad x_n = \pm y_n$$

where each of the n signs $\pm$ is independently $+$ or $-$ the one of the other.

ART. **212.** A form and its associated class was called *general* (allgemein) by Minkowski, if an equation

$$f(x_1, x_2, \cdots, x_n) = f(y_1, y_2, \cdots, y_n)$$

with integral values $x_1, x_2, \cdots, x_n; y_1, y_2, \cdots, y_n$ can never exist except when the system $y_1, y_2, \cdots, y_n$ coincides with $x_1, x_2, \cdots, x_n$ or with $-x_1, -x_2, \cdots, -x_n$.

In particular it is seen that this character exists for $f = \sum a_{hk}x_hx_k$, if among the $n(n+1)/2$ coefficients a_{hk} of f, there is no homogeneous linear relation with integral coefficients, say

$$\sum_{h,\,k} \lambda_{hk} a_{hk} = 0.$$

If we compare in particular the two systems $x_h = 1$, $x_{h+1} = 1$, $x_k = 0$ and $y_h = 1$, $y_{h+1} = -1$, $y_k = 0$ $(k \neq h,\ h+1)$, they offer the two relations $a_{hh} + 2a_{h,\,h+1} + a_{h+1,\,h+1}$ and $a_{hh} - 2a_{h,\,h+1} + a_{h+1,\,h+1}$; and it is clear that, if one of these relations is not equal another, then $a_{h,\,h+1} \neq 0$. Hence in a general form every coefficient $a_{h,\,h+1} \neq 0$. If the class f is a general class then each of its forms is transformed only through the 2^n substitutions (10) into equivalent equally placed forms; and in the class there is always *a single lowest form g which also satisfies the additional conditions* $b_{12} > 0$, $b_{23} > 0$, $\cdots$, $b_{n-1,\,n} > 0$. By E we denote the *identical* substitution. Let S denote any substitution; by its *opposed* (entgegengesetzte) substitution (denoted by $-S$) we understand the one that exists through change of all coefficients s_{hk} into the opposite values $-s_{hk}$.

ART. 213. **Reduced Forms.** There are essentially the lowest forms of a class, which Hermite (*Oeuvres*, T. I, p. 111) introduced as reduced forms with the intention of having in the multitude of these forms a region of discontinuity B of the nature described in the introduction of this chapter. Minkowski, however, as we shall now show, in contrast to Hermite's definition, introduced a simplification in that he put aside certain complicated expressions which were required by Hermite for the lowest forms, but which exerted an influence only upon parts of the boundary of the region of discontinuity.

Let l be one of the integers 1, 2, $\cdots$, n; then by $s_1^{(l)}$, $s_2^{(l)}$, $\cdots$, $s_l^{(l)}$, $\cdots$, $s_n^{(l)}$ we shall understand a system of integers such that the greatest common divisor of $s_l^{(l)}$, $s_{l+1}^{(l)}$, $\cdots$, $s_n^{(l)}$ is unity. Further we define all the quantities $e_h^{(k)}$ as being $=0$, except $e_h^{(h)}$ which $=1$. We next make the substitution $S^{(l)}$ where s_{hk} are any integers so chosen that the determinant of the substitution $=\pm 1$ (*A. N.*, I, Art. 100):

$$S^{(l)}:\quad x_h=e_h^{(1)}y_1+e_h^{(2)}y_2+\cdots+e_h^{(h)}y_h+e_h^{(h+1)}y_{h+1}+\cdots$$
$$+e_h^{(l-1)}y_{l-1}+s_h^{(l)}y_l+s_{h,\,l+1}y_{l+1}+\cdots s_{hn}y_n$$

or

$$x_h=y_h+s_h^{(l)}y_l+s_{h,\,l+1}y_{l+1}+\cdots+s_{hn}y_n \qquad (h<l),$$
$$x_h=s_h^{(l)}y_l+s_{h,\,l+1}y_{l+1}+\cdots+s_{hn}y_n \qquad (h\geqq l).$$

$$S^{(l)}:\begin{cases} x_1=y_1+0+\cdots+0\quad+s_1^{(l)}y_l \\ \qquad\qquad +s_{1,\,l+1}y_{l+1}+\cdots+\quad s_{1n}y_n, \\ x_2=0+y_2+\cdots+0\quad+s_2^{(l)}y_l \\ \qquad\qquad +s_{2,\,l+1}y_{l+1}+\cdots+\quad s_{2n}y_n, \\ \cdots\cdots\cdots\cdots\cdots\cdots\cdots\cdots \\ x_{l-1}=0+0+\cdots+y_{l-1}+s_{l-1}^{(l)}y_l \\ \qquad\qquad +s_{l-1,\,l+1}y_{l+1}+\cdots+s_{l-1,\,n}y_n, \\ x_l=0+0+\cdots+0\quad+s_l^{(l)}y_l \\ \qquad\qquad +s_{l,\,l+1}y_{l+1}\quad+\cdots+s_{ln}y_n, \\ \cdots\cdots\cdots\cdots\cdots\cdots\cdots\cdots \\ x_n=0+0+\cdots+0\quad+s_n^{(l)}y_l \\ \qquad\qquad +s_{n,\,l+1}y_{l+1}+\cdots+s_{nn}y_n. \end{cases}$$

When $l=1$, the determinant of the linear forms is

$$\begin{vmatrix} s_1^{(1)}, & s_{12}, & \cdots, & s_{1n} \\ s_2^{(1)}, & s_{22}, & \cdots, & s_{2n} \\ \cdots & \cdots & \cdots & \cdots \\ s_n^{(1)}, & \cdots & \cdots & s_{nn} \end{vmatrix}=\pm 1$$

where unity is the G.C.D. of $s_1^{(1)}, s_2^{(1)}, \cdots, s_n^{(1)}$; and when $l=2$, the determinant is

$$\begin{vmatrix} 1, & s_1^{(2)}, & s_{13}, & \cdots, & s_{1n} \\ 0, & s_2^{(2)}, & s_{23}, & \cdots, & s_{2n} \\ \cdots & \cdots & \cdots & \cdots & \cdots \\ 0, & s_n^{(2)}, & s_{n3}, & \cdots, & s_{nn} \end{vmatrix}=\pm 1,$$

where the G.C.D. of $s_2^{(2)}, \cdots, s_n^{(2)}$ is unity, etc.

Through the substitution $S^{(l)}$ a form $f=\sum a_{hk}x_hx_k$ becomes $g=\sum b_{hk}y_hy_k$, where $b_{11}=a_{11}$, $b_{22}=a_{22}$, $\cdots$, $b_{l-1,\,l-1}$

$=a_{l-1,\ l-1}$, $b_{ll}=f(s_1^{(l)}, s_2^{(l)}, \cdots, s_n^{(l)})$. If in particular f is a lowest form in its class, we must have $b_{ll}\geqq a_{ll}$.

ART. **214.** We now make the following definition: *A quadratic form*

$$f(x_1, x_2, \cdots, x_n)=\sum a_{hk}x_hx_k$$

is said to be a reduced form, if it satisfies all possible inequalities

$$\text{(I)} \qquad f(s_1^{(l)}, \ s_2^{(l)}, \ \cdots, \ s_n^{(l)})\geqq a_{ll}$$

for every $l=1, 2, \cdots, n$, and for all integral systems $s_1^{(1)}$, $s_2^{(l)}$, $\cdots$, $s_n^{(l)}$, where the G.C.D. of $s_l^{(l)}$, $s_{l+1}^{(l)}$, $\cdots$, $s_n^{(l)}$ is $=1$; with the addition also of the further conditions

$$\text{(II)} \qquad a_{12}\geqq 0, \quad a_{23}\geqq 0, \quad \cdots, \quad a_{n-1,\ n}\geqq 0.$$

In the inequalities (I) the two systems $\begin{cases} s_h^{(l)}=-e_h^{(l)} \\ s_h^{(l)}=e_h^{(l)} \end{cases}$ $(h=1, 2, \cdots, n)$ are to be excluded as (I) has no real significance in the a_{hk} for these systems.

In this definition of a reduced form we have not presupposed that f is a *positive* form.

ART. **215.** In a class of positive forms there exists always a lowest form which satisfies the additional conditions (II) and is a reduced form. And from the results previously given there accordingly *exists in every class of positive forms at least one reduced form.*

Those of the inequalities (I) that belong to the index l show that a_{ll} is the minimum of all values $f(x_1, x_2, \cdots, x_n)$ for all integers $x_1, x_2, \cdots, x_n$ which have unity as their greatest common divisor. Through a substitution $S^{(l)}$ all the integral systems $x_1, x_2, \cdots, x_n$, where unity is the greatest common divisor of $x_l, x_{l+1}, \cdots, x_n$, are transformed into all the integral systems $y_1, y_2, \cdots, y_n$ where the greatest common divisor of $y_l, y_{l+1}, \cdots, y_n$ is unity.

If a positive form satisfies the conditions (I) for $l=1, 2, \cdots, m-1$ but not for m, it is always possible through a substitution $S^{(m)}$ to derive from this form an equivalent form which satisfies the conditions (I) for $l=1, 2, \cdots, m-1$ and also in addition for m. For we have simply to determine all integral systems $s_1^{(m)}, s_2^{(m)}, \cdots, s_n^{(m)}$ for which $F(s_1^{(m)}, s_2^{(m)}, \cdots, s_n^{(m)})<a_{mm}$ while at the same time the greatest common divisor of $s_m^{(m)}, s_{m-1}^{(m)}, \cdots, s_n^{(m)}$ is unity.

By hypothesis there exist such systems and there is a finite number of them. Among them we select the ones that give to f the smallest value and we write an arbitrary one of these as the mth column in $S^{(m)}$ and thereby reach the required result.

If $S^{(l)}$ and $\overline{S}^{(l)}$ are two different substitutions of the type given above where $l<n$, and the lth column is the same in both, then is $\overline{S}^{(l)}=S^{(l)}T$, where T is the substitution of a nature $S^{(l+1)}$.

Proof. In general write $T=R^{-1}S$ where R and S have their first l columns the same and where the determinant of R is ± 1. If the terms of R and S are integers, then $T(=$the product $R^{-1}S)$ is a determinant whose terms are integers, and the determinant of T is the same as the determinant of S. Observe that the first l columns of T are the same as the first l columns of $RR^{-1}=E$. Write the matrices of the substitutions

$$R=\left\|\begin{matrix} r_{11}, & r_{12}, & \cdots, & r_{1n} \\ r_{21}, & r_{22}, & \cdots, & r_{2n} \\ \cdots & \cdots & \cdots & \cdots \\ r_{n1}, & r_{n2}, & \cdots, & r_{nn} \end{matrix}\right\|; \qquad S=\left\|\begin{matrix} s_{11}, & s_{12}, & \cdots, & s_{1n} \\ s_{21}, & s_{22}, & \cdots, & s_{2n} \\ \cdots & \cdots & \cdots & \cdots \\ s_{n1}, & s_{n2}, & \cdots, & s_{nn} \end{matrix}\right\|;$$

then is $r_{lj}=s_{lj}$ (if $j\leqq l$). Write

$$R^{-1}=\left\|\begin{matrix} \overline{r}_{11}, & \overline{r}_{21}, & \cdots, & \overline{r}_{n1} \\ \overline{r}_{12}, & \overline{r}_{22}, & \cdots, & \overline{r}_{n2} \\ \cdots & \cdots & \cdots & \cdots \\ \overline{r}_{1n}, & \cdots & \cdots, & \overline{r}_{nn} \end{matrix}\right\|,$$

where $\overline{r}_{ij}$ is the cofactor of r_{ij}. Then is

$$T=R^{-1}S=\left\| \sum_{k=1}^{k=n} \overline{r}_{ki}s_{kj} \right\| = \| t_{ij} \|.$$

For $j \leqq l$, we have

$$t_{ij} = \sum_1^n \bar{r}_{ki} r_{kj} = \begin{cases} 1, & \text{if } j = i \\ 0, & \text{if } j \neq i \end{cases},$$

which is the first property of an $S^{(l+1)}$ matrix. For $j > l$, the t's are all integers. If S has a determinant ± 1, then T has a determinant ± 1 and consequently $t_{l+1,\, l+1}, \cdots, t_{n,\, l+1}$ have unity as their greatest common divisor, the second property of an $S^{(l+1)}$ matrix.

Note in particular from the above considerations that a reduced form for which the sign of equality appears in none of the inequalities (I) and (II) remains a reduced form by no other substitution save the identical substitution E and its opposed $-E$.

ART. **216.** We may regard the coefficients a_{hk} of a quadratic form as the coordinates of a point f in an $n(n+1)/2$ manifold A. In this manifold we denote by B the region of those points f which satisfy all the inequalities (I) and (II). We call B the *reduced* region (realm). The last article then says:

A form f on the interior of the reduced realm B, *and that is, for which form the equality sign exists in none of the inequalities (I) and (II), is transformed through every unimodular integral substitution that is different from E or −E into a form outside of* B. In particular a complete (allgemeine) class is represented by an interior point of the realm (B).

To clothe this in geometric phraseology observe that every pair of opposed unimodular integral substitutions S, $-S$ transforms the realm (B) into a definite equivalent *room* or *chamber* (Kammer), $B_s = B_{-s}$. And the chambers which correspond to such pairs touch one another at most at points on the boundary. The collectivity of rooms B_s cover the entire region (realm) of the positive forms.

ART. **217. The Walls of the Reduced Realms.** An infinite number of inequalities (I) are presupposed in the definition of a reduced form f. This suggests the necessity of proving the following theorem: There exists a finite number of inequalities among the inequalities (I) whose existence necessitates all the others.

Proof. First take $n=2$, so that $f=a_{11}x_1^2+2a_{12}x_1x_2+a_{22}x_2^2$. Then in (I) put $s_1^{(2)}=\pm 1$, $s_2^{(2)}=1$. It then follows that

$$(11) \qquad a_{11}\pm 2a_{12}+a_{22}\geqq a_{22}, \text{ and hence } \pm a_{12}\leqq \tfrac{1}{2}a_{11}.$$

From these two conditions for the two signs $\pm$ it is seen also that $a_{11}\geqq 0$.

If further we take $s_1^{(1)}=0$, $s_2^{(1)}=1$, we have

$$(12) \qquad a_{22}\geqq a_{11}.$$

Now if $a_{11}=0$, it follows from (11) that also $a_{12}=0$, and as $a_{22}\geqq 0$, all the inequalities (I) necessarily follow. If on the other hand $a_{11}>0$, it follows from (11) and (12) that $a_{12}^2\leqq \frac{1}{4}a_{11}^2\leqq \frac{1}{4}a_{11}a_{22}$ and $D_2=a_{11}a_{22}-a_{12}^2\geqq \frac{3}{4}a_{11}a_{22}$. If we write (Art. 209)

$$f=q_1(x_1+\gamma_{12}x_2)^2+q_2x_2^2,$$

it is seen that $q_1=a_{11}$, $\gamma_{12}=\dfrac{a_{12}}{a_{11}}$, $\pm\gamma_{12}\leqq \frac{1}{2}$, $q_2=D_2/q_1\geqq \frac{3}{4}a_{22}$. Hence D_{22} is $\geqq \frac{3}{4}a_{11}a_{22}$. The general case stated in formula (15) must be proved before we can proceed further. For integers s_1, s_2 it is clear if $|s_1|>1$, and $s_2=1$, that

$$f(\pm|s_1|,1)=a_{11}(s_1^2-|s_1|)+(a_{11}\pm 2a_{12})|s_1|+a_{22}>a_{22};$$

and on the other hand if $|s_2|>1$ and therefore equal at least to 2, we have $f(s_1, s_2)\geqq q_2s_{22}^2\geqq 3a_{22}>a_{22}$. Thus it is seen that when (11) and (12) exist, all inequalities (I) follow.

ART. **218. Next let n be >2.** We write a number of the variables zero and suppose that those of the variables that are left are $x_{h_1}, x_{h_2}, \cdots, x_{h_m}$ $(h_1<h_2<\cdots<h_m)$. We thus derive from f a form $f(x_{h_1}, x_{h_2}, \cdots, x_{h_m})$ and the conditions corresponding to (I) for this form are certain special ones of the conditions (I) that exist for the form f itself. Every

form that is to be derived from a reduced form f in such manner from fewer than n variables has, without regard to the inequalities (II), the character of a reduced form in its number of variables. We may now make certain selections from the inequalities (1). These we shall take seriatim. *First,* select those of the inequalities (I) for f which require that all the binary forms

$$a_{hh}x_h^2+2a_{hk}x_hx_k+a_{kk}x_k^2 \qquad (h<k)$$

satisfy the conditions (I) for reduced forms. We thus derive a finite number of inequalities which may be written

$$(13) \qquad \pm 2a_{hk}<a_{hh} \qquad (h>k),$$

and

$$(14) \qquad 0\leqq a_{11}\leqq a_{22}\cdots\leqq a_{nn}.$$

We next assume that the theorem to be proved is already proved for forms for fewer than n variables and that we may choose from among the inequalities (I) *secondly* a finite number due to which all the forms $f(x_{m+1}, x_{m+2}, \cdots, x_n)$ for $m=1, 2, \cdots, n-2)$ that are derived from f are reduced.

If then $0=a_{11}=a_{22}=\cdots=a_{mm}$ $(1\leqq m<n)$, $0<a_{m+1,\,m+1}$, it follows from (13) that all the coefficients a_{hk} $(h\leqq k)$ where $h=1, 2, \cdots, m$ are zero, so that f becomes simply $f(x_{m+1}, \cdots, x_n)$. The inequalities (I) with respect to the last form have due to the assumption already all the inequalities (I) for f.

We next assume that $a_{11}>0$. And now *thirdly* we select of the inequalities (I) those, of which there is a finite number and due to which all the forms $f(x_1, x_2, \cdots, x_m)$ for $m=2, 3, \cdots, n-1$, that are derived.from f, are reduced forms.

N. B. The induction still remains to be proved. However, we must first prove in Arts. 219–222 the following lemma in which (15) is proved to be true in all cases.

ART. 219. LEMMA. It is possible *fourthly* to select from (I) a finite number of inequalities so that it may be proved by means of them that *the determinant of the form f satisfies the inequality*

(15) $$D_n \geqq \lambda_n a_{11}a_{22}\cdots a_{nn},$$

where λ_n is a certain positive quantity dependent upon n but not upon the constants that appear as coefficients of f. When this has been done, we will finish in Art. 223 the theorem stated in Art. 217.

This has been proved for the case $n=2$, where $\lambda_2=\frac{3}{4}$, and we assume that it is true for fewer than n variables. Using the inductive method we shall prove that it is true for n variables. Observe that we are using another inductive process to prove the lemma.

Let m be any of the values 1, 2, $\cdots$, $n-1$. It is seen that under the above assumption

(16) $$D\begin{pmatrix}1, 2, \cdots, m\\ 1, 2, \cdots, m\end{pmatrix} = D_m \geqq \lambda_m a_{11}a_{22}\cdots a_{mm} \quad (m \leqq n-1);$$

and for the form $f(x_{m+1}, x_{m+2}, \cdots, x_n)$ we also have

(17) $$D\begin{pmatrix}m+1, & m+2, & \cdots, & n\\ m+1, & m+2, & \cdots, & n\end{pmatrix}$$
$$= \bar{D}_{n-m} \geqq \lambda_{n-m} a_{m+1,\, m+1}\cdots a_{nn}.$$

In the cases $m=1$ and $m=n-1$ we put $\lambda_1=1$.

Write down the determinant D_n of f and in it place D_m and D_{n-m} diagonally opposite. It is seen that there are $m!(n-m)!$ terms that belong to the product $D_m D_{n-m}$ and in addition $n!-m!(n-m)!$ terms of the type $\pm a_{1k_1}a_{2k_2}\cdots a_{mk_m}a_{m+1,\,k_{m+1}}\cdots a_{nk_n}$ where $k_1, k_2, \cdots, k_m$, neglecting the sequence, do *not* take any of the values 1, 2, $\cdots$, m while $k_{m+1}, \cdots, k_n$ take at least one of the values 1, 2, $\cdots$, m. Since $a_{hk}=a_{kh}$ it follows from (13) that each of these terms in *absolute* value is

$$\leqq \tfrac{1}{4}a_{11}a_{22}\cdots a_{mm}a_{m+2,\, m+2}\cdots a_{nn}.$$

All these terms are given the negative sign in the following inequality, thereby emphasizing the inequality.

If we observe the inequalities (16) and (17) and let λ_n be a positive constant to be fixed in value later we have identically the inequality

$$D-\lambda_n a_{11}a_{22}\cdots a_{nn}$$
$$\geqq[(\lambda_m\lambda_{n-m}-\lambda_n)a_{m+1,\ m+1}-\tfrac{1}{4}(n!-m!(n-m)!)a_{mm}]$$
$$\times a_{11}a_{22}\cdots a_{mm}a_{m+2,\ m+2}\cdots a_{nn}.$$

We may assume that $1=\lambda_1>\lambda_2\cdots>\lambda_{n-1}$. The positive constant λ_n we shall at first assume taken in any way but less than each of the products $\lambda_m\lambda_{n-m}$ $(m=1, 2, \cdots, n-1)$; and for brevity we put

$$\frac{1}{4}\,\frac{n!-m!(n-m)!}{\lambda_m\lambda_{n-m}-\lambda_n}=k_{m+1}\qquad (m=1, 2, \cdots, n-1).$$

It is seen that the inequality (15) exists if at least one of the following inequalities exists:

$$a_{m+1,\ m+1}\geqq k_{m+1}a_{mm}\qquad (m=1, 2, \cdots, n-1).$$

Even if none of these inequalities exists, we shall prove that even then the inequality (15) exists.

ART. **220.** If none of the above inequalities exists, we may still prove (15) where all the inequalities

$$(18)\qquad k_2a_{11}>a_{11},\quad k_3a_{22}>a_{33},\quad \cdots,\quad k_na_{n-1,\ n-1}>a_{nn}$$

hold. From (16) and (14) it is seen that the determinants $D_1, D_2, \cdots, D_{n-1}$ are all positive and therefore also $q_1=D_1$, $q_2=\dfrac{D_2}{D_1}, \cdots, q_{n-1}=\dfrac{D_{n-1}}{D_{n-2}}$ are all positive and finite. Whether D_n (and with it f) be positive or not, we may at all events, using the results of Art. 209, write

$$(19)\qquad f=q_1\zeta_1^2+q_2\zeta_2^2+\cdots+q_n\zeta_n^2,$$

where

$$(20)\qquad \begin{cases}\zeta_1=x_1+\gamma_{12}x_2+\cdots+\gamma_{1n}x_n,\\ \zeta_2=\qquad\quad x_2+\cdots+\gamma_{2n}x_n,\\ \cdots\cdots\cdots\cdots\cdots\cdots\cdots\cdots\\ \zeta_n=\qquad\qquad\qquad\quad x_n,\end{cases}$$

with

$$q_n=\frac{D_n}{D_{n-1}}, \qquad \gamma_{hk}=\frac{D\begin{pmatrix}1, \cdots, h-1, h\\ 1, \cdots, h-1, k\end{pmatrix}}{D_h}$$

$$\begin{pmatrix}h=1, 2, \cdots, n-1\\ k=h+1, \cdots, n\end{pmatrix}.$$

And it remains to prove that q_n (and therefore also D_n) is positive. The determinant which stands in the denominator of the quotients for γ_{hk} consists of $h!$ terms, of which from (13) the absolute value is $\leqq \frac{1}{2}a_{11}a_{22}\cdots a_{hh}$, while the numerator of this quotient due to (16) is $\geqq \lambda_h a_{11}a_{22}\cdots a_{hh}$. It follows that

(21) $$\gamma_{hk}\leqq\frac{1}{2}\frac{h!}{\lambda_h}.$$

From (19) and (20) we have $q_1=a_{11}$, $q_2<a_{22}$, $\cdots$, $q_{n-1}\leqq a_{n-1,\, n-1}$; and from this due to (18) it follows that

(22) $$q_1=a_{11}, \quad q_2<k_2a_{22}, \quad \cdots, \quad q_{n-1}<k_2k_3\cdots k_{n-1}a_{11}.$$

ART. **221.** It remains next to show that from the inequalities (I) a finite number may be selected by means of which it may be proved that q_n is *positive* and consequently also f is an essentially positive form. For this important proof we may use the elementary principles which were employed by Dirichlet in such masterful manner (see *Alg. Nos.*, II, p. 225) in his treatment of algebraic units. This method consists in distributing a finite number of quantities into a smaller number of compartments (or intervals) so that at least two of the quantities fall within the same compartment (or interval). Corresponding to the expression (19) for f and having the same $\zeta_1, \zeta_2, \cdots, \zeta_n$, we set up the auxiliary form

(23) $$F=\zeta_1^2+k_2\zeta_2^2+\cdots+k_2k_3\cdots k_{n-1}\zeta_{n-1}^2+\mu\zeta_n^2,$$

where μ has the following meaning:

We let $t_1, t_2, \cdots, t_{n-1}$ have respectively the least integral values for which

(24) $$t_1^2\geqq n, \quad t_2^2>nk_2, \quad \cdots, \quad t_{n-1}^2>nk_2k_3\cdots k_{n-1},$$

and put

$$(25) \qquad \mu = \frac{1}{n t_1^2 t_2^2 \cdots t_{n-1}^2}.$$

Accordingly μ is a definite positive quantity and consequently F is a *positive* form of the variables $x_1, x_2, \cdots, x_n$.

We may show that *integral values* $x_1, x_2, \cdots, x_n$ (where $x_n \neq 0$) *may be found so that* $F \leqq 1$ *for them.* Here we have $\zeta_n = x_n$ as in f. We give to x_n successively the values $x_n = 0, 1, 2, \cdots, t_1 t_2 \cdots t_{n-1}$. We determine for each of these values of x_n *integral* values $x_{n-1}, x_{n-2}, \cdots, x_1$ such that

$$(26) \qquad 0 \leqq \zeta_{n-1} < 1, \quad 0 \leqq \zeta_{n-2} < 1, \quad \cdots, \quad 0 \leqq \zeta_1 < 1.$$

For these $t_1 t_2 \cdots t_{n-1} + 1$ values of x_n, we have *different* systems of values $x_1, x_2, \cdots, x_n$ all of which satisfy the conditions (26).

For each of the values $h = n-1, n-2, \cdots, 1$ we distribute the interval $0 \leqq \zeta_h < 1$ into the t_h intervals $0 \leqq \zeta_h < \dfrac{1}{t_h}$, $\dfrac{1}{t_h} \leqq \zeta_h < \dfrac{2}{t_h}, \cdots, \dfrac{t_h - 1}{t_h} \leqq \zeta_h < 1$. Thus there is a distribution of the entire region defined through (26) into $t_1 t_2 \cdots t_{n-1}$ completely separated regions (intervals). And it is seen that there are two systems, say

$$x_1', x_2', \cdots, x_n'; \qquad x_1'', x_2'', \cdots, x_n'',$$

for which $\zeta_1, \zeta_2, \cdots, \zeta_{n-1}$ belong to the same region (interval). Through the system which is had through the subtraction of these two systems, namely $x_1 = x'' - x_1'$, $x_2 = x_2'' - x_2', \cdots, x_n = x_n'' - x_n'$, it is seen that

$$|\zeta_1| < \frac{1}{t_1}, \quad \cdots, \quad |\zeta_{n-1}| < \frac{1}{t_{n-1}}, \quad |\zeta_n| \leqq t_1 t_2 \cdots t_{n-1}$$

while at the same time $x_n > 0$. It follows further from (27), (24) and (25) that each of the $n-1$ first terms of the expression F is $< \dfrac{1}{n}$, while the nth term $\leqq 1/n$. Hence for the integral system in question, namely, $x_1, x_2, \cdots, x_n$ with positive x_n, the expression F is <1. If the integers $x_1, x_2, \cdots, x_n$ have a divisor >1, it is divided out of F leaving $F<1$. On the other hand paying attention to the expressions (20) for $\zeta_1, \zeta_2, \cdots, \zeta_n$ and the inequalities (21) for the coefficients γ_{hk}, we may determine a finite number of definite integral systems $x_1, x_2, \cdots, x_n$ with positive x_n, which have no greatest common divisor other than unity, which are the only systems of the kind in question that may possibly satisfy the inequalities (27). We derive all such systems and *fourthly* we select of the inequalities (I) those which for these particular systems express that always $f(x_1, x_2, \cdots, x_n) \geqq a_{11}$.

It then follows in view of all the inequalities (I) selected that we must necessarily have

$$q_n \geqq \mu a_{11}. \tag{28}$$

For in the expression (19) for f due to (22) the coefficients of $\zeta_1^2, \zeta_2^2, \cdots, \zeta_{n-1}^2$ are not greater than in $a_{11}F$.

If q_n were greater than μa_{11} we would have for a value of $x_n \neq 0$ always $f < a_{11}F$. But we have an integral system $x_1, x_2, \cdots, x_n$ $(x_n \neq 0)$ for which $F \leqq 1$ while for this system necessitated already through one of the inequalities (I) it is required that $a_{11} \leqq f$. This leads to a contradiction. Hence always $q_n \geqq \mu a_{11}$.

ART. **222.** If we multiply (28) by all the inequalities (18), we have $q_n > \frac{\mu}{k_2 k_3 \cdots k_n} a_{nn}$; and, if we multiply this inequality by D_{n-1} as derived from (16), it follows that

$$D_n > \frac{\lambda_{n-1}\mu}{k_2 k_3 \cdots k_n} a_{11} a_{22} \cdots a_{nn}.$$

Observing the significance of μ as evidenced in (24) and (25), we may derive such a value of λ_n that the inequality (15) for D_n is had. Observing that $\lambda_m \lambda_{n-m} - \lambda_n$ appears in the denominator of the expression defining k_{m+1} $(m=1, 2, \cdots, n-1)$, it is seen that λ_n must be chosen smaller than the $n-1$ quantities $\lambda_m\lambda_{n-m}$ $(m<n)$ and in such a way that

$$\lambda_{n-1} \geqq \lambda_n n k_2 k_3 \cdots k_n([\sqrt{n}]+1)^2([\sqrt{nk_2}]+1)^2 \cdots([\sqrt{nk_2\cdots k_{n-1}}]+1)^2$$

where the brackets [ ] denote the "greatest integer" which they include. This requirement for λ_n may always be met, if we observe that the expression on the right simultaneously decreases with λ_n and tends towards zero with λ_n, according to the manner in which $k_2, k_3, \cdots, k_n$ depend upon λ_n. With this determination of λ_n and due to inequalities already selected from the infinite number of inequalities (I) *it is seen that the inequality (15) for D_n is in all cases true.*

ART. **223.** If we apply to the numerator of the quantity $q_h = \frac{D_h}{D_{h-1}}$ the inequality (16) or (15) and to the denominator the inequality $D_{h-1} \leqq a_{11}a_{22}\cdots a_{h-1,\,h-1}$, we have in general

$$q_h \geqq \lambda_h a_{hh} \qquad (h=1, 2, \cdots, n).$$

And now it *may be shown that a finite number of the inequalities (I) may be selected from which all the others follow.* This is the theorem of Art. 217.

To show this write for every value $l=1, 2, \cdots, n$ the following inequalities:

$$(29) \qquad \lambda_n\xi_n^2<1, \quad \lambda_{n-1}\xi_{n-1}^2<1, \quad \cdots, \quad \lambda_l\xi_l^2<1$$

and for the remaining write

$$(30) \qquad \lambda_{l-1}\xi_{l-2}^2<\frac{l-1}{4}, \qquad \lambda_{l-2}\xi_{l-2}^2<\frac{l-2}{4}, \qquad \cdots, \qquad \lambda_2\xi_2^2<\tfrac{2}{4}, \qquad \lambda_1\xi_1^2<\tfrac{1}{4}.$$

Observe that

$$(31) \qquad \begin{array}{l} \zeta_1 = x_1+\gamma_{12}x_2+\cdots+\gamma_{1n}x_n, \\ \zeta_2 = \qquad\quad x_2+\cdots+\gamma_{2n}x_n, \\ \cdots\cdots\cdots\cdots\cdots\cdots\cdots\cdots \\ \zeta_n = \qquad\qquad\qquad\qquad x_n, \end{array}$$

where

$$(32) \qquad |\gamma_{hk}| \leqq \frac{1}{2}\frac{h!}{\lambda_h}.$$

It is clear that only a finite number of integral systems x_1, $x_2, \cdots, x_n$ can satisfy the above conditions. *Among these we choose for the x's all systems* $s_1^{(l)}, s_2^{(l)}, \cdots, s_n^{(l)}$, *where unity is the greatest common divisor of* $s_l^{(l)}, s_{l+1}^{(l)}, \cdots, s_n^{(l)}$, *and we require that the condition (I) be satisfied for the systems so chosen in all cases.*

Those of the inequalities (I) which previously have been selected in such a way necessitate of themselves all the other (infinite in number) inequalities (I). For let $x_1=s_1^{(l)}$, $x_2=s_2^{(l)}, \cdots, x_n=s_n^{(l)}$ be an integral system which does not belong to the ones already segregated and where unity is the greatest common divisor of $s_1^{(l)}, s_2^{(l)}, \cdots, s_n^{(l)}$. It then follows that not all of the inequalities (29) and (30) are true of the quantities $\zeta_1, \zeta_2, \cdots, \zeta_n$ which belong to f. Suppose that one of those in the series (29) is such that, say, $\lambda_h\zeta^2 \geqq 1$ where $h \geqq l$. It then follows from

$$f=q_1\zeta_1^2+q_2\zeta_2^2+\cdots+q_n\zeta_n^2,$$

if we observe that $q_h \geqq \lambda_h a_{hh}$ and $a_{hh} \geqq a_{ll}$, that f is at once $\geqq a_{ll}$ which was to be proved. If on the other hand all the inequalities (29) are satisfied, let h $(<l)$ be the greatest index for which one of the inequalities (30) is not true, so that $\lambda_h\zeta_h^2>\frac{h}{4}$ or when $h=1$, $\zeta_1^2>\frac{1}{4}$ (since $\lambda_1=1$). From the formula

$$f=q_1\zeta_1^2+q_2\zeta_2^2+\cdots+q_h\zeta_h^2+\cdots+q_n\zeta_n^2,$$

it follows that

$$f \geqq q_h\zeta_h^2+\cdots+q_n\zeta_n^2;$$

and as $q_h \geqq \lambda_h a_{hh}$ it is seen that

$$f \geqq a_{hh}\frac{h}{4}+q_{h+1}\zeta_{h+1}^2+\cdots+q_n\zeta_n^2.$$

Since $a_{11} \leqq a_{22} \leqq \cdots \leqq a_{hh}$, it follows that $a_{11}+a_{22}+\cdots+a_{hh}<ha_{hh}$, and consequently

$$(33)\quad f(x_1, x_2, \cdots, x_n) \geqq \tfrac{1}{4}(a_{11}+a_{22}+\cdots+a_{hh}) + q_{h+1}\zeta_{h+1}^2+\cdots+q_n\zeta_n^2.$$

Now consider the integers $x_{h+1}, x_{h+2}, \cdots, x_n$ fixed while the integers $x_h, x_{h-1}, \cdots, x_2, x_1$ take such values $x_h^*, x_{h-1}^*, \cdots, x_2^*, x_1^*$ that the associated expressions (31) satisfy the conditions

$$(34)\quad -\tfrac{1}{2}\leqq \zeta_h^*\leqq \tfrac{1}{2},\quad -\tfrac{1}{2}\leqq \zeta_{h-1}^*\leqq \tfrac{1}{2},\quad \cdots,\quad -\tfrac{1}{2}\leqq \zeta_1^*\leqq \tfrac{1}{2}.$$

We thus have a modified integral system $x_1^*, x_2^*, \cdots, x_n^*$ in which $x_l^*=x_l, \cdots, x_n^*=x_n$; and due to the definition of reduced forms the greatest common divisor of $x_l^*, \cdots, x_n^*$ is unity. And this system $x_1^*, x_2^*, \cdots, x_n^*$ satisfies all the conditions of (29) and (30) for which we have already assumed that $f\geqq a_{ll}$. However, since $a_{kh}>q_k$ it follows from (33) and (34) that

$$f(x_1, x_2, \cdots, x_n)\geqq f(x_1^*, x_2^*, \cdots, x_n^*)\geqq a_{ll}.$$

And this completes the theorem enunciated at the beginning of this article.

ART. 224. **The Edges of the Reduced Realm**. The results of the preceding articles, as we shall now show, are embodied in the following theorem: *The reduced realm* B *is a convex cone with its vertex at the origin $f=0$ which is bounded by a finite number of planes that pass through the origin.* In the entire reduced realm B we have $a_{11}\geqq 0$. The points within this realm for which $a_{11}>0$ correspond to positive forms. The points for which $a_{11}=0$ satisfy also the conditions (Art. 15) $a_{12}=0, a_{13}=0, \cdots, a_{1n}=0$. Accordingly there is a $n(n+1)/2-n=n(n-1)/2$ ply manifold on the boundary of B. The inequalities which serve to characterize the reduced realm have each the form

$$\text{(I, II)}\qquad \sum m_{hk}a_{hk}\geqq 0,$$

where the m_{hk} are certain given numerical coefficients. Among such inequalities are those of (13) and (14). In his *Gesammelte Abhandlungen*, Vol. I, p. 155, Minkowski writes: "There are positive reduced forms f, for which $n(n+1)/2-1$ of the linearly independent inequalities (I, II) become equations. Through these the ratios of the

$n(n+1)/2$ quantities a_{ik} are completely determined in a rational manner." Such reduced forms may be called *limit-forms* (Grenzformen). Among such there is clearly *one* whose coefficients are integers whose G.D.C. $=1$. This is called a *primitive* limit form. Since the number of inequalities is limited, there is only a finite number of primitive forms. These primitive forms are then given by Minkowski for the cases $n=2, 3, 4, 5$.

From the above it follows that *if f is a reduced form then also is every product cf, where c is a positive factor;* and if f and g are two reduced forms then also is every relation $(1-t)f+tg$, where $0<t<1$, a reduced form.

The general principles (Art. 33) offer the following explanations regarding the necessary inequalities chosen from (I, II) that are really necessary for the definition of the realm B. A reduced form φ that does not vanish identically is called an *edge form*, if it is not possible to express φ as a sum of two reduced forms which do not vanish identically and are not positive multiples of each other. Hence $\varphi \neq (1-t)f+tg$, where f and g are reduced forms. Observing that we are now representing forms by points, it is seen that a point which is an edge form can only be on an edge that forms a part of the region B.

An edge form is completely characterized as a reduced form, *if of the inequalities (I, II) any $n(n+1)/2-1$ of them are linearly independent equations in a_{hk}.* We regard forms that are multiples of one another as *not* essentially different. And consequently there is only a finite number of essentially different edge forms (points). The rays from the origin to these points form the edges of the reduced realm.

Of the inequalities (I, II) there may be used as defining the reduced realm only such a one as essential which put $=0$ offers a plane being any one of the $n(n+1)/2-1$ equations that are sufficient to determine the ratios of the coordinates of a_{hk} of the form (point) f.

Thus through $n(n+1)/2-1$ edge forms (points) a plane is uniquely determined. *Those of the inequalities (I, II) thus determined constitute the walls of the reduced realm.* All other inequalities (I, II) by this definition of a reduced realm may be neglected as following from the selected inequalities. On each edge of the reduced realm a form (point) is taken. For example, take one in which the first of the coefficients $a_{11}, a_{22}, \cdots, a_{nn}$ (that $\neq 0$) has the value 1. This may always be done by sliding the point up and down the edge, since it is zero at the origin. We thus have a finite number of completely determined forms $\varphi_1, \varphi_2, \cdots, \varphi_r$. The reduced realm is thus seen to be bounded by a convex cone with the vertex at the origin. There is an infinite number of ways of choosing the forms $\varphi_1, \varphi_2, \cdots, \varphi_r$ dependent upon the positions chosen for the forms (points) on the edges of the cone.

We thus have the theorem: *Every reduced form f may in one (or infinitely many ways) be expressed through the equation*

$$f = c_1\varphi_1 + c_2\varphi_2 + \cdots + c_r\varphi_r, \tag{35}$$

where the coefficients $c_1, c_2, \cdots, c_r$ are all $\geqq 0$; and reciprocally every form that may be expressed in this way is reduced.

ART. 225. **The Neighboring Rooms of the Reduced Realm.** In connection with the reduced forms we may prove further the theorem: *The integral substitutions with determinant ± 1 which are capable of transforming positive reduced forms again into reduced forms are finite in number.*

This theorem may also be expressed in the following manner: *In the realm of the positive forms the reduced region is bound by only a finite number of the equivalent rooms.*

Let S:

$$x_h = s_{h1}y_1 + s_{h2}y_2 + \cdots + s_{hn}y_n \qquad (h=1, 2, \cdots, n)$$

be a unimodular integral substitution which transforms $f = \sum a_{hk}x_hx_k$ into $g = \sum b_{hk}y_hy_k$, where both forms are reduced and $a_{11} > 0$. We thus have

$$f(s_{1k}, s_{2k}, \cdots, s_{nk}) = b_{kk} \qquad (k=1, 2, \cdots, n). \tag{36}$$

If s_{hk} is the last of the integers $s_{1k}, s_{2k}, \cdots, s_{nk}$ that is different from zero, we have, using the previous meaning of q_h (Art. 209, formula (3)),

$$b_{kk} \geqq q_h \geqq \lambda_h a_{hh} \geqq \lambda_n a_{hh}.$$

From this [1] we may show first that

$$b_{ll} \geqq \lambda_n a_{ll} \qquad (l=1, 2, \cdots, n)$$

for every index l. For if for an index l we had $b_{ll} < \lambda_n a_{ll}$, it would follow that

$$b_{11} \leqq b_{22} \leqq \cdots \leqq b_{ll} < \lambda_n a_{ll} \leqq \lambda_n a_{l+1,\, l+1} \leqq \cdots \leqq \lambda_n a_{nn},$$

which is contrary to the above. In these inequalities substitute the left hand side of (36) for b_{kk} and express $f(s_{1k}, s_{2k}, \cdots, s_{nk})$ in terms of a_{kk}. It is seen that when $h \geqq l$ and that is when $h = l, l+1, \cdots, n$, while $k = 1, 2, \cdots, l$, then the quantities s_{hk} are all zero. And since by hypothesis $s_{1k}, s_{2k}, \cdots, s_{h-1,\, k}$ are also zero, we have in the determinant of the substitution S a column consisting of only zeros, while this determinant is by hypothesis $= \pm 1$.

In an analogous manner since g is transformed into f through an unimodular integral substitution, we have always

$$(37) \qquad a_{kk} \geqq \lambda_n b_{kk} \qquad (k=1, 2, \cdots, n).$$

We shall now assume *first* that the following inequalities exist, namely

$$(38) \qquad b_{kk} \geqq \lambda_n a_{k+1,\, k+1} \qquad (k=1, 2, \cdots, n-1).$$

It then follows in virtue of (37) that

$$a_{kk} \geqq \lambda_n^2 a_{k-1,\, k-1}$$

and therefore also

$$a_{11} \geqq \lambda_n^{2k-2} a_{kk} \geqq \lambda_n^{2k-1} b_{kk} \qquad (k=1, 2, \cdots, n).$$

Observe that $q_h \geqq \lambda_n a_{hh} \geqq \lambda_n a_{11}$. It is seen that values of

[1] See also Camille Jordan, *Journ. de l'École Polytechnique*, Vol. 48, p. 217.

$\zeta_1, \zeta_2, \cdots, \zeta_n$ that are associated with $x_1=s_{1k}, \cdots, x_n=s_{nk}$ when account is taken of (36) are such that we have the inequality

$$\begin{aligned} f&=q_1\zeta_1^2+q_2\zeta_2^2+\cdots+q_n\zeta_n^2 \\ &=\lambda_1 a_{11}\zeta_1^2+\cdots+\lambda_n a_{nn}\zeta_n^2 \\ &\leqq \lambda_1\lambda_n^{2k-1}b_{kk}\zeta_1^2+\cdots+\lambda_n\lambda_n^{2k-1}b_{kk}\zeta_n^2, \end{aligned}$$

since b_{kk} is the value of f for the values of ζ's in question. This inequality, when divided through by b_{kk}, becomes

$$1 \geqq \lambda_n^{2k}(\zeta_1^2+\zeta_2^2+\cdots+\zeta_n^2);$$

and from this it is clear that for every vertical column s_{1k}, $s_{2k}, \cdots, s_{nk}$ of S there exist only a finite number of integral systems.

ART. **226.** If the assumption (38) is *not* admissible, let l be the greatest index for which

$$(39) \qquad b_{l-1,\, l-1} < \lambda_n a_{ll}.$$

There are then four sorts of conditions to be considered.

First it is seen as in the preceding article that all the coefficients

$$s_{hk} \qquad \begin{pmatrix} h=l, l+1, \cdots, n \\ k=1, 2, \cdots, l-1 \end{pmatrix}$$

are zero and the substitution S then becomes

$$\begin{aligned} x_h &= s_{h1}y_1+\cdots+s_{h,\,l-1}y_{l-1}+s_{hl}y_l+\cdots+s_{hn}y_n, \quad &\text{if} \quad h<l, \\ x_h &= s_{hl}y_l+\cdots+s_{hn}y_n, \quad &\text{if} \quad h\geqq l. \end{aligned}$$

It is now seen that

$$x_h=s_{h1}y_1+\cdots+s_{h,\,l-1}y_{l-1} \quad (h=1, 2, \cdots, l-1)$$

is an unimodular integral substitution of $l-1$ variables through which the positive form $f(x_1, \cdots, x_{l-1}, 0, \cdots, 0)$ is transformed into $g(y_1, \cdots, y_{l-1}, 0, \cdots, 0)$, both being reduced forms in $l-1$ variables. Using the inductive method of proof, the theorem being evident for forms of one variable, we assume that the theorem to be proved is already proved for forms with fewer than n variables. And that is *secondly* we assume for the coefficients

$$s_{hk} \qquad \begin{pmatrix} h=1, 2, \cdots, l-1 \\ k=1, 2, \cdots, l-1 \end{pmatrix}$$

that there exist only a finite number of systems.

Our assumption regarding the number l carries with it, if $l<n$, the relations $b_{kk} \geqq \lambda_n a_{k+1,\ k+1}$ ($k=l, l+1, \cdots, n-1$), from which and by means of (39) we further have $a_{kk} \geqq \lambda_n^2 a_{k+1,\ k+1}$ ($k=l, l+1, \cdots, n-1$). We thus have

$$a_{ll} \geqq \lambda_n^{2k-2l} a_{kk} \geqq \lambda_n^{2k-2l+1} b_{kk} \quad (k=l, l+1, \cdots, n-1, n),$$

this inequality existing also for $l=n$, $k=n$.

The equation (36) for b_{kk} offers for the values ζ_l, ζ_{l+1}, $\cdots$, ζ_n, which belong to s_{lk}, $s_{l+1,\ k}$, $\cdots$, s_{nk}, the relation

$$\lambda_n^{2k-2l+2}(\zeta_l^2+\zeta_{l+1}^2+\cdots+\zeta_n^2) \leqq 1.$$

And from this in the *third* place it is seen that for the numbers s_{hk} ($h=l, l+1, \cdots, n$; $k=l, l+1, \cdots, n$) there exists only a finite number of systems.

Finally g, as a reduced form, must satisfy in particular all inequalities $g(y_1, \cdots, y_{l-1}, e_l^{(k)}, \cdots, e_n^{(k)}) \geqq b_{kk}$ ($k=l, l+1, \cdots, n$), in which $e_k^k=1$, $e_h^k=0$, and $y_1, \cdots, y_{l-1}$ are arbitrary integers. These equalities exist due to the peculiar form already fixed of the substitution S upon the collective inequalities

$$f(x_1, x_2, \cdots, x_{l-1}, s_{lk}, \cdots, s_{nk}) \geqq f(s_{1k}, \cdots, s_{l-1,\ k}, s_{lk}, \cdots, s_{nk}) \qquad (k=l, l+1, \cdots, n)$$

for arbitrary integers $x_1, \cdots, x_{l-1}$. A similar treatment, as is found at the end of Art. 224, gives for the quantities $\zeta_{l-1}, \cdots, \zeta_1$, expressed in terms of $s_{1k}, \cdots, s_{nk}$ ($k \geqq l$), the conditions

$$\tfrac{1}{4}(q_1+\cdots+q_h) \geqq q_1\zeta_1^2+\cdots+q_h\zeta_h^2 \qquad (h=l-1, l-2, \cdots, 1).$$

From these conditions the following conditions are immediate consequences:

$$\lambda_n \zeta_{l-1}^2 \leqq \frac{l-1}{4}, \qquad \cdots, \qquad \lambda_n \zeta_1^2 \leqq \frac{1}{4}.$$

And from these it further follows in the *fourth* place that for the numbers s_{hk} $(h=1, 2, \cdots, l-1; k=l, l+1, \cdots, n)$ there exist only a finite number of systems.

With this the proof of the theorem in question is completed in every particular.

ART. **227. The Determinant-Surfaces.** Consider all forms f whose determinants have the same value, c $(c\neq 0)$ say, and that is $D(f)=c$. As these forms are denoted by points, it is seen that $D(f)=c$ is a surface in the realm of positive forms (points). As c varies we have sheaves of surfaces that are similar and similarly situated with respect to the origin, so that in the present discussion we may take $c=1$.

We shall prove here the following theorem: *If f and g are two different positive forms of determinant 1 and if t is an arbitrary value >0 and <1, then $(1-t)f+tg$ is also a positive form with determinant >1.*

If only one of the forms is positive, we are always able to find [1] a linear substitution with determinant $=1$ and with real coefficients through which f and g are transformed simultaneously into $\alpha_1 z_1^2+\alpha_2 z_2^2+\cdots+\alpha_n z_n^2$ and $\beta_1 z_1^2+\beta_2 z_2^2+\cdots+\beta_n z_n^2$, expressions which contain only the squares of the new variables.

The determinant of the form $(1-t)f+tg$ takes the product expression

$$\Delta(t)=[\alpha_1+t(\beta_1-\alpha_1)][\alpha_2+t(\beta_2-\alpha_2)]\cdots[\alpha_n+t(\beta_n-\alpha_n)],$$

where by hypothesis

$$\Delta(0)=\alpha_1\alpha_2\cdots\alpha_n=1, \qquad \Delta(1)=\beta_1\beta_2\cdots\beta_n=1.$$

[1] See for example Böcher, *Introduction to Higher Algebra*, p. 171.

It is seen that

$$\frac{d^2 \log \Delta(t)}{dt^2} = -\left[\frac{\beta_1-\alpha_1}{\alpha_1+t(\beta_1-\alpha_1)}\right]^2 - \cdots - \left[\frac{\beta_n-\alpha_n}{\alpha_n+t(\beta_n-\alpha_n)}\right]^2,$$

an expression which is negative in the entire interval $0 \leqq t \leqq 1$. Hence in a plane whose coordinates are t and u, the curve $u = \log \Delta(t)$ in the interval $0 \leqq t \leqq 1$ is convex with respect to the t axis, and as $\log \Delta(t)$ is zero at the two end points $t=1$, $t=0$ respectively, and positive within this interval, it is seen that $\Delta(t) > 1$.

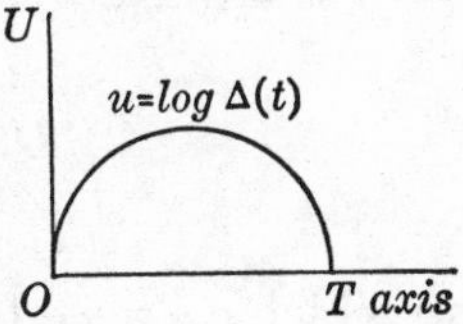

FIG. 139

If we put $c(1-t)\alpha_h = a_h$ and $ct\beta_h = b_h$ $(h=1, 2, \cdots, n)$, where $c>0$, it follows from the inequality $\Delta(t)>1$ that

$$\sqrt[n]{(a_1+b_1)(a_2+b_2)\cdots(a_n+b_n)} > \sqrt[n]{a_1a_2\cdots a_n} + \sqrt[n]{b_1b_2\cdots b_n},$$

if $a_1, a_2, \cdots, a_n$ and $b_1, b_2, \cdots, b_n$ are all positive quantities which are *not* connected by the relation $a_1 : a_2 : \cdots : a_n = b_1 : b_2 : \cdots : b_n$. For, denote the product of any n quantities, say $m_1, m_2, \cdots, m_n$, by π. In the inequality

$$\pi\{(1-t)\alpha_i + t\beta_i\} > 1 \quad (=1-t+t)$$

write $\alpha_i' = (1-t)\alpha_i$, $\beta_i' = t\beta_i$, and we have

$$\sqrt[n]{\pi(\alpha_i'+\beta_i')} > \sqrt[n]{\pi\alpha_i'} + \sqrt[n]{\pi\beta_i'}.$$

Multiply each side of this inequality by c and put $a_i = c\alpha_i$, $b_i = c\beta_i$. This offers the required result, where it may be observed that no restriction is put on the a's or the b's.

The above result, established for the surface $D(f)=1$, may be expressed as follows:

If we construct at any point of the determinant surface $D(f)=1$ which corresponds to a positive form f, the tangent plane to this surface, then in the entire realm of the positive forms it is seen that this determinant surface neglecting the point of contact lies completely on the side of the plane away from the origin.

The position of the point g above, if g is taken as a positive form, relative to the tangential plane to $D(f)=\text{cons.}$, leads to the following interesting inequality: In the space of $n(n+1)/2$ dimensions of which the coordinates are a_{11}, $a_{12}, \cdots, a_{1n}, a_{22}, \cdots, a_{2n}, \cdots, a_{nn}$ we seek the equation of the tangent plane to the surface

$$D(f)=\begin{vmatrix} a_{11}, & \cdots, & a_{1n} \\ \cdots & \cdots & \cdots \\ a_{n1}, & \cdots, & a_{nn} \end{vmatrix}=1,$$

in which $a_{ij}=a_{ji}$ $(i\neq j)$, at the point f_0 of $D(f)=1$ for which $a_{jj}=\alpha_j$ $(j=1, \cdots, n)$, $a_{ij}=0$ $(i\neq j)$. (This point corresponds to the quadratic form $f_0=\alpha_1x_1^2+\alpha_2x_2^2+\cdots+\alpha_nx_n^2$.)

The equation of this tangent plane is

$$(1)\quad (a_{11}-\alpha_1)\left[\frac{\partial D(f)}{\partial a_{11}}\right]_{f=f_0} + (a_{12}-0)\left[\frac{\partial D(f)}{\partial a_{12}}\right]_{f=f_0}+\cdots+(a_{nn}-\alpha_n)\left[\frac{\partial D(f)}{\partial a_{nn}}\right]_{f=f_0}=0.$$

Since $\dfrac{\partial D(f)}{\partial a_{ij}}=A_{ij}$, where A_{ij} is the cofactor of a_{ij} in D, we have

$$\left[\frac{\partial D(f)}{\partial a_{jk}}\right]_{f=f_0}=[A_{jk}]_{f=f_0}=\begin{cases}\prod_{i=1}^{n}\alpha_i/\alpha_j=1/\alpha_j \text{ if } j=k; \; =0 \text{ if } j\neq k.\end{cases}$$

The equation (1) then becomes $\sum_{j=1}^{n}(a_{jj}-\alpha_j)/\alpha_j=0$ or

$$(2)\qquad \sum_{j=1}^{n}\frac{a_{jj}}{\alpha_j}-n=0.$$

The other point of $D(f)=1$ in normal form, namely $g_0 : a_{jj}=\beta_j$ $(j=1, \cdots, n)$, $a_{ij}=0$ $(i\neq j)$ (i.e., the point corresponding to the positive quadratic form $g_0=\beta_1x_1^2+\beta_2x_2^2+\cdots+\beta_nx_n^2$), lies on the opposite side of this plane from the origin. Hence

$$(3)\qquad \sum_{j=1}^{n}\frac{\beta_j}{\alpha_j}-n>0.$$

Since $\prod_{i=1}^{n} \alpha_i = \prod_{i=1}^{n} \beta_i = 1$ we have at once

$$(4) \qquad \frac{1}{n}\left(\frac{\beta_1}{\alpha_1}+\cdots+\frac{\beta_n}{\alpha_n}\right) > \sqrt[n]{\frac{\beta_1\cdots\beta_n}{\alpha_1\cdots\alpha_n}}.$$

This is the well known inequality between the arithmetic and geometric mean of n positive quantities that are not all equal. From the above it is clear that *the determinant surface $D(f)=1$ is in the realm of the positive forms everywhere convex when seen from the origin.*

ART. **228. The Problem of the Densest Lattice-Formed Placement of Spheres.** For the coefficient a_{11} of a positive reduced form f we have always $f(x_1, x_2, \cdots, x_n) \geqq a_{11}$, where $x_1, x_2, \cdots, x_n$ are rational integers, whose G.C.D. $=1$, and are not all simultaneously zero. Accordingly a_{11} is the least quantity that may be expressed through the *form* f by means of integers that do not simultaneously vanish. We call this quantity the *minimum* of the form f and denote it by $M(f)$. It is, as is the reduced form, an *invariant of the class* f.

Due to the inequality (14), it follows from (15) that

$$D(f) \geqq \lambda_n[M(f)]^n.$$

From this it is seen that $\frac{M(f)}{\sqrt[n]{D(f)}}$ does not exceed a certain limit which depends only upon n. The question was raised by Hermite regarding the *precise maximum* of the value of this quotient. Korkine and Zolotareff [1] make the following definition: *A positive quadratic form in n variables is called an* ***extreme*** *form (its class an* ***extreme*** *class) if, with infinitesimal variations of the form, the quotient* $\frac{M(f)}{\sqrt[n]{D(f)}}$ *never increases.* Observe that when the form is subjected to variations we may multiply the form that has undergone the variation by a suitably chosen factor and keep the minimum $M(f)$ un-

[1] *Math. Ann.*, Vol. 6, p. 366 and Vol. 11, p. 242.

changed. Hence we may say: *A positive form is extreme if by no variation of the form, which leaves the minimum unchanged, the determinant never increases.*

ART. 229. A remarkable geometric meaning exists for the extreme classes of forms: If we bring a positive quadratic form $f(x_1, x_2, \cdots, x_n)$ to the form $f=\xi_1^2+\xi_2^2+\cdots+\xi_n^2$, where the ξ's are n real linear forms in the x's, and if we consider $\xi_1, \xi_2, \cdots, \xi_n$ as rectangular coordinates in a space $\mathfrak{R}_n$ of n dimensions, we may regard $f\leqq 1$ as an n-dimensional sphere of radius 1 in $\mathfrak{R}_n$. Its volume in $\xi_1, \xi_2, \cdots, \xi_n$ is

$$\gamma_n=\frac{\pi^{n/2}}{\Gamma\left(1+\frac{n}{2}\right)} \qquad \text{(Art. 80).}$$

The points $x_1=m_1, x_2=m_2, \cdots, x_n=m_n$, where $m_1, m_2, \cdots, m_n$ are integers, constitute in the space $\mathfrak{R}_n$ a lattice with the density $\dfrac{1}{\sqrt{D(f)}}$. For the individual parallelopipeds

$$m_h-\tfrac{1}{2}\leqq x_h\leqq m_h+\tfrac{1}{2} \qquad (h=1, 2, \cdots, n),$$

with these points as centers, collectively fill the space $\mathfrak{R}_n$ without any gaps. They are congruent one to the other and about each lattice point each parallelopiped has a volume $=\sqrt{D(f)}$. (See Art. 148, I, end.)

Next observe that the n-dimensional hyperspheres about the individual lattice points

$$\xi_1^2+\xi_2^2+\cdots+\xi_n^2\leqq\frac{M(f)}{4}=r^2$$

may touch one another only on their boundaries. It follows that

$$\gamma_n(\tfrac{1}{2}\sqrt{M(f)})^n<\sqrt{D(f)},$$

a formula which is of the same nature as (41) though preferable to it. If we keep the meaning of the coordinates $\xi_1, \xi_2, \cdots, \xi_n$ in $\mathfrak{R}_n$ fixed and vary the coefficients of f in such a way that $M(f)$ remains unaltered, then these spheres remain unaltered both in size and in the property of not cutting one another. Only the lattice of their centers is changed. *Hence* (see Arts. 158, 159 and 163) *the question regarding the maximum of* $\frac{M(f)}{\sqrt[n]{D(f)}}$, *and that is regarding the extreme classes of forms, considered geometrically, is of the same significance as the question regarding the densest lattice-formed placement of equal spheres in a space of n dimensions.*

The notion of such problems was introduced by Hermite in his "Introduction des variables continues dans la theorie des nombres," *Oeuvres*, T. I, pp. 164–192.

ART. 230. Determination of the Extreme Classes of Forms. Korkine and Zolotareff proved a series of interesting properties of the extreme classes. The method of reduction that has been developed above the positive forms permits us to bring to a conclusion the theory of the extreme forms in a very satisfactory manner.

We denote a reduced form as an *extreme* form with regard to the reduced realm, if *by all the infinitesimal variations of the form by which the form remains in the reduced realm, the quotient* $\frac{M(f)}{\sqrt[n]{D(f)}}$ *never increases.*

If f is a positive form and if we construct a tangential plane at the point f of the determinant surface $D(f) = \text{const.}$ which goes through f, then as seen above (Art. 226) the surface $D(f)$ lies in the region of the positive forms (the point f excepted) entirely on the side of the tangential plane away from the origin. Hence if we move in this tangent plane away from the point f, the determinant decreases. (See Figs. 140 and 141.) If now f is *reduced*, but is not an *edge form* of the reduced realm, we may express f as the sum of two positive reduced forms φ, ψ which are not multiples of each other. Let φ^*, ψ^* be those multiples of φ, ψ which fall in the tangential plane. Then f lies within the straight line stretch that connects φ^* and ψ^*. Observe that *either the coefficient* a_{11} *increases as we leave* f *and continue on one of the sides of this stretch, or it is constant on the entire stretch.*

And then it would be always possible so to vary f (by multiplying it by a constant, for example) that $D(f)$ decreases and simultaneously $M(f)$ does not increase. Consequently $\frac{M(f)}{\sqrt[n]{D(f)}}$ increases, and f in all events would not be an extreme form in the reduced realm. We accordingly have the result:

An extreme form with respect to the reduced realm can only be an edge form in this realm.

ART. **231.** We now let $f=(a_{hk})$ be a positive edge form of the reduced realm and *extreme* with regard to this realm. We again lay the determinant surface through f and draw the tangent plane to it at f. Let $g=(b_{hk})$ be another *positive edge form* of this realm, and let cg be that multiple of g that falls on the tangent plane. It is seen that by a continuation on the stretch from f to cg the minimum does not increase nor does it remain constant. Hence $cb_{11}<a_{11}$, or $c<a_{11}/b_{11}$. The equation of the tangent plane may be written

$$(a_{11}-a_{11})\left[\frac{\partial D}{\partial a_{11}}\right]_{f=\bar{f}}+\cdots+(a_{1h}-\bar{a}_{1h})\left[\frac{\partial D}{\partial a_{1h}}\right]_{f=\bar{f}}+\cdots$$
$$+(a_{nn}-\bar{a}_{nn})\left[\frac{\partial D}{\partial a_{nn}}\right]_{f=\bar{f}}=0.$$

The negative terms in this expression that are not zero are

$$\bar{a}_{11}\left[\frac{\partial D}{\partial a_{11}}\right]_{f=\bar{f}}+\cdots+\bar{a}_{nn}\left[\frac{\partial D}{\partial a_{nn}}\right]_{f=\bar{f}}=nD(f).$$

It follows that

$$c\sum\frac{\partial D(f)}{\partial a_{hk}}b_{hk}=nD(f).$$

Writing for c its value from above it follows that

$$\text{(43)} \qquad \frac{1}{nD(f)}\sum\frac{\partial D(f)}{\partial a_{hk}}b_{hk}>\frac{b_{11}}{a_{11}}.$$

If on the other hand a positive edge form of the reduced realm satisfies the condition (43) with respect to every other positive edge form g of the realm, then is f an extreme form with regard *to the reduced realm.* For due to formula (35) every arbitrary reduced form may be expressed as an aggregate Σcg of edge forms and then accordingly this inequality (43) would exist for every arbitrary reduced form which was not a multiple of f.

In this generalization the inequality (43) in fact says that with every infinitesimal variation of f, so long as the variation remains in the reduced realm, and not only moving on the ray from the origin to the point f, the quantity $\frac{M(f)}{\sqrt[n]{D(f)}}$ always decreases.

If next a class f is to be an extreme class, it is at all events necessary that every individual reduced form in the class be an extreme form with respect to the reduced realm. The inverse of this theorem is also true and accordingly we have the following theorem as a characterization of the extreme classes.

A positive class of forms f is only then and always then an extreme class if every individual reduced form of the class is an extreme form with regard to the reduced realm.

In fact, let this condition be satisfied for the class of a positive form $f=\Sigma a_{hk}x_hx_k$. We determine all existing unimodular integral substitutions S which transpose f into a reduced form. We further determine in every case for the reduced form $g=\Sigma b_{hk}y_hy_k$, that is brought about by the substitution S, a positive quantity ϵ_S of the following nature: The region of all forms $g^*=\Sigma(b_{hk}+\epsilon_{hk})y_hy_k$ for which all quantities $|\epsilon_{hk}|<\epsilon_S$, so long as it falls in the reduced realm, shall strike only such side walls of this realm that also contain g, and, besides upon the edge drawn from the origin to g, it must offer everywhere smaller values of the function $M(f):\sqrt[n]{D(f)}$ than at the point g. Finally we determine a positive quantity δ such that all forms $\Sigma\delta_{hk}x_hx_k$ where $|\delta_{hk}|<\delta$ are transformed through the substitutions S only into such forms $\Sigma\epsilon_{hk}y_hy_k$ in which the absolute values $|\epsilon_{hk}|<\epsilon_S$. When this has been done, the entire realm of the forms expressed through $f^*=\Sigma(a_{hk}+\delta_{hk})x_hx_k$, where

$|\delta_{hk}| < \delta$, can only strike such walls in the individual rooms $B_{S^{-1}}$ to which f belong that are equivalent to the reduced realm B and cannot fall outside of these rooms $B_{S^{-1}}$. Hence associated with each such form f^* there exists at least one of the substitutions S which transforms it simultaneously with f into a reduced form; and consequently in this entire realm, excepting on the ray drawn from the origin to f, the function $M(f) : \sqrt[n]{D(f)}$ is always smaller than at f.

The positive edge forms on the surface $D(f) = 1$ which have the greatest possible value of a_{11}, necessarily represent extreme classes and *determine the precise upper limit of all values of* $\dfrac{M(f)}{\sqrt[n]{D(f)}}$.

ART. 232. **The Binary, Ternary, and Quaternary Forms.** Due to the Articles 217–223, we may determine the side walls and the edges of the reduced realms for every value of n and we may also determine all the extreme classes of forms.

Minkowski, *Ges. Abhandl.*, Vol. I, p. 156, denoted by $(a)_\nu$ the quadratic form in ν variables where a takes the place of every element in the principal diagonal of the determinant of the form and where unity is the value of all the other elements. Thus $\varphi = (2)_i$ $(i = 2, 3, 4)$ is an extreme form for $n = 2, 3, 4$. (See later in Art. 233.) These values were given by Korkine and Zolotareff, Math. Ann., Vol. 11, where we find on p. 270 as the extreme form (D in all cases is the determinant of the form) for $n = 2$:

$$\sqrt{\frac{4}{3}D}(x_1^2 + x_2^2 + x_1x_2);$$

for $n = 3$:

$$\sqrt[3]{2D}(x_1^2 + x_2^2 + x_3^2 + x_1x_2 + x_1x_3 + x_2x_3);$$

while on p. 273 two extreme forms are given for $n = 4$:

$$2\sqrt[4]{\frac{D}{5}}(x_1^2 + x_2^2 + x_3^2 + x_4^2 + x_1x_2 + x_1x_3 + x_1x_4 + x_2x_3 + x_2x_4 + x_3x_4)$$

and also

$$\sqrt[4]{4D}(x_1^2+x_2^2+x_3^2+x_4^2+x_1x_4+x_2x_4+x_3x_4).$$

On p. 292 three extreme forms are given for $n=5$.

With Minkowski we may determine for any value n the side walls and their edges of the reduced realm and may also derive all the extreme classes of forms. We may show as follows in *the cases $n=2, 3, 4$, when the inequalities* exist, namely

$$f(s_1, s_2, \cdots, s_n) \geqq a_{ll} \qquad (l=1, 2, \cdots, n),$$

where $s_l=1$, and the remaining s_h are $=\pm 1$, or are in part $=0$, that the other inequalities (I) follow themselves. For observe that by making $x_1=\pm y_1$, $x_2=\pm y_2$, $\cdots$, $x_n=\pm y_n$ we may consider in the form $f(m_1, m_2, \cdots, m_n)$ all the m's positive or zero and with the proof of the theorem for the m's all positive, the proof *eo ipso* holds for a less number of variables. The proof is derived by showing that

$$f(m_1, m_2, \cdots, m_n) \geqq f(m_1-u_1, \cdots, m_n-u_n),$$

where the u's are determined as follows: Let m_j be the last of the sequence of numbers $m_1, m_2, \cdots, m_n$ which has the least value and write $u_h=m_j$ except when $h=j$, in which case put $u_j=0$. We then have always

$$m_h-u_h \geqq 0, \qquad m_n-u_n>0;$$

and these n quantities are smaller than the original m's with the exception of one quantity which remains unchanged. We have

$$f(m_1, m_2, \cdots, m_n)-f(m_1-u_1, m_2-u_2, \cdots, m_n-u_n)$$
$$=m_j^2[f(1, 1, \cdots, 1)-a_{jj}]+2\sum_{h\neq j}(m_h-m_j)m_j\sum_{k\neq j}a_{hk}.$$

On the right-hand side of this expression observe that $f(1, 1, \cdots, 1)\geqq a_{jj}$ by hypothesis and that $\sum_{k\neq j}a_{hk}$ remains positive so long as $n\leqq 4$ due to the fact that $a_{hh}\pm 2a_{hk}\geqq 0$. And this proves that

$$f(m_1, m_2, \cdots, m_n)\geqq f(m_1-u_1, m_2-u_2, \cdots, m_n-u_n).$$

A repeated use of this result proves the initial statement.

ART. **233.** If we express a form f as indicated below, the positive edge forms with $M(f)=2$ in the cases $n=2, 3, 4$ are

$$\begin{pmatrix}2, & 1\\ 1, & 2\end{pmatrix}, \quad \begin{pmatrix}2, & 1, & 1\\ 1, & 2, & 1\\ 1, & 1, & 2\end{pmatrix}, \quad \begin{pmatrix}2, & 1, & 1, & 1\\ 1, & 2, & 1, & 1\\ 1, & 1, & 2, & 1\\ 1, & 1, & 1, & 2\end{pmatrix}, \quad \begin{pmatrix}2, & 0, & 0, & 1\\ 0, & 2, & 0, & 1\\ 0, & 0, & 2, & 1\\ 1, & 1, & 1, & 2\end{pmatrix}.$$

The associated determinants are 3, 4, 5 and 4.

All these forms are extreme forms. For example, when $n=3$. The conditions for a reduced form are then

$$a_{11} \leqq a_{22} \leqq a_{33}; \qquad a_{hh} \geqq 2|a_{hk}| \qquad (h, k=1, 2, 3; h \neq k)$$

Write

$$D = \begin{vmatrix}2, & 1, & 1\\ 1, & 2, & 1\\ 1, & 1, & 2\end{vmatrix},$$

$$D+\Delta(D) = \begin{vmatrix}2, & 1-\epsilon_1, & 1-\epsilon_2\\ 1-\epsilon_1, & 2+\epsilon_3, & 1+\epsilon_3/2-\epsilon_4\\ 1-\epsilon_2, & 1+\epsilon_3/2-\epsilon_4, & 2+\epsilon_3+\epsilon_5\end{vmatrix},$$

where the ϵ's are all positive. These variations of f include all forms that are restrained to remain in the reduced region. The latter determinant expanded $=D+$ positive ϵ's, when ϵ's of the second dimension are neglected. Hence $\dfrac{M(f)}{\sqrt[3]{D(f)}}$ never increases.

Similarly it is seen that in a four-dimensional space there exist two essentially different densest lattice-formed placements of equal spheres. The cases $n=5$ and $n=6$ are found in a table on p. 218 of Vol. I of Minkowski's *Gesammelte Abhandlungen.*

ART. **234. Volumes of Reduced Realms that Extend to the Determinant Surfaces.** By the volume of a region in the manifold A of the quadratic forms we understand the value of the $n(n+1)/2$ ply integral

$$\int\int \cdots \int da_{11} da_{12} \cdots da_{nn}$$

taken over this region. This expression integrated offers a quantity of the $n(n+1)/2$ dimension. Let D be any fixed positive value. We shall prove the following theorem: *The region $B(D)$ of the reduced realm, in which $D(f) \leqq D$, and which consequently lies on the side of the origin with respect to the determinant surface $D(f) = D$, has a definite finite volume.* Since the individual realms of this kind, which belong to different values D, are homothetic among one another

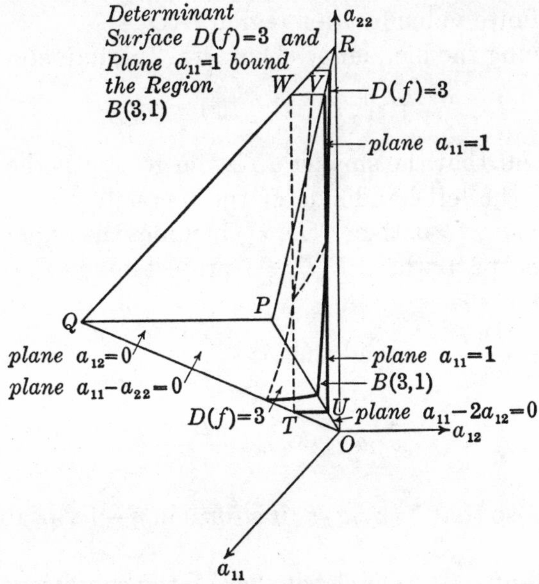

The plane $a_{12}=0$ is the plane of R, Q, and O; the plane $a_{11}-a_{22}=0$ is the plane of P, Q, and O; the plane $a_{11}-2a_{12}=0$ is the plane of P, R, and O; the plane $a_{11}=1$ is the plane of T, U, V, and W.

FIG. 140

starting from the origin, the volume in question will have a value $v_n D^{(n+1)/2}$, where v_n is a constant depending only on n and remains to be computed in the sequel. Observe that D is the nth dimension in the quantities $a_{11}, a_{12}, \cdots, a_{nn}$, and when raised to the $(n+1)/2$ power gives the dimension required in the evaluation of the above integral.

We denote by $B(D, \epsilon)$ the portion of the reduced realm where

$$D(f) \leqq D, \qquad a_{11} \geqq \epsilon. \qquad \text{(See Fig. 140.)}$$

Here ϵ is a positive quantity. These inequalities taken in connection with the inequalities

(44) $$a_{11} \leqq a_{22} \leqq \cdots \leqq a_{nn}, \qquad \pm 2a_{hk} \leqq a_{hh},$$

(45) $$\lambda_n a_{11} a_{22} \cdots a_{nn} \leqq D(f) \quad [\text{see (15)}],$$

$$a_{11} a_{22} \cdots a_{nn} \geqq D(f) \quad [\text{see (4)}]$$

offer (for a reduced form) *upper limits for the absolute values of all coordinates in* $B(D, \epsilon)$ and consequently there exists a definite finite value for this region $B(D, \epsilon)$.

Observing the inequality (I) of Art. 214, namely

(I) $$f(s_1^{(l)}, s_2^{(l)}, \cdots, s_n^{(l)}) \geqq a_{ll},$$

it is evident that the smaller a_{ll} is the greater is the reduced realm on the left-hand side of the inequality (I).

If then $\epsilon > \epsilon^* > 0$, then $B(D, \epsilon^*)$ includes the region $B(D, \epsilon)$ and in the part where $B(D, \epsilon^*)$ projects over $B(D, \epsilon)$ it is seen that $\epsilon^* \leqq a_{11} \leqq \epsilon$, $|a_{lk}| \leqq \frac{1}{2} a_{11}$ $(k=2, 3, \cdots, n)$, $a_{12} \geqq 0$; and $\lambda_n a_{11} \dfrac{\partial D(f)}{\partial a_{11}} \leqq D$ and that is $\dfrac{\partial D(f)}{\partial a_{11}} \leqq \dfrac{D}{\lambda_n a_{11}}$, since

$$a_{22} a_{33} \cdots a_{nn} \geqq \frac{\partial D(f)}{\partial a_{11}}.$$

Observe also that $\sum_2^n a_{hk} x_h x_k$ is a form in $n-1$ variables with determinant $\dfrac{\partial D(f)}{\partial a_{11}}$ which satisfies all the conditions of a reduced form.

If next we assume that the result to be proved is already established for the case of $n-1$ variables, it is seen on the transition from $B(D, \epsilon)$ to $B(D, \epsilon^*)$ that the volume of this region is increased by a smaller amount than the value of the integral $\dfrac{1}{2}\displaystyle\int a_{11}^{n-1} v_{n-1} \left(\frac{D}{\lambda_n a_{11}}\right)^{n/2} da_{11}$ taken over the region $0 < a_{11} \leqq \epsilon$, and that is less than the quantity

$$\frac{v_{n-1}}{n \lambda_n^{n/2}} \epsilon^{n/2} D^{n/2}.$$

With this it follows *that the volume of $B(D, \epsilon)$ tends towards a definite finite limit* as $\epsilon \to 0$, and *this limit defines the volume of $B(D)$.*

Having thus established the existence of the constant v_n, we may add that the volume of $B(D, \epsilon)$ *is*

$$(46) \qquad < v_n D^{\frac{n+1}{2}}$$

and $> v_n D^{\frac{n+1}{2}} - \bar{v}_n \epsilon^{n/2} D^{n/2}$, where *for brevity* $\bar{v}_n$ *stands for*

$$\frac{1}{n} v_{n-1} \lambda_n^{-n/2}.$$

ART. **235.** We remark further that the region defined through

$$(47) \qquad D \leqq D(f) \leqq D^*, \qquad a_{11} \geqq \epsilon$$

of the reduced realm, in which $0 < D < D^*$ and $\epsilon > 0$, has a volume which is

$$(48) \qquad < v_n (D^{*\frac{n+1}{2}} - D^{\frac{n+1}{2}}) \qquad \text{and}$$

$$> \left(v_n - \bar{v}_n \frac{\epsilon^{n/2}}{D^{1/2}} \right) (D^{*\frac{n+1}{2}} - D^{\frac{n+1}{2}}).$$

For observe that the region (47) is entirely contained in the portion $D \leqq D(f) \leqq D^*$ of the reduced realm and from this accordingly we have the *upper* limit in (48)

On the other hand the region (47) contains entirely the region $D \leqq D(f) \leqq D^*$ for the values $a_{11} \geqq \dfrac{\epsilon \sqrt[n]{D(f)}}{\sqrt[n]{D}}$, and that is for $\theta = \dfrac{\epsilon}{\sqrt[n]{D}} \leqq \dfrac{a_{11}}{\sqrt[n]{D(f)}}$ of the reduced realm. Observe that the volume of the last realm is the $(D^{*\frac{n+1}{2}} - D^{\frac{n+1}{2}}) : D^{\frac{n+1}{2}}$ multiple of the volume of the region

$$(49) \qquad D(f) \leqq D, \qquad \theta \leqq \frac{a_{11}}{\sqrt[n]{D(f)}}$$

of the reduced realm, since the realms defined through the last conditions with a fixed value of θ and with different values D represent homothetic cones from the origin.

And finally the region determined through (49) of the reduced realm contains entirely the region $B(D, \epsilon)$. From this follows the *lower* limit named in (48).

ART. **236. Application of the Dirichlet Series.** We shall next present for the derivation of the volume v_n essentially the same methods as those given by Dirichlet for the determination of the class number in the theory of binary forms. Instead of taking the volume integral over the region $B(D)$ we shall consider the integral of a certain function over this region which in a preponderant part of this region is approximately $=1$, and by means of the expression of this function the determination of v_n is made dependent on that of v_{n-1}, that of v_{n-1} on that of v_{n-2}, etc. Let ϵ, G and σ be positive quantities. Then after establishing a certain relation among these quantities, we shall let G become indefinitely large while ϵ and σ decrease towards zero. We shall assume that $\sigma<\frac{1}{2}$, $G>\epsilon$ and $\epsilon\leqq 1$.

We shall now investigate the following expression:

$$\Phi(f)=\sigma(D(f))^{\frac{1}{2}+\frac{\sigma}{n}}\sum\frac{1}{f(x_1, \cdots, x_n)^{\frac{n}{2}+\sigma}}. \tag{50}$$

Here $f(x_1, \cdots, x_n)=\sum a_{hk}x_hx_k$ *denotes a positive reduced form of* n *variables,* $D(f)$ *its determinant, and the summation is to be taken over all systems of integers* $x_1, \cdots, x_n$ *which satisfy the inequalities*

$$\epsilon\leqq f(x_1, \cdots, x_n)<G, \tag{51}$$

where the G.C.D. of $x_1, \cdots, x_n$ *is unity.*

On the other hand let $\psi(f)$ denote the value of the expression (50) where the summation without exception extends over all existing integral systems $x_1, \cdots, x_n$ which satisfy the conditions (51). Thus with the definition of $\psi(f)$ we drop the condition that the G. C. D. of $x_1, \cdots, x_n$ is unity.

We may recall as being of importance here the following fact proved in Art. 225. *If* $x_1, x_2, \cdots, x_n$ *are integers* $\neq 0, 0, \cdots, 0$ *and if* x_h *is the last of these integers that is different from zero, then is*

$$f(x_1, \cdots, x_n) \geqq \lambda_n a_{hh}.$$

The investigation of the expression $\psi(f)$ is founded upon the following facts.

If we let $x_1, x_2, \cdots, x_n$ be the coordinates of a point in an n dimensional realm $\mathfrak{R}_n$, then

$$(52) \qquad f(x_1, x_2, \cdots, x_n) < T,$$

if T is a positive constant, represents the *interior of an n dimensional ellipsoid* in this space. The volume of this ellipsoid in $x_1, x_2, \cdots, x_n$ has the value

$$(53) \qquad \gamma_n \frac{(\sqrt{T})^n}{\sqrt{D(f)}} \qquad \text{(Art. 148, I)},$$

where

$$(54) \qquad \gamma_n = \frac{\pi^{n/2}}{\Gamma\left(1+\frac{n}{2}\right)} = \frac{\pi^{[n/2]}}{\frac{n}{2}\left(\frac{n}{2}-1\right)\cdots\left(\frac{n}{2}-\frac{(n-1)}{2}\right)}$$

is the volume of an n dimensional sphere of radius 1 (Art. 229). We remark further that the entire region of the hypercube

$$(55) \qquad -\tfrac{1}{2} \leqq x_1 \leqq \tfrac{1}{2}, \qquad \cdots, \qquad -\tfrac{1}{2} \leqq x_n \leqq \tfrac{1}{2},$$

due to the inequalities (44), lies wholly in the ellipsoid

$$(56) \qquad f(x_1, \cdots, x_n) \leqq \frac{n(n+1)}{8} a_{nn}.$$

Due to this fact we have an *approximative determination for the number of those lattice points $x_1, \cdots, x_n$ which satisfy the conditions (52).*

To effect this, construct about each lattice point as center with faces parallel to the coordinate planes and with length of edge $=1$, a hypercube which exists through a parallel sliding of the hypercube (55) from the origin toward the lattice point in question. Since we may circumscribe each of these hypercubes through an ellipsoid homologous to the ellipsoid (56), it is seen that *the whole region of these hypercubes in question lies entirely within the realm of the ellipsoid*

$$f(x_1, \cdots, x_n) < \left(\sqrt{T} + \sqrt{\frac{n(n+1)}{8} a_{nn}}\right)^2.$$

Observe that $f(x_1, \cdots, x_n)$ is an accordant function.

All the hypercubes in question do not mutually bound one another and each one of them is of volume 1. Accordingly the number of lattice points in question is at all events

$$< \frac{\gamma_n}{\sqrt{D(f)}} \left(\sqrt{T} + \sqrt{\frac{n(n+1)}{8} a_{nn}}\right)^n.$$

For brevity, we write

$$\kappa_n = \gamma_n \left\{ \left(1 + \sqrt{\frac{n(n+1)}{8\lambda_n}}\right)^n - 1 \right\},$$

and we assert:

The number of integral solutions of

$$f(x_1, \cdots, x_n) < T$$

is clearly

$$(57) \qquad > \frac{1}{\sqrt{D(f)}} \left(\gamma_n T^{n/2} + \kappa_n (\lambda_n a_{nn})^{1/2} T^{\frac{n-1}{2}}\right),$$

if $T \geqq \lambda_n a_{nn}$.

On the other hand if $T > \frac{n(n+1)}{8} a_{nn}$, then *the above hypercubes completely encompass the region of the smaller ellipsoid*

$$f(x_1, \cdots, x_n) < \left(\sqrt{T} - \sqrt{\frac{n(n+1)}{8} a_{nn}}\right)^2;$$

and from this we derive the further fact: *The number of integral solutions of*

$$f(x_1, \cdots, x_n) < T$$

is, if $T \geqq \lambda_n a_{nn}$, *clearly*

$$(58) \qquad > \frac{1}{\sqrt{D(f)}}(\gamma_n T^{n/2} - \kappa_n(\lambda_n a_{nn})^{1/2} T^{\frac{n-1}{2}}).$$

From the two bounds offered in (57) and (58) we have further:

If $T \geqq \lambda_n a_{nn}$ *and t a value* >1, *then the number of integral systems* $x_1, \cdots, x_n$ *which satisfy the inequalities*

$$T \leqq f(x_1, \cdots, x_n) < Tt,$$

lies within the two bounds

$$(59) \qquad \frac{1}{\sqrt{D(f)}}\{\gamma_n(t^{n/2}-1)T^{n/2} \pm \kappa_n(t^{\frac{n-1}{2}}+1)(\lambda_n a_{nn})T^{\frac{n-1}{2}}\}.$$

ART. **237.** Next collect those terms in $\psi(f)$ in which $f \geqq \lambda_n a_{nn}$ and where also $f \geqq \epsilon$. Let T_n be the greater of the two lower bounds ϵ and $\lambda_n a_{nn}$ and equal to either, if they have a common value. From what was given in the preceding article the aggregate of the terms of $\psi(f)$ in question lies between two limits. Let $G > \lambda_n a_{nn}$. We put $G = T_n t^l$, where l is a positive integer and $t > 1$. We distribute f for the various integers $x_1, \cdots, x_n$ which satisfy the inequalities $T_n \leqq f < G$ into the partial intervals $T_n \leqq f < T_n t$, $T_n t < f < T_n t^2$, $\cdots$, $T_n t^{l-1} < f < G$. We determine for each of these intervals from (59) an upper and a lower limit for the number of integral systems $x_1, \cdots, x_n$, for which f falls in the interval in question and we write these in the denominators of the respective terms of $\psi(f)$, substituting for $f(x_1, \cdots, x_n)$ its respective upper and lower limits. We thus have an upper and a lower limit for the aggregate of terms of $\psi(f)$.

It follows, observing the identity

$$\left(\frac{1}{T_n^\sigma} - \frac{1}{G^\sigma}\right) : \left(1 - \frac{1}{t^\sigma}\right)$$

$$= \frac{1}{T_n^\sigma} + \frac{1}{(tT_n)^\sigma} + \frac{1}{(t^2 T_n)^\sigma} + \cdots + \frac{1}{(t^{l-1}T_n)^\sigma} + \frac{1}{G^\sigma},$$

that the portion of $\psi(f)$ corresponding to the interval $T_n \leqq f < G$ is for the upper limit

$$(60)\quad < D(f)^{\sigma/n}\left\{\gamma_n \frac{\sigma(t^{n/2}-1)}{1-\frac{1}{t^\sigma}}\left(\frac{1}{T_n^\sigma}-\frac{1}{G^\sigma}\right)\right.$$

$$\left. + \kappa_n(t^{\frac{n-1}{2}}+1)\frac{\sigma}{1-\frac{1}{t^{\frac{1}{2}+\sigma}}}T_n^{1/2}\left(\frac{1}{T_n^{\frac{1}{2}+\sigma}}-\frac{1}{G^{\frac{1}{2}+\sigma}}\right)\right\}.$$

ART. **238.** Let D be a fixed positive quantity. And for the moment we consider f as situated in the region $B(D, \epsilon)$. It follows then that $a_{11} \geqq \epsilon$ and from (44) and (45) it follows that

$$\lambda_n \epsilon^n \leqq D(f) \leqq D, \qquad \lambda_n \epsilon \leqq \lambda_n a_{11} \leqq \lambda_n a_{nn} \leqq \frac{D}{\epsilon^{n-1}}.$$

With this choice of ϵ, we may take $\sigma(\epsilon) = \sigma$ such that $\lim_{\epsilon \to 0} \epsilon^{\sigma(\epsilon)} \to 1$ and $\lim_{\epsilon \to 0} \sigma(\epsilon) \to 0$ and $\lim T_n^\sigma \to 1$. We then choose $G(\sigma)$ such that $G(\sigma) = \infty$ where $\sigma = \sigma(\epsilon)$ and $\lim_{\epsilon \to 0} G^{-\sigma}(\sigma(\epsilon)) = 0$.

From the relation $G = t^l T_n$, we have $\left(\frac{G}{T_n}\right)^{1/l} = t$; and it is seen that l may be chosen integrally sufficiently large that $t \to 1$. If we take the logarithm of this expression, it is seen that

$$\frac{1}{\log t} = \frac{l}{\log G - \log T_n} = \frac{\sigma l}{\sigma(\log G - \log T_n)} \to \infty,$$

while

$$\frac{\sigma}{\log t} \to 0.$$

Hence $\log t \to 0$, and $t \to 1$. The coefficient of κ_n in (60) approaches zero, while in the first term the factor of γ_n is $\sigma t^\sigma \frac{(t^{n/2}-1)}{t^\sigma - 1}$ which $\to \frac{n}{2}$ as $t \to 1$. Hence the first term in (60) approaches $\frac{n}{2}\gamma_n$.

Under the above conditions a similar procedure for the lower limit of $\psi(f)$ for the interval $T_n \leqq f < G$ leads to the same value $\frac{n}{2}\gamma_n$ as was had for the upper limit.

ART. **239.** We further have to consider those terms of $\psi(f)$ in which $f \geqq \epsilon$ but $< \lambda_n a_{nn}$. Since the constant $\lambda_n < 1$ and as a_{11} is the minimum of f, it is seen that $f > \lambda_n a_{11}$ in all the terms of $\psi(f)$. We separate all those terms of $\psi(f)$ out, if there be such, in which

$$\left.\begin{matrix}\lambda_n a_{hh} \leqq \\ \epsilon \leqq\end{matrix}\right\} f(x_1, \cdots, x_n) < \lambda_n a_{h+1,\ h+1},$$

where h is one of the numbers $1, 2, \cdots, n-1$. Let T_h be the greater of the two numbers $\lambda_n a_{hh}$, ϵ or their common value if these numbers are equal. Since $f < \lambda_n a_{h+1,\ h+1}$, the numbers $x_{h+1}, \cdots, x_n$ must all be zero.

Hence the entire aggregate of the terms in question is at all events less than the value of the infinite series

$$\sigma D(f)^{\frac{1}{2}+\frac{\sigma}{n}} \sum \frac{1}{f(x_1, \cdots, x_h, 0, \cdots, 0)^{\frac{n}{2}+\sigma}}$$

taken over all existing systems $x_1, \cdots, x_h$ for which T_h is $\leqq f(x_1, \cdots, x_h, 0, \cdots, 0)$. We may apply the result expressed in the formula (59) to the case of forms in h variables and we find that the number of integral systems $x_1, \cdots, x_h$ which satisfy the inequalities

$$T_h t^j \leqq f(x_1, \cdots, x_j, 0, \cdots, 0) \leqq T_h t^{j+1} \qquad (j \geqq 0),$$

t being a fixed positive constant >1, say 2, is smaller than the quantity

$$\bar{\gamma}_h \frac{(T_h t^j)^{h/2}}{\sqrt{a_{11}a_{22} \cdots a_{hh}}},$$

where $\bar{\gamma}_h$ represents a certain positive constant that depends only upon h. The aggregate of terms in question is seen to be

$$<\sigma D(f)^{\frac{1}{2}+\frac{\sigma}{n}} \frac{\bar{\gamma}_h}{\left(1-\frac{1}{t^{\frac{n-h}{2}+\sigma}}\right) T_h^{\frac{n-h}{2}+\sigma} \sqrt{a_{11}\cdots a_{hh}}}.$$

Observe that $\lambda_n<1$ so that $\frac{1}{\lambda_n}>1$, and take instead of the denominator of the preceding expression, the larger quantity

$$\lambda_n^{-\frac{n-h-1}{2}} T_h^{\frac{n-h}{2}+\sigma} \sqrt{a_{11}\cdots a_{hh}} \geqq \epsilon^{\frac{1}{2}+\sigma} a_{hh}^{\frac{n-h-1}{2}} \sqrt{a_{11}\cdots a_{hh}} \geqq \epsilon^{\frac{1}{2}+\sigma} a_{11}^{\frac{n-1}{2}}.$$

Making use of this fact it is seen that *the aggregate of all terms in* $\psi(f)$ *which correspond to the conditions*

$$\epsilon \leqq f(x_1, \cdots, x_n) < \lambda_n a_{nn},$$

is

$$<\mu_n \frac{\sigma D(f)^{\frac{1}{2}+\frac{\sigma}{n}}}{\epsilon^{\frac{1}{2}+\sigma} a_{11}^{\frac{n-1}{2}}},$$

where μ_n *is a constant depending only upon* n.

ART. **240.** We again assume that the form f is situated in the region $B(D, \epsilon)$ so that $D(f) \leqq D$, $a_{11} \geqq \epsilon$. (See Fig. 141.) *We determine* σ *as related to* ϵ *in such a way that for the lim* $\epsilon=0$, *we also have* $\lim \left(\frac{\sigma}{\epsilon^{n/2}}\right)=0$. It follows that

$$\log(\epsilon^\sigma) = (\sigma\epsilon^{-n/2})(\epsilon^{n/2} \log \epsilon)$$

converges towards zero and therefore ϵ^σ converges towards 1. Hence also the expression (63) converges towards zero for the form f.

Accordingly we have the result: *If* f *is situated in the region* $B(D, \epsilon)$, *the value of* $\psi(f)$ *may be included in two limits which under the conditions*

$$(64) \qquad \lim \epsilon=0, \qquad \lim \left(\frac{\sigma}{\epsilon^{n/2}}\right)=0, \qquad \lim G^{-\sigma}=0,$$

both converge at the same time towards the value $\frac{n}{2}\gamma_n$.

ART. **241.** *We are assuming always that f lies in the region* $B(D, \epsilon)$. To pass from the expression $\psi(f)$ to the necessary expression $\Phi(f)$, *we shall denote by ψ_d the value of the expression (50), in which the summation is taken over all the integral systems $x_1, \cdots, x_n$, whose G.D.C. $=d$ (where d is a positive integer), that cause $f(x_1, \cdots, x_n)$ to lie within the interval*

$$\epsilon \leqq f(x_1, \cdots, x_n) < G.$$

For values of d which are sufficiently large that $d^2\epsilon \geqq G$, there are no values of $x_1, \cdots, x_n$ that lie within the interval in question. Accordingly, for such values of d we necessarily put $\psi_d = 0$. Hence if such values of d exist the series $\psi_1, \psi_2, \cdots$ is finite. We may write [1]

$$\Phi(f) = \psi_1 - \psi_2 - (\psi_3 - \psi_6) - (\psi_5 - \psi_{10} - \psi_{15} + \psi_{30}) - \cdots \tag{65}$$

where the terms proceed as in the well known infinite product taken over the prime numbers $p = 2, 3, 5, \cdots$, namely

$$\Pi\left(1 - \frac{1}{p^s}\right) = 1 - \frac{1}{2^s} - \left(\frac{1}{3^s} - \frac{1}{6^s}\right) - \left(\frac{1}{5^s} - \frac{1}{10^s} - \frac{1}{15^s} + \frac{1}{30^s}\right) - \cdots. \tag{66}$$

Let $s = n + 2\sigma$ and the series (66) is seen to be absolutely convergent. Its value is the reciprocal of S_s, where

$$S_s = 1 + \frac{1}{2^s} + \frac{1}{3^s} + \frac{1}{4^s} + \cdots. \tag{67}$$

In the terms which constitute ψ_d write $x_h = dy_h$ $(h = 1, 2, \cdots, n)$. It follows that $f(x_1, \cdots, x_n) = d^2 f(y_1, \cdots, y_n)$; and as f is to lie within $B(D, \epsilon)$, the minimum of f therefore by hypothesis being $\geqq \epsilon$, it is seen that in ψ_d we have to extend the summation over all integral systems for which

$$\epsilon \leqq f(y_1, \cdots, y_n) < \frac{G}{d^2}.$$

Next take d^* as an integer independent of σ chosen such

[1] See Lipschitz, "Ueber die asymptotischen Gesetze von gewissen Gattungen zahlentheoretischer Funktionen," *Monatsbericht der Berliner Akademie*, 1865, S. 174.

that the sum of the absolute values of all the terms in (66), for which $d > d^*$, are arbitrarily near zero, and that on the other hand due to the assumptions (64) we have at the same time $\lim (d^{*\sigma}) = 1$. Then notice, due to the results in Art. 240, that for the values $d \leqq d^*$ we have

$$\lim \left(\psi_d \frac{1}{d^{n+2\sigma}} \right) = \frac{n}{2} \gamma_n,$$

and that is

$$\psi_d = \frac{n}{2} \gamma_n \lim \frac{1}{d^{n+2\sigma}};$$

while, when $d > d^*$, we have at least the relation

$$0 \leqq \psi_d \leqq \frac{1}{d^{n+2\sigma}} \psi_1 \to 0.$$

It follows then from (65) that

$$\lim \Phi(f) = \frac{n}{2} \gamma_n \lim \Pi \left(1 - \frac{1}{p^{n+2\sigma}} \right) = \frac{n}{2} \frac{\gamma_n}{S_n}. \tag{68}$$

With this we have reached the following result:

For all forms f in the entire region $B(D, \epsilon)$ the value of the function $\Phi(f)$ lies between two limits, which under the assumptions (64) both simultaneously converge to the value $\frac{n}{2} \frac{\gamma_n}{S_n}$.

ART. **242.** Suppose that the minimum a_{11} of f has an arbitrary value. We may determine an upper limit for the *aggregate of those terms in f for which besides $\epsilon \leqq f$ we also have $\lambda_n a_{nn} \leqq f$. For through (60) we may determine a constant ν_n as an upper limit and for the aggregate of the remaining terms in $\psi(f)$ there is the upper limit (63).* These upper limits obtain for a greater reason for the value of the sum $\Phi(f)$ and we find: *There exist always the inequalities*

$$0 \leqq \Phi(f) < \mu_n \frac{\sigma D(f)^{\frac{1}{2} + \frac{\sigma}{n}}}{\epsilon^{\frac{1}{2} + \sigma} a_{11}^{n - \frac{1}{2}}} + \nu_n, \tag{69}$$

where μ_n and ν_n are two positive constants depending only upon n.

ART. **243.** Now let δ be a positive quantity $\leqq \epsilon$ and consider the $n(n+1)/2$ ple integral

$$J(\delta) = \int\int \cdots \int \Phi(f) da_{11} da_{12} \cdots da_{nn} \tag{70}$$

of the function $\Phi(f)$ defined in (50) and taken over the portion $B(D, \epsilon)$ of the reduced realm determined through $D(f) \leqq D$, $a_{11} \geqq \delta$. If we take first $\delta = \epsilon$ the results of Art. 240 in connection with the theorems of Arts. 234–236 offer under the assumptions (64) the limiting value

$$\lim J(\epsilon) = \frac{n}{2} \frac{\gamma_n}{S_n} v_n D^{\frac{n+1}{2}}.$$

See Art. 234.

Next let $\delta < \epsilon$ and in the region in which the realm $B(D, \delta)$ extends over the region $B(D, \epsilon)$ take the upper bound (69) for the function $\Phi(f)$. The volume of this supplemental region is $< \bar{v} \epsilon^{n/2} D^{n/2}$ (46). In the first term of (69) write for $[D(f)]^{\sigma/n}$ its upper limit $D^{\sigma/n}$. We may then derive an upper limit for the $n(n+1)/2$ ple integral

$$\int\int \cdots \int \frac{[D(f)]^{1/2}}{a_{11}^{(n-1)/2}} da_{11} da_{12} \cdots da_{nn}$$

taken over the entire region $B(D, \delta)$ by proceeding in a similar manner as in Arts. 234–236.

First take the integrations with respect to $a_{22}, a_{23}, \cdots, a_{nn}$ over the surfaces $\frac{\partial D(f)}{\partial a_{11}} = \text{constant}$. Observe that in connection with (45), namely $\lambda_n a_{11} a_{22} \cdots a_{nn} \leqq D(f)$, we had $\lambda_n a_{11} \frac{\partial D(f)}{\partial a_{11}} \leqq D$, so that $\lambda_n a_{11} C \leqq D$. Then integrating with respect to $a_{12}, \cdots, a_{1n}$, we find the integral in question to be

$$< \int \frac{a_{11}^{1/2}}{a_{11}^{(n-1)/2}} \frac{1}{2} a_{11}^{n-1} \, da_{11} \int C^{1/2} v_{n-1} \, d(C^{n/2})$$

the integrations taken over the region

$$0 < \lambda_n a_{11}^n \leqq D, \qquad 0 < \lambda_n a_{11} C \leqq D.$$

The above double integral is seen to be

$$<\frac{n}{n+1}v_{n-1}\left(\frac{D}{\lambda_n}\right)^{\frac{n+1}{2}}\int\frac{1}{2}a_{11}^{-1/2}da_{11}<\frac{n}{n+1}v_{n-1}\left(\frac{D}{\lambda_n}\right)^{\frac{n+1}{2}+\frac{1}{2n}},$$

a finite quantity.

Observe that in the first term of (69) there enters the factor $\frac{\sigma}{\epsilon^{\frac{1}{2}+\sigma}}$, which due to the assumptions (64) converges towards zero. When this is taken into account, we have finally proved the theorem:

The integral $J(\delta)$ taken over the region $B(D, \delta)$, where δ is arbitrarily $\leqq\epsilon$, lies between two limits, both of which under the assumptions (64) converge towards the value

$$\frac{n}{2}\frac{\gamma_n}{S_n}v_nD^{\frac{n+1}{2}}.$$

ART. 244. **Evaluation of the Volume.** Due to the above theorem we may make the calculation of the volume v_n depend upon that of v_{n-1}. If $p_1, p_2, \cdots, p_n$ are n integers, whose G.C.D. $=1$, we may make integral unimodular substitutions P with these integers constituting the first vertical column. Let P_0 be an initial substitution of this kind and P an arbitrary like substitution. Then the first vertical column of $P_0^{-1}P$ is seen to consist of the numbers $1, 0, \cdots, 0$; and we may put $P=P_0QR$, where the substitution Q leaves the first variable unchanged, and consequently has as its first horizontal row the numbers $1, 0, \cdots, 0$, while R is a substitution of the form

$$y_1=z_1+r_2z_2+\cdots+r_nz_n,$$
$$y_2=z_2, \qquad y_3=z_3, \qquad \cdots, \qquad y_n=z_n.$$

To determine more explicitly the nature of the matrices Q and R, write $P_0^{-1}P=QR$, where

$$Q=\begin{Vmatrix}1, & 0, & \cdots, & 0\\ q_{21}, & q_{22}, & \cdots, & q_{2n}\\ \cdots & \cdots & \cdots & \cdots\\ q_{n1}, & q_{n2}, & \cdots, & q_{nn}\end{Vmatrix} \qquad R=\begin{Vmatrix}1, & r_2, & r_3, & \cdots, & r_n\\ 0, & 1, & 0, & \cdots, & 0\\ 0, & 0, & 1, & \cdots, & 0\\ \cdots & \cdots & \cdots & \cdots & \cdots\\ 0, & 0, & 0, & \cdots, & 1\end{Vmatrix}.$$

Observe that in the product of these two matrices, the terms of the first column must be the same as the first column of $P_0^{-1}P$ and that is $1, 0, \cdots, 0$. It follows that $q_{21}=0=q_{31}=\cdots=q_{n1}$. And on the other hand, writing

$$P_0^{-1}P=\left\|\begin{matrix} 1, & s_{12}, & \cdots, & s_{1n} \\ 0, & s_{22}, & \cdots, & s_{2n} \\ \cdots & \cdots & \cdots & \cdots \\ 0, & s_{n2}, & \cdots, & s_{nn} \end{matrix}\right\|,$$

we have

$$P_0^{-1}P=QR=\left\|\begin{matrix} 1, & r_2, & r_3, & \cdots, & r_n \\ 0, & q_{22}, & q_{23}, & \cdots, & q_{2n} \\ 0, & q_{32}, & q_{33}, & \cdots, & q_{3n} \\ \cdots & \cdots & \cdots & \cdots & \cdots \\ 0, & q_{n2}, & q_{n3}, & \cdots, & q_{nn} \end{matrix}\right\|.$$

Hence it is seen that we may write

$$Q=\left\|\begin{matrix} 1, & 0, & 0, & \cdots, & 0 \\ 0, & s_{22}, & s_{23}, & \cdots, & s_{2n} \\ \cdots & \cdots & \cdots & \cdots & \cdots \\ 0, & s_{n2}, & s_{n3}, & \cdots, & s_{nn} \end{matrix}\right\|, \qquad R=\left\|\begin{matrix} 1, & s_{12}, & \cdots, & s_{1n} \\ 0, & 1, & \cdots, & 0 \\ \cdots & \cdots & \cdots & \cdots \\ 0, & 0, & \cdots, & 1 \end{matrix}\right\|.$$

ART. **245.** We shall now let ϵ, G, σ, $\delta\leqq\epsilon$ take such values as were assumed in Arts. 236, 244 and let f be a form in the region $B(D, \delta)$. Let $p_1, p_2, \cdots, p_n$ be integers (whose G.C.D. $=1$), which satisfy the inequalities

$$\epsilon\leqq f(p_1, p_2, \cdots, p_n)=b_{11}<G. \tag{72}$$

We next introduce the substitutions P_0, P, Q, R and observe that the form f when subjected to $P=P_0QR$ has b_{11}, say, as the first coefficient.

We write this form

$$\varphi=\sum b_{hk}y_hy_k=b_{11}\left(y_1+\frac{b_{12}}{b_{11}}y_2+\cdots+\frac{b_{1n}}{b_{11}}y_n\right)^2+\psi, \tag{73}$$

where

$$\psi=c_{22}y_2^2+2c_{23}y_2y_3+\cdots+c_{nn}y_n^2, \tag{74}$$

in which

$$c_{hk}=b_{hk}-\frac{b_{1h}b_{1k}}{b_{11}} \qquad (h, k=2, 3, \cdots, n). \tag{75}$$

Observe that the determinant of ψ is

$$\begin{vmatrix} b_{22}-\frac{b_{12}b_{12}}{b_{11}}, & b_{23}-\frac{b_{12}b_{13}}{b_{11}}, & \cdots, & b_{2n}-\frac{b_{12}b_{1n}}{b_{11}} \\ \cdots & \cdots & \cdots & \cdots \\ b_{2n}-\frac{b_{12}b_{1n}}{b_{11}}, & b_{3n}-\frac{b_{13}b_{1n}}{b_{11}}, & \cdots, & b_{nn}-\frac{b_{1n}b_{1n}}{b_{11}} \end{vmatrix},$$

which determinant bordered is

$$=\begin{vmatrix} 1, & 0, & \cdots, & 0 \\ \frac{b_{12}}{b_{11}}, & b_{22}-\frac{b_{12}b_{12}}{b_{11}}, & \cdots, & b_{2n}-\frac{b_{12}b_{1n}}{b_{11}} \\ \frac{b_{13}}{b_{11}}, & b_{23}-\frac{b_{12}b_{13}}{b_{11}}, & \cdots, & b_{3n}-\frac{b_{13}b_{1n}}{b_{11}} \\ \cdots & \cdots & \cdots & \cdots \\ \frac{b_{1n}}{b_{11}}, & b_{2n}-\frac{b_{12}b_{1n}}{b_{11}}, & \cdots, & b_{nn}-\frac{b_{1n}b_{1n}}{b_{11}} \end{vmatrix}.$$

Multiply the first column by b_{12} and add to the second column, and then multiply the first column by b_{13} and add to the third column, etc. It is seen that

$$b_{11}D(\psi)=D(f).$$

With $p_1, p_2, \cdots, p_n$ as the first vertical column we may choose P_0 in any way as an unimodular substitution, and then so determine the substitution Q that $\psi(y_2, y_3, \cdots, y_n)$ will be a reduced form of $n-1$ variables and therefore in accordance with Arts. 217 and 224 satisfy a finite number of linear inequalities

$$\sum m_{hk}c_{hk}\geqq 0 \qquad (h, k=2, 3, \cdots, n). \tag{76}$$

In general, for Q we have a choice of two opposed substitutions Q^* and $-Q^*$. We may then so determine R that all the inequalities

$$(77)\qquad \pm\frac{b_{12}}{b_{11}}\leqq\frac{1}{2},\qquad \cdots,\qquad \pm\frac{b_{1n}}{b_{11}}\leqq\frac{1}{2}$$

are satisfied, and finally we may effect through a choice between Q^* and $-Q^*$ that

$$(78)\qquad b_{12}\geqq 0.$$

Through these requirements we have brought it about that Q and R and consequently also $P=P_0QR$ are uniquely determined in the case where *equality* enters in none of the inequalities (76), (77) and (78).

ART. **246.** *We shall now take for θ a positive value $\leqq \delta$ and for φ we take the realm of all those forms for which*

$$(79)\qquad \epsilon\leqq b_{11}<G,\qquad D(\varphi)\leqq D,\qquad \theta\leqq c_{22},$$

and in addition we are assuming all the inequalities (76), (77) *and* (78). In Art. 217 we saw in the binary form

$$f=a_{11}x_1^2+2a_{12}x_1x_2+a_{22}x_2^2$$

that

$$D_2=a_{11}a_{22}-a_{12}^2\geqq\tfrac{3}{4}a_{11}a_{22}\geqq\tfrac{3}{4}a_{11}^2.$$

Observe that the minimum of a form φ expressed through (73) and (74) is at all events not greater than the minimum of the binary form

$$b_{11}\left(y_1+\frac{b_{12}}{b_{11}}y_2\right)^2+c_{22}y_2^2,$$

and this minimum, as just indicated, is $\leqq\sqrt{\frac{4}{3}b_{11}c_{22}}$.

Should φ be equivalent to a form f in $B(D,\delta)$ and if (72) is true, then necessarily

$$\delta\leqq\sqrt{\frac{4}{3}Gc_{22}};$$

and φ lies with certainty in the realm indicated in the beginning of this article, if we assume that $\theta=\dfrac{3\,\delta^2}{4G}$.

On the other hand a quantity expressible through φ for values of $y_1, y_2, \cdots, y_n$ that do not all simultaneously vanish is $\geqq c_{22} \geqq \theta$ since c_{22} is the minimum of ψ; or if $y_2, \cdots, y_n$ are simultaneously all zero the quantity expressed through φ is still $\geqq b_{11} \geqq \epsilon \geqq \delta \geqq \theta$. Thus it is seen that the reduced forms f that are equivalent to the forms φ of the above realm, clearly fall within $B(D, \theta)$. For the coefficients $b_{11}, b_{22}, \cdots, b_{nn}$ in φ there exist certain upper limits that depend only upon ϵ, G, θ, D and hence for given values of these quantities there exist only a *finite* number of unimodular integral substitutions in question, through which a reduced form f in $B(D, \theta)$ may be transformed into a form φ with the corresponding conditions (76), (77) and (78). *Accordingly the above region of the forms φ may be distributed entirely into a finite number of the rooms B_p that are equivalent to the reduced realm* B. Assuming further that φ falls neither on the bounding sidewalls of these rooms nor upon one of the surfaces indicated through the signs of equality in (76), (77) and (78), then on the one hand (Art. 212) the reduced form f equivalent to φ as well as the pair of the opposed integral unimodular substitutions P, $-P$ through which f is transformed into φ, are *uniquely* determined; and on the other hand there also does not exist an integral unimodular substitution P^* different from P and $-P$ with the same first vertical column as P or $-P$, through which f is transformed into another form φ^* which likewise satisfies all the inequalities (76), (77), (78) and (79).

ART. **247.** We next form the $n(n+1)/2$-ple integral

$$(80) \qquad K(\theta) = \int\int \cdots \int 2\sigma \frac{D(\varphi)^{\frac{1}{2}+\frac{\sigma}{n}}}{b_{11}^{\frac{n}{2}+\sigma}} db_{11}\, db_{12} \cdots db_{nn},$$

taken over the entire region defined through the inequalities (76), (77), (78) and (79). Through the developments derived above the following ratio of this integral to that given in (70) for $J(\delta)$ may be observed.

We have, if $\delta \leqq \epsilon$,

(81) $$J(\delta) < K(\theta) < J(\theta),$$

where $\theta = \dfrac{3\delta^2}{4G}$ *and* $\epsilon \geqq \delta \geqq \theta$.

To determine the value of the integral $K(\theta)$ we introduce the quantities $c_{22}, c_{23}, \cdots, c_{nn}$ from (75) instead of $b_{22}, b_{23}, \cdots, b_{nn}$ where the associated Jacobian (functional determinant) is 1. The integration is taken with respect to $c_{22}, c_{23}, \cdots, c_{nn}$ and first over surfaces of constant determinant of ψ, then for all values C of these determinants that appear, and finally we integrate with respect to $b_{12}, b_{13}, \cdots, b_{1n}$.

If we make use of the results of (47) and (48) when applied to $n-1$ variables we have in this manner as an upper limit of $K(\theta)$ the value

$$\int 2\sigma b_{11}^{\frac{1}{2}+\frac{\sigma}{n}} \frac{1}{2} \frac{b_{11}^{n-1} db_{11}}{b_{11}^{\frac{n}{2}+\sigma}} \int C^{\frac{1}{2}+\frac{\sigma}{n}} v_{n-1} d(C^{n/2}),$$

taken over the region $\epsilon \leqq b_{11} < G$, $0 < b_{11}C < D$, and that is

(82) $$\frac{n}{n+1+\dfrac{2\sigma}{n}} v_{n-1} D^{\frac{n+1}{2}+\frac{\sigma}{n}} \left[\frac{1}{b_{11}^{\sigma}}\right]_{b_{11}=G}^{b_{11}=\epsilon}.$$

This value approaches $\dfrac{n}{n+1} v_{n-1} D^{\frac{n+1}{2}}$, as $\sigma \to 0$. (See (64)).

A lower limit is had for the integral $K(\theta)$ by decreasing the above upper limit by

$$\int \sigma b_{11}^{\frac{n}{2}-\frac{1}{2}-\sigma+\frac{\sigma}{n}} db_{11} \int C^{\frac{\sigma}{n}} \theta^{\frac{n-1}{2}} \bar{v}_{n-1} d(C^{n/2}).$$

This last expression is

(83) $$= \frac{n}{n+\dfrac{2\sigma}{n}} \bar{v}_{n-1} D^{\frac{n}{2}+\frac{\sigma}{n}} \frac{\sigma}{\dfrac{1}{2}-\sigma} \theta^{\frac{n-1}{2}} \left(G^{\frac{1}{2}-\sigma} - \epsilon^{\frac{1}{2}-\sigma}\right),$$

and converges towards zero for $\theta=\frac{3\epsilon^2}{4G}$ and under the further assumptions (64). Due to the inequalities (81) and the theorem of Art. 242 we derive, due to the process of limits (see (64)), the recursion formula

$$(84)\qquad \frac{n}{2}\frac{\gamma_n}{S_n}v_n=\frac{n}{n+1}v_{n-1}.$$

Since $v_1=1$ we have, if we substitute for γ_n its value (54),

$$(85)\qquad v_n=\frac{2}{n+1}\,\frac{\Gamma(2/2)\Gamma(3/2)\cdots\Gamma(n/2)}{[\Gamma(1/2)]^{2+3+\cdots+n}}S_2S_3\cdots S_n,$$

where S_k stands for the value of the infinite series

$$1+\frac{1}{2^k}+\frac{1}{3^k}+\frac{1}{4^k}+\cdots.$$

This result was announced in a letter to Hermite by Minkowski (*Ges. Abhandl.*, I, p. 269).

ART. 248. **Maximum Density in the Case of Lattice-Formed Placement of Spheres.** *An application may be made of the value of v_n just calculated to the question of the densest placement of spheres in an n-dimensional space.* We assume that the value which the minimum $M(f)$ can reach in the case of all positive forms f of determinant 1 is ρ_n. Hence every positive class of forms f of a determinant $\leqq 1$ contains at least one form

$$\varphi(y_1, y_2, \cdots, y_n)=\sum b_{hk}y_hy_k$$
$$=b_{11}\left[y_1+\frac{b_{12}}{b_{11}}y_2+\cdots+\frac{b_{1n}}{b_{11}}y_n\right]^2+\psi(y_2, \cdots, y_n),$$

where

$$0<b_{11}\leqq \rho_n\sqrt[n]{D(f)},$$

$$\pm\frac{b_{12}}{b_{11}}\leqq\frac{1}{2},\qquad \cdots,\qquad \pm\frac{b_{1n}}{b_{11}}\leqq\frac{1}{2},\qquad b_{12}\geqq 0,$$

$$D(f)=b_{11}\ \text{Det.}\ (\psi)\leqq 1,$$

and ψ is a reduced form of $n-1$ variables $y_2, \cdots, y_n$.

Accordingly the $n(n+1)/2$-ple integral taken over the region just defined of forms φ, namely

$$\int\int\cdots\int db_{11}\, db_{12}\cdots db_{nn},$$

is greater than the volume of the reduced region of the forms with determinants $\leqq 1$. This integral we denote for the moment by v_n. We thus have

$$v_n=\int_0^{\rho_n}\frac{1}{2}b_{11}^{n-1}v_{n-1}\left[\left(\frac{1}{b_{11}}\right)^{n/2}-\left(\frac{b_{11}^{n-1}}{\rho_n^n}\right)^{n/2}\right]db_{11}<\frac{v_{n-1}}{n+1}\rho_n^{n/2}.$$

This value is had, if we observe that

$$b_{11}\leqq\rho_n[D(f)]^{1/n}=\rho_n b_{11}^{1/n}[\text{Det.}(\psi)]^{1/n},$$

so that $D(\psi)=\dfrac{b_{11}^{n-1}}{\rho_n}$ and

$$[C^{n/2}]_{D(\psi)}^{\text{upper limit of } D(\psi)}=\left(\frac{1}{b_{11}}\right)^{n/2}-\left(\frac{b_{11}^{n-1}}{\rho_n^n}\right)^{n/2}.$$

Hence

$$v_n<\frac{v_{n-1}}{n+1}\rho_n^{n/2};$$

and from (84) we have

$$\frac{v_{n-1}}{n+1}=\frac{1}{2}\frac{\gamma_n}{S_n}\nu_n.$$

Accordingly we have finally

$$\rho_n^{n/2}\gamma_n>2S_n,$$

and that is

(86) $$\frac{1}{2^n}\rho_n^{n/2}\gamma_n>\frac{1}{2^{n-1}}S_n.$$

This result may be interpreted in the following manner: *In an n-dimensional space there exists such a parallelopipedic placement of equal sized congruent spheres that the space filled up by the spheres is more than the* $\frac{1}{2^{n-1}}S_n$ *part of the entire space.*

PROBLEM. In this connection the statement (made by Minkowski, *Gesam. Math. Abhandl.*, II, p. 93) is presented as an exercise:

In the case of a *tetrahedral* stratiformed placement of spheres in layers, which doubtless corresponds to the extreme form

$$f=(x_1+x_2+\cdots+x_n)^2+x_1^2+x_2^2+\cdots+x_n^2,$$

there is exactly the $\dfrac{1}{2^{n/2}\sqrt{n+1}}\gamma_n=\dfrac{\pi^{n/2}}{2^{n/2}\sqrt{n+1}\,\Gamma\left(1+\frac{n}{2}\right)}$ part of the infinite space filled through the spheres. And this part in the case of large values of n is essentially smaller than the part named above. In the case of the plane and in space of 3 dimensions this arrangement in layers according to regular triangles or tetrahedra is the *only* densest lattice-formed placement of congruent circles or spheres.

ART. 249. **The Asymptotic Law for the Class-Numbers of Integral Forms.** There exists a special arithmetical meaning for the volume v_n. We consider in particular the positive forms f which have only integral coefficients a_{hk}, and always $a_{11}\geqq 1$. Due to the inequalities (44) and (45) it then follows that *for a given positive integral value $D(f)=D$* there always exists only a finite number of different reduced forms with integral coefficients and therefore also *only a finite number of different classes of integral positive forms.*

This class number for the integer D is denoted by $H(D)$. *We shall prove the Asymptotic Law*

$$\text{(87)}\qquad \lim_{D\to\infty}\left(\frac{H(1)+H(2)+\cdots+H(D)}{D^{\frac{n+1}{2}}}\right)=v_n.$$

ART. 250. In the manifold A of all quadratic forms $f=(a_{hk})$ consider those points (a^0_{hk}), all of whose $n(n+1)/2$ coordinates are rational integers and about each such point as center construct the hypercube

$$\text{(88)}\qquad -\tfrac{1}{2}\leqq a_{hk}-a^0_{hk}\leqq 1 \qquad (h, k=1, 2, \cdots, n).$$

We thus have a net of hypercubes which cover the manifold A simply and without gaps.

Let D be a positive integer, and form the region $B(D, 1)$ which is cut out of the reduced realm B through the

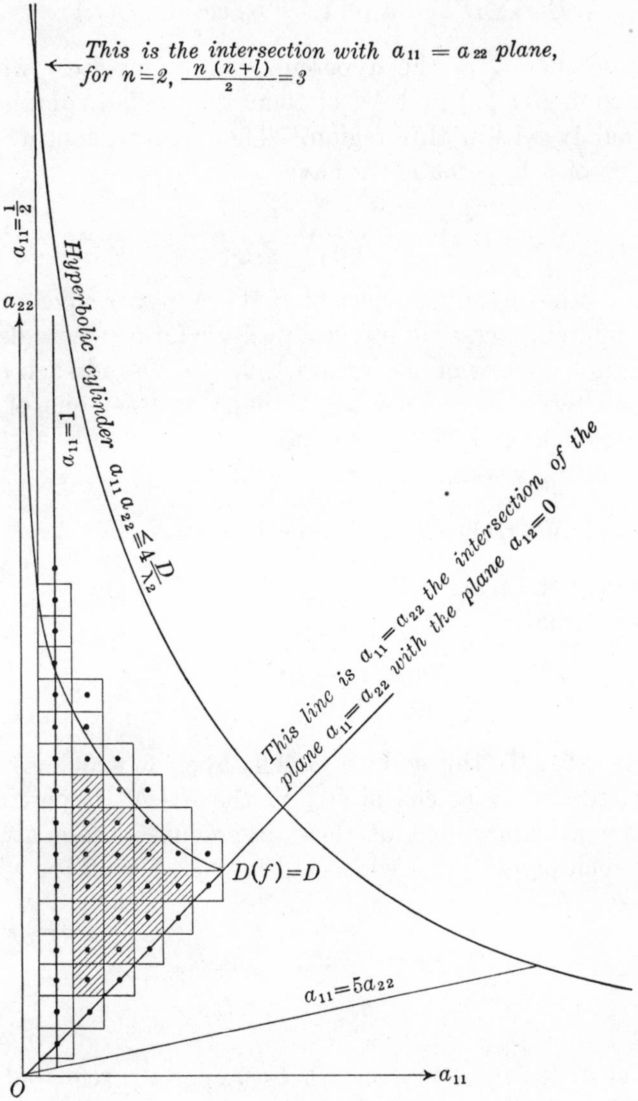

This is the intersection with $a_{11} = a_{22}$ plane,
for $n=2$, $\frac{n(n+l)}{2}=3$
$a_{11}=\frac{1}{2}$
a_{22}
Hyperbolic cylinder $a_{11}a_{22} \leqq 4\frac{D}{\lambda_2}$
$a_{11}=1$
This line is $a_{11}=a_{22}$ the intersection of the
plane $a_{11}=a_{22}$ with the plane $a_{12}=0$
$D(f)=D$
$a_{11}=5a_{22}$
O
a_{11}

FIG. 141

requirement

$$D(f) \leqq D, \qquad a_{11} \geqq 1. \qquad \text{(See Fig. 141.)}$$

Suppose that N of the hypercubes fall completely within the region $B(D, 1)$ and N^* of them do not fall completely but partly within this region. Then *unity* denoting the volume of a hypercube we have (see (46))

$$(89) \qquad N < v_n D^{\frac{n+1}{2}}, \qquad N + N^* > v_n D^{\frac{n+1}{2}} - \bar{v}_n D^{n/2}.$$

On the other hand the centers of the N hypercubes represent different classes of integral positive forms whose determinants have one of the values $1, 2, \cdots, D$ and each class of such forms is represented through at least one of the centers of the $N+N^*$ hypercubes.

Accordingly we have

$$(90) \qquad N \leqq H(1) + H(2) + \cdots + H(D) \leqq N + N^*.$$

To derive the result (87) it is sufficient to show from (89) and (90) that

$$\lim_{D \to \infty} \left(\frac{N^*}{D^{\frac{n+1}{2}}} \right) = 0.$$

ART. **251.** To this end we shall fix a region which is characterized simply as containing all the $N+N^*$ hypercubes. In any arbitrary one of these hypercubes there always exist such points (a^*_{hk}) which fall in $B(D, 1)$ and for which we have

$$(91) \qquad 1 \leqq a^*_{11} \leqq a^*_{22} \cdots \leqq a^*_{nn}, \qquad \pm 2a^*_{hk} < a^*_{hh} \qquad (h<k);$$

$$(92) \qquad \lambda_n a^*_{11} a^*_{22} \cdots a^*_{nn} \leqq D$$

so that $a_{11} < \dfrac{D^{1/n}}{\lambda_n^{1/n}}$. Observe that a^*_{hh} does not refer only to points within the N^* hypercubes but to points a_{hh} in the N hypercubes as well. On the other hand within and on the boundary of every hypercube in question we have from (88)

$$\tfrac{1}{2} \leqq a^*_{hh} - \tfrac{1}{2} \leqq a^0_{hh}.$$

As integers the values a^0_{hh} are necessarily $\geqq 1$.

In the entire hypercube we have

$$\tfrac{1}{2} \leqq a^0_{hh} - \tfrac{1}{2} \leqq a_{hh}.$$

Hence using (91) and (88) it follows always that

$$a_{hh} \leqq a^*_{hh} + 1 \leqq a^*_{h+1,\ h+1} + 1 \leqq a_{h+1,\ h+1} + 2 \leqq 5a_{h+1,\ h+1} \qquad (h<n),$$

and further

$$|a_{hk}| - 1 \leqq |a^*_{hk}| \leqq \tfrac{1}{2} a^*_{hh} \leqq \tfrac{1}{2}(a_{hh} + 1); \qquad |a_{hk}| \leqq \tfrac{7}{2} a_{hh} \qquad (h<k).$$

Finally we have

$$a_{hh} \leqq a^*_{hh} + 1 \leqq 2a^*_{hh}.$$

To these inequalities we add (92). We thus come to the following results: *The $N+N^*$ hypercubes constructed above fall with all their points in the region defined through the conditions*

(93) $$\tfrac{1}{2} \leqq a_{11}, \qquad a_{hh} \leqq 5a_{h+1,\ h+1}, \qquad |a_{hk}| \leqq \tfrac{7}{2} a_{hh} \quad (h<k),$$

(94) $$\frac{\lambda_n}{2^n} a_{11} a_{22} \cdots a_{nn} \leqq D.$$

For the sake of a clearer method of expression we may speak of the ***magnitude*** *of a surface in the manifold A and of* ***orthogonal projections*** *on a plane,* if we make fundamental in the definition of these concepts the formula

$$\sqrt{da^2_{11} + da^2_{12} + \cdots + da^2_{nn}}$$

as the length of a line element. The question now is regarding the surface of the body defined through (93) and (94) and we shall show that for the magnitude of this surface there exists an upper limit

(95) $$\bar{\omega}_2 D \log D \quad \text{for} \quad n=2 \quad \text{and} \quad \bar{\omega}_n D^{\frac{n+1}{2} - \frac{1}{n}} \quad \text{for} \quad n>2,$$

where $\bar{\omega}_n$ is a quantity depending only upon n. When $n=2$, we shall assume that $D \geqq 2$.

In the volume integral of the body indicated through (93) and (94) to an interval a_{11} to $a_{11}+da_{11}$ of the first coefficient there corresponds a certain value

$$\int\int\cdots\int\left[\left\{\int_{-\frac{7}{2}a_{11}}^{\frac{7}{2}a_{11}}\cdots\int_{-\frac{7}{2}a_{11}}^{\frac{7}{2}a_{11}} da_{12}\cdots da_{1n}\right\} da_{11}\right] da_{22}\cdots da_{nn}$$
$$=7^{n-1}a_{11}^{n-1}da_{11}\int\int\cdots\int da_{22}\,da_{23}\cdots da_{nn}.$$

On the other hand if we project this body orthogonally on the plane $a_{11}=0$ and observe how this projection successively increases, when the parameter a_{11} augments in a continuous manner from $\frac{1}{2}$ on, we observe that there corresponds from a_{11} to $a_{11}+da_{11}$ of the parameter an increase of the projection surface by

$$d(7^{n-1}a_{11}^{n-1})\int\int\cdots\int da_{22}\,da_{23}\cdots da_{nn},$$

where the region of integration of a_{22}, a_{23}, $\cdots$, a_{nn} is the same as that of the integral above.

From this it is seen that the bounding surface of this body offered through the equality sign in (94) gives a projection whose surface area is not greater than the value of the integral

$$\int\int\cdots\int (n-1)\frac{da_{11}}{a_{11}}da_{12}\cdots da_{nn}$$

taken over the entire body. From this it is seen *that for the projection of the surface (94) on the plane $a_{11}=0$ there exists an upper limit of the type (95).*

Observe that at an arbitrary point (a_{hk}) of the bounding surface (94) the tangential plane to this surface in the coordinates (b_{hk}), see Art. 227, has the equation

$$\frac{1}{n}\left(\frac{b_{11}}{a_{11}}+\frac{b_{22}}{a_{22}}+\cdots+\frac{b_{nn}}{a_{nn}}\right)=1;$$

and from this we see in connection with the inequalities (93) *that the magnitude of this surface area does not exceed a certain multiple of its projection on the plane* a_{11}, *which multiple depends only upon* n.

On the other hand if we project the entire body defined through (93) and (94) upon the plane

$$b_{11}+b_{22}+\cdots+b_{nn}=0 \tag{96}$$

which is parallel to a tangential plane of the bounding surface (94), the resulting projection is offered *once* exactly from the projection of this bounding surface (94) and a second time it is covered over exactly by the projections of all the remaining plane side walls of the body that are indicated by the inequalities (93), where none of these plane sidewalls is perpendicular to the plane (96).

Accordingly there also exist for the surface area of all the plane sidewalls upper limits of the type (95); and finally also there exists such an upper limit for the entire surface of the body in question.

ART. **252.** Finally we return to the hypercubes enumerated in the number N^*. *Each of these hypercubes* has points in *common with the boundary of the region* $B(D, 1)$. This boundary consists *first* of a portion of the surface $D(f)=D$, *secondly* of portions of the sidewalls of the reduced realm, these sidewalls being planes, and thirdly of a portion of the plane $a_{11}=1$. (Fig. 141.) We consider *first* those of the N^* hypercubes which touch (meet) the surface $D(f)=D$. We arrange these hypercubes in series according to their projections on the plane $a_{11}=0$. Let two of these hypercubes having the same projection upon this plane have their midpoints $a_{11}^0, a_{12}^0, \cdots, a_{nn}^0$ and $a_{11}^0+d, a_{12}^0, \cdots, a_{nn}^0$, where d is a positive integer, and let $a_{11}, a_{12}, \cdots, a_{nn}$ and $a_{11}+\epsilon_{11}$, $a_{12}+\epsilon_{12}, \cdots, a_{nn}+\epsilon_{nn}$ be any point in these respective hypercubes upon the surface $D(f)=D$. We observe that $d-1 \leqq \epsilon_{11} \leqq d+1$ and that the absolute values of $\epsilon_{12}, \epsilon_{13}, \cdots, \epsilon_{nn}$ are $\leqq 1$. For $h \geqq 2$, it follows from $a_{hh}+\epsilon_{hh} \geqq 1$ and

$\epsilon_{hh} \geqq -1$ that also

$$a_{hh} + \epsilon_{hh} \geqq \tfrac{1}{2} a_{hh}.$$

Now form the difference

$$\frac{1}{\dfrac{\partial \text{ Det.}}{\partial a_{11}} |a_{hk} + \epsilon_{hk}|} (\text{Det.} |a_{hk} + \epsilon_{hk}| - \text{Det.} |a_{hk}|) = 0,$$

in which the coefficient of ϵ_{11} is 1, while the other terms in virtue of (91) may be given upper limits which are dependent only upon n (see also (17) for $m=1$).

It follows from this equation that there exists an upper limit depending only upon n for $d+1$ and with it also for the *maximum number of the hypercubes in each of the above series.* The volume of the hypercubes in question does not exceed the product of this maximum number into the projection of the collectivity of those hypercubes upon the plane $a_{11}=0$, and this last projection is at all events not greater than the projection of the body determined through (93) and (94) upon the plane $a_{11}=0$.

In the second place consider those of the N^* hypercubes which touch (meet) a *definite plane sidewall*

(I, II) $$\sum m_{hk} a_{hk} = 0$$

of the reduced realm (region). If we select any coefficient a_{hk} for which the factor m_{hk} is $\neq 0$, we find that the number of hypercubes in question which offer one and the same projection upon the plane $a_{hk}=0$ is not greater than a certain quantity which is derived out of the numerical factors in this equation. And on the other hand the entire projection of all these hypercubes upon the plane $a_{hk}=0$ is not greater than the projection of the entire realm (93) and (94) upon this plane.

Finally the number of those among the N^* hypercubes which cut the plane $a_{11}=1$ is not greater than the sidewall $a_{11}=\frac{1}{2}$ of the body determined through (93) and (94).

Out of all these conditions taken together we derive for the N^* hypercubes an upper limit of the type (95) and therewith we arrive at the following theorem:

The collectivity of all the different classes of integral positive quadratic forms in n variables having the determinants 1, 2, $\cdots$, D is situated between the two limits

$$v_2 D^{3/2} \pm \bar{\omega}_2 D \log D \qquad \text{for} \quad n=2,$$

and

$$v_n D^{\frac{n+1}{2}} \pm \omega_n D^{\frac{n+1}{2}-\frac{1}{n}} \qquad \text{for} \quad n>2,$$

where v_n is the volume of the realm (region) of the reduced forms with determinants $\leqq 1$ and $\bar{\omega}_n$ is a certain positive quantity that depends only upon n.

In case $n=2$, the number D is to be regarded $\geqq 2$. With this the law enunciated in (87) is proved.

INDEX

(The numerals refer to pages. Volume One contains pages 1 through 452; Volume Two contains pages 453 through 833.)

CATALOG OF DOVER BOOKS

BOOKS EXPLAINING SCIENCE AND MATHEMATICS

THE COMMON SENSE OF THE EXACT. SCIENCES, W. K. Clifford. Introduction by James Newman, edited by Karl Pearson. For 70 years this has been a guide to classical scientific and mathematical thought. Explains with unusual clarity basic concepts, such as extension of meaning of symbols, characteristics of surface boundaries, properties of plane figures, vectors, Cartesian method of determining position, etc. Long preface by Bertrand Russell. Bibliography of Clifford. Corrected, 130 diagrams redrawn. 249pp. 5⅜ x 8.
T61 Paperbound **$1.60**

SCIENCE THEORY AND MAN, Erwin Schrödinger. This is a complete and unabridged reissue of SCIENCE AND THE HUMAN TEMPERAMENT plus an additional essay: "What is an Elementary Particle?" Nobel Laureate Schrödinger discusses such topics as nature of scientific method, the nature of science, chance and determinism, science and society, conceptual models for physical entities, elementary particles and wave mechanics. Presentation is popular and may be followed by most people with little or no scientific training. "Fine practical preparation for a time when laws of nature, human institutions . . . are undergoing a critical examination without parallel," Waldemar Kaempffert, N. Y. TIMES. 192pp. 5⅜ x 8.
T428 Paperbound **$1.35**

PIONEERS OF SCIENCE, O. Lodge. Eminent scientist-expositor's authoritative, yet elementary survey of great scientific theories. Concentrating on individuals—Copernicus, Brahe, Kepler, Galileo, Descartes, Newton, Laplace, Herschel, Lord Kelvin, and other scientists—the author presents their discoveries in historical order adding biographical material on each man and full, specific explanations of their achievements. The clear and complete treatment of the post-Newtonian astronomers is a feature seldom found in other books on the subject. Index. 120 illustrations. xv + 404pp. 5⅜ x 8.
T716 Paperbound **$1.50**

THE EVOLUTION OF SCIENTIFIC THOUGHT FROM NEWTON TO EINSTEIN, A. d'Abro. Einstein's special and general theories of relativity, with their historical implications, are analyzed in non-technical terms. Excellent accounts of the contributions of Newton, Riemann, Weyl, Planck, Eddington, Maxwell, Lorentz and others are treated in terms of space and time, equations of electromagnetics, finiteness of the universe, methodology of science. 21 diagrams. 482pp. 5⅜ x 8.
T2 Paperound **$2.00**

THE RISE OF THE NEW PHYSICS, A. d'Abro. A half-million word exposition, formerly titled THE DECLINE OF MECHANISM, for readers not versed in higher mathematics. The only thorough explanation, in everyday language, of the central core of modern mathematical physical theory, treating both classical and modern theoretical physics, and presenting in terms almost anyone can understand the equivalent of 5 years of study of mathematical physics. Scientifically impeccable coverage of mathematical-physical thought from the Newtonian system up through the electronic theories of Dirac and Heisenberg and Fermi's statistics. Combines both history and exposition; provides a broad yet unified and detailed view, with constant comparison of classical and modern views on phenomena and theories. "A must for anyone doing serious study in the physical sciences," JOURNAL OF THE FRANKLIN INSTITUTE. "Extraordinary faculty . . . to explain ideas and theories of theoretical physics in the language of daily life," ISIS. First part of set covers philosophy of science, drawing upon the practice of Newton, Maxwell, Poincaré, Einstein, others, discussing modes of thought, experiment, interpretations of causality, etc. In the second part, 100 pages explain grammar and vocabulary of mathematics, with discussions of functions, groups, series, Fourier series, etc. The remainder is devoted to concrete, detailed coverage of both classical and quantum physics, explaining such topics as analytic mechanics, Hamilton's principle, wave theory of light, electromagnetic waves, groups of transformations, thermodynamics, phase rule, Brownian movement, kinetics, special relativity, Planck's original quantum theory, Bohr's atom, Zeeman effect, Broglie's wave mechanics, Heisenberg's uncertainty, Eigen-values, matrices, scores of other important topics. Discoveries and theories are covered for such men as Alembert, Born, Cantor, Debye, Euler, Foucault, Galois, Gauss, Hadamard, Kelvin, Kepler, Laplace, Maxwell, Pauli, Rayleigh, Volterra, Weyl, Young, more than 180 others. Indexed. 97 illustrations. ix + 982pp. 5⅜ x 8.
T3 Volume 1, Paperbound **$2.00**
T4 Volume 2, Paperbound **$2.00**

CONCERNING THE NATURE OF THINGS, Sir William Bragg. Christmas lectures delivered at the Royal Society by Nobel laureate. Why a spinning ball travels in a curved track; how uranium is transmuted to lead, etc. Partial contents: atoms, gases, liquids, crystals, metals, etc. No scientific background needed; wonderful for intelligent child. 32pp. of photos, 57 figures. xii + 232pp. 5⅜ x 8.
T31 Paperbound **$1.35**

THE UNIVERSE OF LIGHT, Sir William Bragg. No scientific training needed to read Nobel Prize winner's expansion of his Royal Institute Christmas Lectures. Insight into nature of light, methods and philosophy of science. Explains lenses, reflection, color, resonance, polarization, x-rays, the spectrum, Newton's work with prisms, Huygens' with polarization, Crookes' with cathode ray, etc. Leads into clear statement of 2 major historical theories of light, corpuscle and wave. Dozens of experiments you can do. 199 illus., including 2 full-page color plates. 293pp. 5⅜ x 8.
S538 Paperbound **$1.85**

BRIDGES AND THEIR BUILDERS, David Steinman and Sara Ruth Watson. Engineers, historians, everyone who has ever been fascinated by great spans will find this book an endless source of information and interest. Dr. Steinman, recipient of the Louis Levy medal, was one of the great bridge architects and engineers of all time, and his analysis of the great bridges of history is both authoritative and easily followed. Greek and Roman bridges, medieval bridges, Oriental bridges, modern works such as the Brooklyn Bridge and the Golden Gate Bridge, and many others are described in terms of history, constructional principles, artistry, and function. All in all this book is the most comprehensive and accurate semipopular history of bridges in print in English. New, greatly revised, enlarged edition. 23 photographs, 26 line drawings. Index. xvii + 401pp. 5⅜ x 8. T431 Paperbound **$2.00**

FADS AND FALLACIES IN THE NAME OF SCIENCE, Martin Gardner. Examines various cults, quack systems, frauds, delusions which at various times have masqueraded as science. Accounts of hollow-earth fanatics like Symmes; Velikovsky and wandering planets; Hoerbiger; Bellamy and the theory of multiple moons; Charles Fort; dowsing, pseudoscientific methods for finding water, ores, oil. Sections on naturopathy, iridiagnosis, zone therapy, food fads, etc. Analytical accounts of Wilhelm Reich and orgone sex energy; L. Ron Hubbard and Dianetics; A. Korzybski and General Semantics; many others. Brought up to date to include Bridey Murphy, others. Not just a collection of anecdotes, but a fair, reasoned appraisal of eccentric theory. Formerly titled IN THE NAME OF SCIENCE. Preface. Index. x + 384pp. 5⅜ x 8. T394 Paperbound **$1.50**

See also: **A PHILOSOPHICAL ESSAY ON PROBABILITIES, P. de Laplace; ON MATHEMATICS AND MATHEMATICIANS, R. E. Moritz; AN ELEMENTARY SURVEY OF CELESTIAL MECHANICS, Y. Ryabov; THE SKY AND ITS MYSTERIES, E. A. Beet; THE REALM OF THE NEBULAE, E. Hubble; OUT OF THE SKY, H. H. Nininger; SATELLITES AND SCIENTIFIC RESEARCH, D. King-Hele; HEREDITY AND YOUR LIFE, A. M. Winchester; INSECTS AND INSECT LIFE, S. W. Frost; PRINCIPLES OF STRATIGRAPHY, A. W. Grabau; TEACH YOURSELF SERIES.**

HISTORY OF SCIENCE AND MATHEMATICS

DIALOGUES CONCERNING TWO NEW SCIENCES, Galileo Galilei. This classic of experimental science, mechanics, engineering, is as enjoyable as it is important. A great historical document giving insights into one of the world's most original thinkers, it is based on 30 years' experimentation. It offers a lively exposition of dynamics, elasticity, sound, ballistics, strength of materials, the scientific method. "Superior to everything else of mine," Galileo. Trans. by H. Crew, A. Salvio. 126 diagrams. Index. xxi + 288pp. 5⅜ x 8. S99 Paperbound **$1.65**

A DIDEROT PICTORIAL ENCYCLOPEDIA OF TRADES AND INDUSTRY, Manufacturing and the Technical Arts in Plates Selected from "L'Encyclopédie ou Dictionnaire Raisonné des Sciences, des Arts, et des Métiers" of Denis Diderot. Edited with text by C. Gillispie. This first modern selection of plates from the high point of 18th century French engraving is a storehouse of valuable technological information to the historian of arts and science. Over 2000 illustrations on 485 full page plates, most of them original size, show the trades and industries of a fascinating era in such great detail that the processes and shops might very well be reconstructed from them. The plates teem with life, with men, women, and children performing all of the thousands of operations necessary to the trades before and during the early stages of the industrial revolution. Plates are in sequence, and show general operations, closeups of difficult operations, and details of complex machinery. Such important and interesting trades and industries are illustrated as sowing, harvesting, beekeeping, cheesemaking, operating windmills, milling flour, charcoal burning, tobacco processing, indigo, fishing, arts of war, salt extraction, mining, smelting, casting iron, steel, extracting mercury, zinc, sulphur, copper, etc., slating, tinning, silverplating, gilding, making gunpowder, cannons, bells, shoeing horses, tanning, papermaking, printing, dyeing, and more than 40 other categories. Professor Gillispie, of Princeton, supplies a full commentary on all the plates, identifying operations, tools, processes, etc. This material, presented in a lively and lucid fashion, is of great interest to the reader interested in history of science and technology. Heavy library cloth. 920pp. 9 x 12. T421 Two volume set **$18.50**

DE MAGNETE, William Gilbert. This classic work on magnetism founded a new science. Gilbert was the first to use the word "electricity", to recognize mass as distinct from weight, to discover the effect of heat on magnetic bodies; invent an electroscope, differentiate between static electricity and magnetism, conceive of the earth as a magnet. Written by the first great experimental scientist, this lively work is valuable not only as an historical landmark, but as the delightfully easy to follow record of a perpetually searching, ingenious mind. Translated by P. F. Mottelay. 25 page biographical memoir. 90 figures. lix + 368pp. 5⅜ x 8. S470 Paperbound **$2.00**

CHARLES BABBAGE AND HIS CALCULATING ENGINES, edited by P. Morrison and E. Morrison. Babbage, leading 19th century pioneer in mathematical machines and herald of modern operational research, was the true father of Harvard's relay computer Mark I. His Difference Engine and Analytical Engine were the first machines in the field. This volume contains a valuable introduction on his life and work; major excerpts from his autobiography, revealing his eccentric and unusual personality; and extensive selections from "Babbage's Calculating Engines," a compilation of hard-to-find journal articles by Babbage, the Countess of Lovelace, L. F. Menabrea, and Dionysius Lardner. 8 illustrations, Appendix of miscellaneous papers. Index. Bibliography. xxxviii + 400pp. 5⅜ x 8. T12 Paperbound **$2.00**

A HISTORY OF ASTRONOMY FROM THALES TO KEPLER, J. L. E. Dreyer. (Formerly A HISTORY OF PLANETARY SYSTEMS FROM THALES TO KEPLER.) This is the only work in English to give the complete history of man's cosmological views from prehistoric times to Kepler and Newton. Partial contents: Near Eastern astronomical systems, Early Greeks, Homocentric Spheres of Eudoxus, Epicycles, Ptolemaic system, medieval cosmology, Copernicus, Kepler, etc. Revised, foreword by W. H. Stahl. New bibliography. xvii + 430pp. 5⅜ x 8.
S79 Paperbound **$1.98**

A SHORT HISTORY OF ANATOMY AND PHYSIOLOGY FROM THE GREEKS TO HARVEY, Charles Singer. Corrected edition of THE EVOLUTION OF ANATOMY, classic work tracing evolution of anatomy and physiology from prescientific times through Greek & Roman periods, Dark Ages, Renaissance, to age of Harvey and beginning of modern concepts. Centered on individuals, movements, periods that definitely advanced anatomical knowledge: Plato, Diocles, Aristotle, Theophrastus, Herophilus, Erasistratus, the Alexandrians, Galen, Mondino, da Vinci, Linacre, Sylvius, others. Special section on Vesalius; Vesalian atlas of nudes, skeletons, muscle tabulae. Index of names, 20 plates. 270 extremely interesting illustrations of ancient, medieval, Renaissance, Oriental origin. xii + 209pp. 5⅜ x 8. T389 Paperbound **$1.75**

FROM MAGIC TO SCIENCE, Charles Singer. A great historian examines aspects of medical science from the Roman Empire through the Renaissance. Includes perhaps the best discussion of early herbals, and a penetrating physiological interpretation of "The Visions of Hildegarde of Bingen." Also examined are Arabian and Galenic influences; the Sphere of Pythagoras; Paracelsus; the reawakening of science under Leonardo da Vinci, Vesalius; the Lorica of Gildas the Briton; etc. Frequent quotations with translations. New Introduction by the author. New unabridged, corrected edition. 158 unusual illustrations from classical and medieval sources. Index. xxvii + 365pp. 5⅜ x 8. T390 Paperbound **$2.00**

HISTORY OF MATHEMATICS, D. E. Smith. Most comprehensive non-technical history of math in English. Discusses lives and works of over a thousand major and minor figures, with footnotes supplying technical information outside the book's scheme, and indicating disputed matters. Vol I: A chronological examination, from primitive concepts through Egypt, Babylonia, Greece, the Orient, Rome, the Middle Ages, the Renaissance, and up to 1900. Vol 2: The development of ideas in specific fields and problems, up through elementary calculus. Two volumes, total of 510 illustrations, 1355pp. 5⅜ x 8. Set boxed in attractive container. T429, 430 Paperbound, the set **$5.00**

A SHORT ACCOUNT OF THE HISTORY OF MATHEMATICS, W. W. R. Ball. Most readable non-technical history of mathematics treats lives, discoveries of every important figure from Egyptian, Phoenician mathematicians to late 19th century. Discusses schools of Ionia, Pythagoras, Athens, Cyzicus, Alexandria, Byzantium, systems of numeration; primitive arithmetic; Middle Ages, Renaissance, including Arabs, Bacon, Regiomontanus, Tartaglia, Cardan, Stevinus, Galileo, Kepler; modern mathematics of Descartes, Pascal, Wallis, Huygens, Newton, Leibnitz, d'Alembert, Euler, Lambert, Laplace, Legendre, Gauss, Hermite, Weierstrass, scores more. Index. 25 figures. 546pp. 5⅜ x 8. S630 Paperbound **$2.00**

A SOURCE BOOK IN MATHEMATICS, D. E. Smith. Great discoveries in math, from Renaissance to end of 19th century, in English translation. Read announcements by Dedekind, Gauss, Delamain, Pascal, Fermat, Newton, Abel, Lobachevsky, Bolyai, Riemann, De Moivre, Legendre, Laplace, others of discoveries about imaginary numbers, number congruence, slide rule, equations, symbolism, cubic algebraic equations, non-Euclidean forms of geometry, calculus, function theory, quaternions, etc. Succinct selections from 125 different treatises, articles, most unavailable elsewhere in English. Each article preceded by biographical, historical introduction. Vol. I: Fields of Number, Algebra. Index. 32 illus. 338pp. 5⅜ x 8. Vol. II: Fields of Geometry, Probability, Calculus, Functions, Quaternions. 83 illus. 432pp. 5⅜ x 8.
Vol. 1: S552 Paperbound **$1.85**
Vol. 2: S553 Paperbound **$1.85**
2 vol. set, boxed **$3.50**

A HISTORY OF THE CALCULUS, AND ITS CONCEPTUAL DEVELOPMENT, Carl B. Boyer. Provides laymen and mathematicians a detailed history of the development of the calculus, from early beginning in antiquity to final elaboration as mathematical abstractions. Gives a sense of mathematics not as a technique, but as a habit of mind, in the progression of ideas of Zeno, Plato, Pythagoras, Eudoxus, Arabic and Scholastic mathematicians, Newton, Leibnitz, Taylor, Descartes, Euler, Lagrange, Cantor, Weierstrass, and others. This first comprehensive critical history of the calculus was originally titled "The Concepts of the Calculus." Foreword by R. Courant. Preface. 22 figures. 25-page bibliography. Index. v + 364pp. 5⅜ x 8.
S509 Paperbound **$2.00**

HIGHER MATHEMATICS FOR STUDENTS OF CHEMISTRY AND PHYSICS, J. W. Mellor. Not abstract, but practical, building its problems out of familiar laboratory material, this covers differential calculus, coordinate, analytical geometry, functions, integral calculus, infinite series, numerical equations, differential equations, Fourier's theorem, probability, theory of errors, calculus of variations, determinants. "If the reader is not familiar with this book, it will repay him to examine it," CHEM. & ENGINEERING NEWS. 800 problems. 189 figures. Bibliography. xxi + 641pp. 5⅜ x 8. S193 Paperbound **$2.25**

TRIGONOMETRY REFRESHER FOR TECHNICAL MEN, A. Albert Klaf. 913 detailed questions and answers cover the most important aspects of plane and spherical trigonometry. They will help you to brush up or to clear up difficulties in special areas. The first portion of this book covers plane trigonometry, including angles, quadrants, trigonometrical functions, graphical representation, interpolation, equations, logarithms, solution of triangle, use of the slide rule and similar topics. 188 pages then discuss application of plane trigonometry to special problems in navigation, surveying, elasticity, architecture, and various fields of engineering. Small angles, periodic functions, vectors, polar coordinates, de Moivre's theorem are fully examined. The third section of the book then discusses spherical trigonometry and the solution of spherical triangles, with their applications to terrestrial and astronomical problems. Methods of saving time with numerical calculations, simplification of principal functions of angle, much practical information make this a most useful book. 913 questions answered. 1738 problems, answers to odd numbers. 494 figures. 24 pages of useful formulae, functions. Index. x + 629pp. 5⅜ x 8. T371 Paperbound **$2.00**

CALCULUS REFRESHER FOR TECHNICAL MEN, A. Albert Klaf. This book is unique in English as a refresher for engineers, technicians, students who either wish to brush up their calculus or to clear up uncertainties. It is not an ordinary text, but an examination of most important aspects of integral and differential calculus in terms of the 756 questions most likely to occur to the technical reader. The first part of this book covers simple differential calculus, with constants, variables, functions, increments, derivatives, differentiation, logarithms, curvature of curves, and similar topics. The second part covers fundamental ideas of integration, inspection, substitution, transformation, reduction, areas and volumes, mean value, successive and partial integration, double and triple integration. Practical aspects are stressed rather than theoretical. A 50-page section illustrates the application of calculus to specific problems of civil and nautical engineering, electricity, stress and strain, elasticity, industrial engineering, and similar fields.—756 questions answered. 566 problems, mostly answered. 36 pages of useful constants, formulae for ready reference. Index. v + 431pp. 5⅜ x 8. T370 Paperbound **$2.00**

TEXTBOOK OF ALGEBRA, G. Chrystal. One of the great mathematical textbooks, still about the best source for complete treatments of the topics of elementary algebra; a chief reference work for teachers and students of algebra in advanced high school and university courses, or for the mathematician working on problems of elementary algebra or looking for a background to more advanced topics. Ranges from basic laws and processes to extensive examination of such topics as limits, infinite series, general properties of integral numbers, and probability theory. Emphasis is on algebraic form, the foundation of analytical geometry and the key to modern developments in algebra. Prior course in algebra is desirable, but not absolutely necessary. Includes theory of quotients, distribution of products, arithmetical theory of surds, theory of interest, permutations and combinations, general expansion theorems, recurring fractions, and much, much more. Two volume set. Index in each volume. Over 1500 exercises, approximately half with answers. Total of xlviii + 1187pp. 5⅜ x 8.
S750 Vol I Paperbound **$2.35**
S751 Vol II Paperbound **$2.35**
The set **$4.70**

COLLEGE ALGEBRA, H. B. Fine. Standard college text that gives a systematic and deductive structure to algebra; comprehensive, connected, with emphasis on theory. Discusses the commutative, associative, and distributive laws of number in unusual detail, and goes on with undetermined coefficients, quadratic equations, progressions, logarithms, permutations, probability, power series, and much more. Still most valuable elementary-intermediate text on the science and structure of algebra. Index. 1560 problems, all with answers. x + 631pp. 5⅜ x 8. T211 Paperbound **$2.00**

THE CONTINUUM AND OTHER TYPES OF SERIAL ORDER, E. V. Huntington. This famous book gives a systematic elementary account of the modern theory of the continuum as a type of serial order. Based on the Cantor-Dedekind ordinal theory, which requires no technical knowledge of higher mathematics, it offers an easily followed analysis of ordered classes, discrete and dense series, continuous series, Cantor's transfinite numbers. 2nd edition. Index. viii + 82pp. 5⅜ x 8.
S129 Clothbound **$2.75**
S130 Paperbound **$1.00**

A TREATISE ON PLANE AND ADVANCED TRIGONOMETRY, E. W. Hobson. Extraordinarily wide coverage, going beyond usual college level trig, one of the few works covering advanced trig in full detail. By a great expositor with unerring anticipation and lucid clarification of potentially difficult points. Includes circular functions; expansion of functions of multiple angle; trig tables; relations between sides and angles of triangle; complex numbers; etc. Many problems solved completely. "The best work on the subject." Nature. Formerly entitled "A Treatise on Plane Trigonometry." 689 examples, 6 figures. xvi + 383pp. 5⅜ x 8.
S353 Paperbound **$1.95**

FAMOUS PROBLEMS OF ELEMENTARY GEOMETRY, Felix Klein. Expanded version of the 1894 Easter lectures at Göttingen. 3 problems of classical geometry, in an excellent mathematical treatment by a famous mathematician: squaring the circle, trisecting angle, doubling cube. Considered with full modern implications: transcendental numbers, pi, etc. Notes by R. Archibald. 16 figures. xi + 92pp. 5⅜ x 8. T348 Clothbound **$1.50**
T298 Paperbound **$1.00**

* * *

ELEMENTARY MATHEMATICS FROM AN ADVANCED STANDPOINT, Felix Klein.

This classic text is an outgrowth of Klein's famous integration and survey course at Göttingen. Using one field of mathematics to interpret, adjust, illuminate another, it covers basic topics in each area, illustrating its discussion with extensive analysis. It is especially valuable in considering areas of modern mathematics. "Makes the reader feel the inspiration of . . . a great mathematician, inspiring teacher . . . with deep insight into the foundations and interrelations," BULLETIN, AMERICAN MATHEMATICAL SOCIETY.

Vol. 1. ARITHMETIC, ALGEBRA, ANALYSIS. Introducing the concept of function immediately, it enlivens abstract discussion with graphical and geometrically perceptual methods. Partial contents: natural numbers, extension of the notion of number, special properties, complex numbers. Real equations with real unknowns, complex quantities. Logarithmic, exponential functions, goniometric functions, infinitesimal calculus. Transcendence of e and pi, theory of assemblages. Index. 125 figures. ix + 274pp . 5⅜ x 8. S150 Paperbound **$1.75**

Vol. 2. GEOMETRY. A comprehensive view which accompanies the space perception inherent in geometry with analytic formulas which facilitate precise formulation. Partial contents: Simplest geometric manifolds: line segment, Grassmann determinant principles, classification of configurations of space, derivative manifolds. Geometric transformations: affine transformations, projective, higher point transformations, theory of the imaginary. Systematic discussion of geometry and its foundations. Indexes. 141 illustrations. ix + 214pp. 5⅜ x 8.
S151 Paperbound **$1.75**

* * *

COORDINATE GEOMETRY, L. P. Eisenhart. Thorough, unified introduction. Unusual for advancing in dimension within each topic (treats together circle, sphere; polar coordinates, 3-dimensional coordinate systems; conic sections, quadric surfaces), affording exceptional insight into subject. Extensive use made of determinants, though no previous knowledge of them is assumed. Algebraic equations of 1st degree, 2 and 3 unknowns, carried further than usual in algebra courses. Over 500 exercises. Introduction. Appendix. Index. Bibliography. 43 illustrations. 310pp. 5⅜ x 8. S600 Paperbound **$1.65**

MONOGRAPHS ON TOPICS OF MODERN MATHEMATICS, edited by **J. W. A. Young.** Advanced mathematics for persons who haven't gone beyond or have forgotten high school algebra. 9 monographs on foundation of geometry, modern pure geometry, non-Euclidean geometry, fundamental propositions of algebra, algebraic equations, functions, calculus, theory of numbers, etc. Each monograph gives proofs of important results, and descriptions of leading methods, to provide wide coverage. New introduction by Prof. M. Kline, N. Y. University. 100 diagrams. xvi + 416pp. 6⅛ x 9¼. S289 Paperbound **$2.00**

MATHEMATICS, INTERMEDIATE TO ADVANCED

Geometry

THE FOUNDATIONS OF EUCLIDEAN GEOMETRY, H. G. Forder. The first rigorous account of Euclidean geometry, establishing propositions without recourse to empiricism, and without multiplying hypotheses. Corrects many traditional weaknesses of Euclidean proofs, and investigates the problems imposed on the axiom system by the discoveries of Bolya and Lobatchefsky. Some topics discussed are Classes and Relations; Axioms for Magnitudes; Congruence and Similarity; Algebra of Points; Hessenberg's Theorem; Continuity; Existence of Parallels; Reflections; Rotations; Isometries; etc. Invaluable for the light it throws on foundations of math. Lists: Axioms employed, Symbols, Constructions. 295pp. 5⅜ x 8.
S481 Paperbound **$2.00**

ADVANCED EUCLIDEAN GEOMETRY, R. A. Johnson. For years the standard textbook on advanced Euclidean geometry, requires only high school geometry and trigonometry. Explores in unusual detail and gives proofs of hundreds of relatively recent theorems and corollaries, many formerly available only in widely scattered journals. Covers tangent circles, the theorem of Miquel, symmedian point, pedal triangles and circles, the Brocard configuration, and much more. Formerly "Modern Geometry." Index. 107 diagrams. xiii + 319pp. 5⅜ x 8.
S669 Paperbound **$1.65**

NON-EUCLIDEAN GEOMETRY, Roberto Bonola. The standard coverage of non-Euclidean geometry. It examines from both a historical and mathematical point of view the geometries which have arisen from a study of Euclid's 5th postulate upon parallel lines. Also included are complete texts, translated, of Bolyai's THEORY OF ABSOLUTE SPACE, Lobachevsky's THEORY OF PARALLELS. 180 diagrams. 431pp. 5⅜ x 8. S27 Paperbound **$1.95**

ELEMENTS OF NON-EUCLIDEAN GEOMETRY, D. M. Y. Sommerville. Unique in proceeding step-by-step, in the manner of traditional geometry. Enables the student with only a good knowledge of high school algebra and geometry to grasp elementary hyperbolic, elliptic, analytic non-Euclidean geometries; space curvature and its philosophical implications; theory of radical axes; homothetic centres and systems of circles; parataxy and parallelism; absolute measure; Gauss' proof of the defect area theorem; geodesic representation; much more, all with exceptional clarity. 126 problems at chapter endings provide progressive practice and familiarity. 133 figures. Index. xvi + 274pp. 5⅜ x 8. S460 Paperbound **$1.50**

HIGHER GEOMETRY: AN INTRODUCTION TO ADVANCED METHODS IN ANALYTIC GEOMETRY, F. S. Woods. Exceptionally thorough study of concepts and methods of advanced algebraic geometry (as distinguished from differential geometry). Exhaustive treatment of 1-, 2-, 3-, and 4-dimensional coordinate systems, leading to n-dimensional geometry in an abstract sense. Covers projectivity, tetracyclical coordinates, contact transformation, pentaspherical coordinates, much more. Based on M.I.T. lectures, requires sound preparation in analytic geometry and some knowledge of determinants. Index. Over 350 exercises. References. 60 figures. x + 423pp. 5⅜ x 8. S737 Paperbound **$2.00**

ELEMENTS OF PROJECTIVE GEOMETRY, L. Cremona. Outstanding complete treatment of projective geometry by one of the foremost 19th century geometers. Detailed proofs of all fundamental principles, stress placed on the constructive aspects. Covers homology, law of duality, anharmonic ratios, theorems of Pascal and Brianchon, foci, polar reciprocal figures, etc. Only ordinary geometry necessary to understand this honored classic. Index. Over 150 fully worked out examples and problems. 252 diagrams. xx + 302pp. 5⅜ x 8. S668 Paperbound **$1.75**

A TREATISE ON THE DIFFERENTIAL GEOMETRY OF CURVES AND SURFACES, L. P. Eisenhart. Introductory treatise especially for the graduate student, for years a highly successful textbook. More detailed and concrete in approach than most more recent books. Covers space curves, osculating planes, moving axes, Gauss' method, the moving trihedral, geodesics, conformal representation, etc. Last section deals with deformation of surfaces, rectilinear congruences, cyclic systems, etc. Index. 683 problems. 30 diagrams. xii + 474pp. 5⅜ x 8. S667 Paperbound **$2.75**

A TREATISE ON ALGEBRAIC PLANE CURVES, J. L. Coolidge. Unabridged reprinting of one of few full coverages in English, offering detailed introduction to theory of algebraic plane curves and their relations to geometry and analysis. Treats topological properties, Riemann-Roch theorem, all aspects of wide variety of curves including real, covariant, polar, containing series of a given sort, elliptic, polygonal, rational, the pencil, two parameter nets, etc. This volume will enable the reader to appreciate the symbolic notation of Aronhold and Clebsch. Bibliography. Index. 17 illustrations. xxiv + 513pp. 5⅜ x 8. S543 Paperbound **$2.45**

AN INTRODUCTION TO THE GEOMETRY OF N DIMENSIONS, D. M. Y. Sommerville. An introduction presupposing no prior knowledge of the field, the only book in English devoted exclusively to higher dimensional geometry. Discusses fundamental ideas of incidence, parallelism, perpendicularity, angles between linear space; enumerative geometry; analytical geometry from projective and metric points of view; polytopes; elementary ideas in analysis situs; content of hyper-spacial figures. Bibliography. Index. 60 diagrams. 196pp. 5⅜ x 8. S494 Paperbound **$1.50**

GEOMETRY OF FOUR DIMENSIONS, H. P. Manning. Unique in English as a clear, concise introduction. Treatment is synthetic, and mostly Euclidean, although in hyperplanes and hyperspheres at infinity, non-Euclidean geometry is used. Historical introduction. Foundations of 4-dimensional geometry. Perpendicularity, simple angles. Angles of planes, higher order. Symmetry, order, motion; hyperpyramids, hypercones, hyperspheres; figures with parallel elements; volume, hypervolume in space; regular polyhedroids. Glossary. 78 figures. ix + 348pp. 5⅜ x 8. S182 Paperbound **$1.95**

ELEMENTARY CONCEPTS OF TOPOLOGY, P. Alexandroff. First English translation of the famous brief introduction to topology for the beginner or for the mathematician not undertaking extensive study. This unusually useful intuitive approach deals primarily with the concepts of complex, cycle, and homology, and is wholly consistent with current investigations. Ranges from basic concepts of set-theoretic topology to the concept of Betti groups. "Glowing example of harmony between intuition and thought," David Hilbert. Translated by A. E. Farley. Introduction by D. Hilbert. Index. 25 figures. 73pp. 5⅜ x 8. S747 Paperbound **$1.00**

THE WORKS OF ARCHIMEDES, edited by **T. L. Heath.** All the known works of the great Greek mathematician are contained in this one volume, including the recently discovered Method of Archimedes. Contains: On Sphere & Cylinder, Measurement of a Circle, Spirals, Conoids, Spheroids, etc. This is the definitive edition of the greatest mathematical intellect of the ancient world. 186-page study by Heath discusses Archimedes and the history of Greek mathematics. Bibliography. 563pp. 5⅜ x 8. S9 Paperbound **$2.00**

THE THIRTEEN BOOKS OF EUCLID'S ELEMENTS, edited by **Sir Thomas Heath.** Definitive edition of one of the very greatest classics of Western world. Complete English translation of Heiberg text, together with spurious Book XIV. Detailed 150-page introduction discussing aspects of Greek and Medieval mathematics. Euclid, texts, commentators, etc. Paralleling the text is an elaborate critical apparatus analyzing each definition, proposition, postulate, covering textual matters, mathematical analysis, commentators of all times, refutations, supports, extrapolations, etc. This is the FULL EUCLID. Unabridged reproduction of Cambridge U. 2nd edition. 3 volumes. Total of 995 figures, 1426pp. 5⅜ x 8.
S88,89,90, 3 volume set, paperbound **$6.00**

THE GEOMETRY OF RENE DESCARTES. With this book Descartes founded analytical geometry. Excellent Smith-Latham translation, plus original French text with Déscartes' own diagrams. Contains Problems the Construction of Which Requires Only Straight Lines and Circles; On the Nature of Curved Lines; On the Construction of Solid or Supersolid Problems. Notes. Diagrams. 258pp. 5⅜ x 8. S68 Paperbound **$1.50**

See also: **FOUNDATIONS OF GEOMETRY, B. Russell; THE PHILOSOPHY OF SPACE AND TIME, H. Reichenbach; FAMOUS PROBLEMS OF ELEMENTARY GEOMETRY, F. Klein; MONOGRAPHS ON TOPICS OF MODERN MATHEMATICS, ed. by J. W. Young.**

Calculus and function theory, Fourier theory, real and complex functions, determinants

A COLLECTION OF MODERN MATHEMATICAL CLASSICS, edited by R. Bellman. 13 classic papers, complete in their original languages, by Hermite, Hardy and Littlewood, Tchebychef, Fejér, Fredholm, Fuchs, Hurwitz, Weyl, van der Pol, Birkhoff, Kellogg, von Neumann, and Hilbert. Each of these papers, collected here for the first time, triggered a burst of mathematical activity, providing useful new generalizations or stimulating fresh investigations. Topics discussed include classical analysis, periodic and almost periodic functions, analysis and number theory, integral equations, theory of approximation, non-linear differential equations, and functional analysis. Brief introductions and bibliographies to each paper. xii + 292pp. 6 x 9.
S730 Paperbound **$2.00**

MATHEMATICS OF MODERN ENGINEERING, E. G. Keller and R. E. Doherty. Written for the Advanced Course in Engineering of the General Electric Corporation, deals with the engineering use of determinants, tensors, the Heaviside operational calculus, dyadics, the calculus of variations, etc. Presents underlying principles fully, but purpose is to teach engineers to deal with modern engineering problems, and emphasis is on the perennial engineering attack of set-up and solve. Indexes. Over 185 figures and tables. Hundreds of exercises, problems, and worked-out examples. References. Two volume set. Total of xxxiii + 623pp. 5⅜ x 8.
S734 Vol I Paperbound **$1.65**
S735 Vol II Paperbound **$1.65**
The set **$3.30**

MATHEMATICAL METHODS FOR SCIENTISTS AND ENGINEERS, L. P. Smith. For scientists and engineers, as well as advanced math students. Full investigation of methods and practical description of conditions under which each should be used. Elements of real functions, differential and integral calculus, space geometry, theory of residues, vector and tensor analysis, series of Bessel functions, etc. Each method illustrated by completely-worked-out examples, mostly from scientific literature. 368 graded unsolved problems. 100 diagrams. x + 453pp. 5⅝ x 8⅜. S220 Paperbound **$2.00**

THEORY OF FUNCTIONS AS APPLIED TO ENGINEERING PROBLEMS, edited by R. Rothe, F. Ollendorff, and K. Pohlhausen. A series of lectures given at the Berlin Institute of Technology that shows the specific applications of function theory in electrical and allied fields of engineering. Six lectures provide the elements of function theory in a simple and practical form, covering complex quantities and variables, integration in the complex plane, residue theorems, etc. Then 5 lectures show the exact uses of this powerful mathematical tool, with full discussions of problem methods. Index. Bibliography. 108 figures. x + 189pp. 5⅜ x 8.
S733 Paperbound **$1.35**

ADVANCED CALCULUS, E. B. Wilson. An unabridged reprinting of the work which continues to be recognized as one of the most comprehensive and useful texts in the field. It contains an immense amount of well-presented, fundamental material, including chapters on vector functions, ordinary differential equations, special functions, calculus of variations, etc., which are excellent introductions to these areas. For students with only one year of calculus, more than 1300 exercises cover both pure math and applications to engineering and physical problems. For engineers, physicists, etc., this work, with its 54 page introductory review, is the ideal reference and refresher. Index. ix + 566pp. 5⅜ x 8.
S504 Paperbound **$2.45**

CALCULUS OF VARIATIONS, A. R. Forsyth. Methods, solutions, rather than determination of weakest valid hypotheses. Over 150 examples completely worked-out show use of Euler, Legendre, Jacoby, Weierstrass tests for maxima, minima. Integrals with one original dependent variable; with derivatives of 2nd order; two dependent variables, one independent variable; double integrals involving 1 dependent variable, 2 first derivatives; double integrals involving partial derivatives of 2nd order; triple integrals; much more. 50 diagrams. 678pp. 5⅝ x 8⅜. S622 Paperbound **$2.95**

LECTURES ON THE CALCULUS OF VARIATIONS, O. Bolza. Analyzes in detail the fundamental concepts of the calculus of variations, as developed from Euler to Hilbert, with sharp formulations of the problems and rigorous demonstrations of their solutions. More than a score of solved examples; systematic references for each theorem. Covers the necessary and sufficient conditions; the contributions made by Euler, Du Bois Reymond, Hilbert, Weierstrass, Legendre, Jacobi, Erdmann, Kneser, and Gauss; and much more. Index. Bibliography. xi + 271pp. 5⅜ x 8. S218 Paperbound **$**

A TREATISE ON THE CALCULUS OF FINITE DIFFERENCES, G. Boole. A classic in the literature of the calculus. Thorough, clear discussion of basic principles, theorems, methods. Covers MacLaurin's and Herschel's theorems, mechanical quadrature, factorials, periodical constants, Bernoulli's numbers, difference-equations (linear, mixed, and partial), etc. Stresses analogies with differential calculus. 236 problems, answers to the numerical ones. viii + 336pp. 5⅜ x 8. S695 Paperbound **$1.85**

THE ANALYTICAL THEORY OF HEAT, Joseph Fourier. This book, which revolutionized mathematical physics, is listed in the Great Books program, and many other listings of great books. It has been used with profit by generations of mathematicians and physicists who are interested in either heat or in the application of the Fourier integral. Covers cause and reflection of rays of heat, radiant heating, heating of closed spaces, use of trigonometric series in the theory of heat, Fourier integral, etc. Translated by Alexander Freeman. 20 figures. xxii + 466pp. 5⅜ x 8. S93 Paperbound **$2.00**

AN INTRODUCTION TO FOURIER METHODS AND THE LAPLACE TRANSFORMATION, Philip Franklin. Concentrates upon essentials, enabling the reader with only a working knowledge of calculus to gain an understanding of Fourier methods in a broad sense, suitable for most applications. This work covers complex qualities with methods of computing elementary functions for complex values of the argument and finding approximations by the use of charts; Fourier series and integrals with half-range and complex Fourier series; harmonic analysis; Fourier and Laplace transformations, etc.; partial differential equations with applications to transmission of electricity; etc. The methods developed are related to physical problems of heat flow, vibrations, electrical transmission, electromagnetic radiation, etc. 828 problems with answers. Formerly entitled "Fourier Methods." Bibliography. Index. x + 289pp. 5⅜ x 8. S452 Paperbound **$1.75**

THE FOURIER INTEGRAL AND CERTAIN OF ITS APPLICATIONS, Norbert Wiener. The only book-length study of the Fourier integral as link between pure and applied math. An expansion of lectures given at Cambridge. Partial contents: Plancherel's theorem, general Tauberian theorem, special Tauberian theorems, generalized harmonic analysis. Bibliography. viii + 201pp. 5⅜ x 8. S272 Paperbound **$1.50**

INTRODUCTION TO THE THEORY OF FOURIER'S SERIES AND INTEGRALS, H. S. Carslaw. 3rd revised edition. This excellent introduction is an outgrowth of the author's courses at Cambridge. Historical introduction, rational and irrational numbers, infinite sequences and series, functions of a single variable, definite integral, Fourier series, Fourier integrals, and similar topics. Appendixes discuss practical harmonic analysis, periodogram analysis. Lebesgues theory. Indexes. 84 examples, bibliography. xiii + 368pp. 5⅜ x 8. S48 Paperbound **$2.00**

FOURIER'S SERIES AND SPHERICAL HARMONICS, W. E. Byerly. Continues to be recognized as one of most practical, useful expositions. Functions, series, and their differential equations are concretely explained in great detail; theory is applied constantly to practical problems, which are fully and lucidly worked out. Appendix includes 6 tables of surface zonal harmonics, hyperbolic functions, Bessel's functions. Bibliography. 190 problems, approximately half with answers. ix + 287pp. 5⅜ x 8. S536 Paperbound **$1.75**

ASYMPTOTIC EXPANSIONS, A. Erdélyi. The only modern work available in English, this is an unabridged reproduction of a monograph prepared for the Office of Naval Research. It discusses various procedures for asymptotic evaluation of integrals containing a large parameter and solutions of ordinary linear differential equations. Bibliography of 71 items. vi + 108pp. 5⅜ x 8. S318 Paperbound **$1.35**

LINEAR INTEGRAL EQUATIONS, W. V. Lovitt. Systematic survey of general theory, with some application to differential equations, calculus of variations, problems of math, physics. Partial contents: integral equation of 2nd kind by successive substitutions; Fredholm's equation as ratio of 2 integral series in lambda, applications of the Fredholm theory, Hilbert-Schmidt theory of symmetric kernels, application, etc. Neumann, Dirichlet, vibratory problems. Index. ix + 253pp. 5⅜ x 8. S175 Clothbound **$3.50**
S176 Paperbound **$1.60**

ELLIPTIC INTEGRALS, H. Hancock. Invaluable in work involving differential equations containing cubics or quartics under the root sign, where elementary calculus methods are inadequate. Practical solutions to problems that occur in mathematics, engineering, physics: differential equations requiring integration of Lamé's, Briot's, or Bouquet's equations; determination of arc of ellipse, hyperbola, lemiscate; solutions of problems in elastica; motion of a projectile under resistance varying as the cube of the velocity; pendulums; many others. Exposition is in accordance with Legendre-Jacobi theory and includes rigorous discussion of Legendre transformations. 20 figures. 5 place table. Index. 104pp. 5⅛ x 8.
S484 Paperbound **$1.25**

FIVE VOLUME "THEORY OF FUNCTIONS' SET BY KONRAD KNOPP

This five-volume set, prepared by Konrad Knopp, provides a complete and readily followed account of theory of functions. Proofs are given concisely, yet without sacrifice of completeness or rigor. These volumes are used as texts by such universities as M.I.T., University of Chicago, N. Y. City College, and many others. "Excellent introduction . . . remarkably readable, concise, clear, rigorous," JOURNAL OF THE AMERICAN STATISTICAL ASSOCIATION.

ELEMENTS OF THE THEORY OF FUNCTIONS, Konrad Knopp. This book provides the student with background for further volumes in this set, or texts on a similar level. Partial contents: foundations, system of complex numbers and the Gaussian plane of numbers, Riemann sphere of numbers, mapping by linear functions, normal forms, the logarithm, the cyclometric functions and binomial series. "Not only for the young student, but also for the student who knows all about what is in it," MATHEMATICAL JOURNAL. Bibliography. Index. 140pp. 5⅜ x 8.
S154 Paperbound **$1.35**

THEORY OF FUNCTIONS, PART I, Konrad Knopp. With volume II, this book provides coverage of basic concepts and theorems. Partial contents: numbers and points, functions of a complex variable, integral of a continuous function, Cauchy's integral theorem, Cauchy's integral formulae, series with variable terms, expansion of analytic functions in power series, analytic continuation and complete definition of analytic functions, entire transcendental functions, Laurent expansion, types of singularities. Bibliography. Index. vii + 146pp. 5⅜ x 8.
S156 Paperbound **$1.35**

THEORY OF FUNCTIONS, PART II, Konrad Knopp. Application and further development of general theory, special topics. Single valued functions, entire, Weierstrass, Meromorphic functions. Riemann surfaces. Algebraic functions. Analytical configuration, Riemann surface. Bibliography. Index. x + 150pp. 5⅜ x 8.
S157 Paperbound **$1.35**

PROBLEM BOOK IN THE THEORY OF FUNCTIONS, VOLUME 1, Konrad Knopp. Problems in elementary theory, for use with Knopp's THEORY OF FUNCTIONS, or any other text, arranged according to increasing difficulty. Fundamental concepts, sequences of numbers and infinite series, complex variable, integral theorems, development in series, conformal mapping. 182 problems. Answers. viii + 126pp. 5⅜ x 8.
S158 Paperbound **$1.35**

PROBLEM BOOK IN THE THEORY OF FUNCTIONS, VOLUME 2, Konrad Knopp. Advanced theory of functions, to be used either with Knopp's THEORY OF FUNCTIONS, or any other comparable text. Singularities, entire & meromorphic functions, periodic, analytic, continuation, multiple-valued functions, Riemann surfaces, conformal mapping. Includes a section of additional elementary problems. "The difficult task of selecting from the immense material of the modern theory of functions the problems just within the reach of the beginner is here masterfully accomplished," AM. MATH. SOC. Answers. 138pp. 5⅜ x 8.
S159 Paperbound **$1.35**

* * *

LECTURES ON THE THEORY OF ELLIPTIC FUNCTIONS, H. Hancock. Reissue of the only book in English with so extensive a coverage, especially of Abel, Jacobi, Legendre, Weierstrasse, Hermite, Liouville, and Riemann. Unusual fullness of treatment, plus applications as well as theory, in discussing elliptic function (the universe of elliptic integrals originating in works of Abel and Jacobi), their existence, and ultimate meaning. Use is made of Riemann to provide the most general theory. 40 page table of formulas. 76 figures. xxiii + 498pp.
S483 Paperbound **$2.55**

THE THEORY AND FUNCTIONS OF A REAL VARIABLE AND THE THEORY OF FOURIER'S SERIES, E. W. Hobson. One of the best introductions to set theory and various aspects of functions and Fourier's series. Requires only a good background in calculus. Provides an exhaustive coverage of: metric and descriptive properties of sets of points; transfinite numbers and order types; functions of a real variable; the Riemann and Lebesgue integrals; sequences and series of numbers; power-series; functions representable by series sequences of continuous functions; trigonometrical series; representation of functions by Fourier's series; complete exposition (200pp.) on set theory; and much more. "The best possible guide," Nature. Vol. I: 88 detailed examples, 10 figures. Index. xv + 736pp. Vol. II: 117 detailed examples, 13 figures. Index. x + 780pp. 6⅛ x 9¼.
Vol. I: S387 Paperbound **$3.00**
Vol. II: S388 Paperbound **$3.00**

ALMOST PERIODIC FUNCTIONS, A. S. Besicovitch. This unique and important summary by a well-known mathematician covers in detail the two stages of development in Bohr's theory of almost periodic functions: (1) as a generalization of pure periodicity, with results and proofs; (2) the work done by Stepanoff, Wiener, Weyl, and Bohr in generalizing the theory. Bibliography. xi + 180pp. 5⅜ x 8.
S18 Paperbound **$1.75**

COLLECTED WORKS OF BERNHARD RIEMANN. This important source book is the first to contain the complete text of both 1892 Werke and the 1902 supplement, unabridged. It contains 31 monographs, 3 complete lecture courses, 15 miscellaneous papers, which have been of enormous importance in relativity, topology, theory of complex variables, and other areas of mathematics. Edited by R. Dedekind, H. Weber, M. Noether, W. Wirtinger. German text. English introduction by Hans Lewy. 690pp. 5⅜ x 8. S226 Paperbound **$2.85**

See also: **A HISTORY OF THE CALCULUS, C. B. Boyer; CALCULUS REFRESHER FOR TECHNICAL MEN, A. A. Klaf; MONOGRAPHS ON TOPICS OF MODERN MATHEMATICS, ed. by J. W. A. Young; THE CONTINUUM AND OTHER TYPES OF SERIAL ORDER, E. V. Huntington.**

Symbolic logic

AN INTRODUCTION TO SYMBOLIC LOGIC, Susanne K. Langer. Probably the clearest book ever written on symbolic logic for the philosopher, general scientist and layman. It will be particularly appreciated by those who have been rebuffed by other introductory works because of insufficient mathematical training. No special knowledge of mathematics is required. Starting with the simplest symbols and conventions, you are led to a remarkable grasp of the Boole-Schroeder and Russell-Whitehead systems clearly and quickly. PARTIAL CONTENTS: Study of forms, Essentials of logical structure, Generalization, Classes, The deductive system of classes, The algebra of logic, Abstraction of interpretation, Calculus of propositions, Assumptions of PRINCIPIA MATHEMATICA, Logistics, Logic of the syllogism, Proofs of theorems. "One of the clearest and simplest introductions to a subject which is very much alive. The style is easy, symbolism is introduced gradually, and the intelligent non-mathematician should have no difficulty in following the argument," MATHEMATICS GAZETTE. Revised, expanded second edition. Truth-value tables. 368pp. 5⅜ x 8.
S164 Paperbound **$1.75**

THE ELEMENTS OF MATHEMATICAL LOGIC, Paul Rosenbloom. First publication in any language. This book is intended for readers who are mature mathematically, but have no previous training in symbolic logic. It does not limit itself to a single system, but covers the field as a whole. It is a development of lectures given at Lund University, Sweden, in 1948. Partial contents: Logic of classes, fundamental theorems, Boolean algebra, logic of propositions, logic of propositional functions, expressive languages, combinatory logics, development of mathematics within an object language, paradoxes, theorems of Post and Goedel, Church's theorem, and similar topics. iv + 214pp. 5⅜ x 8. S227 Paperbound **$1.45**

A SURVEY OF SYMBOLIC LOGIC: THE CLASSIC ALGEBRA OF LOGIC, C. I. Lewis. Classic survey of the field, comprehensive and thorough. Indicates content of major systems, alternative methods of procedure, and relation of these to the Boole-Schroeder algebra and to one another. Contains historical summary, as well as full proofs and applications of the classic, or Boole-Schroeder, algebra of logic. Discusses diagrams for the logical relations of classes, the two-valued algebra, propositional functions of two or more variables, etc. Chapters 5 and 6 of the original edition, which contained material not directly pertinent, have been omitted in this edition at the author's request. Appendix. Bibliography. Index. viii + 352pp. 5⅝ x 8⅜.
S643 Paperbound **$2.00**

INTRODUCTION TO SYMBOLIC LOGIC AND ITS APPLICATIONS, R. Carnap. One of the clearest, most comprehensive, and rigorous introductions to modern symbolic logic by perhaps its greatest living master. Symbolic languages are analyzed and one constructed. Applications to math (symbolic representation of axiom systems for set theory, natural numbers, real numbers, topology, Dedekind and Cantor explanations of continuity), physics (the general analysis of concepts of determination, causality, space-time-topology, based on Einstein), biology (symbolic representation of an axiom system for basic concepts). "A masterpiece," Zentralblatt für Mathematik und ihre Grenzgebiete. Over 300 exercises. 5 figures. Bibliography. Index. xvi + 241pp. 5⅜ x 8. S453 Paperbound **$1.85**
Clothbound **$4.00**

SYMBOLIC LOGIC, C. I. Lewis, C. H. Langford. Probably the most cited book in symbolic logic, this is one of the fullest treatments of paradoxes. A wide coverage of the entire field of symbolic logic, plus considerable material that has not appeared elsewhere. Basic to the entire volume is the distinction between the logic of extensions and of intensions. Considerable emphasis is placed on converse substitution, while the matrix system presents the supposition of a variety of non-Aristotelian logics. It has especially valuable sections on strict limitations, existence of terms, 2-valued algebra and its extension to propositional functions, truth value systems, the matrix method, implication and deductibility, general theory of propositions, propositions of ordinary discourse, and similar topics. "Authoritative, most valuable," TIMES, London. Bibliography. 506pp. 5⅜ x 8. S170 Paperbound **$2.00**

THE LAWS OF THOUGHT, George Boole. This book founded symbolic logic some hundred years ago. It is the 1st significant attempt to apply logic to all aspects of human endeavour. Partial contents: derivation of laws, signs & laws, interpretations, eliminations, conditions of a perfect method, analysis, Aristotelian logic, probability, and similar topics. xviii + 424pp. 5⅜ x 8. S28 Paperbound **$2.00**

THE PRINCIPLES OF SCIENCE, A TREATISE ON LOGIC AND THE SCIENTIFIC METHOD, W. S. Jevons. Treating such topics as Inductive and Deductive Logic, the Theory of Number, Probability, and the Limits of Scientific Method, this milestone in the development of symbolic logic remains a stimulating contribution to the investigation of inferential validity in the natural and social sciences. It significantly advances Boole's logic, and contains a detailed introduction to the nature and methods of probability in physics, astronomy, everyday affairs, etc. In his introduction, Ernest Nagel of Columbia University says, "[Jevons] continues to be of interest as an attempt to articulate the logic of scientific inquiry." Index. liii + 786pp. 5⅜ x 8. S446 Paperbound **$2.98**

Group theory, algebra, sets

LECTURES ON THE ICOSAHEDRON AND THE SOLUTION OF EQUATIONS OF THE FIFTH DEGREE, Felix Klein. The solution of quintics in terms of rotation of a regular icosahedron around its axes of symmetry. A classic & indispensable source for those interested in higher algebra, geometry, crystallography. Considerable explanatory material included. 230 footnotes, mostly bibliographic. 2nd edition, xvi + 289pp. 5⅜ x 8. S314 Paperbound **$1.85**

LINEAR GROUPS, WITH AN EXPOSITION OF THE GALOIS FIELD THEORY, L. E. Dickson. The classic exposition of the theory of groups, well within the range of the graduate student. Part I contains the most extensive and thorough presentation of the theory of Galois Fields available, with a wealth of examples and theorems. Part II is a full discussion of linear groups of finite order. Much material in this work is based on Dickson's own contributions. Also includes expositions of Jordan, Lie, Abel, Betti-Mathieu, Hermite, etc. "A milestone in the development of modern algebra," W. Magnus, in his historical introduction to this edition. Index. xv + 312pp. 5⅜ x 8. S482 Paperbound **$1.95**

INTRODUCTION TO THE THEORY OF GROUPS OF FINITE ORDER, R. Carmichael. Examines fundamental theorems and their application. Beginning with sets, systems, permutations, etc., it progresses in easy stages through important types of groups: Abelian, prime power, permutation, etc. Except 1 chapter where matrices are desirable, no higher math needed. 783 exercises, problems. Index. xvi + 447pp. 5⅜ x 8. S299 Clothbound **$3.95**
S300 Paperbound **$2.00**

THEORY OF GROUPS OF FINITE ORDER, W. Burnside. First published some 40 years ago, this is still one of the clearest introductory texts. Partial contents: permutations, groups independent of representation, composition series of a group, isomorphism of a group with itself, Abelian groups, prime power groups, permutation groups, invariants of groups of linear substitution graphical representation, etc. 45pp. of notes. Indexes. xxiv + 512pp. 5⅜ x 8.
S38 Paperbound **$2.45**

THEORY AND APPLICATIONS OF FINITE GROUPS, G. A. Miller, H. F. Blichfeldt, L. E. Dickson. Unusually accurate and authoritative work, each section prepared by a leading specialist: Miller on substitution and abstract groups, Blichfeldt on finite groups of linear homogeneous transformations, Dickson on applications of finite groups. Unlike more modern works, this gives the concrete basis from which abstract group theory arose. Includes Abelian groups, prime-power groups, isomorphisms, matrix forms of linear transformations, Sylow groups, Galois' theory of algebraic equations, duplication of a cube, trisection of an angle, etc. 2 Indexes. 267 problems. xvii + 390pp. 5⅜ x 8. S216 Paperbound **$2.00**

CONTINUOUS GROUPS OF TRANSFORMATIONS, L. P. Eisenhart. Intensive study of the theory and geometrical applications of continuous groups of transformations; a standard work on the subject, called forth by the revolution in physics in the 1920's. Covers tensor analysis, Riemannian geometry, canonical parameters, transitivity, imprimitivity, differential invariants, the algebra of constants of structure, differential geometry, contact transformations, etc. "Likely to remain one of the standard works on the subject for many years . . . principal theorems are proved clearly and concisely, and the arrangement of the whole is coherent," MATHEMATICAL GAZETTE. Index. 72-item bibliography. 185 exercises. ix + 301pp. 5⅜ x 8.
S781 Paperbound **$1.85**

THE THEORY OF GROUPS AND QUANTUM MECHANICS, H. Weyl. Discussions of Schroedinger's wave equation, de Broglie's waves of a particle, Jordan-Hoelder theorem, Lie's continuous groups of transformations, Pauli exclusion principle, quantization of Maxwell-Dirac field equations, etc. Unitary geometry, quantum theory, groups, application of groups to quantum mechanics, symmetry permutation group, algebra of symmetric transformation, etc. 2nd revised edition. Bibliography. Index. xxii + 422pp. 5⅜ x 8. S268 Clothbound **$4.50**
S269 Paperbound **$1.95**

ALGEBRAIC THEORIES, L. E. Dickson. Best thorough introduction to classical topics in higher algebra develops theories centering around matrices, invariants, groups. Higher algebra, Galois theory, finite linear groups, Klein's icosahedron, algebraic invariants, linear transformations, elementary divisors, invariant factors; quadratic, bi-linear, Hermitian forms, singly and in pairs. Proofs rigorous, detailed; topics developed lucidly, in close connection with their most frequent mathematical applications. Formerly "Modern Algebraic Theories." 155 problems. Bibliography. 2 indexes. 285pp. 5⅜ x 8. S547 Paperbound **$1.50**

ALGEBRAS AND THEIR ARITHMETICS, L. E. Dickson. Provides the foundation and background necessary to any advanced undergraduate or graduate student studying abstract algebra. Begins with elementary introduction to linear transformations, matrices, field of complex numbers; proceeds to order, basal units, modulus, quaternions, etc.; develops calculus of linear sets, describes various examples of algebras including invariant, difference, nilpotent, semi-simple. "Makes the reader marvel at his genius for clear and profound analysis," Amer. Mathematical Monthly. Index. xii + 241pp. 5⅜ x 8. S616 Paperbound **$1.35**

THE THEORY OF EQUATIONS WITH AN INTRODUCTION TO THE THEORY OF BINARY ALGEBRAIC FORMS, W. S. Burnside and A. W. Panton. Extremely thorough and concrete discussion of the theory of equations, with extensive detailed treatment of many topics curtailed in later texts. Covers theory of algebraic equations, properties of polynomials, symmetric functions, derived functions, Horner's process, complex numbers and the complex variable, determinants and methods of elimination, invariant theory (nearly 100 pages), transformations, introduction to Galois theory, Abelian equations, and much more. Invaluable supplementary work for modern students and teachers. 759 examples and exercises. Index in each volume. Two volume set. Total of xxiv + 604pp. 5⅜ x 8.
S714 Vol I Paperbound **$1.85**
S715 Vol II Paperbound **$1.85**
The set **$3.70**

COMPUTATIONAL METHODS OF LINEAR ALGEBRA, V. N. Faddeeva, translated by **C. D. Benster.** First English translation of a unique and valuable work, the only work in English presenting a systematic exposition of the most important methods of linear algebra—classical and contemporary. Shows in detail how to derive numerical solutions of problems in mathematical physics which are frequently connected with those of linear algebra. Theory as well as individual practice. Part I surveys the mathematical background that is indispensable to what follows. Parts II and III, the conclusion, set forth the most important methods of solution, for both exact and iterative groups. One of the most outstanding and valuable features of this work is the 23 tables, double and triple checked for accuracy. These tables will not be found elsewhere. Author's preface. Translator's note. New bibliography and index. x + 252pp. 5⅜ x 8. S424 Paperbound **$1.95**

ALGEBRAIC EQUATIONS, E. Dehn. Careful and complete presentation of Galois' theory of algebraic equations; theories of Lagrange and Galois developed in logical rather than historical form, with a more thorough exposition than in most modern books. Many concrete applications and fully-worked-out examples. Discusses basic theory (very clear exposition of the symmetric group); isomorphic, transitive, and Abelian groups; applications of Lagrange's and Galois' theories; and much more. Newly revised by the author. Index. List of Theorems. xi + 208pp. 5⅜ x 8. S697 Paperbound **$1.45**

THEORY OF SETS, E. Kamke. Clearest, amplest introduction in English, well suited for independent study. Subdivision of main theory, such as theory of sets of points, are discussed, but emphasis is on general theory. Partial contents: rudiments of set theory, arbitrary sets and their cardinal numbers, ordered sets and their order types, well-ordered sets and their cardinal numbers. Bibliography. Key to symbols. Index. vii + 144pp. 5⅜ x 8.
S141 Paperbound **$1.35**

Number theory

INTRODUCTION TO THE THEORY OF NUMBERS, L. E. Dickson. Thorough, comprehensive approach with adequate coverage of classical literature, an introductory volume beginners can follow. Chapters on divisibility, congruences, quadratic residues & reciprocity, Diophantine equations, etc. Full treatment of binary quadratic forms without usual restriction to integral coefficients. Covers infinitude of primes, least residues, Fermat's theorem, Euler's phi function, Legendre's symbol, Gauss's lemma, automorphs, reduced forms, recent theorems of Thue & Siegel, many more. Much material not readily available elsewhere. 239 problems. Index. I figure. viii + 183pp. 5⅜ x 8. S342 Paperbound **$1.65**

ELEMENTS OF NUMBER THEORY, I. M. Vinogradov. Detailed 1st course for persons without advanced mathematics; 95% of this book can be understood by readers who have gone no farther than high school algebra. Partial contents: divisibility theory, important number theoretical functions, congruences, primitive roots and indices, etc. Solutions to both problems and exercises. Tables of primes, indices, etc. Covers almost every essential formula in elementary number theory! Translated from Russian. 233 problems, 104 exercises. viii + 227pp. 5⅜ x 8. S259 Paperbound **$1.60**

THEORY OF NUMBERS and DIOPHANTINE ANALYSIS, R. D. Carmichael. These two complete works in one volume form one of the most lucid introductions to number theory, requiring only a firm foundation in high school mathematics. "Theory of Numbers," partial contents: Eratosthenes' sieve, Euclid's fundamental theorem, G.C.F. and L.C.M. of two or more integers, linear congruences, etc "Diophantine Analysis": rational triangles, Pythagorean triangles, equations of third, fourth, higher degrees, method of functional equations, much more. "Theory of Numbers": 76 problems. Index. 94pp. "Diophantine Analysis": 222 problems. Index. 118pp. 5⅜ x 8. S529 Paperbound **$1.35**

CONTRIBUTIONS TO THE FOUNDING OF THE THEORY OF TRANSFINITE NUMBERS, Georg Cantor. These papers founded a new branch of mathematics. The famous articles of 1895-7 are translated, with an 82-page introduction by P. E. B. Jourdain dealing with Cantor, the background of his discoveries, their results, future possibilities. Bibliography. Index. Notes. ix + 211 pp. 5⅜ x 8. S45 Paperbound **$1.25**

See also: **TRANSCENDENTAL AND ALGEBRAIC NUMBERS, A. O. Gelfond.**

Probability theory and information theory

A PHILOSOPHICAL ESSAY ON PROBABILITIES, Marquis de Laplace. This famous essay explains without recourse to mathematics the principle of probability, and the application of probability to games of chance, natural philosophy, astronomy, many other fields. Translated from the 6th French edition by F. W. Truscott, F. L. Emory, with new introduction for this edition by E. T. Bell. 204pp. 5⅜ x 8. S166 Paperbound **$1.35**

MATHEMATICAL FOUNDATIONS OF INFORMATION THEORY, A. I. Khinchin. For the first time mathematicians, statisticians, physicists, cyberneticists, and communications engineers are offered a complete and exact introduction to this relatively new field. Entropy as a measure of a finite scheme, applications to coding theory, study of sources, channels and codes, detailed proofs of both Shannon theorems for any ergodic source and any stationary channel with finite memory, and much more are covered. Bibliography. vii + 120pp. 5⅜ x 8. S434 Paperbound **$1.35**

SELECTED PAPERS ON NOISE AND STOCHASTIC PROCESS, edited by **Prof. Nelson Wax,** U. of Illinois. 6 basic papers for newcomers in the field, for those whose work involves noise characteristics. Chandrasekhar, Uhlenbeck & Ornstein, Uhlenbeck & Ming, Rice, Doob. Included is Kac's Chauvenet-Prize winning Random Walk. Extensive bibliography lists 200 articles, up through 1953. 21 figures. 337pp. 6⅛ x 9¼. S262 Paperbound **$2.35**

THEORY OF PROBABILITY, William Burnside. Synthesis, expansion of individual papers presents numerous problems in classical probability, offering many original views succinctly, effectively. Game theory, cards, selections from groups; geometrical probability in such areas as suppositions as to probability of position of point on a line, points on surface of sphere, etc. Includes methods of approximation, theory of errors, direct calculation of probabilities, etc. Index. 136pp. 5⅜ x 8. S567 Paperbound **$1.00**

Vector and tensor analysis, matrix theory

VECTOR AND TENSOR ANALYSIS, A. P. Wills. Covers the entire field of vector and tensor analysis from elementary notions to dyads and non-Euclidean manifolds (especially detailed), absolute differentiation, the Lamé operator, the Riemann-Christoffel and Ricci-Einstein tensors, and the calculation of the Gaussian curvature of a surface. Many illustrations from electrical engineering, relativity theory, astro-physics, quantum mechanics. Presupposes only a good working knowledge of calculus. Exercises at end of each chapter. Intended for physicists and engineers as well as pure mathematicians. 44 diagrams. 114 problems. Bibliography. Index. xxxii + 285pp. 5⅜ x 8. S454 Paperbound **$1.75**

APPLICATIONS OF TENSOR ANALYSIS, A. J. McConnell. (Formerly APPLICATIONS OF THE ABSOLUTE DIFFERENTIAL CALCULUS.) An excellent text for understanding the application of tensor methods to familiar subjects such as dynamics, electricity, elasticity, and hydrodynamics. Explains the fundamental ideas and notation of tensor theory, the geometrical treatment of tensor algebra, the theory of differentiation of tensors, and includes a wealth of practical material. Bibliography. Index. 43 illustrations. 685 problems. xii + 381pp. 5⅜ x 8. S373 Paperbound **$1.85**

VECTOR AND TENSOR ANALYSIS, G. E. Hay. One of the clearest introductions to this increasingly important subject. Start with simple definitions, finish the book with a sure mastery of oriented Cartesian vectors, Christoffel symbols, solenoidal tensors, and their applications. Complete breakdown of plane, solid, analytical, differential geometry. Separate chapters on application. All fundamental formulae listed & demonstrated. 195 problems, 66 figures. viii + 193pp. 5⅜ x 8. S109 Paperbound **$1.75**

VECTOR ANALYSIS, FOUNDED UPON THE LECTURES OF J. WILLARD GIBBS, by E. B. Wilson. Still a first-rate introduction and supplementary text for students of mathematics and physics. Based on the pioneering lectures of Yale's great J. Willard Gibbs, can be followed by anyone who has had some calculus. Practical approach, stressing efficient use of combinations and functions of vectors. Worked examples from geometry, mechanics, hydrodynamics, gas theory, etc., as well as practice examples. Covers basic vector processes, differential and integral calculus in relation to vector functions, and theory of linear vector functions, forming an introduction to the study of multiple algebra and matrix theory. While the notation is not always modern, it is easily followed. xviii + 436pp. 5⅜ x 8. S656 Paperbound **$2.00**